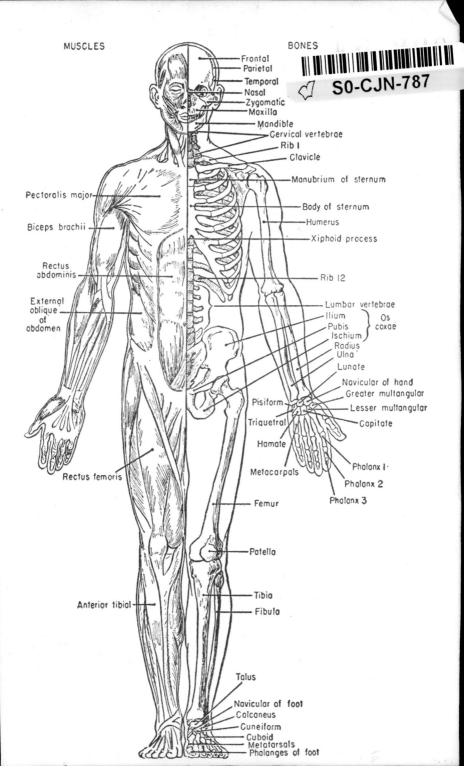

MUSCLES

BONES

Frontal
Parietal
Temporal
Nasal
Zygomatic
Maxilla
Mandible
Cervical vertebrae
Rib I
Clavicle
Manubrium of sternum
Pectoralis major
Body of sternum
Biceps brachii
Humerus
Xiphoid process
Rectus
abdominis
Rib 12
External
oblique
of
abdomen
Lumbar vertebrae
Ilium
Pubis   Os
Ischium   coxae
Radius
Ulna
Lunate
Navicular of hand
Greater multangular
Pisiform
Lesser multangular
Triquetral
Capitate
Hamate
Phalanx I
Metacarpals
Phalanx 2
Rectus femoris
Phalanx 3
Femur
Patella
Tibia
Anterior tibial
Fibula
Talus
Navicular of foot
Calcaneus
Cuneiform
Cuboid
Metatarsals
Phalanges of foot

PHYSIOLOGY AND ANATOMY

PHYSIOLOGY

By

ESTHER M. GREISHEIMER

B.S. IN EDUCATION, M.A., PH.D., M.D.

EMERITUS PROFESSOR OF PHYSIOLOGY, RESEARCH
PROFESSOR OF ANESTHESIOLOGY, TEMPLE UNI-
VERSITY SCHOOL OF MEDICINE, PHILADELPHIA;
FORMERLY PROFESSOR OF PHYSIOLOGY, WOMAN'S
MEDICAL COLLEGE OF PENNSYLVANIA, PHILADEL-
PHIA; FORMERLY ASSOCIATE PROFESSOR OF PHYSI-
OLOGY, THE UNIVERSITY OF MINNESOTA, MINNE-
APOLIS

With the Assistance of

ANN A. MIRALDO

R.N., B.S.

SCIENCE INSTRUCTOR
TEMPLE UNIVERSITY SCHOOL OF NURSING

SEVENTH EDITION
REWRITTEN and RESET

and ANATOMY

with Practical Considerations

*430 Illustrations
Including 48 in Color*

J. B. LIPPINCOTT COMPANY

PHILADELPHIA   MONTREAL

This book
is dedicated affectionately to
MISS KATHARINE J. DENSFORD
who first suggested that it be written
and to
those innumerable nurses whom it
has been my privilege and joy to teach

Preface
to the Seventh Edition

Since Miss Katharine J. Densford suggested, about 25 years ago, that the J. B. Lippincott Company ask the author to write a textbook of anatomy and physiology, the book has achieved 6 editions. The complete rewriting of the seventh gives this work its most complete revision of recent editions. Such a scope has permitted the author to use the experience acquired in her many years of teaching classes as small as 10 and as large as 300 student nurses in central schools of nursing.

The author has continued to engage in active research in laboratories of physiology, and this training in careful planning and accurate observation undoubtedly has influenced her in the desire to present material in a logical and accurate manner. The constant reading required for scientific research, as well as for effective teaching, has enabled the author to present theories and the status of theories which are accepted by scientists of today.

Again, the nervous system is presented early, since this knowledge is essential to understanding the circulatory, the respiratory and the other systems. The material on the nervous system has been condensed into 2 chapters, one dealing with the peripheral (including the autonomic) and the other with the central nervous system. All other chapters are completely rewritten with a view to improved presentation and organization, but the revisions are less drastic than those in the nervous system. The chapter on endocrines, in addition to its complete recasting, has received special attention.

Many chapters begin with short introductions. It is hoped that such over-all views will orient the reader before the details are encountered. Throughout the book analogies are used with applications to situations in one's daily life.

Variations in type size have been utilized to facilitate selection of material.

Many new illustrations have been added. These have been selected for their teaching qualities. A large number of other illustrations have been redrawn and labels re-evaluated for appropriateness and clarity. It is hoped that the abundant illustrations will be a valuable asset to the text.

The summaries are in outline form; this is intended to facilitate review after study of the chapter has been completed. The practical considerations have been retained, refreshed and enlarged. Situations, with relevant questions, are found at the end of each chapter.

In order to increase the applicability of the present edition to the student nurse, the aid of Miss Ann Miraldo, an instructor in Temple University School of Nursing, was sought. Miss Miraldo made suggestions for improvement, then read the first and the second drafts of the seventh edition and made additional suggestions of value, for both the text and the practical considerations. She contributed all the situations and questions. Her valuable assistance is gratefully acknowledged.

Mrs. John R. Ayers, a teacher in the Philadelphia public schools, has read both drafts of the seventh edition, and her criticisms, as a lay reader, have contributed to the clarity of the text.

Mr. Barton Lippincott has read the first and the second drafts, and his suggestions have contributed also to the clarity of the text. The author is deeply indebted to him for his kindness, consideration and willingness to help in every way to make this edition superior to its predecessors. It has been a great privilege and a pleasure to work with him.

The author wishes to express her thanks to Miss Dorothy Ellis who assisted with proofreading and the making of the index.

Thanks are due also to Mr. Walter Kahoe, Mr. Stanley A. Gillet and other staff members of the J. B. Lippincott Company whose joint efforts have helped to make this a useful book.

It is hoped that the students who use this text enjoy studying it as much as the author has enjoyed trying to make it a book well suited to their needs.

E. M. G.

Preface
to the First Edition

This book represents an attempt to present the essentials of anatomy and present-day physiology logically, simply and graphically. It is abundantly supplied with illustrations which should prove an aid, as they have been carefully selected with this in mind. A glossary is added, which may prove of value to many students.

So far as arrangement is concerned, the anatomy of a system is presented first, and then the physiology of the same system. The study of structure is essential to an understanding of the function, and it is natural to most of us to wish to know how something works, once we have seen how it is made. In a few cases, such as the special senses, the reproductive system and the glands of internal secretion, it seemed advisable to present both the anatomy and physiology in one chapter.

At the end of most of the chapters, practical considerations are presented. These are not to be considered a part of the regular required course; they are added because they are of general interest, and they may help to clear up a few of the pathologic conditions which one meets in everyday life. They have developed as a result of the inevitable questions asked by alert students over a great many years of teaching. It is earnestly hoped they will never be studied, but merely read by the interested student. Including them seems justified since the normal structures and functions of the human body have often an added significance when considered in the light of the deviations from the normal.

It will be found that occasionally material is included which one might expect to be covered in other courses, such as chemistry or physics. Some students may not have had these supporting courses, and such material is included for them. As much or as little as may be desired may be selected for study. Surely there are some students who do not need to study the skeletal system in detail. The anatomy of the muscular system is most important to students of physical education, but less important to other groups. The muscles are considered not only in groups, but also according to the joints across which they act, since the physical education student is especially interested in joints and the muscles which move them. Other students may omit this without loss of continuity. The teacher must select the material essential to her particular group, and omit such as may not be needed.

This must be considered as an introductory course, whether given as one aspect of a general education or as a basis for further study of the human body in health and disease. It is hoped that it contains much which should prove of value and interest to all students, and that it is a worth-while addition to any student's general knowledge, for whatever career he pursues. It is intended to help explain things which one is constantly meeting at every turn.

It should be kept in mind that physiology is a young science in comparison with anatomy. The problems of human disease, especially disorders of internal secretions and vitamin deficiency, have necessitated an investigation of the normal functions of the body. So physiology is a growing subject, in answer to demands; new knowledge is constantly added and old theories must be either discarded or re-interpreted in the light of recent experimental results. The physiologist must keep abreast of these rapid changes in medical science which make the present age such a fascinating one. It is earnestly hoped that the student may enjoy this glimpse of how the body is made and of how it functions, and that he may develop an interest in the growing medical science.

THE AUTHOR

Contents

UNIT TWO

THE ERECT AND MOVING BODY

UNIT FIVE

THE REPRODUCTIVE SYSTEM

Prologue

WHAT HAPPENS TO THE BODY IN CLIMBING STAIRS

In order to emphasize the correlation between the various systems of the body, as well as between the somatic and the visceral parts of the nervous system, an analysis is presented of the part played by each system as a person climbs stairs.

The skeletal system, of course, is moved upward step by step. It takes no active part except to furnish places of attachment for skeletal muscles and to serve as levers on which muscles may exert their force of contraction.

The skeletal muscles are brought into action in their entirety. In moving from one step to the next, some muscles are contracting, and their antagonists are relaxing. In addition, other muscles are acting as synergists and fixation muscles. The burden of lifting the body depends on the skeletal muscles. In climbing a flight of stairs, a great amount of work is done, and the energy is furnished by chemical changes that take place in the muscles.

There is a difference between slow climbing and running up the stairs. If we climb slowly enough, we can breathe in sufficient oxygen to take care of the requirements of the active muscles from moment to moment. The pyruvic acid (and its derivative, lactic acid) that is formed in the muscles is disposed of almost as rapidly as it appears. In other words, the muscles recover completely after each step is taken and before the next one is attempted, in very slow climbing. We do not get out of breath, and we can climb for quite a time.

If we run up the stairs, we find that we cannot run up many flights before we are entirely "out of breath," even if we are in excellent physical condition. The amount of oxygen that we can supply to the active muscles is much less than they need at the time. Consequently, pyruvic acid changes to lactic acid, which accumulates in the muscles and escapes into the blood and the urine in fairly large amounts. We can do work far in excess of the greatest supply of oxygen that the heart and the lungs can provide at the moment, due to the ability to accumulate lactic acid. In other words, we can run into debt for oxygen, to a limited extent and for a very short period of time.

After we stop climbing, we find that we are out of breath, and it is several minutes before we settle down to normal breathing again. This happens only after we have paid the oxygen debt in full. During the labored breathing after the exercise is over, sufficient oxygen is supplied to the muscles to permit complete recovery.

The nervous system plays an important role in climbing stairs. Impulses are transmitted at a rapid rate from the central nervous system to each participating motor unit in every active skeletal muscle. The two types of gradation are used to produce maximal contractions. This means that all motor units are active in the contracting muscles, and the rate of impulses reaching each motor unit is such as required to produce a short, complete tetanic type of contraction. Antagonistic muscles receive few impulses, so they are completely relaxed momentarily. Of course, each muscle group acts as prime mover and then as antagonist, in rapid succession.

The afferent impulses from muscles, tendons and joints are as important as efferent impulses. They keep the brain informed of the amount and the duration of contraction; climbing would be impossible without this information. The somatic portion of the nervous system handles the situation thus far.

Changes in the circulatory system involve the visceral portion of the nervous system. There is a redistribution of blood which increases the blood supply to active muscles. The arterioles of the skeletal muscles are dilated by impulses in visceral efferent nerve fibers. The coronary vessels that supply the heart muscle are dilated likewise. The vessels in the splanchnic area (abdominal viscera) are constricted, which makes more blood available to the skeletal muscles. The metabolites produced in the active muscles (carbon dioxide, for example) have a local effect, in that they dilate the capillaries and keep them all widely open. The concentration of carbon dioxide in the blood increases, and this acts as a stimulus to the vasoconstrictor center in the medulla. The end result is a still further constriction of the arterioles in the skin and the viscera, making more blood available for the active muscles. Meanwhile, the blood pressure rises, and this in itself improves the blood flow to the active muscles.

The venous return to the heart is increased, due chiefly to 2 factors. One is the squeezing effect of the contracting skeletal muscles (called the *muscular pump mechanism*) which pushes blood along in the veins. The second factor that aids venous return is the deeper movements of respiration, which exert a greater sucking effect in the thorax due to the negative pressure.

Since more blood is returned to the heart, it is filled better, and its fibers are stretched more than usual. This means that the ventricular contractions will be more forceful than usual, and the stroke volume (output per beat) will be increased greatly. With an increase in rate of contraction and an increased stroke volume, the cardiac output is increased greatly.

Respiration. Both the rate and the depth of respiration increase. In addition to getting in more oxygen and getting out more carbon dioxide, these respiratory movements increase the venous return, as stated above.

The oxygen use increases markedly; the blood gives up more of its oxygen than during rest. This is described as an increase in oxygen utilization.

The digestive system is rather inactive during strenuous exercise. Both the movements and the secretions are decreased temporarily by visceral efferent nerves. There is a mobilization of liver glycogen; if exercise is carried to exhaustion, the blood sugar falls.

The excretory system plays a minor role. Urine production is decreased temporarily during strenuous exercise. Perspiration for purposes of regulating body temperature occurs.

The endocrine system is involved to some extent. Even very moderate exercise is accompanied by an increase in the secretion of epinenephrine by the adrenal medullae. This, in turn, aids in the redistribution of the blood, increases the rate and the force of the heart beat, dilates the coronaries, mobilizes liver glycogen, relaxes the smooth muscles of the bronchioles and increases the output of ACTH by the anterior lobe of the pituitary gland. ACTH, in turn, increases the production of adrenal cortical hormones, which aid in meeting the stress of exercise.

Body temperature may rise during strenuous exercise; this, in itself, increases the rate of respiration and the rate of the heart. Reflexes are set up that tend to prevent a great rise in temperature. The blood vessels of the skin dilate now, in contrast with the earlier constriction, and the sweat glands are stimulated. Both of these responses tend to increase heat loss, but heat loss cannot keep pace with heat production in strenuous exercise, and the temperature rises.

The special senses play an important role. The eyes are very useful; if you doubt this, try to run up stairs rapidly with your eyes closed. There surely will be a difference in your rate of speed with eyes closed. Your hand on the banister gives you information of value. Impulses from the soles of the feet and from every active muscle flood the central nervous system. Even your ears are used; try stuffing your ears with cotton and see if you run up stairs as rapidly as before.

Many systems co-operate in the act of running up the stairs. The greatest burden falls on the circulatory and the respiratory systems, but several other systems have a share to contribute. You must think of the body acting as a unit, and then you can appreciate fully the importance of each of the many systems in most of the acts of everyday life. The somatic and the visceral portions of the nervous system are involved in practically all of our responses to both external and internal changes, and in every "threat" to homeostasis the resources of the body are mobilized.

UNIT 1

THE BODY AS AN INTEGRATED WHOLE

PART 1

THE BODY AS AN INTEGRATED WHOLE

1. Introduction to Anatomy

Throughout the study of anatomy you will be confronted with new terminology. If you try to link each new word with its origin or meaning you will make the subject "live"; otherwise, anatomy will become more bewildering day by day. Anatomic terms are as essential to the student of anatomy as tools are to a carpenter.

Many of the terms in use today have been derived from Greek and Latin sources, and they consist of prefixes, suffixes and two or more roots. An example of a prefix which will be encountered frequently is *peri*, which means "around"; *pericardium* means "around the heart," and *periosteum* means "around a bone." A common suffix is *al*, which means "pertaining to"; *radial* means "pertaining to the radius," and *femoral* means "pertaining to the femur." The root *myo* means "muscle"; *myocardium* means the "muscle of the heart," and *myoneural* junction means the junction between "muscle and nerve."

Many of the anatomic terms have been used for more than 2,500 years. Frequently, parts of the body were given certain names because they resembled common objects or because they were thought to perform certain functions. Even if the supposed function has been found to be untrue, the old name still is used to designate the structure.

7

You will encounter the same terms again and again throughout the course, so you may as well learn to recognize them as old friends. The use of the Glossary in the back of the book and the use of a medical dictionary will help you to understand and remember new terms. Early in the course you will find a staggering number of bones to identify; if you master this step you will find it a great help when you study later the attachments of muscles, nerves, arteries and veins. Study with the intent to remember; write the difficult words, spell them aloud, use them in conversation. Since you need to learn countless terms, you may as well make a game of it and have fun doing it. If you really put forth some effort you will be gratified with your daily progress. Probably never again in your educational journey will you be able to see daily progress so clearly as in anatomy. But if you neglect your study for a few days and "get behind" you will find a mountainous task awaiting you. Your attitude is about the most important feature of the course.

As you study anatomy or structure and correlate it with physiology or function, you will begin to see and appreciate deeply the beauty and the wonder of each system in turn, for each truly is a miracle. The fascinating concept of *homeostasis* or the maintenance of the "normal" will grow upon you as you see how all reflexes tend to keep blood pressure, heart rate, body temperature, respiration and the composition of the blood constant. It is only when the "odds" become so great and the reactions of the body fail to maintain homeostasis that sickness results, necessitating medical and nursing care.

The acquisition of a working knowledge of anatomy and physiology is like laying a foundation for a house; it should be done well so that the base for advanced study in medicine and surgery is sound. The text, the illustrations, the charts and the page references all have been planned to help you learn, and, as you learn the normal structure and function of the body, you will be preparing yourself to give effective care to patients who come to hospitals because of disturbance in anatomy or physiology.

DEFINITIONS

The word "anatomy" is of Greek origin; it is derived from the prefix *ana* meaning "apart" and the root *tome* meaning "a cutting," so it literally means "a cutting apart." The Latin word "dissection" is derived from the prefix *dis* meaning "apart" and the root *secare* meaning "to cut," so it likewise means "to cut apart." Although both

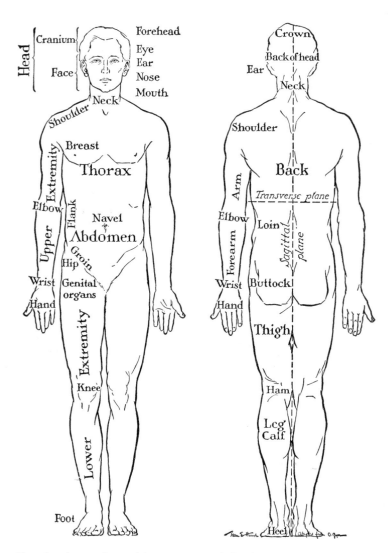

FIG. 1. Anatomic position; regions of the body; midsagittal and transverse planes indicated.

terms, anatomy and dissection, mean cutting apart, the former has acquired a much broader application and now includes many subdivisions. The terms indicate that the anatomy of early days consisted of that learned by dissecting human bodies.

SUBDIVISIONS OF ANATOMY

Gross anatomy refers to a study of structure as seen by the unaided eye, or that studied in the dissecting room.

Microscopic anatomy or **histology** is a study of cells and tissues as seen by the aid of a microscope.

Cytology is that branch of anatomy which deals only with the structure of cells.

Embryology includes the study of the origin, the growth and the development of an organism from inception until birth.

Neuroanatomy is the study of the origin, the development, the gross structure and the microscopic structure of the nervous system.

Comparative anatomy, commonly called "cat anatomy" by students, is a study of the gross structure of a mammal and its relation to the human body.

Human anatomy includes embryology, histology and gross anatomy of the human body.

There are many other subdivisions; each year brings new branches, as scientific investigations become more and more specialized. Anatomy today is a very comprehensive science with its unlimited number of branches.

Our study of anatomy will be taken up according to systems of the body, so it might be called "systematic" anatomy; it will include small amounts of embryology and histology, together with larger amounts of gross anatomy.

TERMS OF LOCATION AND POSITION

It is essential to become well acquainted with the following terms that are in common use.

Anatomic Position. An individual who is standing, facing forward, with arms at the sides and palms turned forward is said to be in the anatomic position. This position is illustrated in Figure 1.

Superior indicates the position of a structure which is nearer the head; **inferior** indicates a structure farther from the head. An example of these terms is *superior* vena cava and *inferior* vena cava; these are the two great veins which return blood to the heart from the upper and the lower portions of the body, respectively.

Anterior and **ventral** indicate structures nearer the front or belly-side of the body; their opposites are **posterior** and **dorsal,** which mean nearer the back. The roots of the spinal nerves which enter or leave the spinal cord are examples of these terms. The anterior or ventral roots are those nearer the front of the spinal cord, and the posterior or dorsal roots are those nearer the back.

Cranial means toward the head end, and **caudal** means toward the feet.

There are some differences between man and quadrupeds with respect to the preceding terms; these differences are indicated in Figure 2.

Medial means nearer the mid-line of the body, and **lateral** means farther from the mid-line. The medial rectus muscle of the eye is the one toward the nose; the lateral rectus muscle of the eye is the one toward the ear.

Internal means deeper within or nearer the mid-line of the body; **external** means nearer the external surface or farther from the mid-line. You will notice that the medial rectus muscle may

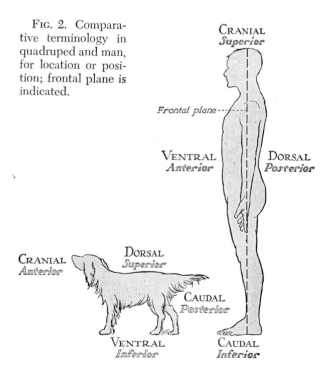

FIG. 2. Comparative terminology in quadruped and man, for location or position; frontal plane is indicated.

CRANIAL
Superior

Frontal plane

VENTRAL
Anterior

DORSAL
Posterior

CRANIAL
Anterior

DORSAL
Superior

CAUDAL
Posterior

VENTRAL
Inferior

CAUDAL
Inferior

be called the internal rectus also, and the lateral rectus may be
called the external rectus; both names are correct for each muscle.
Other meanings of internal and external are noted in the names of
the muscles of the abdominal wall; here the internal oblique muscles lie deeper in the wall than the external oblique muscles do.

Proximal means nearer the origin of a part and **distal** means
farther from the origin. With respect to the upper extremity, the

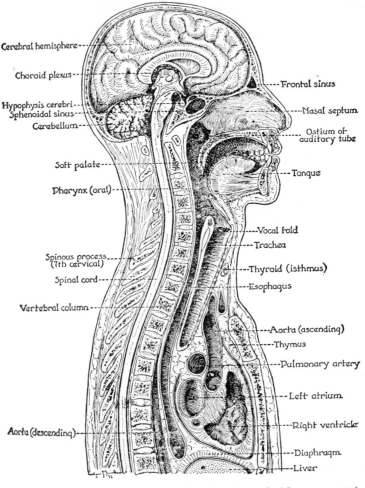

Cerebral hemisphere

Choroid plexus

Hypophysis cerebri
Sphenoidal sinus
Cerebellum

Soft palate

Pharynx (oral)

Spinous process
(7th cervical)
Spinal cord

Vertebral column

Aorta (descending)

Frontal sinus

Nasal septum

Ostium of
auditory tube

Tongue

Vocal fold
Trachea
Thyroid (isthmus)
Esophagus

Aorta (ascending)
Thymus
Pulmonary artery

Left atrium

Right ventricle

Diaphragm
Liver

Fig. 3. Midsagittal section of head, neck and trunk (diagrammatic).

shoulder is proximal to the elbow, and the hand is distal to the elbow.

Central refers to the principal part; **peripheral** means extensions from the principal part. The central nervous system refers to the brain and the spinal cord; the peripheral nervous system refers to the nerves which go out to, or come in from, all parts of the body.

Parietal refers to the walls of a cavity, and **visceral** refers to the organs within the cavity. We speak of parietal branches of arteries as those which supply the structures of the walls of the abdomen and the thorax; the visceral branches are those which supply the viscera or organs within the abdomen and the thorax.

After a bit of practice, the preceding terms will become part of your anatomic vocabulary and will cause you no difficulty.

FUNDAMENTAL PLANES

In order to enable one to see the various internal structures of the body in relation to each other, sections are cut in different planes. Three fundamental planes are the midsagittal, the coronal or frontal, and the transverse or horizontal. The **midsagittal** plane passes through the body from top to bottom, as indicated in Figure 1. It is so named because it passes through the sagittal suture of the skull (p. 9). The cutting blade passes through the body from front to back, or in an anteroposterior direction, and thus the body is divided into right and left halves. Any other plane which divides the body into right and left portions but does not pass through the mid-line of the body is called a sagittal plane. The slices of the body are called sections; a midsagittal section of the head, the neck and the trunk is shown in Figure 3.

The **coronal or frontal** plane takes its name from the coronal suture of the skull (p. 11). It passes through the body from top to bottom, as indicated in Figure 2. To section along this plane, the blade passes through the body from right to left and divides it into front (anterior, ventral) and back (posterior, dorsal) portions. A coronal or frontal section is shown in Figure 4.

The **transverse, or horizontal,** plane passes through the body as indicated in Figure 1. A blade passed along this plane divides the body into upper (superior, cranial) and lower (inferior, caudal) portions. A transverse or horizontal section is shown in Figure 5.

By a careful study of these illustrations and by referring to them as various organs are studied later, you will come to know the positions of the organs and their relation to each other.

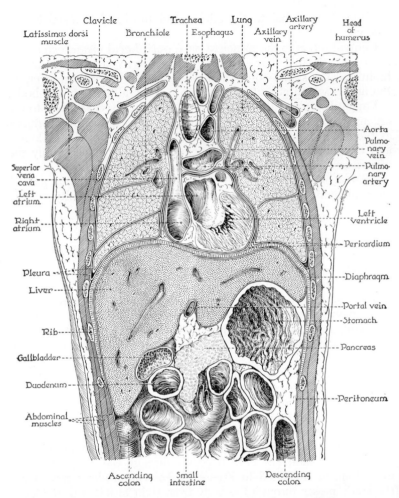

Fig. 4. Coronal or frontal section through the thorax and the upper abdomen (diagrammatic).

VERTEBRATE STRUCTURE OF MAN

Vertebrates are animals which have a vertebral column, a backbone or a spine. Fishes, amphibia, reptiles, birds and mammals are members of the vertebrate group. Man belongs to the mammalian subgroup of vertebrates. The characteristic of this subgroup is the

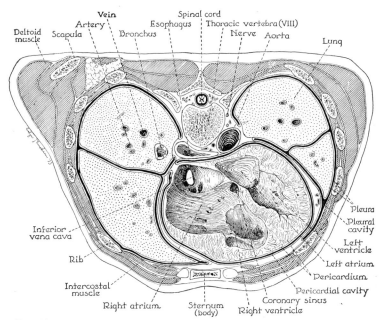

Vein
Artery
Spinal cord
Esophagus
Thoracic vertebra (VIII)
Deltoid muscle
Scapula
Bronchus
Nerve
Aorta
Lung

Inferior vena cava

Rib

Intercostal muscle

Right atrium

Sternum (body)

Right ventricle

Coronary sinus

Pericardial cavity

Pericardium

Left atrium

Left ventricle

Pleural cavity

Pleura

FIG. 5. Transverse or horizontal section through the trunk at the level of the heart (diagrammatic).

presence of mammary glands, in the female, which secrete milk to nourish the young.

In addition to possessing a vertebral column, vertebrates are characterized by the presence of dorsal and ventral cavities. A diagram of the vertebrate structure of man is shown in Figure 6.

The dorsal cavity lies within the skull and the backbone. It consists of two portions: (1) the cranial portion, which is occupied by the brain, and (2) the vertebral portion, which is occupied by the spinal cord.

The ventral cavity is divided into thoracic and abdominal portions by a muscular partition called the diaphragm, as shown in Figure 6. Each of these portions may be subdivided further. The thoracic cavity comprises two pleural cavities, each of which is occupied by a lung, and the pericardial cavity, which is occupied by the heart. In addition to the heart, the space between the lungs (called the mediastinum, p. 538) contains the following: trachea, esophagus, thymus gland, large blood vessels, lymphatic vessels and nodes, and nerves.

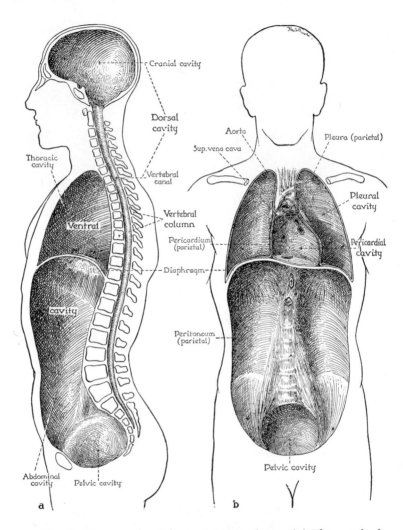

FIG. 6. Diagram of vertebrate structure of man. (a) The vertebral column, the dorsal cavity and the ventral cavity are shown. The diaphragm separates the abdominal from the thoracic portion; the lower portion of the abdominal cavity is called the pelvic cavity. (b) The divisions of the ventral cavity are shown. The thoracic division of the ventral cavity is subdivided into the pleural and the pericardial cavities.

The abdominal cavity lies inferior to the diaphragm. It is occupied by the stomach, the small intestine, most of the large intestine, the liver, the gallbladder, the pancreas, the spleen, the kidneys, the adrenal glands and the ureters. The lowermost portion of the abdominal cavity is called the pelvic cavity; it is occupied by the urinary bladder, the end of the large intestine (called the rectum) and parts of the reproductive system.

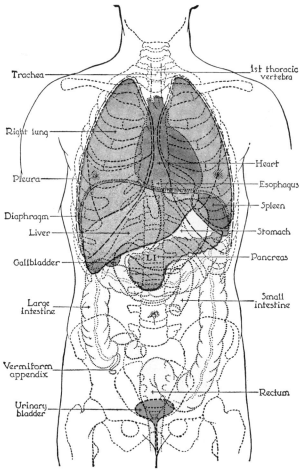

FIG. 7. The anterior surface projection of some of the thoracic, abdominal and pelvic viscera.

Figures 7 and 8 illustrate anterior and posterior surface projections of the various viscera to help orient you as to the location of organs.

ORGANIZATION OF THE BODY

Let us compare the organization of the body with the organization of a hospital. When you walk into a hospital corridor you

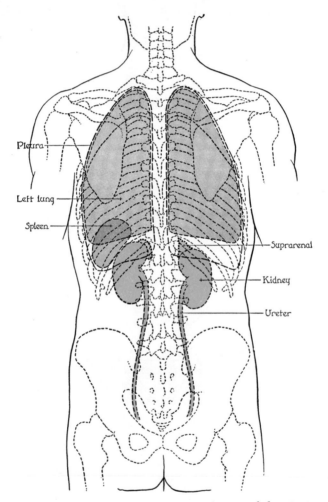

FIG. 8. Posterior surface projection of some of the viscera.

see a large number of individuals, each walking briskly about, apparently busy with his own tasks.

Each individual may be thought of as a unit and is comparable with a cell in the body. There is a great difference in appearance between the individuals whom you see and also in the work that each does. There is an even greater difference between the various cells of the body and the functions that they perform.

As you become a little better acquainted with the hospital, you realize that the individuals who do a certain type of work, such as scrub nurses, constitute one large group; and each large group carries out certain definite tasks. The nurses give nursing care to patients; the physicians take histories, do physical examinations and prescribe certain tests, medications and treatments for patients. Each of these groups, the nurses and the physicians, is made up of individuals who are performing specific functions. Similarly, in the body there are groups of cells which perform specific functions. Such groups of cells are called tissues.

In a larger sense, nurses and physicians work together to improve the health of patients; another way of stating this is that two groups with different individual functions work together for one purpose. Likewise, in the body tissues of various kinds are grouped together to form organs, which perform a surprising number of related functions.

No matter how efficient nurses and physicians may be, hospitals would not exist long without supervisors, maintenance men, elevator operators, telephone operators, cooks, maids and a host of other workers to carry out innumerable duties. In the body, groups of organs work together to accomplish a particular function, such as to supply the body with oxygen; these groups of organs are called systems. It is as impossible for the body to function properly without the co-operation of each individual cell as it is for a hospital to run efficiently without the co-operation of each individual, no matter whether the work is giving nursing care or cooking meals.

Without carrying the analogy further, we shall list the systems of the body. They are: skeletal, muscular, nervous, circulatory, respiratory, digestive, excretory, endocrine and reproductive systems. Our plan is to have you study cells, then tissues and finally systems, in the order listed above.

CELLS

A cell is the smallest unit of living matter; its substance is called protoplasm. Each cell is separated from its environment by a membrane, which regulates all the exchanges of materials between the cell and the tissue fluid surrounding it. Cell membranes possess selective permeability. (The properties of cell membranes are dealt with on p. 62.) The only facts to which we wish to call your attention at this time are that cell membranes are somewhat elastic, and if they are destroyed at one point a new membrane is formed immediately from the cytoplasm.

Cells are so small that they cannot be seen without the aid of a microscope. The only exception is the human ovum (p. 782), which is just visible to the unaided eye as a tiny speck; it is the largest single cell in the body. The human body, which begins as one cell (fertilized human ovum, p. 781) grows until the number of cells is so great that it is beyond human comprehension.

Structure

Each cell is made up of two parts: the *cytoplasm* and the *nucleus.* The nucleus contains granules of chromatin, which is the primary carrier of hereditary factors from one individual to the next generation. A small spherical body, called the *nucleolus,* is seen in the nucleus. The nuclear membrane which separates nuclear material from cytoplasm is from 2 to 4 times as thick as the cell membrane. An important constituent of all nuclei is desoxyribonucleic acid (abbreviated to DNA), which is the chief nucleic acid of chromosomes.

In the cytoplasm of a typical cell (such as a liver cell) there are two types of substances. Those substances which form part of the living protoplasm are called *organelles* (specialized structures in cells, with definite functions to perform); the substances which are nonliving are called *inclusions* (present, but not essential to the life of the cell). The organelles comprise the centrosome, the mitochondria, a Golgi apparatus, ergastoplasm and fibrils. The centrosome, which contains a still smaller body called a centriole, is called the attraction sphere and also the cell center; it is very important in cell division (p. 22). Mitochondria may appear as threads, rods or granules, and there may be as many as 2,500 in the cytoplasm of a single normal rat liver cell. Mitochondria vary in number with the physiologic condition of the cell. They contain enzymes which are substances aiding the transformation of food into living protoplasm and the burning of food materials with the release of energy. Enzymes are present in every cell; they are specific, which means that each acts on a particular material called its substrate, like a special key which fits only one Yale lock.

The Golgi apparatus is a network of black, twisted rods, which possibly may be related to the secretory activity of the cells in whose cytoplasm it appears. The ergastoplasm is the ribonucleic acid of the cytoplasm and is important in cell differentiation and growth. It is important in cell division and is present in abundance in cells that are dividing. Fibrils are chains of molecules of protein in cells of nervous, muscular and epithelial tissues, in which they are called neurofibrils, myofibrils and tonofibrils, respectively.

Inclusions are stored foods (fat in cells of fat depots, glycogen or carbohydrate in liver and muscle, and protein), secretory granules (in gland cells), globules, pigments and crystals.

A diagram of the parts of a typical cell is shown in Figure 9. It should be emphasized that each part of the cell has definite functions to perform. The nucleus is the vital part, and any cytoplasm which becomes separated from the nucleus dies. Each living cell is in dynamic equilibrium with its environment; this means that there are exchanges going on constantly between the cell and the tissue fluid which bathes it. Food and oxygen must be brought to it, and waste products must be removed from its vicinity. It is like a factory, bustling with activity. The nucleus not only controls growth, maintenance and metabolism of the cell but also controls cell division.

Cell Division

When cells are not undergoing division they are said to be in the "interphase," during which they carry on their specialized tasks.

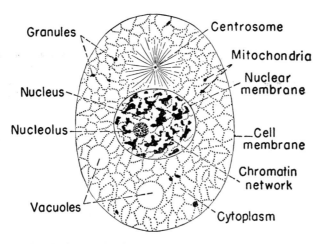

FIG. 9. Structure of a typical cell shown in diagram.

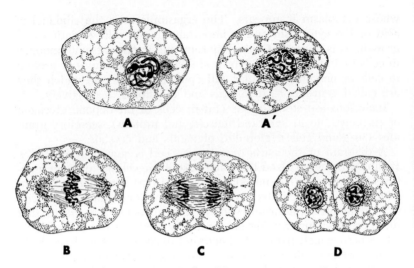

FIG. 10. Mitosis in eggs of whitefish. A and A′ are in the prophase. In A′ the chromatin material is present in rodlike bodies called *chromosomes;* the nuclear membrane has disappeared, and the centriole has divided. B represents the metaphase. The centrioles give off rays that form a spindle; the chromosomes are attached to the equator of the spindle. C represents the anaphase in which the chromosomes split and migrate toward the centrioles. D represents the telophase in which cytoplasm is dividing and 2 daughter cells are forming.

Apparently, they never rest, since they use oxygen and produce carbon dioxide as long as they are alive.

When cells reproduce, they usually do so by the type of cell division known as *mitosis.* We do not know what starts mitosis or what factors control it, but always the following pattern is followed.

Although mitosis is a continuous process, it is divided into 4 stages for convenience of description (Figure 10). The first stage is called the *prophase;* in this stage there are 3 changes in the nucleus and 1 in the cytoplasm. The 3 changes in the nucleus are: (1) the chromatin material changes from granules into a network and then breaks up into rodlike bodies called chromosomes; (2) the nucleolus disappears; and (3) the nuclear membrane disappears. In the cytoplasm the centriole divides, and the two parts begin to move to opposite sides of the cell.

The second stage is called the *metaphase.* During this phase the centrioles appear to give off rays, and the rays extend until those from one centriole meet those from the other at the middle of the cell, or equator of the spindle, formed by the rays. Meanwhile, the chromosomes become attached to the equator of the spindle.

The third stage is called the *anaphase*. During this phase each chromosome splits in two. Normally, there are 48 chromosomes in the cells of man, and during the anaphase there are 96. Immediately, 48 chromosomes migrate from the equator along the rays of the spindle toward each centriole.

The fourth stage is called the *telophase*. During this phase of mitosis a new nuclear membrane forms around each group of 48 chromosomes, and a nucleolus is formed in each nucleus. The chromosomes become chromatin material again, and, finally, the cytoplasm divides, and two complete daughter cells are formed. Each cell is capable of undergoing mitosis in the future.

The process of mitosis may take a few minutes or several hours, according to the type of cell dividing. Some cells in the body undergo mitosis throughout life; this is true of the germinal layer of the skin (p. 41), blood-forming tissue (p. 391), lining of the gastro-intestinal tract, glandular cells and the male germinal epithelium (p. 758). Other cells do not seem to undergo mitosis after the birth of the individual; this is true of the cells of the central nervous system. After cells have "lived their lives," they die; death of a cell is shown by a shrunken or fragmented nucleus. Dead cells eventually dissolve or are engulfed by phagocytes (p. 396).

TISSUES

A tissue is a group of cells which are similar in structure and in their intercellular substance. There are 4 basic or primary types of tissue in the human body: epithelial, connective, muscular and nervous tissue. This classification is based on the types of cells and the kind and the amount of intercellular substance or matrix present. Each type of tissue is specialized for a particular function. Epithelial and connective tissues will be described in this chapter; muscular tissue is described on p. 145; and nervous tissue on p. 248.

Epithelial Tissue

General Functions of Epithelial Tissue. The epithelial tissues of the body are highly specialized to perform 4 kinds of functions: protect, absorb, secrete and filter. The protective function is performed by sheets of epithelial tissues which cover the body (skin) and line the intestinal tract, the respiratory passages and the urinary passages. Epithelial cells, which are specialized for absorption, are found in the small intestine and in the kidney tubules. In the small intestine the lining cells permit the passage of water and other food materials from the lumen of the intestine into the capillaries in the walls. This passage from the intestine into the blood is called absorption. In the kidney tubules the epithelial cells permit the absorption of materials useful to the body (p. 683).

The epithelial cells which are specialized for secretion are found in the glands. The process of secretion is the removal of materials from the blood and pouring them out onto the skin, into the digestive tract or onto the membranes lining the respiratory passages.

The cells which are specialized for filtration are those which line the capillaries of the circulatory system. These permit the passage of water and dissolved substances from the blood into the tissue fluid (p. 401).

Characteristics of Epithelial Tissues. Epithelial tissues exist in the form of sheets or membranes. Such membranes are not sturdy; consequently, they are found firmly attached to strong supporting tissues called "basement membranes" which are composed of connective tissue. The cells of epithelial tissues are packed together closely. Tiny fibers are present in some cells; they pass from one cell to another and help hold them together (tonofibrils). The edges of adjacent cells are joined by a film of cement which is the only intercellular substance present in epithelial tissues.

There are no blood vessels in epithelial tissues; the cells receive oxygen and food from blood in capillaries in the basement membranes; likewise, epithelial cells eliminate their waste by way of the same capillaries. Epithelial cells have an unlimited capacity for regeneration so that cells which are subjected to the wear and tear of everyday living are replaced readily by mitosis of remaining cells.

Types of Epithelial Tissue (Ham's Classification). The following types of epithelial tissue exist in the human body:

1. Division of covering and lining membranes

(a) Simple: squamous, cuboidal, columnar (ciliated and nonciliated)

(b) Pseudostratified: columnar (ciliated and nonciliated)

* Ham, A. W.: Histology, ed. 2, chap. 12, Philadelphia, Lippincott, 1953.

Fig. 11. Three-dimensional diagrams illustrating the different types of epithelial membranes found on wet surfaces. (1) Nucleus of epithelial cell. (2) Cell of supporting connective tissue. (3) Connective tissue. (4) Goblet cell. The basement membrane is shown as a space merely to emphasize boundary between epithelial cells and connective tissue. (Modified from Ham, A. W.: Histology, ed. 2, Philadelphia, Lippincott.)

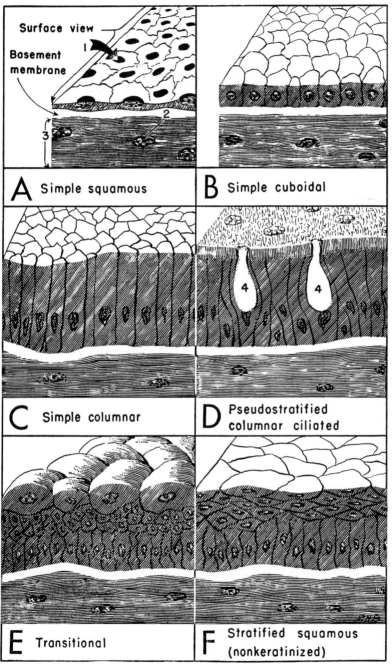

A Simple squamous

B Simple cuboidal

C Simple columnar

D Pseudostratified columnar ciliated

E Transitional

F Stratified squamous (nonkeratinized)

Surface view

Basement membrane

FIGURE 11 *(Caption on facing page)*

(c) Stratified: squamous (keratinized and nonkeratinized), columnar, transitional

2. Division of glandular epithelial tissue

(a) Endocrine glands: cord and clump type, follicle type

(b) Exocrine glands: simple (tubular and alveolar), compound (tubular, alveolar and tubo-alveolar)

THE CHARACTERISTICS OF EACH TYPE ARE AS FOLLOWS:

1. Covering and lining epithelial membranes.

(a) *Simple* epithelial membranes consist of one layer of cells. In simple squamous epithelium there is one layer of thin, flat cells, with a small amount of cement between them. This type of epithelial tissue lines the serous cavities (p. 38) and is called mesothelium. Simple squamous epithelium also lines blood and lymph vessels and in these localities it is called endothelium. The appearance of simple squamous epithelium is shown in Figure 11a.

Simple cuboidal epithelium consists of a single layer of cells of medium height, as shown in Figure 11b. This type of epithelial tissue is found covering the surface of the ovaries and in the thyroid gland.

In simple columnar epithelium the cells are tall, and there are hairlike processes on the free surface of some of the cells, as illustrated in Figure 11c. These processes are called *cilia;* they are capable of performing a beating movement by which they move particles and secretions along the surface of the membranes. This type of epithelium is found in the respiratory passages. In the nonciliated type of simple columnar epithelium no hairlike processes are present.

In both the ciliated and the nonciliated types of simple columnar epithelium, some of the cells are specialized to secrete a slippery substance called mucus. In these cells the nucleus lies near the basement membrane, and the remainder of the cell is shaped like a goblet which gives such cells the name of *goblet cells.* The goblet is filled with mucinogen (precursor from which mucus is made). The mucus secreted by goblet cells keeps epithelial membranes moist, and the cilia move the mucus along over the surface. Goblet cells are illustrated in Figure 11c.

(b) *Pseudostratified* columnar epithelium is so named because it appears at first glance to be composed of several layers of cells, but on closer inspection it is seen to be composed of one layer. Some of the cells are very short and do not reach the free surface of the membrane, while others are tall and extend to the free surface. The nuclei of the short cells are near the basement membrane

THE HUMAN BODY

Anatomic Relationships in *Videograf**

The following superimposed drawings reveal the components of the body in depth perspective. Various layers of the body are shown. The front views occur on pages A, C, E and G. A back view of each of these layers is shown on pages B, D, F and H, respectively. Thus you can "read through" the body as though leafing through a book, from the front (A) through successive layers, until finally the back (H) is reached.

Trademark,
J. B. Lippincott Co.

Printed in West German

and those of the tall cells are at a higher level. Both cilia and goblet cells are present (Figure 11d).

(c) *Stratified* epithelium consists of several layers of cells and is named according to the shape of the cells in the top layer.

Stratified squamous keratinized epithelium is found in the epidermis of the skin. The surface cells, which are exposed to air, die, fuse together and form a horny material called keratin. This layer is waterproof; it protects the body from drying out. (See Figure 20.)

In stratified squamous nonkeratinizing epithelium the deeper cells are columnar, and the cells on the surface are squamous, as shown in Figure 11f. This type of epithelium is protective; it is found on wet surfaces which must endure wear and tear, such as the inside of the mouth where coarse foods may damage the epithelial surface. It is found also in the cornea of the eye (p. 356); in which the outer layer of cells is protected from drying out by the layer of tears which covers the surface.

Stratified columnar epithelium is found only in the ducts of large glands.

Transitional epithelium is a peculiar type of stratified epithelial tissue found in structures which are subjected to periodic distention, such as the urinary bladder. It is like stratified squamous nonkeratinizing epithelium except that the superficial cells are rounded when the bladder is empty and flattened when it is distended. In the latter case they are stretched and drawn out into squamouslike cells without breaking apart. (See Figures 11e and 369.)

2. Glandular division of epithelial tissue.

The mucous-secreting goblet cells found in simple and pseudo-stratified columnar epithelium cannot produce more than a small fraction of the various secretions needed in the body. To meet the needs for additional secretions, epithelial cells in many regions have turned inward from the covering or lining surfaces and grown into or invaded the underlying supportive connective tissue. The manner in which such masses of secreting cells (called glands) develop is shown in Figure 12. These cells are highly specialized to secrete; this means that they remove materials from the blood and manufacture new substances which they then extrude from their cytoplasm.

(a) *Endocrine Glands.* These glands lose their connection with the epithelial surface from which they developed, consequently they possess no ducts through which they can extrude their secretions. The secretions which are produced by endocrine glands are

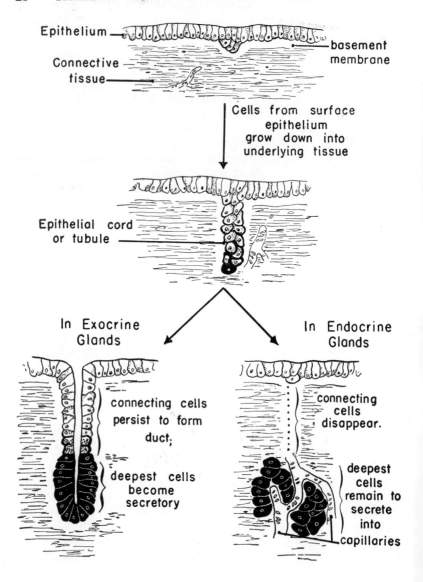

Epithelium

Connective tissue

basement membrane

Cells from surface epithelium grow down into underlying tissue

Epithelial cord or tubule

In Exocrine Glands

In Endocrine Glands

connecting cells persist to form duct;

deepest cells become secretory

connecting cells disappear.

deepest cells remain to secrete into capillaries

FIG. 12. Diagram showing how exocrine and endocrine glands develop. (Modified from Ham, A. W.: Histology, ed 2, Philadelphia, Lippincott.)

TYPES OF EXOCRINE GLANDS

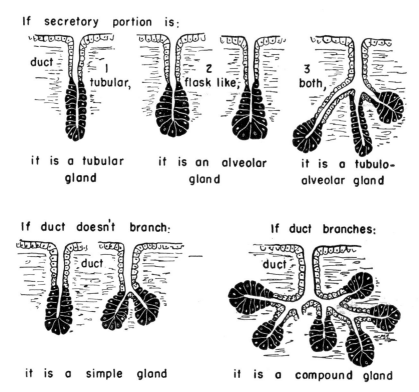

If secretory portion is:

duct — 1 tubular,   2 flask like;   3 both,

it is a tubular gland   it is an alveolar gland   it is a tubulo-alveolar gland

If duct doesn't branch: If duct branches:

duct   duct

it is a simple gland   it is a compound gland

Fig. 13. Diagram showing the different kinds of secretory units of exocrine glands and the difference between simple and compound glands. (Modified from Ham, A. W.: Histology, ed. 2, Philadelphia, Lippincott.)

extruded into blood or lymph. The endocrine glands comprise the endocrine system to which Chapter 19 is devoted.

(b) *Exocrine Glands.* The exocrine glands retain their connection with the epithelial surface from which they originated. The connections are called the ducts of the glands, and they convey the secretions from the glands to the surface. The secretory units are clusters of cells found at the ends of the ducts. Exocrine glands are classified according to the shape of the clusters of secreting cells. If the clusters are tubular in shape, the gland is called a tubular gland; if the clusters are round, the gland is called an alveolar gland. If the duct of the gland is unbranched, the term "simple" is used.

The glands whose ducts branch are called compound glands. The shape of the secreting units determines the type of gland; there are compound tubular and compound alveolar glands. In some instances tubular and round clusters of secretory cells are both present, and these are called compound tubo-alveolar glands. Various types of glands are illustrated in Figure 13.

Connective tissue may form capsules which practically enclose all the secretory units of glands. Partitions of connective tissue penetrate the large glands and divide them into large lobes. The lobes, in turn, are divided into small lobules by additional partitions of connective tissue.

Connective Tissue

Occurrence and Origin. Connective tissue is the most widely distributed tissue, and is found everywhere in the body. In the embryo it develops from the mesenchyme, which is a subdivision of the mesoderm (p. 789) and spreads as a loose, soft tissue into and between all other parts of the body.

General Functions. Connective tissue performs a variety of functions, some of which are due to the cells and others to the intercellular substance.

(1) Connective tissue serves as a binding tissue; it binds organs together, muscles to bones, bones to other bones and one type of tissue to another.

(2) Connective tissue serves as a storehouse for fat.

(3) Connective tissue is important as a supporting tissue, as in cartilage and bone.

(4) Connective tissue is important in the production of new blood corpuscles and the removal of worn out ones from the blood stream. This is called the hemopoietic (meaning blood production) function.

(5) Certain cells of connective tissue help to protect the body against invasion by bacteria and other cells help to produce immunity to disease.

Characteristics of Connective Tissue. Connective tissue is abundantly supplied with blood vessels. It is characterized by having few cells and a large amount of intercellular substance or matrix, which differs markedly in various types of connective tissue.

THE INTERCELLULAR SUBSTANCE or matrix is the nonliving material found between the cells of connective tissue. It is produced by the cells and consists of two basic types: fibrous and amorphous (meaning without form). Three types of fibers are present in the *fibrous type* of intercellular substance: collagenic, reticular and elastic.

The collagenic, or white, fibers are very tough and strong, yet flexible, and resistant to a pulling force. They may occur singly or in bundles. Reticular fibers are delicate and serve to support the cells of connective tissue. They are arranged in networks and are found wherever connective tissue joins other tissues. Elastic, or yellow, fibers permit connective tissue to be stretched and return to the original form when the force is removed. They are arranged in plates or sheets.

Amorphous intercellular substance, or ground substance, varies from a fluid (in blood) through a soft, jellylike material to the hard substance of bone. Oxygen and food materials pass through amorphous intercellular substance between blood capillaries and tissue cells; likewise, carbon dioxide and waste products pass through amorphous intercellular substance on their way from the tissue cells to the blood capillaries.

Since the amorphous intercellular substance, as well as the fibrous intercellular substance, is nonliving, it tends to deteriorate with age. The skin becomes wrinkled, the arteries lose their elasticity, and the crystalline lens of the eye (p. 376) undergoes a change. The change in the arteries may lead to high blood pressure (p. 519), and the change in the lens makes it necessary for most older people to wear glasses (p. 376).

THE CELLS OF CONNECTIVE TISSUE produce the intercellular substance, store fat, make new blood corpuscles, eat bacteria and cell debris (called phagocytosis), produce antibodies which give us immunity to certain diseases and make heparin which prevents coagulation of blood (p. 401).

Several types of cells are present in connective tissue.

(1) *Fibroblasts* are the most numerous cells in connective tissue. They appear in various shapes, have large oval nuclei and long processes which extend from the body of the cell. There are no granules in the cytoplasm.

(2) A primitive or embryonic type of cell is the *undifferentiated mesenchymal cell.* This type of connective tissue cell is found especially along blood capillaries. Such cells may develop into

any of the other types of cells found in connective tissue (in pathologic conditions).

(3) *Macrophages* are large cells which ingest bacteria, other
cells and any foreign material which enters the tissues. They are
called scavengers. The nucleus is small and indented on one side;
cytoplasmic processes extend from the cell body into the intercellular substance.

We shall digress for a moment to discuss the *reticuloendothelium*.
This term is used to designate certain modified endothelial cells
which occur in various parts of the body and have the ability to
take up foreign matter which comes in contact with them. In addition to the macrophages of connective tissue, the reticuloendothelium comprises the cells of the spleen, the lymph nodes and the
bone marrow, as well as the Kupffer cells of the sinusoids of the
liver (p. 609). The main function of all of these cells is phagocytosis, which means that they protect the body from injury by
foreign substances, they rid the body of worn-out red blood corpuscles and other cellular debris and build up immunity to infecting
agents.

(4) *Mast cells* are connective tissue cells whose cytoplasm is
stuffed with granules. They are thought to be the cells which
make heparin.

(5) *Fat cells* are fibroblasts which are specialized to store fat.
One very large droplet of fat fills the cell, and the nucleus is flattened on one side of the cell, making the cell look like a signet ring.

(6) *Plasma cells* are small spherical cells which have a small
cart-wheel nucleus, placed on one side of the cell.

(7) *Pigment cells* are found especially in the dense connective
tissue of the skin and in the choroid layer of the eye (p. 356).

Types of Connective Tissue (Ham's Classification).* The
following are the types of connective tissue which are found in the
human body: (1) areolar, (2) adipose, (3) dense fibrous, regularly and irregularly arranged, (4) cartilage (hyaline, fibrous and
elastic), (5) bone (cancellous and compact) and (6) hemopoietic
(myeloid and lymphatic).

(1) *Areolar* connective tissue contains all types of fibers, loosely
woven together and embedded in an amorphous intercellular substance. It is white and sticky and is found as packing between
organs, along blood vessels and as a framework for all organs. Exchanges between blood and tissue cells take place through areolar

----

* *Op. cit.*

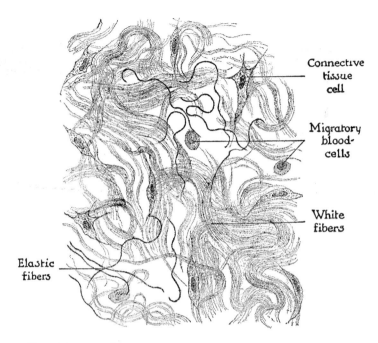

Connective
tissue
cell

Migratory
blood-
cells

White
fibers

Elastic
fibers

Fɪɢ. 14. Teased preparation of areolar connective tissue from subcutaneous area. Elastic fibers normally are straight; they are coiled here, due to the method of preparation. ×300.

connective tissue. It is the most common type and undergoes changes during inflammation. Areolar connective tissue is illustrated in Figure 14.

(2) *Adipose* connective Tissue. In this type of connective tissue the cells are closely packed. There is little intercellular substance, but in that which is present both collagenic and elastic fibers run in all directions. The blood supply is abundant. Adipose tissue is found under the skin, beneath the serous membranes, around the kidneys, in the omentum (p. 585) and as soft elastic pads between organs. It forms padding around joints and occurs in the marrow of the long bones. It is a reserve food, an insulator against heat loss and a support and protection for various organs. Figure 15 illustrates adipose connective tissue.

(3) *Dense fibrous connective tissue* in which the fibers are regularly arranged is found in tendons. The collagenic fibers are ar-

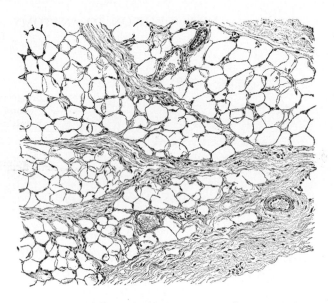

FIG. 15. Adipose connective tissue from omentum. The fat cells are arranged as groups between bundles of fibers in intercellular substance. ×160.

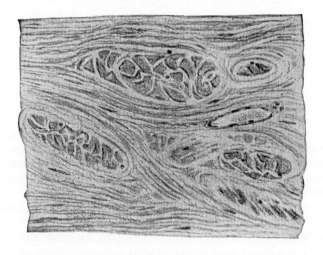

FIG. 16. Subcutaneous dense fibrous connective tissue, showing bundles cut in various directions, irregularly arranged.

ranged in parallel rows, with rows of fibroblasts between them. This type of tissue is glistening white, strong and flexible.

In the irregularly arranged dense fibrous connective tissue, the bundles of collagenic fibers run in all directions, as shown in Figure 16. This type of tissue is found in the derma of the skin (p. 41), in the submucous layer of the intestinal tract (p. 584), in the capsules of various organs and in the deep fascia (p. 38). It contains all types of cells, but they are few in number.

(4) *Cartilage* is a special kind of dense connective tissue in which the amorphous intercellular substance exists in the form of a very firm jelly or gel. Often it is called gristle. The fibers form a dense network. Cartilage cells, called chondrocytes, lie in little cavities called lacunae, usually in groups of 2 or 4. There are no blood vessels in cartilage; it is nourished by materials which reach it from the blood capillaries by diffusion through the tissue fluid (p. 401), and the waste products diffuse from chondrocytes through tissue fluid to the blood capillaries to be eliminated. Cartilage is

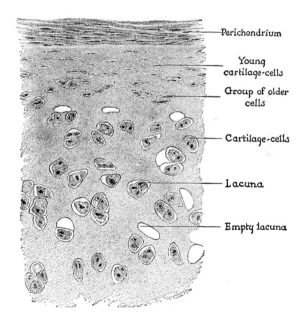

FIG. 17. Hyaline cartilage; cartilage cells are shown in lacunae; the matrix is firm and homogeneous. The perichondrium is shown. ×250.

covered by a membrane composed of fibrous connective tissue called perichondrium.

Three types of cartilage are found in the body: hyaline, fibrous and elastic. Hyaline cartilage is the most common type; it is pearly white and glassy or translucent in appearance. It forms the skeleton in the embryo and provides models in which most of the bones develop. It covers the articulating ends of bones in movable joints (p. 126), makes up the costal cartilages (p. 112) and the cartilages of the nose and the larynx.

Hyaline cartilage makes possible the growth of long bones in length (p. 79). It is very sensitive to disturbances in metabolism and undergoes changes whenever there is deficiency of proteins, minerals or certain vitamins. (See Figure 17.)

Fibrous cartilage or fibrocartilage is less firm than hyaline cartilage but has great strength. The collagenic fibers are arranged in parallel rows as they are in regularly arranged dense fibrous connective tissue. The chondrocytes are arranged in rows between the large bundles of fibers. Fibrous cartilage is closely associated

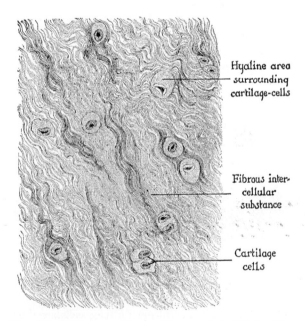

Hyaline area surrounding cartilage-cells

Fibrous inter-cellular substance

Cartilage cells

FIG. 18. Fibrous cartilage. The matrix is filled with collagenic fibers. ×225.

with dense fibrous connective tissue in the capsules and the ligaments of joints. It is found also in the intervertebral disks (p. 108) and in the pubic symphysis (p. 98). (See Figure 18.)

Elastic cartilage contains a network of elastic fibers in its intercellular substance, together with some collagenic fibers, as shown in Figure 19. It is flexible and elastic and occurs in the external ear, the epiglottis and some of the laryngeal cartilages.

The remaining two types of connective tissue, bone and hemopoietic tissue, are discussed on pages 81 and 391, respectively.

TISSUES AS BUILDING MATERIALS

MEMBRANES

Now we shall consider the manner in which different types of tissues are combined and used as building materials. The simplest

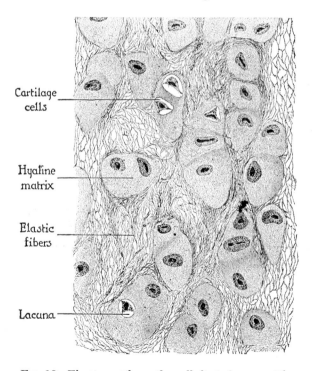

Cartilage cells

Hyaline matrix

Elastic fibers

Lacuna

FIG. 19.   Elastic cartilage; the cells lie in lacunae. The matrix is filled with elastic fibers.

combination encountered is the use of tissues in the formation of membranes. A membrane is a sheet of tissues used to cover or line surfaces or to divide organs into lobes. The two principal types of membranes are epithelial and fibrous, in each of which there are several subgroups.

Epithelial membranes consist of two subgroups: the mucous and the serous membranes. *Mucous* membranes have epithelium on the free surface and a layer of connective tissue, called the lamina propria, beneath. They line the alimentary (digestive), the respiratory (air passages), the reproductive and the urinary tracts, all of which open to the outside. They are wet and slippery. The cells in the mucous membrane secrete mucus, absorb food material (in the intestine) and protect (as in the mouth) underlying tissues.

Serous membranes are composed of an outer layer of mesothelium on the free surface and a thin layer of areolar connective tissue beneath. Serous membranes are thin, transparent and glistening. They line closed cavities (peritoneal, pleural and pericardial) and cover and join organs in these cavities. The serous membrane which lines the walls of the cavities is called the parietal layer, and that which covers the organs is called the visceral layer. The serous membranes protect against friction when the viscera glide over each other. They are kept moist by a thin fluid which covers the free surface. The omentum is an important membrane which consists of mesothelium, areolar connective tissue and some adipose connective tissue. The cellular elements in the omentum are numerous and active.

Fibrous membranes are composed entirely of connective tissue. The subcutaneous tissue, which is also called the *superficial fascia,* is an example of a fibrous membrane. It is a combination of areolar and adipose connective tissue. It underlies the skin of the whole body and is a continuous sheet. It is firmly attached to the derma of the skin. The amount of adipose tissue varies in different individuals; those who possess a generous amount of adipose tissue are said to be "well padded." The superficial fascia is connected with the deeper tissues, such as the deep fascia and the covering of bones (periosteum) and cartilage (perichondrium). It is chiefly in the superficial fascia that abnormal collections of fluid (edema, p. 411) occur.

The *deep fascia* lies under the superficial fascia and is composed of dense fibrous and elastic connective tissue. It contains no fat and is in close relation to bones, ligaments and muscles. Sheets of deep fascia enclose glands and viscera, and it forms sheaths for nerves and blood vessels. In the distal portions of the extremities there are special thickenings of the deep fascia or bands which act as pulleys around which tendons work. They also form tunnels in which tendons lie (p. 153).

The *periosteum* is another example of a fibrous membrane. In this the external layer is composed of a network of dense connective tissue containing blood vessels. The deeper layer, which lies adjacent to the bone, is composed of areolar connective tissue and contains both bundles of collagenic fibers and a network of thin elastic fibers. The *perichondrium,* the *dura mater* (p. 314) and the *sclera* of the eye (p. 355) also are fibrous membranes.

The final example of a fibrous membrane is the *synovial membranes.* These are the membranes which line joint cavities (p. 126). The free surface of a synovial membrane is covered with flattened connective tissue cells; this layer may rest on areolar, dense fibrous or adipose connective tissue. A small amount of fluid, called synovial fluid, is present and permits movement of the joint without friction.

Skin

Structure. The skin is an example of a complex combination of tissues. It may be thought of as a cutaneous membrane and furnishes an example of a more complex combination of tissues as building materials than is found in epithelial and fibrous membranes.

Since one of the duties of the nurse is to give the proper care to the skin of the patient, it is considered worthwhile to pay special attention to the structure of the skin.

The skin covers the entire surface of the body. It consists of two main layers which are very different in character and originate from different germ layers of the embryo (p. 789). The two layers are the epidermis and the derma or corium, which are cemented together firmly. Immediately under the derma, but not part of the skin, there is a layer of areolar connective tissue, called the subcutaneous tissue or superficial fascia, described above as a fibrous membrane. Other names which are given to this layer of subcutaneous tissue are the *tela subcutanea* and the *panniculus adiposus.* Bundles of collagenic fibers extend from the dermis of the skin into the subcutaneous tissue to provide anchorage for the skin.

If you look at your finger tips and palms you can see ridges in the skin; these are the papillae of the corium which project into the epidermis. The ridges develop during the third and the fourth fetal months, and the pattern never changes except to enlarge. The pattern is peculiar to the individual and serves to identify him. Occasionally, criminals try to eradicate the pattern by having operations performed which leave scars on the finger tips, thus obliterating the pattern.

EPIDERMIS. The epidermis is the outer, thin layer of skin. It is composed of stratified squamous keratinizing epithelium. Since it contains no blood vessels its cells obtain their nourishment from tissue fluid derived from the capillaries of the dermis. Numerous nerve endings penetrate the epidermis, and specialized endings or receptors (p. 338), as well as free nerve endings, are located in the epidermis. The outer layers of the epidermis are exposed to the air, hence are keratinized, or cornified, to prevent dehydration of the deeper layers. The surface of the skin is difficult to moisten because it is covered by a film of oil produced by the sebaceous glands (p. 43).

The epidermis varies in thickness in different parts of the body. It is thickest on the palms and the soles. An individual who stands

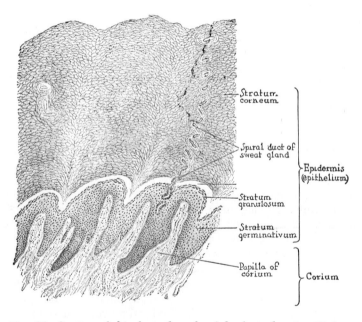

FIG. 20. Section of skin from the sole of the foot, showing all the layers of the epidermis and a part of the corium. ×70.

a great deal may develop callouses on the feet, as one who does difficult manual work may have callouses on his hands. The thickest skin has the most layers in the epidermis. The 4 layers of the epidermis present on the sole of the foot are shown in Figure 20. The layers are (1) the horny layer or stratum corneum, which consists of dead scales of keratinized material; (2) the stratum lucidum, whose cells contain eleidin, which is formed during the process of keratinization; (3) the stratum granulosum, in which layer the epithelial cells die and keratohyalin appears; and (4) the stratum germinativum, which is adjacent to the derma or corium. The cells of the horny outer layer are being shed constantly (desquamated) and are replaced constantly by cells from the deeper layers of epidermis. Blisters extend down to the stratum granulosum. The growth of the epidermis takes place exclusively in the stratum germinativum by mitosis; these cells proliferate continuously.

The color of the skin depends on the pigment granules (melanin) in the basal cells of the fourth layer or stratum germinativum.

DERMA, OR CORIUM. The inner layer of the skin is the derma or corium. It is composed of dense connective tissue. The surface of the derma is uneven, due to the presence of papillae. The outer-

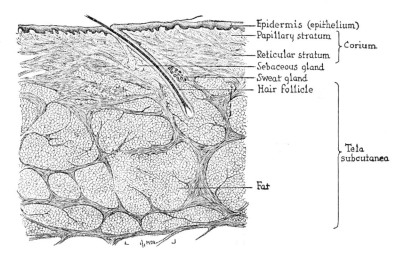

FIG. 21. Section of skin, showing the epidermis, the corium and the tela subcutanea. A hair follicle, a sweat gland and a sebaceous gland are shown; the deep fascia is omitted in the drawing. ×17.

most layer of the derma, called the papillary layer, contains fine bundles of collagenic fibers closely woven together. Next, there is the reticular layer in which there are coarse bundles of interlacing collagenic fibers as shown in Figure 21. Elastic fibers form networks between the bundles of collagenic fibers. The cells in this connective tissue are fibroblasts, fat cells and some macrophages. The fibers give strength, extensibility and elasticity to the skin. The extensibility of the skin is evident when one has swollen extremities; it is even more evident when the skin over the abdomen is stretched during pregnancy, in extreme obesity, when there is an accumulation of a large amount of fluid in the abdomen or a large ovarian tumor or cyst. The stretched skin is smooth and glistening and can be injured by excessive stretching. The little tears which occur during stretching remain visible afterward as silvery white streaks called striae.

Age Changes. In youth the skin is extensible and elastic. As one grows older, the skin becomes thinner and less elastic. The fat disappears from the subcutaneous tissue (superficial fascia), and the skin appears wrinkled.

Blood Supply. The largest arteries of the skin are arranged in the form of a network in the subcutaneous tissue just below the derma. From this network branches pass inward to supply the adipose tissue of the fascia and parts of the hair follicles; other branches pass outward to supply the skin. When the vessels reach the outer part of the reticular layer of the dermis they form a second network or subpapillary plexus. The capillaries of the skin are found only in the connective tissue beneath the epidermis.

The veins of the derma can become distended with blood, and when this happens the skin serves as a reservoir for blood. When the skin is exposed to cold the small arteries of the skin constrict, and less blood flows through them. This means that less heat is lost from the body (p. 708). When the skin is exposed to heat the vessels dilate and more blood flows through the skin, thus favoring loss of heat from the body (p. 708).

Lymphatic Vessels. Lymphatic vessels are particularly numerous in the skin and are arranged in superficial and deep networks. The skin cannot be pricked anywhere without penetrating lymphatic vessels.

Nerves to and from the Skin. The nerves which reach the skin from the central nervous system are distributed to the smooth muscle in the walls of the small arteries in the derma, to the smooth muscle around the roots of the hairs and to the sweat glands of

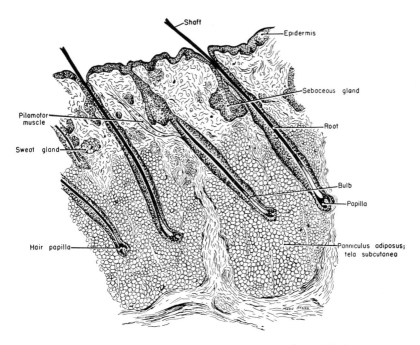

FIG. 22. Section of scalp showing all parts of hair follicle, sweat and sebaceous glands and pilomotor muscle. ×14. (Piersol, G. A.: Normal Histology, Philadelphia, Lippincott.)

the skin. The nerves which carry messages from the skin to the central nervous system show specialized endings (receptors, p. 338) of many types. They are affected by changes in the environment of the individual, and the messages which they transmit to the central nervous system arouse sensations in the brain. By this means we acquire information about the world in the immediate vicinity of the body.

Appendages of the Skin. The cutaneous glands, the hair and the nails comprise the appendages of the skin, and are protective in character. All are specializations or differentiations of the epidermis.

CUTANEOUS GLANDS. The *cutaneous* glands are of 3 types: sebaceous, sweat and ceruminous. The sebaceous glands are found everywhere on the surface of the body except on the palms and the soles. They lie in the superficial layer of the derma, and their excretory ducts usually open into the necks of the hair follicles, as shown in Figure 22. Sebaceous glands produce an oily secretion (called sebum) which prevents the hair from becoming brittle. This secretion likewise acts as a waterproof layer on the skin and decreases the loss of water from the skin.

Sweat glands are distributed over the entire skin; they are most numerous in the axillae and on the palms, the soles and the forehead. It is estimated that there are about 2 million sweat glands in the skin of an adult. These glands are located in the derma, and their ducts pass through the epidermis, in a spiral manner, to the surface of the skin where they open in pores. Sweat glands are shown in Figures 22 and 23.

Sweat glands are supplied by nerves which carry messages to cause perspiration when the outside temperature is high or when there is fever (an elevation of body temperature). The sole purpose of sweat glands is to act as an emergency mechanism when

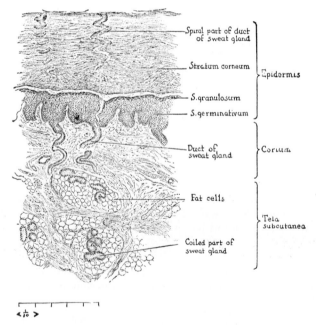

FIG. 23. Section of skin from palm, showing parts of sweat glands extending from the tela subcutanea (panniculus adiposus, superficial fascia) to the surface. ×65.

it is necessary for the body to lose heat by the evaporation of water from its surface. The pores of the sweat glands are rather prominent, and many individuals use astringents on the skin to close the pores and make them appear smaller.

Ceruminous glands are modified sweat glands; they are found only in the skin of the passages leading into the ear (external auditory meatus). They secrete wax which helps to protect the ear drum. If wax is allowed to accumulate in large amounts it may harden and cause earache.

The *mammary* glands are really specialized cutaneous glands which produce milk for the nourishment of the young (p. 805).

HAIR. Hairs develop from the epidermis and vary in length and thickness in different parts of the body. They are present over almost the entire surface of the body, with the exception of the palms and the soles, but they are thickest on the scalp. The parts of the hair are the shaft and the root. The shaft is pigmented and projects beyond the surface of the skin. When the pigment is lost the hair turns gray.

The root and its coverings comprise the follicle. The outer covering of the root is a continuation of the stratum germinativum. Hairs are being lost throughout life and are replaced by the continued division of the epidermal cells of the germinal layer.

Two or more sebaceous glands are associated with each hair follicle, as shown in Figure 22. Their ducts open into the follicle near the surface of the skin. Bundles of smooth muscle are present around the root of the hair and are called the *arrectores pilorum.* When the smooth muscles contract they make the hair stand on end or draw the shaft into the vertical position. The skin around the hair is elevated and is responsible for the appearance of "gooseflesh."

Hair is straight or curly, depending on the difference of curvature of the follicle and the form of the hair. If the follicle is unbent, and if the shaft is cylindrical the hair is straight. If the follicle is bent and if the shaft is flattened, the hair is curly. The primary development of the hair begins about the end of the third month of fetal life. During postnatal life the maximal rate at which hair grows is about one half inch per month. Cutting and shaving have no effect on the growth of hair.

THE NAILS are the horny scales of epidermis that overlie the dorsal surfaces of the fingers and the toes. The corium, which the nail covers, is modified to form the nail bed. New formation of nail takes place in the epithelium at the proximal portion of the nail bed. As new formation takes place the nail moves forward and thus grows in length. The crescent at the base of the nail is called the lunula.

Functions of the Skin. The skin performs many functions. It is protective; it acts as a mechanical barrier to prevent injury to underlying tissues. The horny layer acts as a chemical barrier; if the skin is allowed to remain dirty, its protective power is less efficient. When a break occurs in the epidermis the ever-present bacteria enter and eventually reach the deeper tissues, and infection results. The skin is a nearly waterproof covering and makes it possible for the body to maintain a high content of water even in dry air. The skin enables the body to be immersed in fresh water without being swollen and in salt water without being shrunken.

The skin is an important sense organ, containing receptors which are responsive to touch, pain, and changes of temperature. It is a source of information regarding one's immediate environment.

The skin is important in the regulation of body temperature; its sweat glands constitute an emergency mechanism for cooling the body by evaporation of sweat from its surface, thus facilitating the loss of heat on hot days. The amount of blood brought to the skin likewise aids in temperature regulation, and the amount of blood varies with the size of the blood vessels in the skin. When the vessels are dilated, more heat is lost; and when they are constricted, less heat is lost.

Water, sodium chloride and glucose can be stored in the skin. Some substances are absorbed through the skin. Lead and aniline dyes may be absorbed in sufficient amounts to produce symptoms of poisoning, which makes this an industrial hazard. Methyl salicylate (oil of wintergreen) is rubbed on the skin to relieve painful joints in rheumatism. Vitamin D (p. 623) is produced in the skin when one is exposed to the ultraviolet light which is present in sunlight.

ORGANS

As stated previously, tissues are combined to form organs. We have considered the structure of some of the tissues of the body and have had examples of simple combinations of tissues to form membranes, and a complex combination of tissues to form the skin. The next step in considering the organization of the body is to think of the component parts of organs.

An organ is a part of the body which performs a definite function. Organs have connective tissue frameworks, with special blood, lymph and nerve supplies, in addition to highly specialized cells which are characteristic for each organ. The specialized cells form the "parenchyma" of the organ, which is the important and predominant tissue. The accessory supporting tissues form the "stroma" of the organ. The stomach, the kidney and the liver are examples of organs.

SYSTEMS

The final units of organization in the body are called systems. A system is a group of organs, each of which contributes its share to the function of the whole. The systems of the body are skeletal, muscular, nervous, circulatory, respiratory, digestive, excretory, endocrine and reproductive.

The skeletal system is composed of bones and joints. This system supports and protects the viscera and the central nervous system and makes possible the movements of various parts of the body by supplying levers upon which skeletal muscles can act. Each bone is an organ; connective tissue predominates in this system. The cells of this system carry out highly specialized functions (p. 82).

The muscular system is composed of muscles. Movements of the body are due to the contraction of skeletal or striated muscles (p. 145). Movements of materials along the digestive tract are due to the contraction of smooth muscle (p. 146). Blood is pumped around the body by the heart muscle. Each muscle is an organ, and muscular tissue is the predominant tissue in this system. The cells in each type of muscular tissue are highly specialized.

The nervous system is made up of the brain, the spinal cord and the peripheral nerves. The organs of special sense are included with the nervous system. This is the great correlating and controlling system of the body. Messages flash with great rapidity over all parts of this system, as over telephone and telegraph wires. The nervous system is intimately connected with all other systems and, by means of the organs of special sense, it is the source of information about the outside world and about one's own interior. Each part of the central nervous system is an organ. Nervous tissue predominates, and the cells are highly specialized for the conduction of messages.

The circulatory system comprises the heart, blood vessels, lymph vessels and nodes. The heart is the pump, while the blood vessels carry food and oxygen to all parts of the body and return waste to the organs of excretion. The heart and each vessel are organs. Many types of tissue are present in the circulatory system, and many types of specialized cells are found.

The respiratory system comprises the respiratory passages and the lungs. It makes possible the oxygenation of the blood and the elimination of carbon dioxide. The lungs and each part of the passageway are organs, and many types of cells and tissues are found in this system.

The digestive system comprises the alimentary tract and its associated glands, and the tongue and the teeth. It converts food into substances which can be absorbed and utilized by the various tissues of the body. Each part of the system, such as the stomach, the pancreas, and the liver, is an organ. Many types of tissues and an even greater number of types of specialized cells are found in this system.

The excretory system proper includes the kidneys and the excretory ducts. Each kidney and ureter and the urinary bladder are organs. Nitrogenous waste, excess inorganic salts and water are eliminated by this system. Many types of tissue and cells are found in the excretory system.

The endocrine system comprises the glands of internal secretion; these are the pituitary, the thyroid, the parathyroids, the adrenal glands, the gonads and the islet cells of the pancreas. The function of this system is chemical correlation, which is slower than nervous correlation. An apt comparison is that the speed of nervous correlation is like the telephone, while that of chemical correlation is like postal or freight service. Each gland is an organ, and the cells of each are highly specialized to produce the particular secretion (hormone) characteristic of that gland.

The reproductive system, in the male, comprises the testes and a system of excretory ducts (epididymis, ductus deferens, ejaculatory ducts) with their accessory structures (seminal vesicles, prostate gland, bulbo-urethral glands and penis). The female reproductive system comprises the ovaries and the ducts (uterine tubes, uterus and vagina) with their associated structures (external genitalia). This system is concerned with the perpetuation of the species. Each part of the system is an organ. Many tissues are found in this system, and the cells in each are highly specialized to carry out their particular functions.

All of the systems are interrelated and correlated functionally, and it is impossible to alter one system without producing changes in the others.

PRACTICAL CONSIDERATIONS

Cellulitis is an inflammation of the subcutaneous tissue or super-ficial fascia. As this is continuous throughout the body, cellulitis may be widespread and diffuse.

Decubitus ulcers (bed sores), occur where there are pressure areas in the body. Frequent turning of the patient's body and alcohol rubs help to prevent this distressing condition. Sometimes it is said that the nursing care of any hospital can be judged by the presence or the absence of bed sores.

Syphilitic ulcers occur in the late stages of untreated syphilis. They are seen less frequently now than formerly, due to the dissemination of information about venereal disease.

Acne (pimples) is due to infection of sebaceous glands.

Boils are due to infection of hair follicles.

Hives is the lay term for urticaria, a skin condition characterized by the sudden appearance of raised patches which are white in the center and itch severely. Hives occur after the ingestion of certain foods, such as strawberries or seafood, to which some individuals are sensitive. The condition usually disappears within a day or two.

Sunburn is a condition in which the skin is swollen and red after long exposure to the sun, especially to its ultraviolet light, and can happen even on a cloudy day. It is thought to be due to the production of a substance like histamine, which dilates the capillaries and leads to swelling or edema. An individual who has large areas of sunburn usually is quite ill and complains of constitutional disturbances, such as fever, malaise and headache. A moderate exposure to sunlight stimulates the production of vitamin D from ergosterol in the skin. This is discussed in textbooks of chemistry.

Anesthesia of the skin refers to a loss of feeling in the skin. It is due to injury of peripheral nerves or central nervous system. In patients with this condition, as well as in unconscious patients, great care is needed in the use of hot water bottles or heating pads, as there is no warning signal, and severe burns may occur. The sense organs in the skin are exceedingly important in protecting us from various types of danger, and when messages cannot reach our conscious centers we are likely to experience damage to the skin.

Skin Signs. Nurses should form the habit of observing the differences in color and condition of the skin in various patients. The appearance reflects the existence of a general disease. The skin is red in hypertension (high blood pressure) and in any other condition in which the blood vessels of the skin are dilated. A pale skin suggests anemia (too few red corpuscles or too little hemoglobin). The color of the skin may be blue or purple (cyanosis) in severe heart disease and in such pulmonary diseases as pneumonia (in which the blood is not being adequately supplied with oxygen). A yellow skin (jaundice) indicates the presence of bile pigments in the blood in larger than normal amounts. A bronzing of the skin is characteristic of Addison's disease (deficiency of secretion of the adrenal cortex, p. 736). The alert nurse will find many clues of interest if she observes color and condition of the skin of her patients.

The skin of the hyperthyroid patient (p. 729) is unusually moist and hot. Such a person produces more heat than normal, and, in order to keep the body temperature from rising to fever levels, more heat is lost by evaporation of sweat.

Rashes are common in many infectious diseases.

The skin is usually *rough* in vitamin deficiencies and often is cracked and scaly around the corners of the mouth.

Grafts. Skin from one part of the body may be "grafted" to another part in the same individual after such injuries as burns.

SUMMARY

1. Definitions

A. Subdivisions of anatomy: gross, microscopic, cytologic, embryologic, neuro-anatomic, comparative, human

B. Terms of location and position: anatomic position, superior, inferior, anterior or ventral, posterior or dorsal, cranial, caudal, medial, lateral, internal, external, proximal, distal, central, peripheral, parietal, visceral

C. Fundamental planes: sagittal, coronal or frontal, transverse or horizontal

2. Vertebrate structure of man: vertebral column, dorsal cavity, ventral cavity (thoracic and abdominal)

3. Organization of the body: cells, tissues, organs, systems

A. Cells

a. Structure. Nucleus: chromatin, nucleolus. Cytoplasm: organelles (centrosome, mitochondria, Golgi apparatus, ergastoplasm, fibrils). Inclusions: stored foods, secretory granules, globules, pigments, crystals

b. Cell division: stages of mitosis (prophase, metaphase, anaphase, telophase)

B. Tissues
    a. Definition
    b. Types: epithelial, connective, muscular, nervous
        (1) Epithelial: general functions, common features, types

            (A) Covering and lining membranes: simple squamous, simple cuboidal, simple columnar (ciliated and nonciliated); pseudostratified; stratified squamous (keratinized and nonkeratinized), stratified columnar and transitional

            (B) Glandular division: endocrine and exocrine glands

        (2) Connective: occurrence and origin, general functions, characteristics, types: areolar, adipose, dense fibrous, cartilage (hyaline, fibrous and elastic), bone (cancellous and compact) and hemopoietic (myeloid and lymphatic) tissues

  4. Tissues as building materials
    A. Membranes
      a. Epithelial: mucous and serous
      b. Fibrous: superficial fascia, deep fascia, periosteum, synovial membrane
    B. Skin
      a. Structure: epidermis (4 layers) and derma or corium (2 layers)
      b. Age changes
      c. Blood supply
      d. Lymphatic vessels
      e. Nerves
      f. Appendages: cutaneous glands (sebaceous, sweat and ceruminous); hairs; nails
      g. Functions: protection, sense organ, regulation of body temperature, storage, absorption
  5. Organs
  6. Systems: skeletal, muscular, nervous, circulatory, respiratory, digestive, excretory, endocrine and reproductive

SITUATION AND QUESTIONS

When the hot water heater at a summer camp exploded, John Brian received scattered second-degree and third-degree burns over his entire body.

1. Second-degree burns involve the superficial and the underlying layers of the skin; therefore, the primary tissues which were

totally or partially destroyed are: _____(a) epithelial and connective tissues; _____(b) epithelial and muscular tissues; _____(c) connective and muscular tissues; _____(d) adipose and fibrous tissues.

2. The function of the sebaceous glands, which are located in the derma of the skin, was impaired. They have as their function the secretion of: _____(a) sweat; _____(b) salt; _____ (c) oil; _____(d) milk.

3. With proper care new tissue will be formed. The formation of new tissue depends upon the process of division of the cells making up the tissues. The usual type of cell division is called: _____(a) binary fission; _____; (b) mitosis; _____ (c) budding; _____(d) segmentation.

4. Epithelial tissues are classified according to the arrangement and the shape of their cells. The type found in the skin is: _____(a) stratified squamous; _____(b) simple cuboidal; _____(c) simple columnar; _____(d) simple squamous.

5. Connective tissue is found not only with the skin but also is found widely distributed throughout the body. Which of the following is *not* an example of connective tissue?: _____(a) Blood. _____(b) Bone. _____(c) Muscle. _____ (d) Tendon.

~~~~~~

2. Introduction to Physiology

~~~~~~

DEFINITION

Physiology is the study of the phenomena presented by living organisms; also, it includes a study of the functions of each organ and the conditions which determine each function.

RELATION TO OTHER SCIENCES

Physiology is a very young science in comparison with anatomy. It is not an independent science; it is very dependent upon several other branches of knowledge. A knowledge of physics is essential in understanding the function of the heart and the blood vessels, the mechanics of respiration, the formation of images in the eye and the transmission of sound waves to the inner ear. A knowledge of chemistry is indispensable in unraveling the secrets of digestion and metabolism and in understanding the way in which oxygen and carbon dioxide are carried in the blood.

The science of pathology (the study of disease) has contributed much information to physiology regarding the function of the endocrine glands and the importance of vitamins. The pathologic changes in the body which follow disturbances in the endocrine system or occur when one is deprived of certain vitamins disclose facts of great importance to the physiologist. The functions of various parts of the nervous system have been made more understandable by the contributions of psychology and psychiatry. Surgery has extended the boundaries of physiologic knowledge by noting the effects which follow removal of various organs or parts of organs. The newly born science of electronics is making it possible for investigators to study many functions of the body by entirely new methods and is responsible for the revision of some of the ideas of function.

CHARACTERISTICS OF LIVING MATTER

The characteristics, or properties, of living matter depend upon the differentiation of cells which compose it. Differentiation means that certain cells are highly specialized for particular functions.

Excitability is one of the most obvious properties of living organisms. This is the ability to be affected by a change in the environment (called a stimulus). This means that a living organism is sensitive to its surroundings. We constantly use this fundamental characteristic of excitability as a test of "aliveness" or awareness in another person or in an animal. Children pinch each other, call each other names, poke animals, make loud noises to see if they can call forth responses in any living organism in their vicinity. This property is developed most highly in nerve cells. The activities it initiates depend on changes in the environment, either external or internal and tend to make such adaptations as are essential to the preservation of the individual.

Conductivity refers to the ability of specialized cells to transmit a wave of excitation from the part of the body stimulated to other parts of the nervous system. This property is developed most highly in nerve cells.

Contractility refers to the ability of long cells to undergo shortening and, thereby, produce movement. Contractility is highly developed in muscle cells.

Absorption and Assimilation. Absorption is the ability of specialized cells to take substances into their protoplasm; it is highly selective. This property is developed highly in the epithelial cells of the small intestine; through the activity of these cells the food we eat is absorbed from the lumen of the intestine. Assimilation refers to the processes within cells by which absorbed material is used to build protoplasm.

Excretion and Secretion. Excretion is the ability of the cell to eliminate waste products which it has produced. Cells also can eliminate substances which are useful to the body, such as digestive juices or hormones (internal secretions). They remove materials from the blood, build them into characteristic secretions and then extrude them into ducts or into blood and lymph. This process is called secretion.

Respiration. The use of oxygen and production of carbon dioxide constitute respiration. These are essential phases of metabolism, or the burning, of food materials with the production of energy. The process of metabolizing foods may be thought of as the transformation of potential energy of foods into kinetic energy, or work, and thermal energy, or body heat.

Growth and Reproduction. Growth is the increase in the amount of protoplasm from sources within an organism. It is due to an increase in the number of cells by mitosis, rather than to an increase in the size of cells. It includes the process of repair by which damaged parts are replaced. When one reaches the adult stage the body no longer increases in size, and repair becomes predominant as growth ceases.

Another meaning for reproduction is the formation of new individuals of the next generation; this type of reproduction keeps life going from one generation to the next.

Organization of Living Matter. Perhaps the most striking property of living matter is its organization. Each part of a cell, and each cell as a whole, is so organized that it performs a special function. Each tissue, in turn, is specialized for the performance of characteristic functions. Each organ and each system perform particular functions for the benefit of the body as a whole.

Whenever something happens in one part of the body to disturb the existing condition, compensatory responses occur in other parts of the body to restore the original condition. The adjusting mechanisms tend to maintain the body in a "steady state" which is called homeostasis. Suppose you suddenly look at your watch and see that it is time for class. You run up the steps, and your muscles require more oxygen than they had been using when you were sauntering along toward school. To supply extra oxygen, you breathe more rapidly, the heart beats faster, and the blood pressure rises in order to bring a more abundant supply of blood to the active muscles. You may feel warm and perspire by the time you reach the classroom. This is a brief list of the changes which occur during a bout of exercise.

As you would anticipate, damage to any part of the body has widespread effects on other parts. The whole field of medicine is concerned with the changes that occur in the human body when there is damage to such organs as the heart, the lungs or the liver. It is interesting to know that there are some organs which function for a time and then undergo "involution" or atrophy. This is the case with the thymus gland, which ceases to function at the onset of puberty, and the ovaries in women, which cease to function after the menopause (p. 768). Normal adjustments are made by the body when such organs undergo involution.

The beauty of the organization of the body should make a lasting impression upon you. It is truly remarkable how well the body works if properly nourished and given adequate rest. It is equally remarkable how few difficulties are due to defective parts present at birth or to natural breakdowns of parts of the body before one reaches old age. Intricate integration and correlation of functions enable us to maintain life with a feeling of "well-being" and to perpetuate the species by reproduction.

COMPOSITION OF PROTOPLASM

The chief constituents of protoplasm are water, inorganic salts, proteins, carbohydrates and lipids (substances which are somewhat like fats). The most abundant elements of the body are carbon, hydrogen, nitrogen and oxygen. The entire body of a man has the following composition:

	Percentage	Percentage
Inorganic substances	70.3	
Water		65.9
Mineral matter		4.4
Organic substances	29.7	
Carbon		18.4
Oxygen		6.0
Hydrogen		2.7
Nitrogen		2.6
Total	100.0	100.0

The elementary composition of the human body, including inorganic and organic substances, is presented as follows.

	Percentage		Percentage
Oxygen	65.00	Sulfur	0.25
Carbon	18.00	Chlorine	0.15
Hydrogen	10.00	Sodium	0.15
Nitrogen	3.00	Magnesium	0.05
Calcium	2.00	Iron	0.004
Phosphorus	1.00	Other elements	0.046
Potassium	0.35		

The composition of different tissues varies widely; that for dead mammalian striated muscle and for white matter of brain are presented below.

	Striated muscle	White matter of brain
Water	75.0	70.7
Protein	20.0	10.0
Lipids	2.0	18.5
Carbohydrates and extractives	2.0	—
Inorganic salts	1.0	0.8

IMPORTANCE OF THE VARIOUS CONSTITUENTS OF LIVING MATTER

WATER

There is a large amount of water in all living tissue; life can continue only a few days without water. Water holds the various components of protoplasm in solution; the chemical reactions which occur in cells require the presence of water. Many substances ionize in water. For example, such substances as sodium chloride split into ions which bear electric charges, Na^+ and Cl^-, and are called electrolytes. The properties and the classes of electrolytes are determined by the kinds of ions they yield when they dissolve in water. These classes are acids, alkalies or bases, and salts. All of these are of great importance in living matter.

Neutrality, acidity and alkalinity. In order to explain these terms satisfactorily, a discussion of pure water must be presented. Pure water consists almost entirely of molecules of H_2O. However, a few molecules dissociate into H and OH ions. In pure water the number of H ions is exactly equal to the number of OH ions. Because of this, pure water is called a neutral solution. The amounts of H and OH ions found in pure water are expressed in terms of gram equivalents per liter of pure water. The concentration of H ions is 10^{-7} gram equivalent per liter at 22° C.

This concentration may be expressed in several ways, such as 1×10^{-7},

0.0000001,1/10^7 and 1/10,000,000, and means that there is one gram equivalent of H in the ionic form in 10 million liters of pure water. The number of OH ions is exactly equal, as stated previously.

The product of H and OH ions in pure water is $10^{-7} \times 10^{-7}$, or 10^{-14}. In fact, if the concentration of H ions is multiplied by the concentration of OH ions, the product is constant, not only for water, but also for any aqueous solution, regardless of whether it is neutral, acid or alkaline. Therefore, if the H ions increase, the OH ions must decrease correspondingly. For example, if, in a given solution, the concentration of H ions is 10^{-5}, the concentration of OH ions must be 10^{-9}. If the concentration of H ions is 10^{-10}, the concentration of OH ions must be 10^{-4}. In other words, the product of H ions and OH ions is always 10^{-14}.

The reaction of any aqueous solution depends on the relative numbers of H and OH ions. When the number of each is 10^{-7}, or equal, the solution is said to be neutral in reaction, as is the case in pure water. If the number of H ions is in excess of 10^{-7}, such as 10^{-5}, or 0.00001, the solution is acid in reaction. If the number of H ions is less than 10^{-7} (which means that the number of OH ions is greater than 10^{-7}), for example, H ions 10^{-11}, or 0.00000000001, and the OH ions 10^{-3}, or 0.001, the solution is alkaline in reaction.

It will be seen that a determination of the number of either the H ions or the OH ions in any electrolytic solution will give an accurate estimate of its reaction. It is evident, also, that in order to express the acidity or alkalinity of an electrolytic solution it is sufficient to state the number of either H or OH ions present.

This method of expressing acidity or alkalinity becomes unwieldy, because of the large numbers that need to be used. Sorenson suggested that it would be more convenient to express the concentration of H ions in a simplified form, in terms of the logarithm (to the base 10) of its reciprocal. Arbitrarily, he chose the letter "p" to signify that the negative exponent to the base 10 is used. Since Sorenson's time the term pH has come into general use. The pH of a solution is the logarithm of the reciprocal of its H ion concentration.

A few examples to illustrate the method of changing the H ion concentration into terms of pH follow. In a neutral solution, the concentration of H ions, as stated above, is 10^{-7} or 1×10^{-7}; the pH is the log of the reciprocal, which may be written as 1/1 $\times 10^{-7}$, 1/0.0000001, 10,000,000 or 10^7; thus, the pH of a neutral solution is 7.0.

Let us assume that the concentration of H ions in a given solution of electrolyte is 2×10^{-6}; this may be written as 0.000002. The pH is the log of the reciprocal, 1/0.000002 or 500,000, and is 5.699.

In blood the concentration of H ions is 0.4×10^{-7}; the pH is the log of the reciprocal, 1/0.4 $\times 10^{-7}$, 1/0.00000004 or 25,000,000, and is 7.399.

In summary, the pH of a neutral solution is 7.0; that of an acid solution is less than 7.0, for example, 5.0, and that of an alkaline solution is greater than 7.0, for example 9.0. One must keep in mind that a solution with a pH of 3.0 is more acid than one of pH 4.0, and that a solution with a pH of 9.0 is more alkaline than one of pH 8.0. The pH of gastric juice is about 1.4, which means that it is strongly acid. The pH of the urine is about 6.0, which means that it is weakly acid.

The following table of approximate values will prove of value.

Normality	Conc. H ions	Conc. OH ions	pH
Normal HCl	1	10^{-14}	0
0.1 N HCl	10^{-1}	10^{-13}	1
0.01 N HCl	10^{-2}	10^{-12}	2
0.001N HCl	10^{-3}	10^{-11}	3
0.0001N HCl	10^{-4}	10^{-10}	4
0.00001 N HCl	10^{-5}	10^{-9}	5
0.000001N HCl	10^{-6}	10^{-8}	6
Pure water	10^{-7}	10^{-7}	7
0.000001 N NaOH	10^{-8}	10^{-6}	8
0.00001 N NaOH	10^{-9}	10^{-5}	9
0.0001 N NaOH	10^{-10}	10^{-4}	10
0.001 N NaOH	10^{-11}	10^{-3}	11
0.01 N NaOH	10^{-12}	10^{-2}	12
0.1 N NaOH	10^{-13}	10^{-1}	13
Normal NaOH	10^{-14}	1	14

By looking at the table it is evident that every rise of 1 in pH means lowering of the concentration of H ions to 1/10 of its previous value.

H and OH ions are involved in all the chemical processes which take place in living cells, and the functions of cells are modified greatly by any departure from the normal reaction. Acids are formed constantly in the body as a result of metabolic activity; carbonic acid (or its derivative, carbon dioxide) is produced by the oxidation of all types of foods. Phosphoric and sulfuric acids are formed by oxidation of phosphorus and sulfur of protein foods. Lactic acid and pyruvic acid are produced during muscular activity. Substances which produce bases, such as Na,K,Ca and Mg, are taken into the body in foods. Since living cells are so sensitive to changes in reaction, either toward acidity or alkalinity, there are ample means of keeping the pH relatively constant in the body, despite ingested acids and bases and those produced by metabolism of foods and during muscular activity.

The respiratory system and the excretory system play major roles in the maintenance of the acid-base balance of the body (p. 563). A slight shift in the pH of the blood, which indicates the condition of the entire body, can alter the functions of many cells. Such variations arise when (1) one loses large amounts of gastric juice containing hydrochloric acid by prolonged vomiting, and the reaction of the blood becomes decidedly alkaline; (2) there is a failure to eliminate carbonic acid (as carbon dioxide) as rapidly as it is formed, in pulmonary disease; or (3) the kidneys fail to excrete phosphoric and sulfuric acids produced by protein metabolism, and they accumulate in the blood. In the above situations, and in many others as well, the patient is said to be in a state of "acidosis" or "alkalosis," according to the reaction of the blood, and, as a result of this, bodily functions are altered. One example of alteration is evident in the nervous system; in alkalosis, excitability is increased and convulsions may occur, while in acidosis, excitability is decreased, and coma or unconsciousness may occur.

Water is important in the regulation of body temperature. When one is exposed to heat the sweat glands become active, and the evaporation of water from the surface of the skin cools it and helps to prevent a rise in body temperature. Cells perform their various functions most efficiently at normal body temperature. During fever, many of their activities may be altered.

Water is important in the excretion of waste. Waste products are eliminated chiefly in urine; if there is a lack of sufficient water for this purpose, waste products accumulate in the blood. Normally, one's thirst is the best guide in determining how much water should be taken in daily to maintain the body in "water balance."

INORGANIC SALTS

Many inorganic salts are found in the body; they occur in the cells and the fluids (blood, tissue fluid and lymph). The chlorides of sodium, potassium, calcium and magnesium are most abundant, while many other salts are present in minute traces. Sodium and chloride ions are present in higher concentrations than other ions in the fluids; inside the cells, potassium and phosphate ions are more abundant than other ions.

Inorganic salts are essential to the maintenance of proper osmotic conditions (movement of water through membranes), acid-base balance, the coagulation of blood (requires calcium), formation of bones (calcium and phosphorus), formation of internal secretion of the thyroid gland (iodine), transport of oxygen and carbon dioxide (iron in hemoglobin of red blood corpuscles).

The chlorides of sodium, potassium and calcium are indispensable so far as conductivity in nerves and contractility of muscles are concerned. A slight increase in the concentration of sodium chloride increases excitability of muscles, and they undergo convulsive contractions. The contractility and the conductivity of heart muscle are disturbed by either too low or too high a concentration of potassium chloride in the blood. Too low a concentration of calcium in the blood can lead to convulsions.

These few examples of the importance of various salts and the disturbances which follow alterations in their concentration will indicate to you the need for having the proper concentration and distribution of salts when giving fluids by vein or in any situation in which patients are not eating well-balanced diets. Many of the glands of internal secretion aid in maintaining the proper salt balance in the body; among these are the adrenal cortex (p. 735) and the posterior lobe of the pituitary gland (p. 723). In other words, the intake of water, the activity of various glands and the kidneys all share in the responsibility of maintaining the proper concentrations of various salts for the welfare of the body.

PROTEINS

Proteins constitute the framework of protoplasm. They also supply energy when they are oxidized, and are the source of enzymes and hormones which are synthesized (meaning "built up") in cells. Growth of new tissue and repair of old tissue depend on available protein. Growing children, elderly individuals and patients who have undergone surgical operations need more protein in the diet than a healthy, young adult.

CARBOHYDRATES

Carbohydrates comprise sugars and starches. They are oxidized easily and are the most readily available source of energy. Glucose, which is the sugar present in the blood, is as essential to the functions of the brain as oxygen. One loses consciousness within a very few minutes in the absence of oxygen. If the concentration of sugar in the blood is too low, convulsions occur. When one goes without food, part of the protein of protoplasm is transformed into glucose in order to keep the concentration in the blood above the convulsive level. This transformation of protein into glucose requires the presence of a normal liver and normal glands of internal secretion.

LIPIDS

The term "lipid" comprises both fats and fat-related substances. Such substances are a source of energy and are stored as reserve food in adipose tissue. The adipose tissue in the superficial fascia is not only a reserve food, but it acts also as an insulator, preventing loss of heat from the body. Lipids are present in high concentration in cell membranes, in which they play an essential role in maintaining a normal permeability. Lipids are important for one more reason—they assist in transportation of fat-soluble vitamins (p. 623) which always are associated with lipids.

As you have noted, each foodstuff has its own individual contribution to make to the welfare of the body. Attention has been called to the transformation of protein into carbohydrate on certain occasions, and already you have learned that it is possible for carbohydrate to be transformed into fat and stored as adipose tissue, for you have witnessed the obese people who are constantly eating "sweets." The detailed consideration of transformation of one foodstuff into another is dealt with in chemistry textbooks.

ORGANIZATION OF LIVING CELLS

Even though the chemical composition of living cells has been determined with accuracy, scientists cannot make synthetic protoplasm in their laboratories. The organization of protoplasm is unique and apparently cannot be duplicated. Some constituents of protoplasm are in the form of colloidal particles (single large molecules or aggregations of smaller molecules) and they may change readily in living cells from the sol state (particles suspended in a liquid) to the gel state (in which the particles absorb the liquid and swell to form a semisolid mass similar to gelatin).

By dissecting various types of cells under the microscope it has been learned that the cell membrane is fairly resistant to damage, and, if it is destroyed in one place (by dissecting needles), it is rapidly repaired by the cytoplasm of the cell.

Cell membranes possess selective permeability. This means that they keep some molecules from entering and permit other molecules of the same size to pass through the membrane into the cells. For example, potassium and phosphate are present inside the cell in higher concentrations than in the tissue fluid bathing the cell. On the other hand, sodium and chloride are present in the tissue fluid in higher concentrations than they are inside the cell. This situation requires a cell membrane with highly selective properties. As long as a cell is alive it permits the entry and exit of molecules which play a part in its metabolism and rejects those for which it has no need.

COMPARISON OF CELL MEMBRANES WITH ARTIFICIAL MEMBRANES

The artificial membranes which we have chosen to compare with the cell membrane are: filter paper, cellophane or collodion, and copper-ferrocyanide membranes. Filter paper contains large pores which allow water and dissolved substances (including large col-

TYPES OF ARTIFICIAL MEMBRANES.

FILTER PAPER	COLLODION OR CELLOPHANE	COPPER FERROCYANIDE
Water and all dissolved substances can pass through. Solid particles, such as grains of sand, are too large to pass.	Water and dissolved crystalloids can pass through. Colloids are held back.	Only water passes through. Crystalloids and colloids held back. Semipermeable.

FACTORS OF IMPORTANCE IN PERMEABILITY.

1. SIZE OF OPENINGS in membranes, as illustrated above.

2. FAT SOLUBILITY.

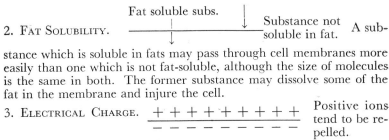

A substance which is soluble in fats may pass through cell membranes more easily than one which is not fat-soluble, although the size of molecules is the same in both. The former substance may dissolve some of the fat in the membrane and injure the cell.

3. ELECTRICAL CHARGE. $+ + + + + + + + +$ $- - - - - - - - -$ Positive ions tend to be repelled.

4. SELECTIVE PERMEABILITY.

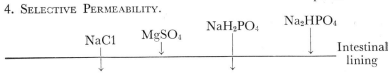

FIG. 24. Types of membranes and factors of importance in permeability. The membranes represented include filter paper, cellophane and copper ferrocyanide. The size of the pores, fat-solubility, electrical charges and selective action of the membrane itself all play a part in determining permeability.

loidal particles or aggregates) to pass through readily but hold back particles as large as grains of sand. Figure 24 illustrates the large size of the pores in filter paper; there are no cell membranes in the body with pores as large as these.

Cellophane or collodion membranes have smaller pores than filter paper, as indicated in Figure 24. Pores of this size permit water and dissolved particles of small size to pass through but hold back large colloidal particles such as protein molecules. It is probable that the pores in the walls of our blood capillaries are of the same size as those in cellophane membranes.

Copper-ferrocyanide membranes (which you can easily make by placing a crystal of ferrocyanide in a copper sulfate solution) have pores which are smaller than those in cellophane, as indicated in Figure 24. Such pores permit only water molecules to pass; all larger molecules are held back. Copper-ferrocyanide membranes are called semipermeable membranes. This means they are permeable to water but hold back all dissolved substances, regardless of the size of the molecules.

Cell membranes behave as semipermeable membranes, in some respects. However, the permeability of cell membranes varies with the condition of the cells, and with their metabolic requirements. Therefore, factors in addition to size of pores help to determine the permeability of cell membranes. One of these other factors is lipid-solubility. If a substance which dissolves easily in fats (such as ether) is brought in contact with the cell membrane it dissolves in the lipid of the cell membrane and penetrates the cell immediately. A third factor is the electric charge on the substance in contact with the cell; if this substance bears a positive charge, the cell membrane repels it and refuses entrance. A fourth factor is the "vital activity" of the cells themselves. An example of this is in the behavior of the cells of the intestinal lining toward sodium acid phosphate (NaH_2PO_4) and disodium phosphate (Na_2HPO_4). The former is admitted readily to the cells which line the wall of the small intestine, and the latter is refused admission. These factors are indicated in the lower section of Figure 24.

PHYSICAL FACTORS INVOLVED IN EXCHANGES THROUGH MEMBRANES

Filtration is the passage of water and dissolved substances through a membrane, due to differences in pressure on the two sides of the membrane. In filtering a solution in the laboratory, the weight of the column of fluid in the funnel, together with atmospheric pressure, supplies the force which is necessary for filtration. This force is called hydrostatic pressure. Figure 25 illustrates filtration.

Filtration occurs in the body and is important in the production of tissue fluid (p. 401) and urine (p. 682). Water and small dissolved particles pass through the capillary walls readily. Occasionally, a large particle (protein molecule) passes through the capillary wall. The pressure of the blood in the capillaries is the driving force for filtration in the body and is an important means of getting nutriment from blood to tissue cells. Likewise, it is important in removing waste from the blood by the kidneys. Filtration in the kidneys is illustrated in Figure 26.

Diffusion is the spreading out of molecules of gas or liquid until equal concentration is reached throughout the container. It is due to the spontaneous movement of molecules, always from a higher

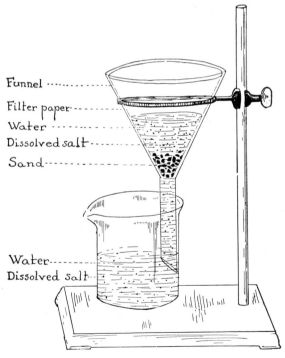

Funnel
Filter paper
Water
Dissolved salt
Sand

Water
Dissolved salt

FIG. 25. Diagram representing filtration.

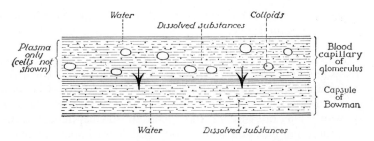

Fɪɢ. 26. Diagram representing filtration in the capillaries. A capillary of a glomerulus of the kidney is used as an example.

to a lower concentration (as if Nature abhorred inequalities). For example, when you enter a room in which there are flowers, like lilies of the valley, you immediately note the odor. Molecules of the perfume diffuse from the flowers to all parts of the room, and, within a short space of time, the odor is uniform throughout the room.

In the body there is diffusion of gases between the air sacs or alveoli of the lungs and the blood. Molecules of oxygen diffuse from the air in the lungs into the blood, and carbon dioxide molecules diffuse from the blood into the air in the lungs. When the blood reaches the capillaries in the tissues of the body, oxygen diffuses from the blood into the tissue fluid and on into tissue cells, while carbon dioxide diffuses from the tissue cells into the tissue fluid and on into the blood. In every instance the molecules diffuse from the region in which they are highly concentrated to the region in which they are less highly concentrated. A diagram of diffusion is shown in Figure 27.

Diffusion of liquids also occurs in the body. An example is the diffusion of glucose. The concentration of glucose is high in the blood immediately after meals, and it diffuses out into tissue fluid and on into tissue cells. As the cells use the glucose, more diffuses from blood into tissue fluid and on into cells. In the opposite direction, waste products diffuse from the cells, in which the concentration is higher, into the tissue fluid and on into the blood, in which the concentration is lower.

Osmosis is the passage of water through semipermeable membranes due to differences in concentration of dissolved substances on the two sides of the membrane. Since dissolved substances do not pass through these membranes, the only way in which equaliza-

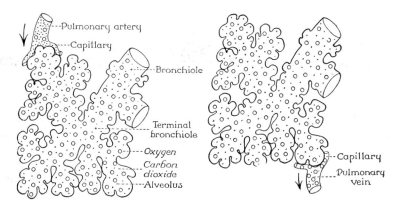

Fig. 27. Diffusion of gases in the alveoli of the lungs. In the diagrams circles represent oxygen, and dots represent carbon dioxide. The diagrams show diffusion of carbon dioxide and oxygen through the alveoli of the lungs by changes in the number of dots and circles in the pulmonary artery and the pulmonary vein.

tion of concentration can be attained on the two sides of the membrane is for water to pass through from the less concentrated to the more concentrated solution. Water is drawn into the concentrated solution in order to dilute it.

Osmosis can be demonstrated easily by the use of red blood corpuscles and salt solutions. Normally, the red corpuscles are suspended in the plasma of the blood (p. 397), the concentration of dissolved substances, such as salts, inside the corpuscles being the same as the concentration of dissolved substances in the plasma. In this case, the plasma is said to be "isotonic" (same concentration) with the corpuscles, and no passage of water through the membrane occurs.

If the red corpuscles are removed from the plasma and placed in a concentrated (hypertonic) salt solution, water leaves the corpuscles and enters the salt solution by osmosis. As a result, the corpuscles shrivel and appear to be *crenated,* or notched. If the corpuscles are placed in a dilute (hypotonic) salt solution, water enters the corpuscles by osmosis. The corpuscles swell and may burst, and then the hemoglobin escapes from the corpuscles and colors the solution. Bursting of red corpuscles with release of hemoglobin is called *laking,* or *hemolysis* (meaning "blood solution"). Crenation and hemolysis are illustrated in Figure 28.

The osmotic effects between body tissues, blood corpuscles and injected solutions are of great importance. Solutions which are injected into the blood stream (intravenously) and those which are injected under the skin (hypodermically or by hypodermoclysis) or into the muscles (intramuscularly) must be isotonic in order to prevent undesirable shrinking or swelling with damage to blood corpuscles and tissue cells. The two solutions used most frequently for intravenous injection, exclusive of whole blood or plasma, are 0.9 per cent sodium chloride, which is called normal or physiologic saline, and 5.4 per cent glucose. Both of these are isotonic with the cells of the body. Water can be taken by mouth, since osmotic adjustments are made in the intestine during its absorption, but it is not given by any other channel.

SPECIALIZED ACTIVITIES OF CELLS

Secretion. Certain specialized cells take materials from the blood and tissue fluid and synthesize (meaning "build up," or place together) them into characteristic secretions, which they then extrude. This is true of the cells of the salivary glands, the gastric glands, the pancreas and the intestinal glands, all of which pour their secretions into the lumen (space within the walls) of the ali-

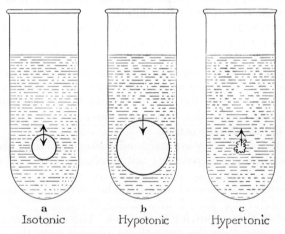

| a | b | c |
| Isotonic | Hypotonic | Hypertonic |

Fig. 28. Osmosis. (a) Red blood corpuscles undergo no change in size in isotonic solutions. (b) They increase in size in hypotonic solutions. (c) They decrease in size in hypertonic solutions.

mentary tract. The cells of the glands of internal secretion are very highly specialized, also; each gland produces one or more typical hormones (p. 718) which influence many activities of the body. The cells of the sweat glands transfer water, salts and urea from the blood to the surface of the body but do not synthesize secretions. The cells of sebaceous glands synthesize an oily secretion called "sebum." The cells of the ceruminous glands synthesize a waxy secretion. Secretory cells produce their secretions by vital activity, that is, they work, as is shown by the extra amounts of oxygen that they use while secreting.

Ameboid Movements. Some cells have the ability to move about the body. The cytoplasm of these cells bulges out into foot-like processes called pseudopodia (false feet), and then the entire cell follows the foot. This type of locomotion is slow indeed but enables white blood cells to leave the blood vessels and migrate to sites of infection or inflammation. When the cells collect at the site of injury they surround and digest bacteria and broken-down cells *(phagocytosis)*. The collection of white blood cells, bacteria and debris of tissue cells is called "pus."

Ciliary Movement. Cilia are fine, protoplasmic extensions of cells. Cilia act together to move fluids or particles which come in contact with the ciliated surface. Repeatedly, they bend down rapidly with a forceful stroke in one direction and return slowly to the original position. The movement passes over the ciliated surface in waves. The cilia are rigid when bending down and limp when returning to the erect position.

Other specialized activities are contractility (p. 218) and conductivity (p. 252).

PRACTICAL CONSIDERATIONS

Water. In conscious, healthy individuals, thirst is a guide to the amount of water needed. Infants, unconscious patients, extremely ill patients and paralyzed patients cannot tell the nurse when they are thirsty. Such patients need to be given enough water to take care of the daily requirements and to maintain water balance, since water is lost continuously whether or not any is taken in.

Foods. We have called attention to the important functions of each type of foodstuff. A balanced diet is a necessity if one is to remain in good health. Dietary fads should be avoided.

Inorganic Salts. A proper balance of sodium, potassium and calcium chlorides is essential for the contraction of muscles and the conductivity of nerves. When fluids are to be administered by vein this must be taken into account. Difficulties with the heart occur if there is either too much or too little potassium in the blood.

Acid-base Balance. Acids are produced during metabolism, and alkalies are taken in as constituents of food. In order to maintain homeostasis there must be a balance between the two. Carbonic acid is eliminated by the lungs; in pulmonary disease there may be an accumulation of this acid in the blood. Sulfuric and phosphoric acids are excreted by the kidneys, and in kidney disease they accumulate in the blood. Lactic acid is taken care of in two ways: some of it is excreted by the kidneys, and some is synthesized to glycogen in the liver. In either kidney or liver disease lactic acid may accumulate in the blood. Hydrochloric acid is produced by the glands of the stomach, and if one experiences a siege of vomiting, so much hydrochloric acid is lost from the body that the acid-base balance is upset, and alkalosis results. The balance may be upset also in starvation and in diabetes mellitus. If the reaction of the blood inclines toward the acid side (pH lower than 7.3) the patient is said to be in acidosis; if the reaction moves toward the alkaline side (pH above 7.4) the patient is said to be in alkalosis). In either case the condition is decidedly serious, and adjustments should be made to restore a slightly alkaline reaction (pH 7.40).

Homeostasis. In order for the body to function properly, correlation by the nervous system and by the glands of internal secretion is needed. If a part of the nervous system is diseased or removed, or if one of the glands of internal secretion is diseased or removed, widespread effects on other parts of the body occur. In most of the patients whom you encounter you will find that the correlation of the body is at fault; some organ or system is failing to perform its function normally, and this alters activity of other organs and systems. Homeostasis occurs only in health.

SUMMARY

1. Definition of physiology
2. Relation of physiology to other sciences: physics, chemistry, pathology, psychology, psychiatry, surgery and electronics
3. Characteristics of living matter
    A. Excitability
    B. Conductivity
    C. Contractility

D. Absorption and assimilation

E. Excretion and secretion

F. Respiration

G. Growth and reproduction

H. Organization

4. Composition of protoplasm

5. Importance of the various constituents of living matter

    A. Water: amount. Functions: solvent, ionization, regulation of body temperature, excretion of waste

    B. Inorganic salts: most abundant salts. Functions: osmosis, acid-base balance, coagulation of blood, formation of bones, formation of internal secretions, transport of oxygen and carbon dioxide, conductivity and contractility

    C. Proteins. Functions: framework of protoplasm, source of energy, source of enzymes and hormones, growth, tissue repair

    D. Carbohydrates. Functions: source of energy, essential to function of nervous system

    E. Lipids (fats and fat-related substances). Functions: source of energy, reserve food in adipose tissue, insulation, cell permeability, association with fat-soluble vitamins

6. Organization of living cells

    A. Organization unique, cannot be duplicated

    B. Characteristics of cell membranes: selective permeability

    C. Comparison of cell membranes with artificial membranes

        a. Filter paper

        b. Cellophane or collodion

        c. Copper-ferrocyanide membranes

7. Physical factors involved in exchanges through membranes

    A. Filtration: in the laboratory; in the body

    B. Diffusion: in a room; in the body

    C. Osmosis: in red corpuscles; importance of isotonic solutions for injection into body

8. Some specialized activities of cells

    A. Secretion

    B. Ameboid movement

    C. Ciliary movement

SITUATION AND QUESTIONS

John Brian was admitted to the hospital for treatment of his burns. One of the problems in his management was that of hydration. Intravenous injections were given, and, by a series of physical processes, there was an exchange of material across membranes.

The process by which these materials will leave the blood vessels to be utilized by the cells is called: _____(a) diffusion; _____(b) osmosis; _____(c) filtration; _____(d) dialysis.

Based on the laws of osmosis, if a hypertonic solution was injected into the blood stream, you would expect the red blood corpuscles to appear: _____(a) crenated; _____(b) hemolyzed; _____(c) laked; _____(d) sludged.

What force causes the physical process of filtration to occur? _____(a) Difference in concentration of dissolved substances on two sides of a membrane; _____(b) Molecular movement; _____(c) Difference in pressure on two sides of a membrane; _____(d) Difference in volume on two sides of a membrane.

The repair of the tissue burned and the growth of new tissue will depend greatly on the following food material: _____(a) protein; _____(b) carbohydrate; _____(c) fats; _____ (d) vitamins.

The addition of salts to the intravenous fluids given John Brian is important to ensure proper body function. A special property of nerve tissue dependent on various salts is: _____(a) growth and repair; _____(b) conductivity; _____(c) metabolism; _____(d) contractility.

UNIT 2

THE ERECT AND MOVING BODY

3. The Skeletal System

INTRODUCTION

The skeletal system forms a solid framework around which the body is built. It is composed of bones and cartilage. It supports the softer tissues and provides protection for them. In addition, it furnishes surfaces for attachment of muscles, tendons and ligaments. Some parts of the skeletal system connect with each other in such a way that they form structures like cages or boxes in which internal organs are lodged. Examples of this are the thorax, or chest, in which the lungs and the heart occupy a protected position; the skull, which houses the brain; and the vertebral column, which houses the spinal cord.

Many of the bones play the part of passive levers by means of which various movements of the body are performed.

Bones are not solid structures; within each bone there is a central cavity filled with bone marrow, which is yellow in some locations and red in others. The cells in the red bone marrow are as

75

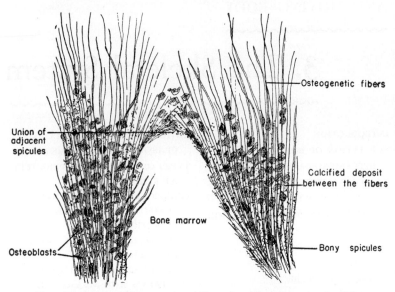

FIG. 29. Part of the growing edge of a developing parietal bone of a fetal cat. (After J. Lawrence.) (Lewis, W. H.: Gray's Anatomy, ed. 26, Philadelphia, Lea & Febiger.)

busy with "production" as the workers in any factory. The products which these cells manufacture are blood corpuscles. It has been estimated that between 600 million and 1.5 billion red blood corpuscles are destroyed daily in the body, and it is essential that as many new ones be formed each day to replace those that are destroyed. This will give you an idea of the bustling activity that goes on within the bones. The skeletal system is far from being the "inert" system that you might think.

FORMATION OF BONE

Bone begins to be formed in the embryo at an early age. It is formed by two methods: the intramembranous and the cartilaginous, or endochondral.

INTRAMEMBRANOUS BONE FORMATION

Bones of the skull are formed by the intramembranous method. At an early age, the developing brain of the embryo is covered with three layers of tissue, but only the middle one is of interest to us now. This layer consists of a fibrous membrane, composed of fine bundles of collagenic fibers and fibroblasts. In the center

FIG. 30. Part of a longitudinal
section of the developing femur
of a rabbit. (*a*) Flattened cartilage cells. (*b*) Enlarged cartilage cells. (*c* and *d*) Newly
formed bone. (*e*) Osteoblasts
(*f*) Giant cells or osteoclasts. (*g*
and *h*) Shrunken cartilage cells.
(From Atlas of Histology, Klein
and Noble Smith.) (Lewis, W.
H.: Gray's Anatomy, ed. 26,
Philadelphia, Lea & Febiger.)

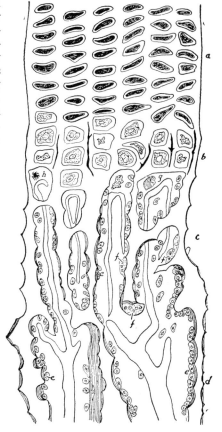

of an area, which corresponds to a bone that is to be formed, the
fibroblasts differentiate into bone-forming cells or *osteoblasts*. They
produce an intercellular substance or matrix in which calcium is
deposited. From this center, ossification, or bone formation, advances in radiating columns of calcified fibers, between which the
osteoblasts construct bone. This type of bone formation is illustrated in Figure 29. Ossification of the bones of the skull is not
complete at birth (p. 124), but, eventually, it is completed, and
the cranial bones then consist of hard, strong, outer and inner
plates, or tables, of bone, with soft, spongy bone between. This
spongy layer of bone is called diploë (meaning "double" or
"folded").

How a layer of bone is formed on a surface
(Appositional growth)

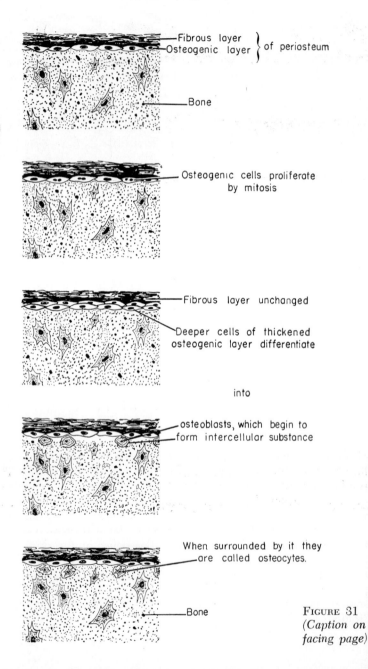

Fibrous layer
Osteogenic layer } of periosteum

Bone

Osteogenic cells proliferate
by mitosis

Fibrous layer unchanged

Deeper cells of thickened
osteogenic layer differentiate

into

osteoblasts, which begin to
form intercellular substance

When surrounded by it they
are called osteocytes.

Bone

FIGURE 31
(*Caption on
facing page*)

CARTILAGINOUS OR ENDOCHONDRAL BONE FORMATION

Most of the bones of the body are formed by the cartilaginous, or endochondral, method, in which there are cartilage models of future bones. There is a skeleton of hyaline cartilage fully formed by the second month of embryonic life. Ossification begins soon after the second month and much of it is completed before birth. This method of bone formation reminds one of the building of a bridge, in which a temporary wooden structure is erected first, and then gradually is replaced by a permanent steel structure.

The first change is an increase in the size of cartilage cells in certain areas. These areas, so far as long bones are concerned, are in the center of the shaft, or diaphysis, and in the ends, or epiphyses, of the bone. After the cartilage cells enlarge they begin to degenerate and, eventually, leave spaces into which bone-forming cells grow. The two processes go on simultaneously; that is, destruction of cartilage and formation of bone take place in adjacent areas, as illustrated in Figure 30. Bone formation spreads out from the centers of ossification in the diaphysis and the epiphyses until only two thin strips of cartilage remain, one at each end of the bone between the diaphysis and the epiphyses. These strips persist as epiphyseal cartilages until growth of the bone is completed, at which time these cartilages also become transformed into bone, and the epiphyses are said to be "closed." The final stages in the replacement of cartilage occur long after birth in some bones.

GROWTH OF BONE

In Circumference. Bones continuously grow in circumference by the deposit of bone beneath the periosteum by the appositional method. The deeper layer of the periosteum is composed of osteoblasts, which are responsible for the new bone that is formed (Fig. 31). As new bone is formed on the external surface, other cells called osteoclasts dissolve the bony tissue adjacent to the medullary cavity and in this way enlarge the marrow cavity to keep pace with the increase in circumference of the shaft.

In Length. Bones grow in length due to the activity of the

FIG. 31. Diagram of the process by which bone increases in circumference. New layers of bone are produced by cells of the osteogenic layer of periosteum in appositional growth. (Modified from Ham, A. W.: Histology, ed. 2, Philadelphia, Lippincott.)

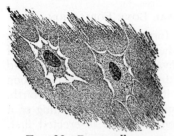

Fig. 32. Bone cells or osteocytes lying within lacunae in the matrix. ×700.

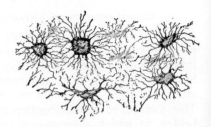

Fig. 33. Lacunae and canaliculi from dried bone (cut parallel with the lamellae). ×300.

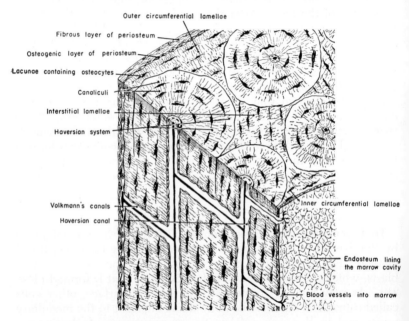

Outer circumferential lamellae

Fibrous layer of periosteum

Osteogenic layer of periosteum

Lacunae containing osteocytes

Canaliculi

Interstitial lamellae

Haversian system

Volkmann's canals

Haversion canal

Inner circumferential lamellae

Endosteum lining the marrow cavity

Blood vessels into marrow

Fig. 34. Wedge-shaped section from a mature long bone drawn in three dimensions. The fibrous and osteogenic layers of periosteum, osteocytes in lacunae, haversian canals and Volkmann's canals are shown. The circumferential lamellae are shown at the boundaries, the outer toward the periosteum, and the inner toward the marrow cavity. The interstitial lamellae are shown between the haversian systems; these lamellae probably are the remains of former haversian systems. (Modified from Ham, A. W.: Histology, ed. 2, Philadelphia, Lippincott.)

cartilage cells in the epiphyseal cartilages and the replacement of these by osteoblasts. As ossification occurs in the cartilage adjacent to the shaft of the bone, new cartilage cells are formed at the distal end. The length of the shaft is increased in this manner, and growth in length continues until the epiphyses are closed, which means that all the cartilage has been transformed into bone. Cessation of growth in bones occurs at about 18 years in females and soon after 20 in males. An immature long bone is illustrated in Figure 45.

STRUCTURE OF ADULT BONE

MICROSCOPIC STRUCTURE

Bone, or osseous tissue, is a form of dense connective tissue in which the intercellular substance, or matrix, is infiltrated with calcium salts. It is hard, and cannot be cut with a knife. One striking difference between cartilage and bone is that the inter-

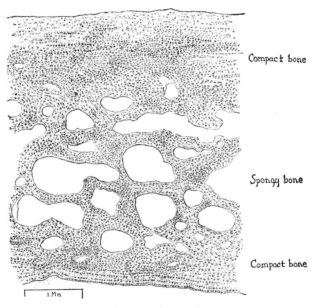

FIG. 35. Section of frontal bone; the diploë (spongy or cancellous bone) is shown, bounded above and below by layers of compact bone.

cellular substance of the latter is permeated by a system of tiny canals called *canaliculi*. These canaliculi are filled with tissue fluid which makes it possible for oxygen and nutrient material to diffuse to the bone cells from the blood and for their waste to be removed, so that they may remain alive although they are surrounded by calcified intercellular substance.

The unit of bone structure is a bone cell, or *osteocyte*, with the matrix which it has deposited around it. The spaces in which osteocytes lie are called *lacunae;* two osteocytes lying in lacunae are shown in Figure 32. As osteocytes grow, they send out cytoplasmic processes which deposit matrix around them. Later, the processes are withdrawn, and the spaces which they occupied formerly remain as tunnels or canaliculi in the matrix. The canaliculi around one osteocyte communicate with those around other osteocytes and form a network of permeating channels throughout the matrix. Several empty lacunae, with communicating canaliculi, as seen in dried bone, are shown in Figure 33.

Osteocytes are arranged in layers; such a layer of cells, together with the matrix around them, forms a sheet called a *lamella* (Fig. 34). Lamellae are arranged in two general designs, each of which gives rise to a characteristic type of bony structure. The first type is **spongy or cancellous bone,** in which the lamellae are arranged as a scaffolding or latticework of spicules (spike-shaped or needle-shaped) of bone, with marrow-filled spaces between, as illustrated in Figure 35. The second type is **compact bone,** in which the lamellae are arranged to form an apparently solid mass, as shown in Figure 34.

There are small spaces between the lamellae in compact bone, but they can be seen only with the aid of a microscope. The unit of structure in compact bone is the haversian system or canal with concentric lamellae surrounding it. The central canal is called a *haversian canal.* In the living state, the canals are occupied by arteries, veins, lymphatic vessels and nerves. The contents of the haversian canal are shown in Figure 36, *4.*

Gross Structure

A typical long bone consists of a shaft, or **diaphysis,** and two ends, or **epiphyses** (Fig. 36, *a*). The diaphysis consists mainly of compact bone, although the innermost layer is composed of spongy, or cancellous, bone. In the center of the diaphysis there is a large space called the medullary cavity, which is filled with bone marrow, (as are the spaces between the spicules of spongy

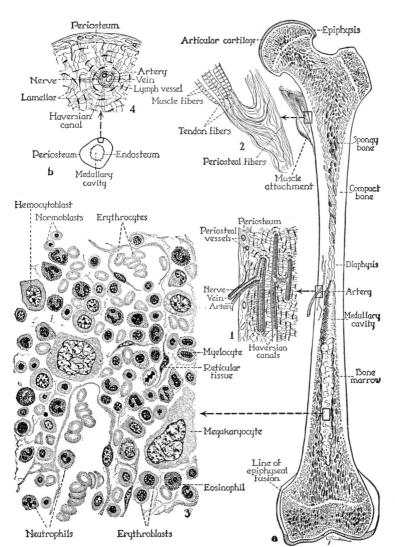

Fig. 36. (a) Longitudinal section of long bone; union of epiphyses and diaphysis at line of epiphyseal fusion. Squares and arrows indicate sections enlarged in (1), (2) and (3). (1) Periosteum and compact bone showing structures entering haversian canal; longitudinal section. (2) Portion of muscle attachment enlarged; fusion of tendon fibers with periosteal fibers. (3) Microscopic section of bone marrow. (Red bone marrow shown, although, for convenience of illustration, not removed from correct location.)

(b) Cross section of long bone through diaphysis. (4) Periosteum and compact bone in cross section; contents of haversian canal.

bone). The bone marrow extends into the larger haversian canals. The microscopic appearance of bone marrow is illustrated in Figure 36, 3. In the embryo (p. 793), bone marrow arises from the vascular mesenchyme which, in turn, invades the cartilage as it is being replaced by bone.

In adult bone, two types of marrow are present: red and yellow. **Yellow marrow** is found, especially, in the medullary cavities of long bones and consists largely of adipose tissue. **Red bone marrow** is found in the bodies of the vertebrae, diploë of the cranial bones, the sternum, the ribs and the proximal epiphyses of femur and humerus. The red marrow consists of a large number of cells contained in the meshes of a delicate connective tissue which is abundantly supplied with blood vessels.

The types of cells found in red bone marrow are: (1) ameboid marrow cells, or myelocytes; (2) white blood corpuscles; (3) erythroblasts; (4) reticulocytes; (5) red blood corpuscles; (6) a few giant cells; and (7) a few large, fat cells. The giant cells resemble osteoclasts.

The functions of red bone marrow are: (1) formation of red blood corpuscles, (2) formation of granular leukocytes, (3) possible formation of some lymphocytes, (4) formation of platelets, (5) production and dissolution of bone and (6) phagocytosis, as in other parts of the reticuloendothelium. It is the only source of red corpuscles and granular leukocytes after birth. Red marrow, in some areas, is changed to yellow marrow by invasion of fat cells. This begins soon after birth, and, in the adult, the red marrow remains only in the locations listed previously.

The outside of the bone is covered with a fibrous membrane called the **periosteum.** Some prolongations of the periosteum extend into the bone and are called Sharpey's fibers. Blood vessels, lymphatic vessels and nerves are present in the periosteum. The vascular supply of the bone is derived from two sources: from the vessels in the periosteum and from a large artery, called the nutrient artery, which enters the diaphysis and reaches the medullary cavity. The vessels from the periosteum which enter the bone become the vessels of the haversian canals. The canals which convey the periosteal vessels into the haversian canals are called Volkmann's canals (Fig. 34).

The cells of the deeper layer of the periosteum, which normally produce bone in the immature individual, may again take on this special function if there is an injury in adult bone.

The **endosteum** is the membrane that lines the marrow cavities of bones (Fig. 34), covers the spicules of cancellous, or spongy bone and lines the haversian canals of compact bone. It consists of a single layer of cells which may be osteoblasts or osteogenic cells.

TYPES OF BONES

Bones are divided into 4 classes according to their shape: long, short, flat and irregular. **Long bones** are found in the extremities. Each has a shaft and two ends, as described above. **Short bones** are cubical in shape; they consist of cancellous, or spongy, bone enclosed in a thin shell of compact bone. The bones of the wrist (carpal bones) are examples of short bones. **Flat bones** are thin, each being made up of two plates of compact bone which enclose between them a layer of cancellous, or spongy, bone. The ribs, the scapula or shoulder blade, and the bones of the skull are examples of flat bones. **Irregular bones** appear in various shapes and comprise all that are not in one of the preceding classes. Some of the skull bones are irregular, as are the vertebrae. The thinner parts of irregular bones consist of two plates of compact bone with cancellous bone between them, while the bulky parts consist of cancellous bone surrounded by a layer of compact bone.

Sesamoid bones, with the exception of the patella, or knee cap, are very small, rounded bones. They develop in the capsules of joints or in tendons. One surface is covered with cartilage and enters either into the formation of a joint, or, if separated by a bursa, plays upon another bone, cartilage or ligament. The function of sesamoid bones is to eliminate friction. The number is variable, the usual number being 2 in the hand and 4 or more in the lower extremity.

DESCRIPTIVE TERMS

Many bones show **projections** which bear different names. Eight types of projections are encountered frequently. These are:

(1) *Condyle,* a rounded projection for articulation (at a joint) with another bone. An example of this is found at the lower end of the femur where it articulates with the tibia (Fig. 48).

(2) *Crest* (a ridge), an example of which is the flaring, upper border of the hip bone or the ilium (Fig. 46).

(3) *Head,* an expanded end beyond a constricted portion called a neck. An example of this is the head of the femur, at the end of the neck of the bone (Fig. 48).

(4) *Process,* a marked prominence. An example of this is the

olecranon process of the ulna, which you can feel at the back of the elbow (Fig. 42).

(5) *Spine,* a sharp projection. Examples of this are the spines of the vertebrae, which you can feel on yourself (Figs. 56 and 57).

(6) *Trochanter,* a very large process. This is used to identify two large projections near the upper end of the femur (Fig. 48).

(7) *Tubercle,* a small rounded projection. An example is the deltoid tubercle of the humerus (Fig. 41).

(8) *Tuberosity,* a large, roughened projection. The largest tuberosities of the body are those of the ischium (part of the hip bone, (Fig. 46); these bear the weight of the body in the sitting position, and undoubtedly you are sitting on these very tuberosities as you read this.)

There are **depressions,** or even holes, in bones, which likewise help to describe and identify them. Five types are listed: foramen, fossa, groove, sinus and meatus. A *foramen* is a hole in a bone. An example of a large foramen is the foramen magnum in the occipital bone (Fig. 71), through which the spinal cord passes. A *fossa* is a shallow or hollow place in a bone. An example of this is the mandibular fossa of the temporal bone (Fig. 70). Another example is the supraspinous fossa of the scapula (Fig. 39). A *groove* is a long, shallow place on a bone. There is such a depression on the anterior surface of the humerus (Fig. 41). A *sinus* is an air cavity in a bone. An example of this is found in the maxilla (Fig. 66). A *meatus* is a tube-shaped opening in a bone, the best example of which is the external auditory meatus or canal which leads to the eardrum (Fig. 70).

Other examples of projections and depressions will be encountered as you continue your study of bones.

DIVISIONS OF THE SKELETON

For purposes of study, the skeleton is divided into two parts. These are: (1) the appendicular skeleton, which comprises the bones of the upper and the lower extremities, together with those of the shoulder and the pelvic girdles, and (2) the axial skeleton which comprises the bones of the vertebral column, the thorax and the skull. The skeleton is shown in Figure 37—the appendicular portion in yellow and the axial in blue. The number of bones in each division (exclusive of small sesamoid bones) is given below:

Appendicular: total 126 bones
    Shoulder girdles, 4
    Two upper extremities, 60. Distributed as follows: 1 humerus, 1 ulna, 1 radius, 8 carpal bones, 5 metacarpal bones, 14 phalanges, in each

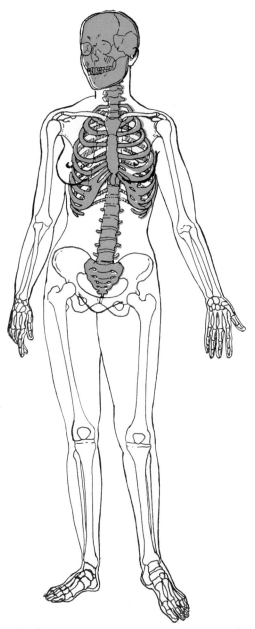

Fig. 37. The skeleton. The bones of the head and the trunk forming the axial skeleton, are shown in blue; and those of the extremities
forming the appendicular skeleton, are shown in yellow.

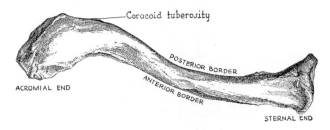

FIG. 38. Right clavicle.

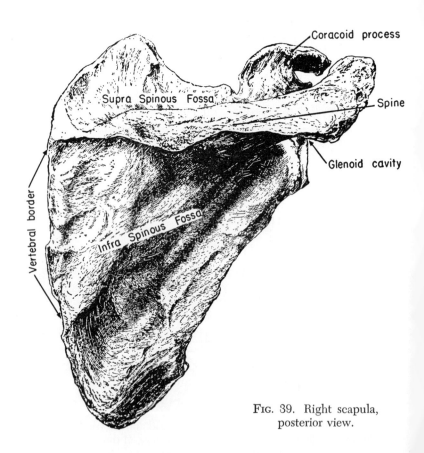

FIG. 39. Right scapula,
posterior view.

Pelvic girdle, 2

Two lower extremities, 60. Distributed as follows: 1 femur, 1 patella, 1 tibia, 1 fibula, 7 tarsal bones, 5 metatarsal bones, 14 phalanges, in each

Axial: total 80 bones

Vertebral column, 26 bones

Thorax (sternum and ribs), 25 bones

Skull, 29 bones; of these 8 are cranial bones, 14 are bones of the face, 6 are small bones in the middle ears, and there is 1 hyoid bone

The total number of bones in the skeleton is 206.

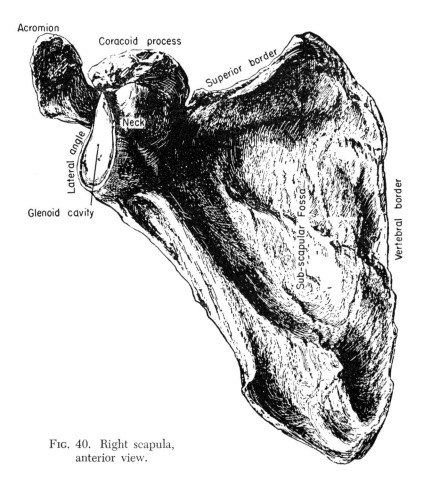

Fig. 40. Right scapula, anterior view.

Upper Extremity

The bones of the upper extremity may be divided into 4 groups: shoulder girdle, arm, forearm and hand.

Shoulder Girdle. The shoulder girdle is made up of the clavicle and the scapula, on each side of the body. The clavicles join the sternum in front. The shoulder girdles serve to attach the bones of the upper extremities to the axial division of the skeleton, and they also provide places of attachment for many muscles.

THE CLAVICLE, or collar bone, is a long, slender, double-curved bone (Fig. 38). It lies in the root of the neck between the upper end of the sternum and the acromial end of the scapula, to which it is joined. It serves as a prop for the shoulder. You can feel it throughout its entire length, if you are not too well-padded with adipose tissue.

THE SCAPULA, or shoulder blade, lies on the upper part of the back. You can feel its triangular shape if you reach over the right shoulder with your left hand and feel your back when you move your right shoulder in various directions. The scapula is shown in Figures 39 and 40. You can feel the spine of the scapula as it passes across the dorsal surface and ends in the large flat acromial process, which forms the tip of the shoulder. You can feel the junction of this process with the clavicle. In Figure 40 you will see the glenoid cavity, which is the smooth area for articulation with the head of the humerus. Above the glenoid cavity you will see the hooklike projection which is called the coracoid process. This is not a good name for it—it was given the name "coracoid" because it was thought to resemble the beak of a crow or raven, but the crow's beak is not hooked. In the body the coracoid process curls forward beneath the clavicle. Place your finger near the outer end of the clavicle and then bring it down over the clavicle, and you can feel the coracoid process. You can palpate the axillary border of the right scapula with your opposite hand, if you keep the right arm at your side. The scapula furnishes places of attachment for many muscles.

The coraco-acromial ligament completes the arch between the coracoid process and the acromion, and helps to protect the shoulder joint. The coracoclavicular ligament is a strong ligament which binds the acromial end of the clavicle to the coracoid process of the scapula. The interclavicular ligament is formed by a broad band of fibrous tissue which is attached to the apex of the

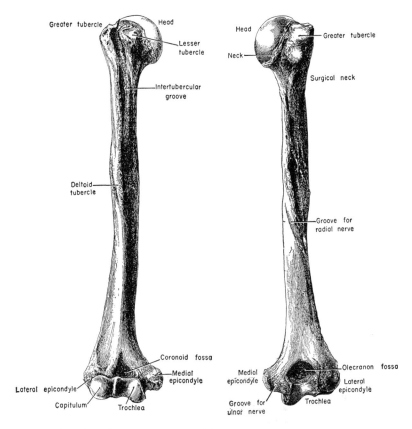

FIG. 41. (*Left*) Anterior view of humerus. (*Right*) Posterior view of humerus.

sternal end of the clavicle and to the margins of its articular surface. The fibers pass across the interclavicular notch to become attached to the fibers from the opposite clavicle.

Arm. The bone of the arm is the *humerus.* This is the largest and longest bone of the upper extremity; it extends from the shoulder to the elbow. It is illustrated in Figure 41. At the upper end of the humerus you can feel the head, which articulates with the glenoid cavity of the scapula. Below the head there are two tubercles: the one on the lateral side is called the *greater,* and the one on the medial side the *lesser* tubercle. Locate the acromial

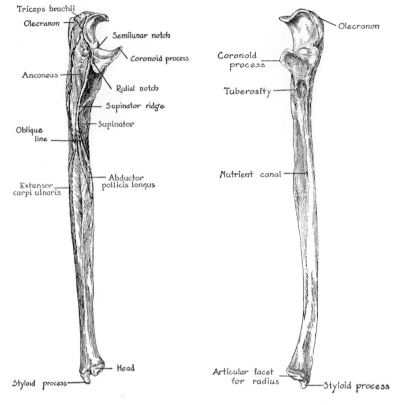

Fig. 42. (*Left*) Right ulna, lateral or outer aspect. (*Right*) Right ulna, medial or inner aspect.

process of the scapula (tip of shoulder) and just below this you can feel the greater tubercle of the humerus moving when you rotate or twist your arm medially and laterally.

The shaft is long and rather slender. The lower end of the humerus widens and shows two smooth areas on its under surface. These are the capitulum, on the outer side, for articulation with the radius, and the trochlea on the inner side, for articulation with the ulna. Just above the articular surfaces, depressions are noted; the depression on the anterior aspect is called the *coronoid fossa* and receives the coronoid process of the ulna when the forearm is flexed. The depression on the posterior aspect is the *ole-*

cranon fossa, which receives the olecranon of the ulna when the forearm is extended. The deltoid tubercle is near the middle of the anterolateral surface of the shaft. The two projections from the medial and lateral margins of the lower end of the humerus are called the medial and lateral epicondyles. At the elbow you can feel 3 bony prominences: the epicondyles of the humerus and the olecranon of the ulna. When the elbow is extended these 3 prominences lie in a horizontal line, and when it is flexed they form the points of a triangle.

Forearm. THE ULNA lies on the medial side of the forearm. You can feel it in its extent from the tip of the elbow to the small projection on the wrist near the little finger. The ulna, shown in Figure 42, consists of a long, slender shaft with an enlarged upper end. The upper end exhibits two beaklike processes; the one which curves upward and forward is called the olecranon. The other is called the coronoid process. The semilunar notch between the olecranon and the coronoid process is the articular surface for the trochlea of the humerus. The tuberosity is near the junction of the coronoid process and the shaft.

The distal end of the ulna is small; the knobbed portion is called the head; the small projection on the medial side is the styloid process. On the lateral surface, at both the upper and the lower ends, are small areas for articulation with the radius.

THE RADIUS lies on the lateral, or thumb side, of the forearm. It is more difficult to feel than the ulna as it is better padded with muscles. It consists of a shaft, with a large lower end and a small upper end, as shown in Figure 43. The upper end is a disklike head which articulates with the capitulum of the humerus and the side of the ulna. A tuberosity is noted on the shaft a short distance below the head. On the under surface of the lower end is a smooth surface which articulates with the navicular and the lunate bones of the wrist, or carpus, and with the head of the ulna. There is a styloid process on the lateral side of the lower end. The radius and the ulna are parallel in supination (p. 129); in the movement of pronation (p. 129), the lower end of the radius is carried forward and medially around the lower end of the ulna, and the shafts of the radius and the ulna cross each other.

The annular ligament of the radius forms part of the anterior and the posterior ligaments of the elbow joint. It is attached to the volar and the dorsal margins of the radial notch of the ulna and forms about four fifths of a tendinous ring. It encircles the proximal part of the neck of the radius and tends to prevent displacement of its head. The anterior and the posterior radio-ulnar ligaments pass transversely between the nonarticular surfaces of the radius and the ulna.

Hand. The bones of the hand are the carpal bones, the metacarpal bones and the phalanges.

THERE ARE 8 CARPAL BONES, arranged in 2 rows of 4 each, as shown in Figure 44. In the proximal row, beginning on the lateral side, are the navicular, the lunate, the triquetral and the pisiform. In the distal row are the greater multangular, the lesser multangular, the capitate and the hamate bones. The carpal bones are fitted closely together and are united by ligaments. The projection

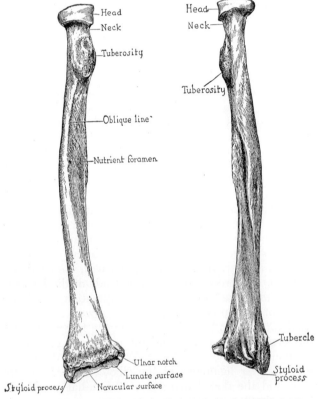

FIG. 43. Right radius. (*Left*) Anterior view. (*Right*) Posterior view.

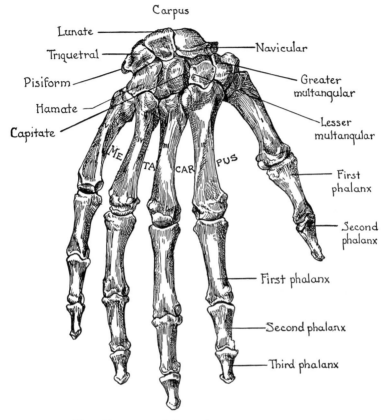

Carpus
Lunate
Triquetral
Pisiform
Hamate
Capitate
Navicular
Greater multangular
Lesser multangular
First phalanx
Second phalanx
First phalanx
Second phalanx
Third phalanx

FIG. 44. Bones of the right hand, dorsal view.

at the front of the wrist on the medial side is due to the pisiform bone.

THERE ARE 5 METACARPAL BONES which form the bony structure of the palm of the hand (Fig. 44). The metacarpal bones are long and cylindrical, and their rounded distal ends form the knuckles. At their proximal ends they articulate with the carpal bones and with each other, and distally with the proximal phalanges.

THERE ARE 14 PHALANGES, or bones of the fingers, in each hand. The thumb contains 2, and each finger 3 (Fig. 44). They are called the first, or proximal; the second, or middle; and the third, or distal phalanx.

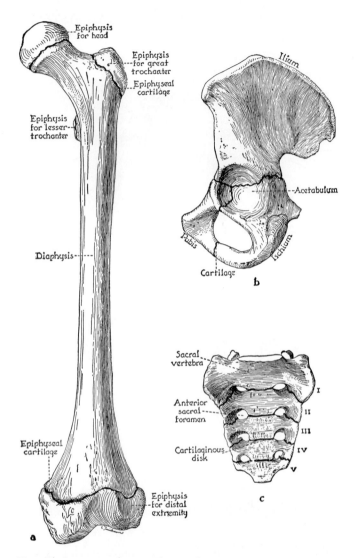

Fig. 45. Immature bone. The epiphyseal cartilages separating the individual bone elements are shown. (a) Femur, showing diaphysis and epiphyses for head, trochanter and the lower end of the bone. (b) Os coxae; the epiphyseal cartilages at which growth is taking place between the ilium, ischium and pubis are shown. The relation of these parts in the formation of the acetabulum is indicated clearly. (c) Sacrum. Five individual vertebral elements which later fuse to form the sacrum are here shown separated by epiphyseal cartilages.

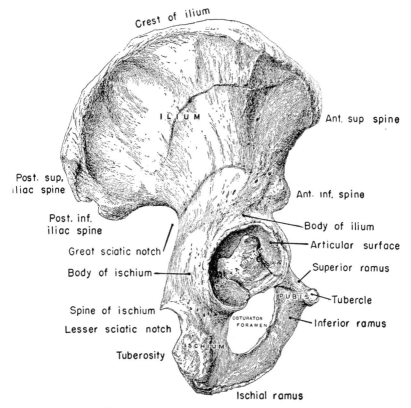

Crest of ilium

ILIUM

Ant. sup spine

Post. sup.
iliac spine

Ant. inf. spine

Post. inf.
iliac spine

Body of ilium

Great sciatic notch

Articular surface

Body of ischium

Superior ramus

PUBIS

Tubercle

Spine of ischium

OBTURATOR
FORAMEN

Inferior ramus

Lesser sciatic notch

Tuberosity

ISCHIUM

Ischial ramus

FIG. 46. Right os coxae, lateral aspect.

Lower Extremity

The bones of the lower extremity may be divided into 4 groups: hip bones, thigh, leg and foot.

Hip Bones. The hip bone is called the *os coxae;* the old terminology was innominate bone. This is the broadest bone in the body. The 2 hip bones meet in front in the mid-line of the body and form the lateral and anterior walls of the pelvis. Each starts out as 3 separate bones—the ilium, the ischium and the pubis (Fig. 45). Eventually, the 3 bones fuse in the acetabulum, which is a socket on the lateral surface into which the head of the femur fits.

THE ILIUM (Fig. 46) is the largest of the 3 bones; it forms the superior, broad, expanded portion, or prominence, of the hip.

There is a large fossa on the medial surface. You can feel the crest of the ilium from one end to the other in the living body. There is a spine at each end, but the anterior is the only one you can feel. The articulation of the ilium with the sacrum forms the sacro-iliac joint. Frequently the ligaments around this joint are torn. This is a source of great pain in many individuals.

THE ISCHIUM is the lowest and strongest portion (Fig. 46). It extends downward from the acetabulum and expands into a large tuberosity. A ramus curves forward from the body of the ischium to unite with the pubis.

THE PUBIS consists of a body and two rami (Fig. 46). The body unites with its fellow in the mid-line in front, to form a joint known as the symphysis pubis. The ascending ramus passes to the ilium, and the descending ramus passes to the ischium. A tubercle projects forward from the upper border of the pubis. The obturator foramen is a large hole in the os coxae and is bounded by the ischium and the pubis and the rami.

THE PELVIS is the lower portion of the body cavity and is bounded by the pelvic girdle, or bony pelvis, which is a rigid bony ring made up of the two hip bones, the sacrum, the coccyx and strong ligaments. The pelvic girdle provides large surfaces for the attachment of the muscles of the lower extremities. The pelvic girdle protects the urinary bladder, some of the organs of reproduction and the distal end of the large intestine; also, it serves as a firm base by means of which the trunk can rest upon the thighs.

The brim of the pelvis marks off the greater, or false, pelvis above from the lesser, or true, pelvis below. The greater pelvis is bounded by the ilia and the muscular walls of the abdomen. The lesser pelvis is bounded in front and on the sides by the pubis, the ilia and the ischia, and behind by the sacrum and the coccyx. It consists of an inlet, an outlet and a cavity. The brim is the inlet; the outlet is the space between the tip of the coccyx and the tuberosities of the ischia. The cavity is a short, curved canal from 13 to 15 cm. long in the region of the sacrum and the coccyx and only 4 to 5 cm. long in the region of the symphysis pubis. The urinary bladder lies behind the symphysis pubis. The rectum lies in the curve along the sacrum and the coccyx. In women, the uterus, the uterine tubes, the ovaries and the vagina lie between the urinary bladder and the rectum.

There are important sexual differences in the pelvis. In women, the pelvis is adapted for pregnancy and parturition (delivery, or birth of children), the cavity of the lesser pelvis being roomier,

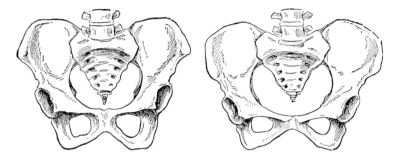

FIG. 47. Male and female pelves (*Left*) Male pelvis, narrow, heavy and compact. (*Right*) Female pelvis, broad, light and capacious.

the inlet and outlet larger and pubic arch wider than in men. In the former, the pelvic bones are lighter, and the coccyx is more movable than in men. Figure 47 shows the pelves of the male and the female.

Bones of the Thigh. THE FEMUR is the bone of the thigh; *the patella* is included for convenience. The femur is the heaviest, longest and strongest bone in the body. It is covered so thickly with muscles that you can feel it only near its ends. It transmits the entire weight of the trunk from hip to tibia. At its upper end the femur has a head, a neck and two trochanters (Fig. 48). The rounded head is directed upward and inward toward the acetabulum and is attached to the shaft by a neck which is nearly 5 cm. long. This long neck enables the femur to be moved freely, even though the head is firmly buried in muscles. At the top of the shaft, on the posterior aspect, two prominent elevations are noted, which are connected by a ridge, or crest. The elevation on the lateral side is the greater trochanter, and can be felt on the outer side of the thigh about 14 cm. below the highest point of the iliac crest. The smaller elevation on the medial side is the lesser trochanter.

The linea aspera, a ridge for the attachment of muscles, can be seen on the posterior surface. The lower end of the femur is larger than the upper, and the two large masses at its distal end are the lateral and the medial condyles. They can be felt at the sides of the knee. On the under surface of the distal end, there are large articular areas which receive the head of the tibia. The femur articulates with the patella also.

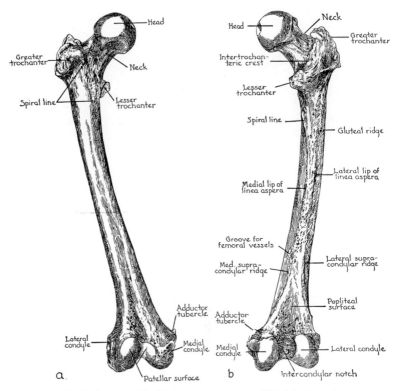

Fig. 48. Right femur. (*Left*) Anterior aspect. (*Right*) Posterior aspect.

The patella is the knee cap (Fig. 49) and forms the prominence in front of the knee when the leg is extended. The patella is the largest sesamoid bone in the body and is embedded in the tendon of the quadriceps femoris muscle (p. 172). It is held in position by muscles and ligaments and is surrounded by many bursae (cavities filled with fluid). The most important bursa is the prepatellar which lies in the subcutaneous tissue between the skin and the patella. Often it is injured and it is irritated easily, which leads to its enlargement and the condition known as "housemaid's knee."

The iliofemoral ligament consists of a triangular group of fibers attached proximally to the inferior part of the antero-inferior iliac spine and adjoining part of the rim of the acetabulum. They are attached distally to the line between the trochanters. The iliotibial band is a thick layer of fascia attached to the iliac crest, proximally,

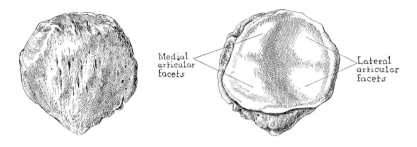

anterior view   posterior view

FIG. 49.   Right patella, anterior and posterior views.

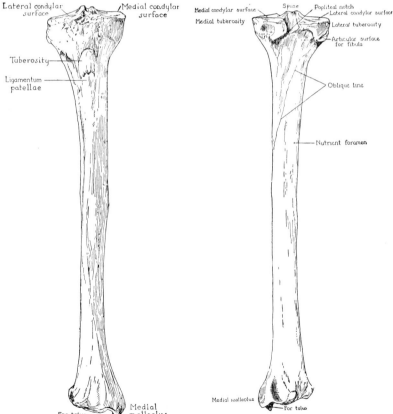

FIG. 50. (*Left*) Anterior aspect of right tibia. (*Right*) Posterior aspect of right tibia.

and to the capsule of the knee joint, distally. It receives the insertion of the tensor fasciae latae and part of the gluteus maximus.

Bones of the Leg. THE TIBIA, or shin bone, is the medial and larger bone of the leg. It is second to the femur in length and transmits the weight of the trunk to the foot. The proximal end shows two smooth surfaces for articulation with the condyles of the femur. Between these surfaces is a projection called the intercondylar eminence. The projection on the anterior surface near the proximal end of the bone is called the tuberosity (Fig. 50) and it can be felt in the living subject. When one kneels, the

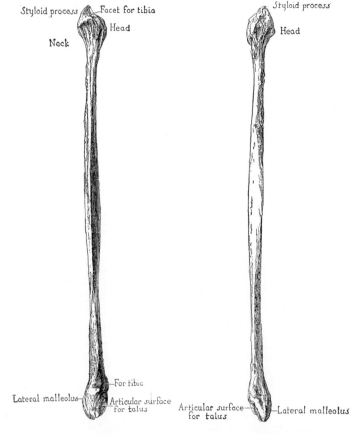

FIG. 51. Right fibula. (*Left*) Anterior aspect. (*Right*) Posterior aspect.

body rests on the tuberosity of the tibia, the ligamentum patellae and the lower part of the patella. The anterior border of the shaft is sharp and can be palpated easily.

The lower end of the tibia widens out and has on its under-surface an articular area for the talus (one of the tarsal bones). On the medial side, the tibia projects downward as the medial mal-leolus and forms the prominence on the inner side of the ankle. The tibia articulates both above and below with the fibula.

THE FIBULA is the long, slender bone on the lateral side of the leg. It is attached above and below to the lateral aspect of the tibia but does not enter into formation of the knee joint. The upper end is expanded slightly to form a head (Fig. 51), and the lower end projects downward to form the lateral malleolus. The fibula articulates with the talus and thus enters into formation of the ankle joint. The talus lies between the lateral and the medial malleoli.

Foot. The bones of the foot may be divided into 3 groups: tarsus or ankle bones, metatarsals and phalanges.

THERE ARE 7 TARSAL BONES. The talus, the highest of the group (Fig. 52), is relatively large and articulates with the undersurface of the tibia and the fibula. The calcaneus is the largest of the tarsal bones; it lies below and behind the talus and is shaped like a revolver handle. The calcaneus forms the base of the heel and transmits the weight of the body to the ground. The navicular ar-ticulates with the anterior end of the talus. Anterior to the navicu-lar are the 3 small cuneiform bones. The cuboid, which lies on the lateral side of the foot, articulates with the anterior end of the calcaneus.

The long plantar ligament is attached to the plantar surface of the calcaneus. It runs forward and is fixed to the plantar surface of the cuboid ridge, but many of its fibers extend to the bases of the third, fourth and fifth metatarsal bones.

THERE ARE 5 METATARSAL bones lying anterior to the tarsus (Fig. 52); the bases of the inner 3 articulate with the 3 cuneiform bones, and those of the outer 2 articulate with the cuboid. The heads of the 5 metatarsal bones form the ball of the foot.

THERE ARE 14 PHALANGES in each foot. Of these, 2 are in the great toe and 3 in each of the other toes.

AXIAL SKELETON

Components of the Vertebral Column

The vertebral column, or backbone, extends the full length of the back and consists of 26 bones—24 vertebrae, the sacrum and the coccyx. There are 3 groups of vertebrae, based on their location—7 cervical in the neck, 12 thoracic in the thorax and 5 lumbar in the loin.

Characteristic differences exist between the groups, despite similarities in general structure. Each vertebra, with the exception of the first two cervical, consists of an anterior mass which is called the *body* and a posterior portion called the *vertebral arch*. These

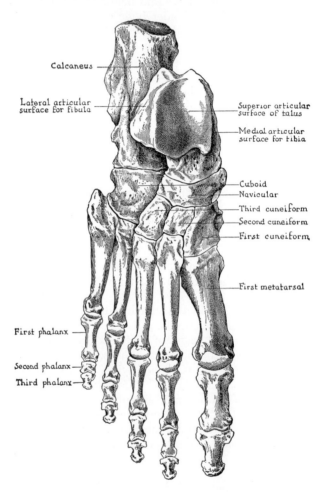

Calcaneus

Lateral articular
surface for fibula

Superior articular
surface of talus

Medial articular
surface for tibia

Cuboid
Navicular
Third cuneiform
Second cuneiform
First cuneiform

First metatarsal

First phalanx

Second phalanx
Third phalanx

FIG. 52. Bones of the right foot, dorsal aspect.

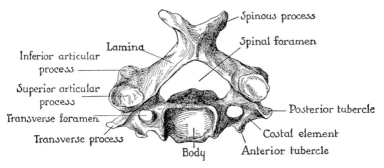

FIG. 53. Fourth cervical vertebra, superior aspect.

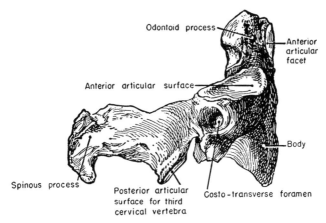

FIG. 54. The epistropheus, lateral view.

parts enclose a space called the *vertebral foramen* (Fig. 53). The vertebral arch is made up of a pair of pedicles and a pair of laminae, and it supports 7 processes (Fig. 56). The pedicles are short, thick processes which project backward, on either side, to join the laminae. The laminae are broad plates which project backward and medially from the pedicles. The 7 processes are 4 articular (2 for the vertebra above and 2 for that below), 2 transverse (one on each side where the pedicle and lamina join) and one spinous process which projects downward and backward from the junction of the laminae. These processes serve as places of attachment for muscles and ligaments.

The Vertebrae. CERVICAL VERTEBRAE. The distinguishing characteristic of these vertebrae is the transverse processes which are very wide and exhibit a canal for the transmission of the vertebral artery. The fourth cervical vertebra is shown in Figure 53. The seventh cervical has a very prominent spinous process called the vertebra prominens. The second cervical, called the epistropheus (meaning axis or pivot), has a small body and a projection called the odontoid process (Fig. 54). The odontoid process passes through a canal in the first cervical vertebra and forms the axis of rotation for the skull and the first cervical vertebra. The first cervical is a bony ring called the *atlas* (Fig. 55). The cavity of the atlas is divided by a transverse ligament into two parts: the larger, posterior part transmits the spinal cord; the smaller, anterior one receives the odontoid process of the epistropheus. There are

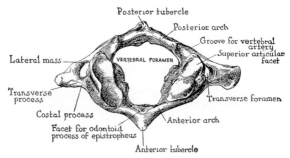

FIG. 55. The atlas, superior aspect.

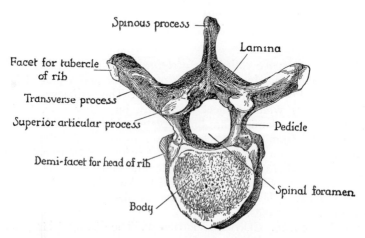

FIG. 56. Sixth thoracic vertebra, superior aspect.

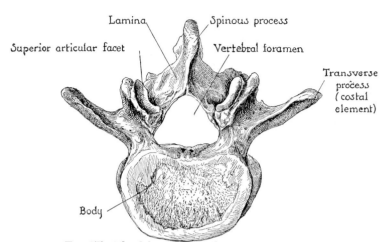

Lamina

Spinous process

Superior articular facet

Vertebral foramen

Transverse process (costal element)

Body

FIG. 57. Third lumbar vertebra, superior aspect.

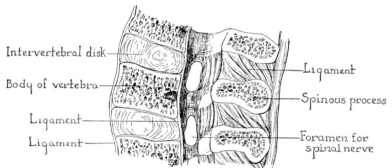

Intervertebral disk

Body of vertebra

Ligament

Ligament

Ligament

Spinous process

Foramen for spinal nerve

FIG. 58. Sagittal section through part of the vertebral column, with the position of ligaments, intervertebral disks, bodies of vertebrae, spinous processes and intervertebral foramina indicated. (After Spalteholz)

two smooth oval areas on the upper surface of the atlas for articulation with the condyles of the occipital bone. By means of this articulation it is possible for a person to rock his skull back and forth on the atlas. As he turns his head from side to side, the atlas moves with the skull, and the two turn on the epistropheus, using the odontoid process as the center of rotation.

THE THORACIC VERTEBRAE become progressively larger from above downward. The transverse processes give partial attachment to the ribs. The sixth thoracic vertebra is shown in Figure 56.

THE LUMBAR VERTEBRAE are larger than the thoracic and lack

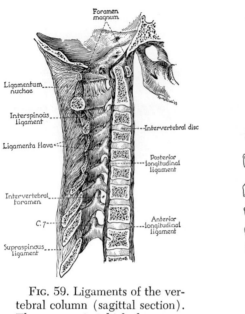

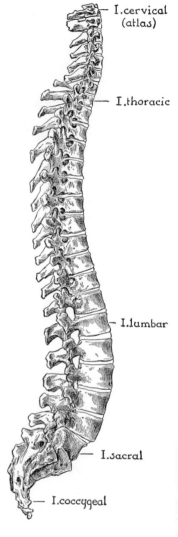

Fig. 59. Ligaments of the vertebral column (sagittal section). The manner in which these pass between the various parts of the vertebrae and skull is indicated. Intervertebral foramina also are shown.

Fig. 60. (*Right*) Lateral view of adult vertebral column showing curves.

the processes for attachment to the ribs. The third lumbar is shown in Figure 57.

INTERVERTEBRAL JOINTS. Between each pair of vertebrae there is a disk of cartilage, called the intervertebral disk (Fig. 58), which acts as a cushion and a shock absorber. The vertebrae are bound together by strong ligaments, as shown in Figure 58 and 59. Since the ligaments are somewhat extensible, and the disks compressible, movements of flexion, extension, abduction and rotation (p. 128) are possible.

The sacrum lies below the fifth lumbar vertebra and is triangular in shape (Figs. 45 and 60), with the apex extending downward. The sacrum is formed by the fusion of 5 sacral vertebrae. The prominent lip at the upper anterior margin of the body is called the sacral promontory. The sacrum is wedged between the 2 hip bones.

The coccyx is formed by the fusion of 4 rudimentary coccygeal vertebrae and is attached to the tip of the sacrum (Fig. 60).

Vertebral Column as a Whole

The vertebral column is a strong, flexible pillar for the support of the trunk and cranium, and serves as a protection for the spinal cord and roots of the spinal nerves (p. 256). The vertebral column normally exhibits 4 curves (Fig. 60). The thoracic and the sacral curves are primary and are present at birth. The cervical curve appears when the infant begins to hold up his head at about 3 months and becomes more pronounced when he begins to sit up at about 9 months. The lumbar curve appears when the infant begins to walk. These curves give the resilience and spring to the vertebral column so essential in walking and jumping.

Ligaments of the Vertebral Column. Some of the ligaments which help to hold the vertebrae together are illustrated in Figures 58 and 59. The bodies of the vertebrae are connected by anterior and posterior longitudinal ligaments. The former extends from the epistropheus to the sacrum and consists of short and long fibers which arise from the edges of the vertebrae and from the disks and blends with the periosteum of the vertebrae below. The posterior longitudinal ligament extends from the epistropheus to the sacrum and attaches to the disks and the edges of the bodies of all the vertebrae.

THE LIGAMENTA FLAVA are elastic membranes that join the laminae, extending from the epistropheus to the sacrum. They are attached firmly to the articular capsules which surround the articular processes.

THE SUPRASPINOUS LIGAMENT extends along the tips of the spines from the last cervical vertebra to the sacrum.

THE INTERSPINOUS LIGAMENTS connect the spinous processes between the tips and the laminae and extend from the ligamenta flava to the supraspinous ligament.

THE LIGAMENTUM NUCHAE extends from the external occipital

protuberance (p. 121) to the spine of the seventh cervical vertebra. It is composed of yellow elastic tissue and helps to hold up the head in quadrupeds.

Bones of the Thorax

The bony thorax is made up of the ribs, the thoracic vertebrae and the sternum (Fig. 61). It is covered with muscles and skin, and the floor is formed by the diaphragm. The thorax protects and supports the heart and the lungs, plays an important role in respiration and helps to support the bones of the shoulder girdle. Red corpuscles are formed in the red bone marrow of the ribs and sternum.

Ribs. There are 12 pairs of ribs, which are long, slender, curved bones. They are attached to the thoracic vertebrae posteriorly. The first 7 pairs are attached to the sternum by separate costal

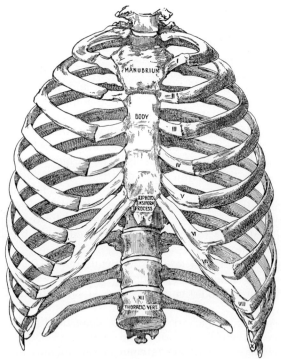

FIG. 61. The bony thorax, anterior view, showing sternum and ribs.

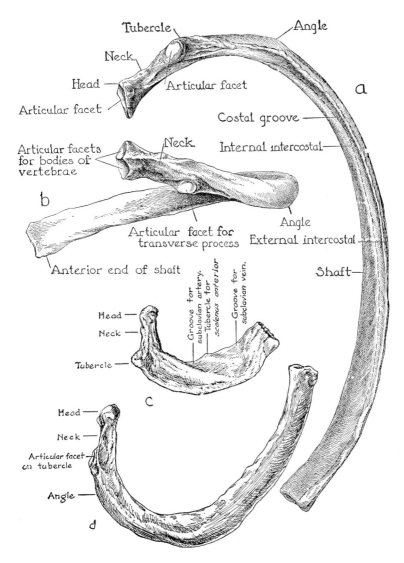

FIG. 62. (a and b) Typical rib (fifth rib, right side). (a) Inferior view; (b) posterolateral view. (c) First rib, right side, superior surface. (d) Second rib, right side, superior surface.

cartilages and are called the *true ribs.* The remaining 5 pairs are called *false ribs;* of these, the eighth, the ninth and the tenth pairs have cartilages which attach to the cartilage above. The last 2 pairs are unattached in front and are called the free or floating ribs. You can identify your ribs easily; the first can be felt just below the inner end of the clavicle where its costal cartilage joins the sternum. The spaces between the ribs are called the *inter-costal spaces* and are filled with muscles.

A typical rib has a head, which articulates with the body of a thoracic vertebra; a short neck; a tuberosity, which articulates with the transverse process of the vertebra; and a shaft (Fig. 62). The upper ribs are shorter than the lower, with the exception of the last two. The ribs curve around the sides of the chest, slanting downward and forward, making the sternal end lower than the vertebral end. The thorax is wider below than it is above and is wider from side to side than it is from front to back.

The sternum, or breast bone, lies in the mid-line of the thorax in front. It is about 15 cm. long and is made up of the manubrium, above; a body; and a xiphoid process, below (Fig. 61). The upper end of the sternum articulates with the clavicle and the first rib on each side. Some of the abdominal muscles are attached to the xiphoid process.

Bones of the Skull

The skull is the skeleton of the face and the head. It is composed of 21 bones which are joined together and move as a whole, plus one freely movable bone (mandible or lower jaw). Eight of the bones form the cranium, and 14 are bones of the face. The *cranial bones* are frontal, occipital, sphenoid, ethmoid, 2 temporal and 2 parietal bones. The *bones of the face* are the paired zygomatic, lacrimal, nasal, maxillae, inferior nasal conchae and palatine, and the unpaired vomer and mandible. There are 6 small bones in the middle ears (p. 368) and there is 1 hyoid bone in the neck.

The Skull from the Front. If you look at the front of the skull, as it appears in Figure 63, you will see most of the bones of the face and some of those of the cranium.

THE FRONTAL BONE is noted at the front of the skull. It consists of a vertical portion, which forms the forehead, and an orbital portion, which extends backward and enters into the formation of the roofs of the orbital and the nasal cavities. The superciliary ridges are the elevations above the orbital margins. Beneath these, inside the bone, are cavities known as the *frontal sinuses.* The sinuses communicate with the nasal cavity.

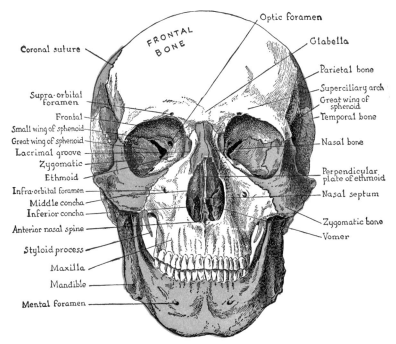

FIG. 63. Anterior view of the skull, showing some of the cranial bones, the facial bones, the orbits, and part of the nasal cavity.

THE ORBITS. These are the bony sockets for the eyeballs and are formed by the cranial and the facial bones. The upper rim is formed by the frontal bone. The medial and part of the lower rim is formed by the *maxilla.* The lateral rim is formed by the *zygomatic* bone, and the *sphenoid* forms part of the posterior wall. The medial wall is formed by part of the *ethmoid* bone, with the small *lacrimal* bone in the medial corner.

THE ETHMOID BONE is a light spongy, bone located at the base of the cranium, between the orbits, at the roof of the nose. It consists of 4 parts: (1) the *horizontal,* or *cribriform,* plate, which forms part of the base of the cranium and the roof of the nasal cavity; (2) the *perpendicular* plate, which forms part of the nasal septum; and (3) and (4) 2 lateral masses (Fig. 64). On the medial side these masses form the lateral walls of the nasal cavity. Two scroll-like ridges project from them and are called the *superior* and *middle conchae,* as shown in Figure 77. Laterally, the masses form part of the walls of the orbit. The ethmoid has canals in it through which the fibers of the olfactory nerve pass. It also contains air cells which open into the nasal cavity.

THE LACRIMAL BONES are thin, scalelike bones, about as large as a fingernail, which lie in the medial wall of the orbit on the ethmoid bone. These are the smallest and most fragile bones of the face. Each lacrimal bone contains a groove which is part of the lacrimal canal from the orbit to the nasal cavity. The tear duct passes through the canal (p. 355).

EACH PALATINE BONE is L-shaped, the upright portion forming a part of the lateral wall of the nasal cavity, the horizontal piece forming part of the floor of the nasal cavity and part of the roof of the mouth. Each palatine bone lies between the maxilla and the pterygoid process of the sphenoid bone.

Returning to the orbit, you note that it is a cone-shaped cavity at the apex of which there is a large opening called the optic foramen. The optic nerve, together with blood vessels, passes through this foramen. In the living subject the orbit contains the eyeball, the extrinsic eye muscles, nerves, blood vessels, the lacrimal gland and some adipose tissue.

THE NASAL CAVITY is prominent in the front view of the skull. The nasal *septum* separates the two halves of the nasal cavity. The septum is formed principally by the ethmoid and the *vomer*, together with parts of the frontal, the nasal, the sphenoid, the maxilla and the palatine (or palate) bones. In the living subject the septal cartilage completes the septum in front. The bones that enter into the formation of the roof of the nasal cavity are the nasal, the frontal, the ethmoid, the sphenoid, the vomer and the palatine (or palate) bones. The floor is formed by the maxilla

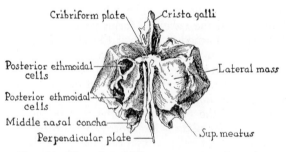

FIG. 64. The ethmoid bone, posterior view, showing the perpendicular plate and the lateral masses. The ethmoidal cells are shown on the left.

and the palatine bones. The lateral wall is formed by the maxilla, the lacrimal, the ethmoid, the palatine and the sphenoid bones.

THE JAWS. The upper jaw is formed by the fusion of the two *maxillae,* which articulate with the frontal bone. The maxillae not only form part of the floor of the orbits but also form most of the roof of the mouth, the floor and the lateral walls of the nasal cavity and part of the wall of the nasolacrimal duct. Each maxilla consists of a *body* and several *processes* (Figs. 65 and 66). The

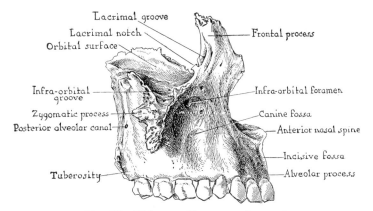

FIG. 65. Right maxilla, external aspect.

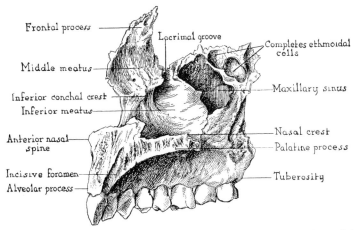

FIG. 66. Right maxilla, inner aspect, showing some of the ethmoidal cells and the maxillary sinus.

anterior and lateral aspects of the body form part of the face below the eyes and above the teeth. On the medial aspect, the body
forms part of the lateral wall of the nasal cavity. The superior
aspect assists in the formation of the floor of the orbit. A large
single cavity inside the body, called the *maxillary sinus,* communicates with the nasal cavity. The alveolar process carries the upper
teeth. The horizontal or palatine processes form the anterior and
larger part of the hard palate.

The *mandible* or lower jaw is the largest bone of the face. It consists of a horseshoe-shaped body and 2 rami (Figs. 67 and 68).
The lower teeth are found at the upper margin of the body. There
are 2 processes on top of each ramus. The posterior process is

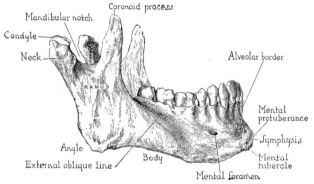

FIG. 67. Mandible, external aspect.

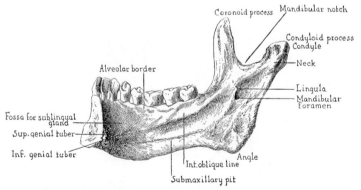

FIG. 68. Mandible, inner aspect.

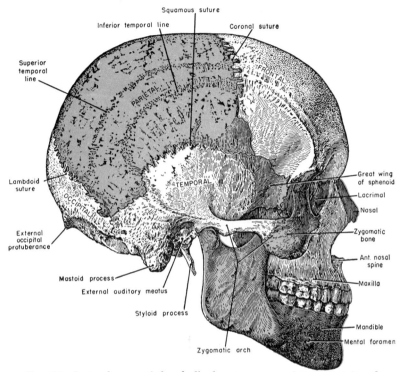

FIG. 69. Lateral view of the skull, showing some of the cranial and facial bones and sutures.

called the condyloid process; it articulates with the temporal bone to form the mandibular joint (Fig. 79*b*). The anterior process is the coronoid, to which the temporal muscle (p. 190) is attached. On the inner side of the ramus is the *mandibular foramen* which transmits the nerves and the arteries to the lower teeth. The *mental foramen* also transmits nerves and blood vessels. The angle of the mandible is formed by the posterior border of the ramus and the lower border of the body. The mandible can be felt easily through the skin; if the finger is placed just in front of the opening of the external ear, the condyle of the mandible can be felt sliding back and forth during the movements of the lower jaw.

Age Changes in the Mandible. At birth, the 2 halves of the mandible are connected by fibrous tissue; during the first year the 2 halves unite. As the teeth erupt, the child chews, and the depth of the body increases, due to the growth of the alveolar border.

The lower part of the bone becomes thicker, the rami enlarge, and the angle becomes less obtuse. As growth continues the body increases in depth and length. In old age, after the teeth are lost, the alveoli are absorbed, and the chin appears more prominent, and the angle again becomes obtuse.

THE ZYGOMATIC BONE is the cheek bone, situated at the upper and lateral part of the face. It forms the prominence of the cheek and part of the lateral wall and part of the floor of the orbit. A process projects backward from it to articulate with the zygomatic process of the temporal bone. These 2 processes together form the zygomatic arch, which can be felt on the side of the face in front of the ear.

THE NASAL BONES are small flat bones which form the upper part of the bridge of the nose.

Lateral View of the Skull. Let us now turn to the lateral view of the skull as it appears in Figure 69. In this view we can see parts of the frontal, the parietal, the temporal, the occipital and the sphenoid bones. The PARIETAL bone lies between the FRONTAL and OCCIPITAL bones.

THE TEMPORAL BONE is a very complicated bone (Fig. 70), which forms part of the sides and part of the base of the skull. It contains

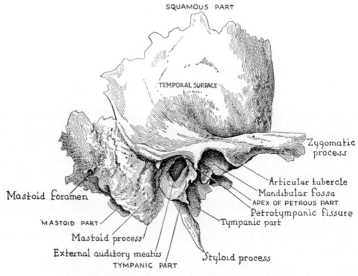

FIG. 70. External view of right temporal bone.

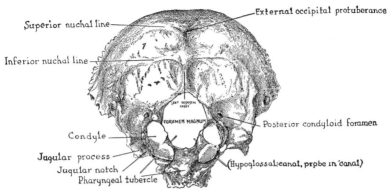

Superior nuchal line

Inferior nuchal line

External occipital protuberance

EXT OCCIPITAL CREST

FORAMEN MAGNUM

Condyle

Jugular process
Jugular notch
Pharyngeal tubercle

Posterior condyloid foramen

(Hypoglossal canal, probe in canal)

FIG. 71. External aspect of the occipital bone.

the organ of hearing and articulates with the lower jaw. It is divided into 4 parts, for ease of description: petrous, squamous, tympanic and mastoid portions.

The petrous portion contains the organ of hearing. On the cranial side there is a foramen called the *internal acoustic meatus* which allows the passage of the facial, the cochlear and the vestibular nerves. The styloid process projects downward from the inferior surface and an oval opening on the posterior surface leads into the internal acoustic meatus.

The squamous part is a scalelike plate of bone at the side of the skull. The zygomatic process projects forward from the lower part of its lateral surface and articulates with the temporal process of the zygomatic bone to form the zygomatic arch. The inferior surface is occupied largely by the mandibular fossa, which receives the condyle of the mandible. The articular tubercle is a prominence in front of the fossa. The temporal surface forms part of the floor of the temporal fossa.

The tympanic part is a curved plate, the upper surface of which forms the anterior, the inferior and part of the posterior wall of the external acoustic meatus. The external acoustic meatus is a canal about 15 mm. long, directed medially and slightly forward.

The mastoid portion lies behind the squamous and the tympanic parts. The mastoid process projects from its inferior border. The mastoid foramen for the passage of blood vessels opens near the posterior border of the lateral surface. The mastoid portion contains air spaces called *mastoid air cells,* which communicate with the middle ear by means of the mastoid antrum (Figs. 112 and

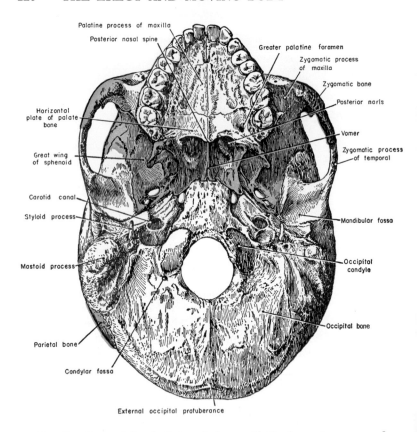

Palatine process of maxilla
Posterior nasal spine
Greater palatine foramen
Zygomatic process of maxilla
Zygomatic bone
Posterior narls
Horizontal plate of palate bone
Vomer
Zygomatic process of temporal
Great wing of sphenoid
Carotid canal
Styloid process
Mandibular fossa
Occipital condyle
Mastoid process
Parietal bone
Occipital bone
Condylar fossa
External occipital protuberance

FIG. 72. Base of the skull from below, with the lower jaw removed, showing some of the cranial bones and the bony roof of the mouth.

148). A groove, which is continuous with that of the occipital bone, is evident on the inner surface of the mastoid portion (Fig. 73). The transverse venous sinus (p. 451) that occupies this groove is very near the mastoid air cells, being separated only by a thin plate of bone. The ease with which infection may pass from the middle ear to the mastoid air cells and on to the transverse sinus is obvious.

THE OCCIPITAL BONE forms the back and a large part of the base of the skull. The foramen magnum is the large opening seen in Figure 71. On each side of the foramen magnum are the articular

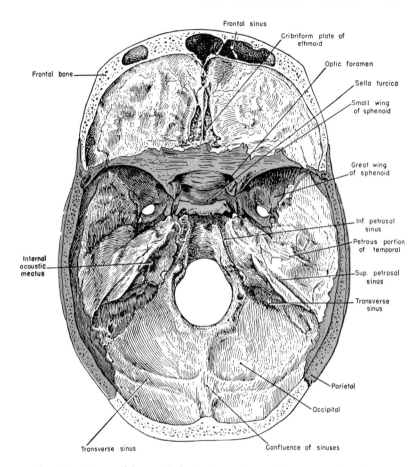

FIG. 73. View of base of skull, from above. The internal surfaces
of some of the cranial bones are shown.

surfaces for the atlas. This atlanto-occipital joint between the skull
and the first cervical vertebra permits the backward and forward
movement of the head. The external occipital protuberance is
located behind, in the mid-line, at the junction of the skin of the
neck with that of the head. This projection can be felt in the living
subject between the muscular columns at the back of the neck.
The superior nuchal line passes laterally from the protuberance on
each side and can be followed laterally to the mastoid portion of

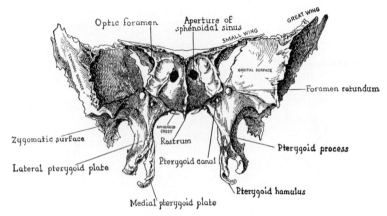

Optic foramen   Aperture of
                 sphenoidal sinus   GREAT WING
                              SMALL WING

TEMPORAL WING   ORBITAL SURFACE   GREAT WING

                                    Foramen rotundum

Zygomatic surface   SPHENOID CREST
                     Rostrum   Pterygoid process

Lateral pterygoid plate   Pterygoid canal

                              Pterygoid hamulus
Medial pterygoid plate

Fig. 74. The sphenoid bone, anterior view, showing the great
and small wings, pterygoid plates, and the aperture of the sphenoid
sinus.

the temporal bone. The ligamentum nuchae takes origin from this
protuberance.

Before you leave the lateral view of the skull, note the opening
of the external auditory meatus, the zygomatic arch and the articulation of the mandible with the temporal bone.

Base of the Skull from Below. We look next at the base of
the skull from below (Fig. 72). Note the largest opening, which
is the *foramen magnum,* the openings of the nasal cavity and the
hard palate or roof of the mouth. The bony roof of the mouth is
made up of the hard palate and part of the maxillae and the palatine bones. The hard palate separates the mouth from the nasal
cavity and also serves as the floor for the latter.

Base of the Skull from Above. Now look at the base of the
skull as it appears from above (Fig. 73). The top of the cranium
and its contents must be removed to permit this view. THE
SPHENOID BONE (shown in blue), which is located at the base of
the skull in front of the temporal bones, may be seen. The sphenoid
fills the space between the orbital plates of the frontal bone an-
teriorly and the temporal and the occipital bones posteriorly. It
bears some resemblance to a bat with its wings extended (Fig. 74).
The sphenoid is divided into a middle portion or body, 2 great
and 2 small wings, which extend outward from the sides of the
body, and 2 pterygoid processes, which project below and form
part of the lateral walls of the nasal cavity.

The upper surface exhibits a depression in the form of a saddle called the *sella turcica*. The hypophysis or pituitary gland (p. 720) lies in this depression. The undersurface of the body forms part of the roof of the nose. The body contains 2 sphenoid air cells which open into the nasal cavity.

Hyoid Bone. We shall bring our consideration of the bones of the skull to a close by calling attention to the hyoid bone (Fig. 75), which is an isolated bone lying in the anterior part of the neck a short distance above the larynx. It consists of a central

Fig. 75. (*Right*) The hyoid bone, anterior view.

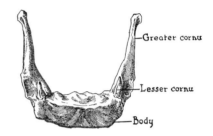

Fig. 76. (*Bottom*) Infant's skull showing fontanels and sutures.

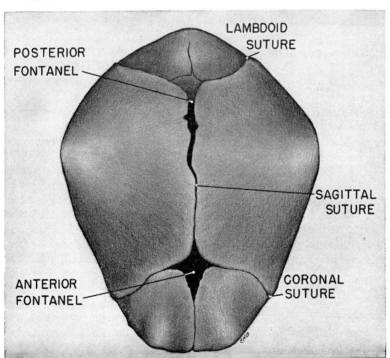

portion, called the body, and 2 cornuae, the greater and the lesser, which project backward. The hyoid bone is suspended from the tip of the styloid processes of the temporal bones by the stylohyoid ligaments. It serves for the attachment of those muscles which move the tongue and aid in speaking and swallowing. It can be felt in the neck above the margins of the thyroid cartilages.

Sutures Between Cranial Bones. The articulations between the cranial bones are called *sutures,* and the following may be seen in Figure 69: (1) coronal, between the frontal and the parietal bones; (2) lambdoid, between the parietal and the occipital bones; and (3) squamous, between part of the temporal and the parietal bones. The sagittal suture (Fig. 76) unites the two parietal bones. The place at which the coronal and the sagittal sutures meet is called the *bregma* (front of the head). The place at which the sagittal and the lambdoid sutures meet is called the *lambda* (from the Greek letter which it resembles).

The Fontanels. There are several places in which the intramembranous ossification of the cranial bones is not complete at birth. These areas are called fontanels. There are 6 fontanels at the angles of the parietal bones; 2 of these, called the *anterior* and the *posterior,* are situated in the mid-line (Fig. 76). The anterior is the largest of the fontanels, and it normally closes at about 18 months of age. The posterior fontanel normally closes at about 1 month of age. The other fontanels, the anterolateral and the posterolateral, on each side, normally close within a month or two after birth.

Air Sinuses. You will recall that it was stated during the description of the skull that many of the cranial bones and one of the bones of the face contain air spaces. The bones that contain such spaces are the frontal, the temporal, the ethmoid, the sphenoid and the maxilla. The air spaces or sinuses may be divided into 2 groups: the paranasal sinuses, which communicate with the nasal cavity, and the mastoid sinus, which communicates with the middle ear. These sinuses are lined with mucous membrane which serves also as periosteum. Consequently, it is called mucoperiosteum and is continuous with the mucous membrane that lines the air passages. The sinuses are illustrated in Figures 77, 302 and 303. The mastoid sinus is shown in Figures 112 and 148. The paranasal sinuses, together with the bones that enter into the formation of the walls of the orbits and the nasal fossae, are illustrated in the frontal section of the skull (Fig. 78). The sinuses are important as resonance chambers in the production of voice and they decrease the weight of the skull.

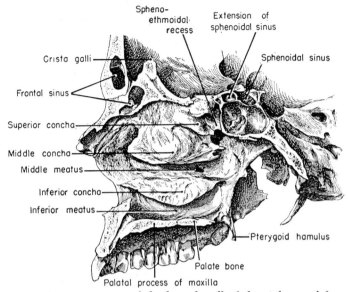

FIG. 77. Inner aspect of the lateral wall of the right nasal fossa. The frontal and the sphenoidal sinuses, the nasal conchae and the meatuses are shown.

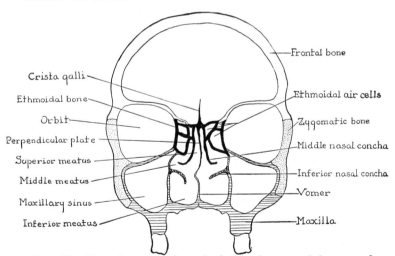

FIG. 78. Frontal section through skull, orbits, nasal fossae and paranasal sinuses. The individual bones which enter into the formation of the walls of each structure are shown. (Modified from Callander and Corning)

ARTICULATIONS OR JOINTS

The parts of the skeleton are bound together by fibrous bands or by capsules, cartilage or bone. The places of contact of bones are called articulations or joints, and the tendons, the muscles and the fasciae around the joints lend support to them.

CLASSIFICATION OF JOINTS

There are several ways of classifying joints, and we shall classify them according to their structure or on a morphologic basis. On this basis there are 5 classes of joints or articulations: syndesmoses, synchondroses, synostoses, symphyses and synovial joints.

Syndesmoses (meaning "together" and "band") are articulations in which bones are held together by bands of dense fibrous tissue. Examples of this type of union are the sutures of the skull and the union between the lower end of the tibia and the fibula.

Synchondroses (meaning "together" and "cartilage") are joints in which 2 bones are held together by means of cartilage: epiphyseal disks are examples of synchondroses. These disks consist of hyaline cartilage and connect bone of the epiphyses with the bone of the diaphysis.

Synostoses (meaning "together" and "bone") are joints in which 2 bones are united firmly with connecting bone. They connect bones that developed separately and remained separate as long as they were growing. During the growth period the bones are connected by cartilage or fibrous tissue, but when growth ends the connecting link undergoes ossification. Most syndesmoses and synchondroses become synostoses.

Symphyses (meaning "a growing together") are joints in which the bones are covered with cartilage at the site of union, and the cartilage caps are held together by dense fibrous tissue or fibrocartilage. This forms a strong joint with limited movement. Examples of this type of articulation are the symphysis pubis and the intervertebral joints (called intervertebral disks).

Synovial joints (meaning "with egg," since the *synovial fluid* resembles egg white) are joints in which fluid is present in a closed cavity between 2 bones. These are called *diarthroses* (through joints) by some authors, since they permit great freedom of movement. The bones entering into the formation of this type of joint have smooth articular surfaces which are covered with articular cartilage. The articular cartilages of the 2 bones come in contact with each other. An articular capsule is attached to both bones near the periphery of the articular surfaces, and this capsule closes the articular cavity. The wall of the joint capsule consists of 2 layers—an outer fibrous layer composed of white fibrous tissue, and an inner synovial layer composed of areolar connective tissue, elastic fibers and fat cells. The articular cavity is the space enclosed by the synovial layer and the articular cartilages, and it contains the synovial fluid. This fluid is watery and clear and contains salts, mucus, protein and fat. It lubricates the joint. The structure of a typical synovial joint is illustrated in Figure 79. In some synovial

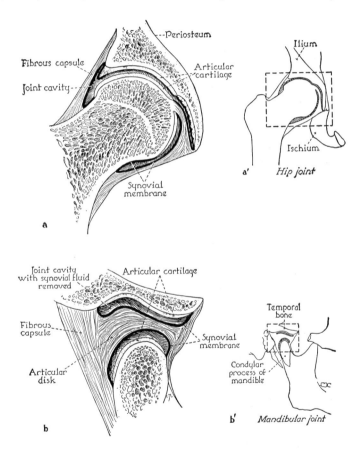

FIG. 79. Structure of synovial joint, semidiagrammatic. Joint cavity shown enlarged. (*Top*) Hip joint. (*Right*) Relations of the bones which articulate at the acetabulum. (*Bottom*) Mandibular joint. (*Right*) Relations of the bones which articulate. This joint is modified by an articular disk with which each articular cartilage normally is in contact.

joints there is an articular disk between the articular cartilages.

On the basis of the forms of the articular surfaces of the bones, diarthroses may be divided into the following subgroups: spheroidal, hinge, screw, ellipsoidal, trochoidal, saddle and irregular.

In the **spheroidal** joint, a rounded head of one bone is received in a concave surface of the other in a ball-and-socket arrangement. The shoulder and the hip joints are of this type.

In the **hinge** type, a convex cylindrical surface meets a concave cylindrical surface, such as the joints between the phalanges.

The joint between the atlas and the epistropheus is an example of the **screw** type of joint.

The **ellipsoidal** type occurs between the radius and the carpus.

The radio-ulnar joints are examples of **trochoidal** joints, in which the articular surface of one bone is the edge of a disk that glides in a corresponding concave articular surface of the other bone.

In the **saddle** joint, the end of one bone is convex in one direction and concave in the other; the end of the second bone is exactly the opposite, as in the metacarpophalangeal joint of the thumb.

The intertarsal joints are examples of **irregular** joints.

Types of Movements Permitted at Synovial Joints

The movements of parts of the body result chiefly from the revolving of joint surfaces. The surfaces revolve around axes that are located in or near the joint.

Angular movement is that type which changes the angle between bones. It may be divided into 4 kinds: flexion, extension, abduction and adduction. *Flexion* decreases the angle between bones or brings the bones closer together. *Extension* increases the angle between bones or separates them more widely. In the case of the ankle joint we use the term *plantar flexion* instead of extension and *dorsal flexion* instead of flexion. *Abduction* is movement away from the median plane of the body and *adduction* is movement toward the median plane of the body. The movements of the digits are exceptions; in the fingers, adduction is movement toward the third digit; in the toes, adduction is movement toward the second digit.

Circumduction. When all of the above angular movements are combined in succession so that the end of the limb describes a circle and the shaft of the limb describes the surface of a cone, the result is *circumduction*.

In rotation there is a revolving movement or twisting of a part of the body around the longitudinal axis of that part, without a change in the position of the part. *Medial* rotation is rotation or twisting toward the median plane of the body; *lateral* rotation is rotation or twisting away from the median plane of the body. You can demonstrate rotation on yourself by holding your shoulder steady and twisting the upper extremity about on its longitudinal axis.

Special Movements. There are two special movements of the forearm: supination and pronation. In the anatomic position the forearm is supinated, with palm forward; the radius and the ulna are parallel. *Supination* is the movement that brings the forearm into this position. In *pronation* the back of the hand is turned forward, and the radius is crossed over the ulna. Demonstrate supination and pronation on yourself by flexing your forearm at the elbow joint, placing your opposite hand on the flexed forearm and then turning your palm downward and upward, in alternation. You can feel the radius change its position with respect to the ulna.

There are 2 special movements at the ankle joint: inversion and eversion. *Inversion* is the act of turning the sole of the foot inward and *eversion* is the act of turning the sole of the foot outward.

Two other special movements are performed by the lower jaw, the clavicle and the tongue. These are protraction and retraction. *Protraction* is the act of moving the part forward, and *retraction* is drawing it backward.

PRACTICAL CONSIDERATIONS

COMPOSITION OF BONE

The matrix of bone is impregnated with calcium (lime) salts. The composition of fresh bone is as follows: water 50 per cent and solid material 50 per cent. Of this solid material, 67 per cent is inorganic and 33 per cent organic. Calcium phosphate is the chief inorganic constituent; the chief organic constituent is collagen, which is converted to gelatin by boiling.

The following shows the difference between a 7 months' fetus and a 4-year-old child:

	7 MONTHS' FETUS	4-YEAR-OLD CHILD
Water %	69.11	45.29
Fat %	0.38	12.29
Ash %	13.28	51.59

Calcium is present in bone, not only as phosphate, but also as carbonate and fluoride; magnesium is present as phosphate; sodium is present as oxide and chloride.

The inorganic portion of bone may be removed by dilute hydro-chloric acid. The portion that remains maintains the shape of the bone; it is tough and flexible and may be tied in a knot.

The organic portion of bone may be removed by oxidation in air, the shape of the bone remaining, but the residue is fragile and brittle.

The bones of children contain less inorganic matter and more organic matter than the bones of adults. Consequently, the former

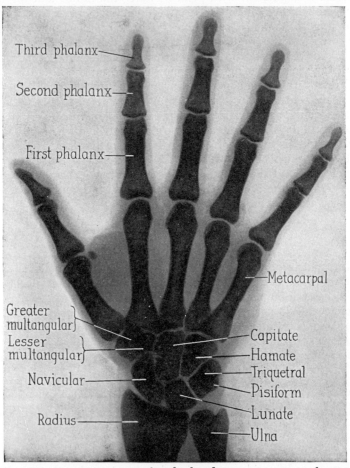

FIG. 80. Roentgenogram of right hand, posterior view, showing bones. (Farris)

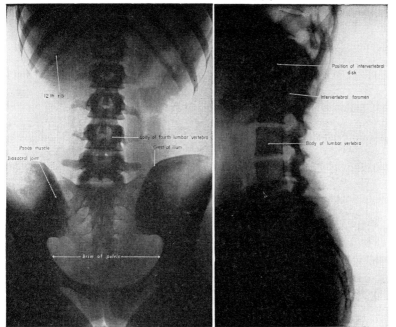

FIG. 81. (*Left*) Roentgenogram of vertebral column, lumbar and upper sacral regions. The lower ribs and the psoas muscles are visible. Anteroposterior view. (From T. A. Pearson, M.D.)

FIG. 82. (*Right*) Roentgenogram of vertebral column, lumbar region. Lateral view. Position of intervertebral disk indicated; disk not visible by x-rays. (From T. A. Pearson, M.D.)

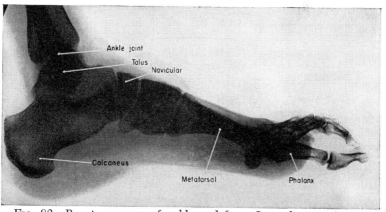

FIG. 83. Roentgenogram of ankle and foot. Lateral view. (From T. A. Pearson, M.D.)

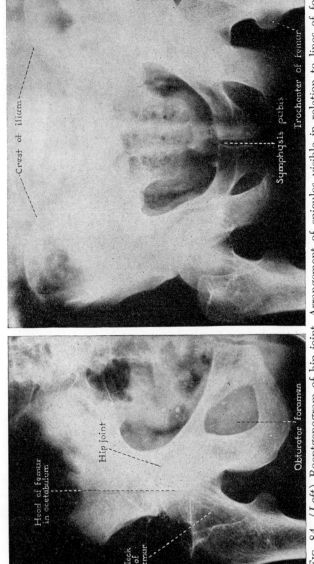

FIG. 84. (*Left*) Roentgenogram of hip joint. Arrangement of spicules visible in relation to lines of force. (*Right*) Roentgenogram of pelvis. (From University of Minnesota Hospital)

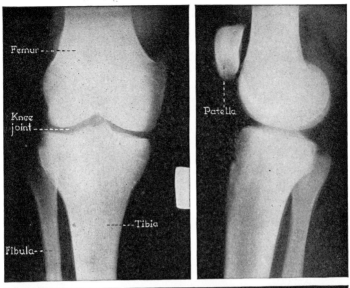

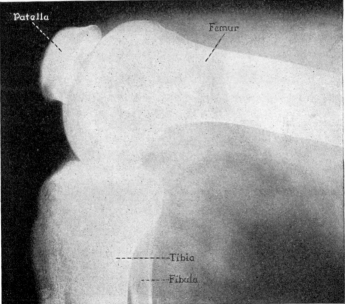

FIG. 85. Roentgenogram of knee. (*Top, left*) Anteroposterior and (*Top, right*) lateral views in extreme extension. (*Bottom*) Lateral view, in extreme flexion. Position of patella is shown. (From University of Minnesota Hospital) (Farris)

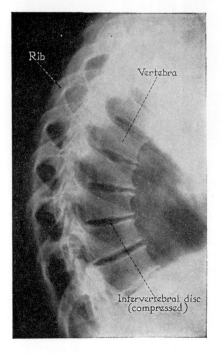

Rib

Vertebra

Intervertebral disc
(compressed)

FIG. 86. Roentgenogram
showing kyphosis of the
thoracic portion of vertebral
column, with secondary
changes on the anterior borders of the vertebrae. (From
University of Minnesota
Hospital)

are less brittle and much more flexible. They bend easily, but do
not break easily. If they do happen to be fractured they break like
a green stick. The unossified epiphyseal lines of the long limb
bones of children are weak places in the bones, and in accidents
an epiphysis sometimes separates from the diaphysis. If this happens the cartilage may be so damaged that the bone ceases to grow
in length at that end after the diaphysis and the epiphysis have
reunited.

As one grows older the amount of inorganic matter increases
more and more, and the brittle bones of the aged break easily and
heal with difficulty. Nurses see more fractured hips now than were
seen a generation ago because more people now live to a "ripe
old age."

INFECTION OF BONE

A bone may become infected, and the resulting inflammation of
the bone and its marrow is called *osteomyelitis*. As you may imag-
ine, this is indeed a serious condition. Bone may be the seat of

tuberculous infection. Any bone may be so involved, but when there is tuberculosis of the vertebrae we speak of it as Pott's disease.

ROENTGENOGRAMS OF BONES

A roentgenogram is a shadow picture. Such pictures are valuable in the diagnosis of fractures and they give valuable information in the course of reduction and treatment of fractures. The following roentgenograms are presented for your observation: Figures 80, 81, 82, 83, 84, 85 and 86.

JOINT DISORDERS

Dislocation. Joints may be dislocated, in which case there is displacement of one of the bones or a derangement of the parts that compose the joint. An incomplete or partial dislocation is called a *subluxation* of a joint.

Bursitis. Bursae are situated at places where friction would develop in their absence. Some of the important bursae are: *acromial, olecranon, subdeltoid, subscapular* and *prepatellar.* Bursae may become inflamed (bursitis), and movements then elicit pain (as in housemaid's knee).

Ankylosis refers to fixation of a joint so that it can move no longer. Usually it is preceded by an infection.

Arthritis refers to inflammation of the tissues around joints and is accompanied by swelling, redness and pain. Rheumatoid arthritis resembles rheumatism.

Sprain. A sprain refers to the wrenching of a joint, during which the attachments are ruptured or torn, but there is no displacement of bones. Sprains are accompanied by swelling, redness and pain. A sacro-iliac sprain is a frequent cause of backache.

Occasionally, an individual suffers from a painful arthritis which migrates from one joint to another. This condition often is accompanied by damage to the heart, resulting in chronic valvular disease of the heart. There is no permanent damage to the joints. This condition is called rheumatic fever, and it may follow a streptococcal infection of the pharynx.

DIAMETERS OF THE FEMALE PELVIS AND MEASUREMENTS OF FETAL SKULL

The various diameters of the female pelvis should be measured during pregnancy; these are important in relation to the size of the average fetal skull. If the pelvic measurements are small, there may be difficulty during the delivery of the head of the fetus. When difficulty seems to be imminent, serious consideration should be given to operative delivery by cesarean section. The incomplete ossification of the cranial bones of the fetus permits some overlapping of the bones or "molding of the head" during delivery. Probably you have noted the difference in the shape of the head between a baby born by delivery through the birth canal, during which molding occurs, and one delivered by cesarean section, during which no molding occurs.

Sometimes obstetricians aid delivery by placing forceps on the head of the fetus and pulling as the mother pushes to get the head through the birth canal. This is called instrumental delivery. Unless great care is observed, damage may be produced to the brain, especially to the motor cortex (p. 309) underlying the bony region to which forceps are applied, and a "spastic" child (p. 236) is the result.

DEFORMITIES

The curves of the vertebral column may become exaggerated and lead to a poor standing position or posture. An increase in the thoracic curve is called *kyphosis* (Fig. 86). An increase in the lumbar curve is called *lordosis*. A lateral curvature is called *scoliosis*. Abnormal curvatures may follow erosion (wearing away) of the bodies of vertebrae due to tuberculosis.

The intervertebral disks are composed of fibrous tissue and cartilage and are compressible. The disks are thin in the cervical region, thicker in the thoracic region and still thicker and resilient in the lumbar region. The disks act as buffers or shock absorbers, as well as cushions, which permit certain kinds of spinal movements. Each bone is bound to the one above and below by strong ligaments, yet in spite of this arrangement one hears occasionally of a "slipped" or herniated disk. A *laminectomy* is an operation in which the vertebral arches, especially the posterior parts, together with the vertebral spines, are removed.

In rickets there is defective calcification of bones, which can lead to a series of deformities. In young children, *knock knees* may occur in which the thighs slant inward from the pelvis to the knees. *Bowlegs*, in which the bowing is outward, are seen frequently. *Pigeon breast* is a deformity in which the sternum and the costal cartilages protrude, and the line of junction between ribs and the cartilages becomes a deep groove. The sides of the chest are flattened. Changes may take place also at the junctions of ribs and the cartilages which have the appearance of beaded ribs, giving

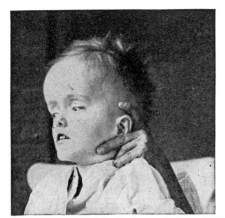

FIG. 87. (*Left*) Hydrocephalus. This child was 11 years of age at the time the photograph was taken. (From Minnesota School for the Feeble Minded)

FIG. 88. (*Right*) Microcephalic twins. The twins were 28 years of age at the time the photograph was taken. The intelligence quotient was 11. They are active and affectionate toward each other. They can comb hair and button clothes; the memory is fair; the powers of attention are slight. (From Minnesota School for the Feeble Minded)

rise to the term *rachitic* (rickets) *rosary. Craniotabes* refers to a thinning of the bones of the cranium, which may accompany rickets. There may be various types of deformities of the pelvis which can interfere with normal delivery of children by a rachitic mother. A deficiency of vitamin D is one of the contributing causes in rickets.

Under some conditions the parathyroid glands are overactive (p. 733), and calcium and phosphorus are withdrawn from the bones, leaving them soft and susceptible to deformities.

Clubfoot is a congenital malformation, either single or bilateral, in which the front part of the foot is inverted and rotated. It is accompanied by shortening of the Achilles tendon (*tendo calcaneous*) and contracture of the fascia in the sole of the foot.

A bunion is a swelling of a bursa of the foot, especially of the metatarsophalangeal joint of the great toe. It may develop as a result of pressure or friction from badly fitting shoes. The great toe is forced outward, and the joint is made unduly prominent.

Hydrocephalus is a condition in which there is marked enlargement of the head and prominence of the forehead, atrophy of the brain and an abnormal increase in the amount of cerebral fluid with dilatation of the ventricles of the brain. Figure 87 illustrates hydrocephalus in a child of 11 years.

When the pituitary gland secretes too much of its growth hormone in an adult, the head, the hands and the feet increase in size, as illustrated in Figure 387. The condition is called *acromegaly*.

In **microcephalus** there is diminution in the size of the cranium due to premature ossification of the sutures. Such individuals are idiotic, and the arrested growth of the skull is thought to be secondary to the arrested development of the brain. Microcephalic twins are shown in Figure 88.

FAILURE OF UNION OF BONES

Sometimes bones that should unite before birth fail to do so. One such failure leads to *harelip,* in which there is a cleft in the lip. The frontal and the maxillary processes fail to unite, either on one side or on both. *Cleft palate* is caused by the faulty union between the palatal plates of the horizontal processes of the maxillary arches. The cleft is in the hard palate or roof of the mouth.

Spina Bifida. The vertebral canal is formed by the laminae of the vertebrae arching over and uniting posteriorly. If the laminae fail to unite the condition is called spina bifida. It occurs most frequently in the lumbar and the sacral regions. The contents of the spinal canal, either the meninges or spinal cord, or both, may protrude.

Amputation refers to the removal, most often by surgical means, of a whole or a part of a limb. In may occur nonsurgically as a result of gangrene or as the result of an accident.

Sternal Puncture. In various types of anemia a sternal puncture is made. This really is a biopsy (examination of tissue from a living subject). The types of cells and the phases of development are noted, and the condition of the red bone marrow is determined.

Craniotomy is the cutting into pieces of the fetal head when delivery would be impossible otherwise—the fetus is abnormal. In neurosurgery, the term *craniotomy* refers to any operation that involves opening the cranium.

Sinusitis is infection of the mucoperiosteum lining the air spaces of the cranial bones (paranasal sinuses).

SUMMARY

1. Formation of bone
   A. Intramembranous
   B. Cartilaginous or endochondral
2. Bone growth
   A. In circumference
   B. In length
3. Structure of adult bone
   A. Microscopic
      a. Cancellous or spongy
      b. Compact
   B. Gross; parts of a typical long bone
      Shaft or diaphysis; epiphyses; periosteum; blood supply; bone marrow (yellow and red); endosteum
4. Types of bones
   A. Long
   B. Short
   C. Flat
   D. Irregular
   E. Sesamoid
5. Descriptive terms
   A. Projections: condyle, crest, head, process, spine, trochanter, tubercle, tuberosity
   B. Depressions: foramen, fossa, groove, sinus, meatus
6. Divisions of the skeleton
   A. Appendicular
      a. Upper extremity
         (1) Shoulder girdle
            (A) Clavicle
            (B) Scapula
         (2) Arm (humerus)
         (3) Forearm
            (A) Ulna
            (B) Radius

(4) Hand
    (A) Carpus
    (B) Metacarpals
    (C) Phalanges

b. Lower extremity
  (1) Hip bones
    (A) Ilium
    (B) Ischium
    (C) Pubis
    (D) Pelvis
  (2) Thigh
    (A) Femur
    (B) Patella
  (3) Leg
    (A) Tibia
    (B) Fibula
  (4) Foot
    (A) Tarsal
    (B) Metatarsal
    (C) Phalanges

B. Axial
  a. Vertebral column
    (1) Components: (vertebrae, sacrum, coccyx)
    (2) As a whole
  b. Thorax
    (1) Ribs
    (2) Sternum
  c. Bones of skull (face and cranium)
    (1) As a whole
      (A) From the front: frontal, maxilla, zygomatic, ethmoid, lacrimal, palatine; orbits; nasal cavity; jaws
      (B) Lateral view: parietal, temporal, occipital
      (C) Base from below: foramen magnum
      (D) Base from above: sphenoid
    (2) Hyoid
    (3) Sutures between cranial bones; fontanels
    (4) Air sinuses

8. Articulations or joints
  A. Classes according to morphology
    a. Syndesmoses
    b. Synchondroses

  c. Synostoses
  d. Symphyses
  e. Synovial joints
B. Types of movement permitted at synovial joints
  a. Angular: flexion, extension, abduction and adduction
  b. Circumduction
  c. Rotation: medial and lateral
  d. Supination and pronation
  e. Inversion and eversion
  f. Protraction and retraction

SITUATIONS AND QUESTIONS

A 76-year-old woman tripped on a loose rug and fell down 10 steps. Upon x-ray examination, it was found that Mrs. Keith had a fractured hip and a possible break of the medial leg bone.

Older folks are more prone to breaks in bones because: _____(a) the bones of adults contain more inorganic salts causing them to become hard and brittle; _____(b) the bones are worn thin because of extended use, through the years; _____(c) adults have more spongy bone than children; _____(d) calcium is removed from bones, thereby making them more fragile.

The hip joint is an example of: _____(a) a diarthrotic joint; _____(b) a syndesmosis joint; _____(c) a hinge type joint; _____(d) a symphysis.

The doctor discovered that the rounded projection of the femur, which fits into the hip socket, was splintered. In his report he referred to this projection as the: _____(a) acetabulum; _____(b) greater trochanter; _____(c) head; _____ (d) tubercle.

The medial leg bone involved in this fall is the: _____(a) femur; _____(b) tibia; _____(c) fibula; _____(d) patella.

A student viewing Mrs. Keith's x-ray pictures could observe readily the characteristics of the female pelvis. In comparing the male and the female pelvis, it can be said that: _____(a) the female pelvis is composed of the same bones as the male pelvis; _____(b) the male pelvis has a wider pubic arch than the female; _____(c) the ilium is less flared in the female pelvis; _____(d) the bones of the female pelvis are larger than those of the male.

Mr. Stehe is suffering from bursitis of the left shoulder. The doctor explained to him that: _____(a) a bursa is a sesamoid bone found at a joint; _____(b) a bursa is the depression that is occupied by bone cells; _____(c) a bursa is a cavity within long bones; _____(d) a bursa is a small sac containing fluid.

The bone of the arm which articulates with the scapula to form the shoulder joint is the: _____(a) clavicle; _____(b) humerus; _____(c) atlas; _____(d) ulna.

Mrs. Moore found the growth and the development of her 6-weeks-old son very interesting. She discovered that the skull bones of her son were not fused together. These soft places of the infant's head are called: _____(a) fontanels; _____(b) sutures; _____(c) fissures; _____(d) fossae.

There are several normal curvatures to the vertebral column. The curve that develops as the child begins to hold up his head is the _____(a) lateral curvature; _____(b) anterior curve of cervical vertebrae; _____(c) posterior curve of thoracic vertebrae; _____(d) anterior curve of lumbar vertebrae.

The structure involved in growth in length of long bones is: _____(a) periosteum; _____(b) marrow cavity; _____(c) epiphyseal cartilage; _____(d) endosteum.

Mrs. Moore soon discovered the one movable bone of the son's skull. The name of this bone is: _____(a) ethmoid; _____(b) mandible; _____(c) maxilla; _____(d) frontal.

~~~~~~

4. Anatomy of the Muscular System

~~~~~~

INTRODUCTION

Muscular tissue is specialized for contractility. Its general functions are exceedingly numerous and varied. The first function, which begins long before you are born and continues until your last minute of life, is the pumping of blood around your body by contraction of heart muscle. Another function that is present long before birth is the movement of the extremities; when this begins the mother says that she "feels life," and she is assured that the fetus is alive within her.

A third function of muscular tissue is that of respiration or getting oxygen into, and carbon dioxide out of, the lungs. The first gasp or cry of the newborn infant indicates that the muscles of respiration have begun to function. When your training takes you to the delivery room you will realize that everyone present at a delivery is tense until these respiratory muscles of the newborn begin to function. The respiratory muscles normally continue to function as long as you live, but if they should become paralyzed by poliomyelitis or some other misfortune their function can be replaced by an "iron lung."

Other general functions that appear soon after birth are the movement of food material along the gastro-intestinal tract, the transport of urine to the urinary bladder and the emptying of the urinary bladder. These particular functions are due to the activity of "smooth" muscular tissue.

The gradual mastery of many of the "skeletal" muscles by the developing child is fascinating to watch. Within a few months after birth the infant begins to hold his spoon and then his cup. A little later he learns to walk. But it takes several years before the movements can be co-ordinated properly to permit a child to wring a wash cloth, button his clothes, brush his teeth, lace his shoes, tie his shoe strings and write. Still more years pass before the muscular control is sufficient for playing the piano, fingering the violin or typing. In fact, some individuals who are "all thumbs" never do acquire skill in using their hands for such fine work as sewing, embroidering, threading needles and using very fine tools such as watchmakers employ.

The above examples will give you an idea of the variety of functions carried out by muscular tissue. All of us should appreciate our normally functioning muscles, and the realization of the intricacy and the beauty of the muscular system should make a lasting impression on us. Consider what a difference it would make in our lives if we could not walk, feed ourselves and perform the hundreds of tasks that make up the day's work. You can see easily how complicated life may be if some of your skeletal muscles become paralyzed, such as the muscles of respiration, in poliomyelitis,

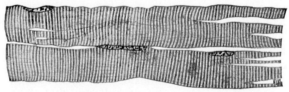

FIG. 89. Longitudinal section of striated muscle showing cross-striations and the nuclei at the periphery. ×275.

or the muscles of the extremities, after a stroke. Paralysis of smooth muscle leads to death, if it involves the smooth muscle of the intestine.

TYPES OF MUSCULAR TISSUE

The muscles are the engines of the body, and there are different types for the performance of various functions. Three types of muscular tissue are present in the body.

The first is **skeletal**, which is attached to bones. This type is called *striated,* also, due to its appearance under the microscope, and sometimes a third name, *voluntary,* is used, since this type is under the control of the will. This muscular tissue is like a high-speed engine; it can develop great power but runs for short periods of time.

The second type is **smooth** (also called visceral, plain and involuntary) muscular tissue. It is present in the walls of the viscera and is not under the control of the will. This type is like an engine that is geared for slow speed and heavy duty; it continues to function day after day in a slow but steady manner.

The third type is **cardiac** or heart muscular tissue. It works steadily day after day, yet it can respond more vigorously for short periods, such as when we make a dash for a streetcar or a bus or run up stairs.

STRUCTURE OF MUSCULAR TISSUE

MICROSCOPIC STRUCTURE

If you examine muscular tissue under a microscope you will see that each type has a characteristic structure.

Skeletal muscle is made up of parallel bundles of long, cylindrical fibers, which are muscle cells drawn out into long threadlike structures. Each fiber has many nuclei arranged around its periphery (external surface or circumference), as shown in Figure 89. Such a fiber is a "multinucleated" cell. The cytoplasm of the muscle fiber (sarcoplasm) contains many fine fibers which are called *myofibrils.* These are cytoplasmic organelles (p. 20). The cell membrane of a skeletal muscle fiber is called *sarcolemma* (from *sarco,* meaning "flesh," and *lemma,* meaning "rind" or "husk"). Although you cannot see the structure of the myofibrils by ordinary microscopic observation, it is known that they are composed of long chains of protein molecules. They exhibit alternating light and dark disks which are responsible for the striated appearance of the muscle. Skeletal muscle fibers vary from 1 to 80 mm. in length in different muscles.

Smooth muscular tissue is made up of spindle-shaped cells, which means that they are long and tapering. Each cell or fiber has a single nucleus that lies in the center or widest part of the cell, as shown in Figure 90. Smooth muscle fibers vary markedly in length in different parts of the body. The smallest are found in the walls of small blood vessels, where they are 0.02 mm. long, or one fiftieth as long as the shortest skeletal muscle fiber. The largest fibers are found in the pregnant uterus, in which they may be 0.5 mm. long or one half as long as the shortest skeletal muscle fiber. In other words, the longest skeletal muscle fibers are about 160 times as long as the longest smooth muscle fibers. Myofibrils are present in the sarcoplasm, but the striated appearance is lacking.

Cardiac muscular tissue is made up of a network of branching fibers. Myofibrils are present, as are the alternating light and dark disks which are responsible for the striated appearance under the microscope. Heart muscle differs from skeletal in that each section of fiber has only one nucleus, located in the center of the cell. The dark-stained bands noted at intervals are called *intercalated disks*. The structure of heart muscle is illustrated in Figure 91.

Fig. 90. Smooth muscle from the intestine. Several isolated cells are seen at the top. ×200.

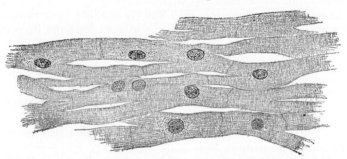

Fig. 91. Human cardiac muscle. Branching fibers, centrally placed nuclei, striations and intercalated disks are evident. ×375.

Gross Structure

There is connective tissue in muscles. The entire skeletal muscle is wrapped in a connective tissue covering called *epimysium* ("upon the muscle"). Partitions of connective tissue extend from the epimysium into the muscle to divide it into bundles called *fasciculi.* These partitions are called *perimysium* ("around mus-

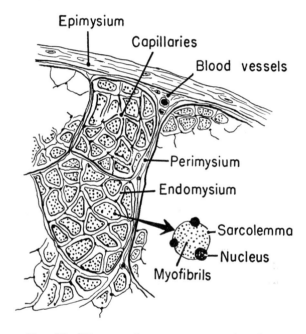

Fig. 92. Diagram of a cross section of a skeletal muscle, showing the connective tissue component. The connective tissue sheath that covers the muscle is called *epimysium.* The perimysium surrounds bundles of muscle fibers or "partitions" the muscles into groups of fibers. Endomysium surrounds individual muscle fibers. An enlarged cross section of a single muscle fiber (cell) is shown by the arrow at the right. The cell contains many nuclei located peripherally just under the cell membrane or sarcolemma. The myofibrils are organelles in the cytoplasm or sarcoplasm. (Modified from Ham, A. W.: Histology, ed. 2, Philadelphia, Lippincott)

cle"), since they surround bundles of muscle fibers. Very delicate connective tissue extends from the perimysium, which surrounds each bundle of fibers, into the interior of the bundle and penetrates between its fibers. This constitutes the *endomysium* ("within muscle"). Capillaries form a network within it. Figure 92 is a diagram of a cross section of a muscle, in which the epimysium, the perimysium and the endomysium are shown in their proper relationships. The epimysium, the perimysium and the endomysium are all continuous with the connective tissue structures to which a muscle is attached and on which it exerts its pull by contraction. The sarcolemma or cell membrane blends with the connective tissue of the muscle.

The connective tissue component of skeletal muscles has been compared with a harness, by means of which the pull exerted by a horse can be brought to bear on a wagon.

Smooth muscular tissue is arranged in sheets or bundles, either circular or longitudinal, which form a layer in the walls of blood vessels, intestine and other viscera. The smooth muscle layer is bound firmly to other components of the wall by connective tissue.

Cardiac muscular tissue is arranged in bundles, some of which are common to the two atria (p. 489) and others are common to the two ventricles (p. 490). The bundles are arranged as spirals or figures-of-eight.

LOCATION OF VARIOUS TYPES OF MUSCULAR TISSUE

Skeletal muscles are attached to the bones. They cover the skeleton; surround the oral, the abdominal and the pelvic cavities; separate the thoracic from the abdominal cavities; form the body of the tongue; and are attached to the outer layer of the eyeball.

Smooth muscle is present in the walls of the blood vessels, the gastro-intestinal tract, the ureters, the urinary bladder, the ducts of the reproductive system, the uterus, the respiratory passages, the lymphatic vessels, the capsule of spleen, around the hair follicles of the skin, within the connective tissue of the skin and within the eyeball.

Cardiac muscle is present only in the walls of the heart.

BLOOD SUPPLY OF THE MUSCULAR TISSUE

All types of muscular tissue are supplied abundantly with blood. Arteries are carried by the perimysium from the epimysium into the substance of the muscle. The arteries subdivide and, finally, the capillaries are carried by the endomysium to each muscle fiber.

Most of the arterioles run parallel with the muscle fibers and give off branches at right angles to the fibers. It is thought that a layer of tissue fluid exists between the sarcolemma and the wall of the capillary, and that exchanges between the muscle fiber and blood take place through this tissue fluid.

Lymphatic vessels are found in the perimysium and the epimysium of striated muscle. In cardiac muscle they are found also in the endomysium.

NERVE SUPPLY OF MUSCULAR TISSUE

All 3 types of muscular tissue are supplied with nerve fibers that carry messages from the muscles to the brain. Thus, the brain is kept informed of the degree of contraction of skeletal muscles. This information is essential to the proper co-ordination of muscular movements. The brain, likewise, is kept informed of undue stretching of smooth muscle, such as when gas accumulates in the intestine and gives rise to gas pains. Information about excessive contraction or spasm of smooth muscle is sent to the brain. The information sent from the heart muscle is concerned with the amount

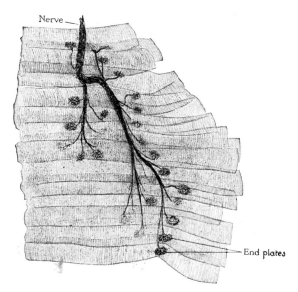

Fig. 93. Motor end-plates or neuromuscular junctions in striated muscle. The axon divides and sends branches to the individual muscle fibers. ×135.

of oxygen supplied to the heart. Whenever the heart is not getting enough oxygen to carry out its work efficiently, one feels a
warning pain or angina (suffocation). It is evident that the messages which are sent from each type of muscular tissue to the brain
are important for the proper functioning of that particular type of
muscle.

As you might expect, the messages that travel from the brain to
each type of muscular tissue are of even greater importance. The
messages to **skeletal muscle** travel over the *somatic efferent nerves*
(p. 245). The nerve fibers penetrate the sarcolemma and come in
contact with the sarcoplasm in an area called the *neuromuscular*
junction, the *myoneural* junction or *motor end-plate* (Fig. 93). One
nerve fiber supplies varying numbers of muscle fibers. In muscles
in which fine, accurate movements are essential, such as in the
muscles which move the eyes, each nerve fiber supplies only 3 to
6 muscle fibers. On the other hand, in muscles in which such fine
control is unnecessary, as in the muscles of the leg, each nerve
fiber divides extensively and supplies as many as 150 muscle fibers.
A nerve cell, its outgoing fiber and all the muscle fibers supplied
constitute a "motor unit." Each skeletal muscle is made up of an
enormous number of motor units.

The messages to **smooth muscle** travel over the *autonomic* or
visceral efferent nerves (fibers which carry messages away from
the central nervous system to visceral structures). Smooth muscle
differs markedly from skeletal muscle with respect to its dependence on messages from the brain—skeletal muscles contract only
when they receive messages from the brain, while smooth muscles
contract quite independently of such messages. The only reason
that any messages are needed by smooth muscle is that there are
times when its activity must be increased or decreased to meet
changing needs. Consequently, there is a double nerve supply to
carry messages from the brain to smooth muscle; one nerve increases the activity and the other decreases the activity that is
already going on in smooth muscle. This regulation of activity in
smooth muscle is entirely unconscious, that is, we have no voluntary control over this type of muscular tissue.

The messages to **cardiac muscle** travel over the autonomic or
visceral efferent nerves, as is the case for smooth muscle. The
heart beats spontaneously and is in no way dependent on messages
from the brain. However, there are times when its activity must
be increased or decreased temporarily, and messages from the
brain are essential at such times.

INDIVIDUAL SKELETAL MUSCLES

Skeletal muscles make up the so-called red flesh of the body, and they comprise about 36 per cent of the body weight in women and 42 per cent in men. The combined weight of all the skeletal muscles in the body is about 3 times as great as that of all the bones in the body.

NAMES OF SKELETAL MUSCLES

Each skeletal muscle in the body has a name; some of these are now in English, and others are still in Latin. You will need to learn the names of some of the important skeletal muscles, as you needed to know the names of some of the bones. The names of muscles have been determined by various circumstances.

Some are given names appropriate to their **location.** Examples of this are: the intercostal muscles, between the ribs; femoris, in the region of the femur; and brachii, in the region of the arm.

A second way of naming muscles is determined by the **direction of their fibers.** Examples of this are: rectus, straight; transversus, across; and obliquus, in an oblique direction.

A third means of naming is derived from the **action,** as abductor, adductor, flexor, extensor and levator (lifter).

A fourth means is derived from the **shape or size,** such as deltoid (from the Greek letter *delta*); trapezius, like a trapezoid or four-sided; maximus, largest, minimus, smallest, longus, long; and brevis, short.

A fifth means is derived from the *number of heads of origin,* as biceps, 2 heads; triceps, 3 heads; and quadriceps, 4 heads.

A sixth means is derived from the **points of attachment,** such as sternocleidomastoid (sternum, clavicle, mastoid process of temporal bone), and styloglossus (styloid process and tongue).

You will note as you progress that some names of muscles are combinations of two of the above, such as adductor magnus, biceps brachii and quadriceps femoris.

PARTS OF A SKELETAL MUSCLE

The end of the skeletal muscle that is the relatively more fixed point of attachment is called the *origin.* The end that is freely movable is called the *insertion.* When the muscle contracts, the insertion is pulled toward the origin. However, you will note later that the origin is fixed absolutely in only a small number of muscles, such as those of the face. In many other muscles, the origin and the insertion are "functionally" interchangeable, which means that these muscles can "act from either end." Examples of this will be encountered as you progress. The portion of the muscle between the origin and the insertion is called the *body* or *belly* of the muscle. The parts of a typical muscle (biceps brachii) are shown in Figure 94.

ATTACHMENTS OF SKELETAL MUSCLES

Prolongations of the connective tissue of muscle attach the muscles to bone, cartilage, skin, mucous membrane or fasciae. The attachments to periosteum of bone or perichondrium of cartilage are broad. This type of attachment is found in the intercostal muscles and in some of the muscles attached to the shoulder and the hip girdles.

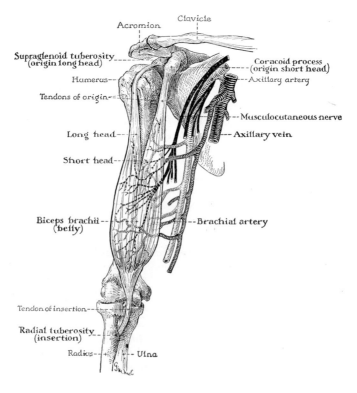

FIG. 94. The biceps brachii with all the parts essential to a complete description. Semidiagrammatic.

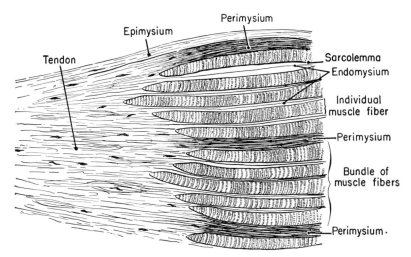

FIG. 95. Diagram of a longitudinal section of a muscle showing
its termination in a tendon. The sarcolemma, the endomysium, the
perimysium and the epimysium are continuous with the connective
tissue of the tendon. The connective tissue forms a harness, against
which the pull of contracting muscle fibers is exerted. (Modified
from Ham, A. W.: Histology, ed. 2, Philadelphia, Lippincott)

The connective tissue may be prolonged in the form of tendons,
as shown in Figure 95. Tendons attach to bone, cartilage or other
structures. They vary greatly in appearance; some are like flat
ribbons, and others are broad sheets called *aponeuroses*. Some
tendons are enclosed in sheaths (Fig. 117): this arrangement is
found in the flexors of the hand. The type of attachment in each
case is eminently suited to the particular work that muscle performs. Muscles are separated from one another and held in position
by deep fasciae, which are sheets of tough, fibrous, connective
tissue.

In some regions bursae are found. They are closed sacs that
contain a small amount of fluid and are located between surfaces
that glide over each other. They prevent friction between the
muscles and their underlying parts. The inner lining of a bursa
acts as a synovial membrane, which means that it secretes fluid.
Bursae of importance are found at the elbow, the knee, the hip,
the heel and under the deltoid, the gluteus maximus and the
trapezius muscles.

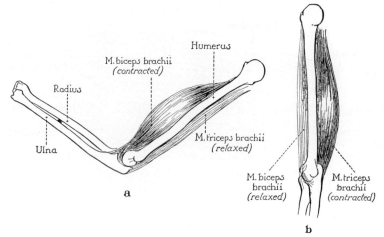

FIG. 96. Diagram of co-ordinated movement. (*Left*) In flexion
of the forearm the biceps brachii is contracted and the triceps is
inhibited. (*Right*) In extension, the reverse condition holds. (Redrawn from Keith.)

MUSCULAR ACTION

Skeletal muscles shorten and exert pull on their attachments when
they contract. The muscles that are atttached to bones move those
bones at the synovial joints. Skeletal muscles are responsible for
the movements of parts of the body or the body as a whole and
are used in both voluntary and reflex movements.

Many skeletal muscles are arranged in pairs; when one of a pair
contracts the other muscle of the pair relaxes. The first is called
the *prime mover,* and the second the *antagonist.* The relaxation
of the antagonist makes possible co-ordinated movement. A diagram of co-ordinated movement is illustrated in Figure 96. When
the opposite movement is performed, the prime mover becomes
the antagonist, and vice versa.

When you wish to perform a particular act, such as rubbing your
eye, the act as a whole is thought of, and you do not analyze it
into the individual muscles that you are going to use. Even our
simplest acts require the co-ordinated use of many muscles in different functional capacities; this is essential to the precision of the
act. Other muscles act as *synergists* (meaning "working together")
and enable the prime movers to perform the desired act efficiently
and smoothly. In some instances, the synergists control the posi-

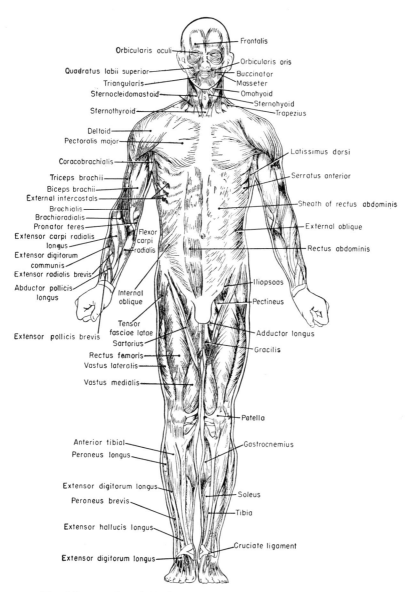

FIG. 97. Muscles of the body, anterior view. The deeper muscles are shown on the left side of the face and on the right side of the abdomen.

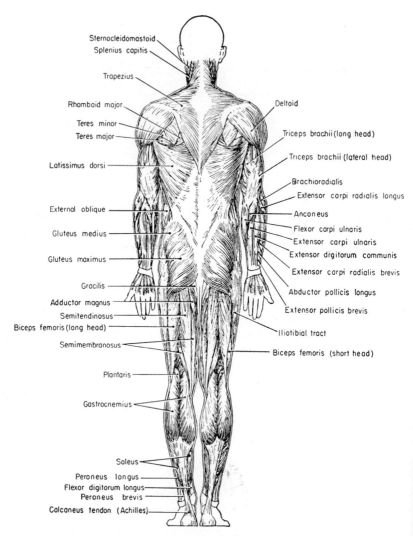

Sternocleidomastoid
Splenius capitis
Trapezius
Rhomboid major
Teres minor
Teres major
Latissimus dorsi
External oblique
Gluteus medius
Gluteus maximus
Gracilis
Adductor magnus
Semitendinosus
Biceps femoris (long head)
Semimembranosus
Plantaris
Gastrocnemius
Soleus
Peroneus longus
Flexor digitorum longus
Peroneus brevis
Calcaneus tendon (Achilles)

Deltoid
Triceps brachii (long head)
Triceps brachii (lateral head)
Brachioradialis
Extensor carpi radialis longus
Anconeus
Flexor carpi ulnaris
Extensor carpi ulnaris
Extensor digitorum communis
Extensor carpi radialis brevis
Abductor pollicis longus
Extensor pollicis brevis
Iliotibial tract
Biceps femoris (short head)

FIG. 98. Muscles of the body, posterior view.

tion of intermediate joints, so that the prime mover may exert its action on a distal joint. Suppose you wish to clench your hand; in order to do this the prime movers flex the fingers and the antagonists (extensors of the fingers) relax. The synergistic muscles fix the wrist in the extended position. If you have something in your

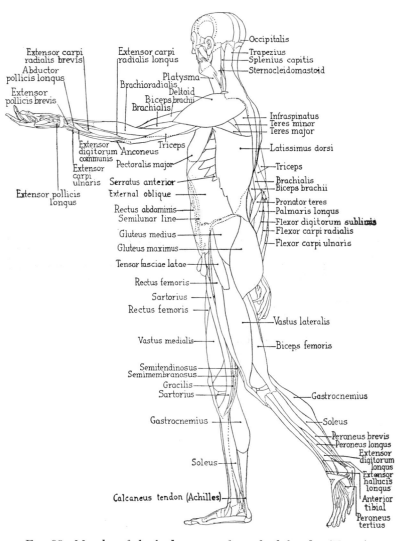

Extensor carpi radialis brevis
Abductor pollicis longus
Extensor pollicis brevis
Extensor carpi radialis lonqus
Brachioradialis
Platysma
Deltoid
Biceps brachii
Brachialis
Occipitalis
Trapezius
Splenius capitis
Sternocleidomastoid
Infraspinatus
Teres minor
Teres major
Latissimus dorsi
Extensor digitorum communis
Extensor carpi ulnaris
Extensor pollicis longus
Anconeus
Triceps
Pectoralis major
Serratus anterior
External oblique
Rectus abdominis
Semilunar line
Gluteus medius
Gluteus maximus
Tensor fasciae latae
Rectus femoris
Sartorius
Rectus femoris
Vastus medialis
Semitendinosus
Semimembranosus
Gracilis
Sartorius
Gastrocnemius
Soleus
Calcaneus tendon (Achilles)
Triceps
Brachialis
Biceps brachii
Pronator teres
Palmaris longus
Flexor digitorum sublimis
Flexor carpi radialis
Flexor carpi ulnaris
Vastus lateralis
Biceps femoris
Gastrocnemius
Soleus
Peroneus brevis
Peroneus lonqus
Extensor digitorum longus
Extensor hallucis lonqus
Anterior tibial
Peroneus tertius

FIG. 99. Muscles of the body as seen from the left side. (Farris)

hand which someone wants to take from you, he will flex your
wrist, and your grip will be lost, since your fingers will no longer
remain flexed. Even though he knows nothing of prime movers,

antagonists and synergists, he can get what he wants by interfering with the co-ordinated movements that accompany clenching your hand.

GROUPS OF SKELETAL MUSCLES

The two principal groups of skeletal muscles are appendicular and axial. The appendicular group comprises the muscles of the upper and the lower extremities. The axial group comprises the muscles of the trunk, the head and the neck. Figures 97, 98, 99 and 100 will give you an idea of the muscles of the body as a whole.

APPENDICULAR MUSCLES

MUSCLES OF THE UPPER EXTREMITY

The muscles of the upper extremities are used in writing, eating, manipulating tools and machines, climbing, defending, attacking and innumerable other activities. They even play a part in expressing one's emotions.

The movements of the scapula are of great importance in the movements of the arm. The scapula can be moved forward, backward, upward, downward and rotated as it follows the movements of the arm. The head of the humerus is kept in the glenoid cavity during these movements. The arm can be abducted, adducted, flexed, extended and rotated at the shoulder joint. During all of these movements the scapula moves in proper co-ordination to keep the shoulder joint intact.

Perform the following acts, and in each case try to determine the direction of the movements of the arms and the shoulders: Look at the sky directly above you; fold your arms across your chest; make yourself round-shouldered; throw out your chest and throw your shoulders back; zip a dress up the back; tie your shoestrings; tie your apron strings; pick up an object from the floor on your right; scratch your back; place a book on your head and move your arms in various directions without dropping the book. If you have been a careful observer during the above acts you noted that one muscle takes part in several acts, and that different parts of one muscle may take part in opposite acts, according to variations in the relative fixation of the attachments.

Not all of the skeletal muscles are described in the text; for information about those not described, make use of the Muscle Table at the end of this chapter.

The muscles of the upper extremity may be divided into the following groups: (1) muscles that connect the upper extremity to

FIG. 100. Male figure as seen from the left side. (Farris)

the trunk: (a) dorsal or superficial muscles of the back, and (b) ventral, or muscles of the pectoral region; (2) muscles of the shoulder; (3) muscles of the arm; (4) muscles of the forearm; (5) muscles of the hand.

Dorsal Muscles. The dorsal or superficial muscles of the back are the trapezius, the latissimus dorsi, the levator scapulae and the major and minor rhomboids.

THE TRAPEZIUS is a very large muscle that lies superficially at the back of the neck and the upper part of the thorax (Fig. 98). The right and the left trapezius muscles together form a trapezoid, which is the reason the muscle was so named. Each trapezius arises from, or has its origin from, the occipital bone, the ligamentum nuchae, the spines of the seventh cervical and all of the thoracic vertebrae. Each is inserted on the clavicle, the acromion and the spine of the scapula on its own side.

The degree of contraction of the trapezius muscles determines the position of the shoulders, and this indicates the general well-being or physical condition of the individual. If you allow your shoulders to droop, you broadcast to those about you that you are not feeling "fit" or are a little below "par."

Depending upon which part of the muscle is more fixed, the trapezius can take part in many acts, such as (1) raising and shrugging the shoulders, (2) extending the head, (3) turning the head from side to side and (4) bracing back the shoulders.

THE LATISSIMUS DORSI (meaning "widest of the back") is shown in Figures 98 and 101. It is a large, flat, triangular muscle that covers the loin and the lower half of the thoracic region. It arises mainly from the spines of the lower thoracic, the lumbar and the sacral vertebrae and the iliac crest. There is some variation in different individuals, in that a few slips of the muscle may arise from the lower 3 or 4 ribs, in addition to the above points of origin. The fibers of each latissimus dorsi muscle converge to a narrow tendon and insert on the anterior surface of the upper part of the humerus on its side of the body.

With the trunk fixed, the latissimus dorsi draws the arm powerfully downward in a backward sweep and simultaneously rotates it inward in the well-known swimming stroke. The latissimus dorsi is the chief muscle used in giving a downward blow with the upper extremity. When both arms are fixed, the latissimus dorsi muscles assist the abdominal and the pectoral muscles in pulling the trunk forward, as in climbing. These muscles also raise the

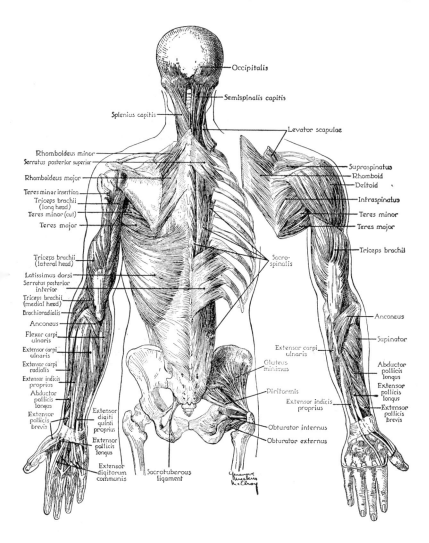

FIG. 101. Deep muscles of neck, back and hip region and muscles of upper extremity, posterior view. Right upper extremity has been removed from the body by cutting the rhomboids and levator scapulae muscles. Certain muscles have been removed to show deeper layers and to expose the underlying bones.

lower ribs and, in this way, can act as muscles of respiration when a person is breathing forcibly.

THE LEVATOR SCAPULAE AND THE MAJOR AND THE MINOR RHOM-BOIDS (Fig. 101) are flat muscles that extend from the upper part of the vertebral column to the medial border of the scapula, beneath the trapezius, on each side. They elevate the scapula, rotate it and draw it backward.

Ventral Muscles. The ventral muscles or those of the pectoral region are the pectoralis major, the pectoralis minor, the subclavius, and the serratus anterior.

THE PECTORALIS MAJOR (Figs. 97 and 108) is a large, thick, fan-shaped muscle on the upper, anterior part of the chest. The fibers of the two pectoralis major muscles form the anterior axillary folds in front of the armpits. Each muscle arises from the clavicle, the sternum and the upper 6 costal cartilages and is inserted on the greater tubercle of the humerus of its side of the body. Part of this muscle is removed in radical operations for cancer of the breast.

The pectoralis major adducts, flexes and rotates the humerus in-ward. It draws the shoulder girdle forward and depresses it. If the arm has been raised, the pectoralis major helps to bring it back to the side. These are the chief flying muscles in birds.

THE PECTORALIS MINOR (Fig. 107) is a thin, triangular muscle that lies under the pectoralis major. It depresses the tip of the shoulder and helps to rotate the scapula downward. It is always removed in radical breast operations for cancer.

THE SUBCLAVIUS (Fig. 107) is a small triangular muscle that lies between the clavicle and the first rib. If the arms are fixed, the subclavius muscles, together with the pectoral muscles, draw the ribs upward and expand the chest, thereby aiding in forced in-spiration.

THE SERRATUS ANTERIOR is a large muscle that occupies the side of the chest and the medial wall of the axilla or armpit (Figs. 107 and 108). Its fibers arise like the teeth of a saw or in a jagged fashion, suggesting the name "serratus." It arises from the upper 8 or 9 ribs along the front and the sides of the thorax and is inserted on the vertebral border of the scapula.

The serratus anterior muscles are the fixation muscles for the scapulae. They are important in pushing, during which motion they carry the scapulae forward. These muscles assist the trapezius muscles in supporting weights on the shoulders, and they aid in raising the arms above the horizontal level.

Muscles of the Shoulder. The muscles of the shoulder are the deltoid, the supraspinatus, the infraspinatus, the teres major, the teres minor and the subscapularis (Figs. 101 and 107).

THE DELTOID is a large, thick, powerful, shield-shaped muscle that covers the shoulder joint and gives roundness to the upper part of the arm just below the shoulder (Figs. 97, 98 and 101). It arises from the clavicle, the acromion and the spine of the scapula. Its fibers unite to form a thick tendon that inserts on the deltoid tubercle on the lateral aspect of the humerus.

When the whole deltoid contracts, it abducts the arm and raises it laterally to the horizontal position. Various fibers assist other muscles in flexing, extending and rotating the arm. The deltoid muscles are common sites for intramuscular injections.

THE OTHER 5 MUSCLES of the shoulder arise from the scapula and insert on the humerus.

The *supraspinatus,* the *infraspinatus* and the *teres minor* pass over the capsule of the shoulder joint, to which their tendons adhere, and insert on the greater tubercle of the humerus. They help to protect the shoulder joint, as well as to assist in lateral rotation of the arm. The supraspinatus, in addition, aids the deltoid in abducting the arm and helps to fix the head of the humerus in the glenoid cavity.

The *teres major* assists in adduction and medial rotation of the arm.

The *subscapularis* (Fig. 107) helps to protect the front of the shoulder joint and prevents displacements of the head of the humerus. It is the chief medial rotator of the arm.

Muscles of the Arm. The muscles of the arm are the biceps brachii, the coracobrachialis, the brachialis and the triceps brachii. The term *brachii* used in all of these means "arm." The muscles of the arm act chiefly on the forearm, flexing, extending and rotating it. Flexion is brought about by the contraction of the ventral arm muscles, which are inserted on the radius and the ulna, and, also, by the more superficial muscles of the forearm. Extension is brought about by the contraction of the dorsal muscles of the arm.

THE BICEPS BRACHII (Fig. 97) lies anterior to the humerus and forms a large part of the substance of the arm. This is the muscle which small boys show when boasting of their physical strength. As indicated in the name, the biceps brachii has two heads of origin, one from the glenoid fossa and the other from the tip of the coracoid process of the scapula. The tendon of this muscle inserts on the tuberosity at the proximal end of the radius. You can feel this tendon if you place the fingers of the opposite hand in the crease of the elbow and flex and extend the forearm. The biceps brachii flexes the forearm and aids powerfully in supination; this means that when the radius lies across the ulna as the palm faces downward, the pull of the biceps brachii helps to draw the radius back into a position parallel with the ulna as the palm faces upward.

THE CORACOBRACHIALIS is a bandlike muscle that extends from the scapula to the humerus (Fig. 107). It assists in flexion and adduction of the arm at the shoulder joint and helps to keep the head of the humerus in the glenoid fossa.

THE BRACHIALIS (Fig. 107) extends from the humerus to the ulna, covering the front of the elbow joint and protecting it. It assists in flexion of the forearm.

THE TRICEPS BRACHII (Figs. 98 and 101) is the chief muscle on the posterior aspect of the arm. It arises by 3 heads, 2 from the humerus and a long one from the scapula. It is inserted on the tip of the olecranon of the ulna.

The triceps brachii is the antagonist of the biceps brachii, which means that it extends the forearm. This muscle is important in boxing, since it converts the arm into a solid rod. It helps to support the shoulder joint, by means of its long head, and helps to hold the head of the humerus in place.

Muscles of the Forearm. The great variety of movements of the thumb and the fingers are due to the contractions of the muscles of the forearm, together with those of the hand. For ease of description the muscles of the forearm are divided in subgroups of anterior-medial and dorsal-lateral muscles.

ANTERIOR-MEDIAL MUSCLES are pronators and flexors of the wrist and the fingers. They are arranged in 3 layers: (1) superficial layer—pronator teres, flexor carpi radialis, palmaris longus and flexor carpi ulnaris; (2) intermediate layer—flexor digitorum sublimis; and (3) deep layer—flexor digitorum profundus, flexor pollicis longus and pronator quadratus.

The 4 superficial muscles listed above arise by means of a common tendon from the medial epicondyle of the humerus.

The pronator teres (Fig. 107) extends from its humeral and ulnar origins obliquely across the forearm and ends in a flat tendon which inserts on the body of the radius. This muscle forms the medial boundary of the hollow of the elbow. It assists in pronation of the forearm.

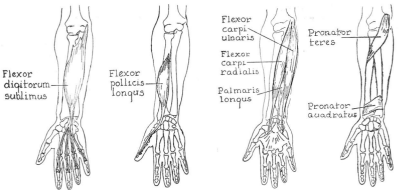

FIG. 102. Anterior muscles of the forearm arranged in functional groups. (*Left* to *Right*) Flexors of fingers, of which only the digitorum sublimis is shown; flexor of thumb; flexors of wrist; and pronators of forearm. (Slightly modified and redrawn from Marshall, Clyde, and Lazier, E. L.: Introduction to Human Anatomy, Philadelphia, Saunders)

The flexor carpi radialis (Fig. 107) extends from the humerus to about the midpoint of the forearm where it becomes a long, flat tendon and inserts on the base of the second metacarpal bone.

The flexor carpi ulnaris (Fig. 107) lies on the medial border of the forearm, and its tendon inserts on the pisiform bone, and on the third, fourth and fifth metacarpal bones.

The palmaris longus terminates in the palmar aponeurosis (Fig. 107).

The flexor digitorum sublimis arises from the humerus, the ulna and the radius and inserts by long tendons on the middle phalanx of each of the 4 fingers (Fig. 107).

The flexor digitorum profundus arises from the ulna, extends down the front of the forearm and inserts by 4 tendons on the distal phalanx of each of the 4 fingers (Fig. 107).

The flexor pollicis longus is a special muscle for flexion of the thumb. It arises from the anterior aspect of the radius and inserts on the distal phalanx of the thumb.

The pronator quadratus is a flat, quadrangular sheet of muscle that extends between the lower portions of the ulna and the radius and assists in pronation.

The above muscles may be divided into 4 functional groups, as illustrated in Figure 102. The flexors of the fingers are the flexor

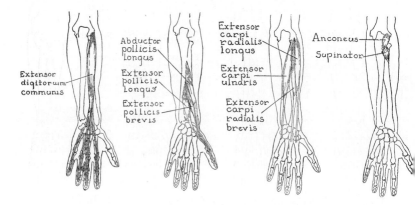

Fig. 103. Posterior muscles of the forearm arranged in functional groups. (*Left* to *right*) Common extensor of fingers, muscles acting on thumb, extensors of wrist and anconeus and supinator. (Slightly modified and redrawn from Marshall, Clyde, and Lazier, E. L.: Introduction to Human Anatomy, Philadelphia, Saunders)

digitorum sublimis and profundus. The flexor of the thumb is the flexor pollicis longus. The flexors of the wrist are the flexor carpi radialis and ulnaris and the palmaris longus. The pronators of the forearm are the pronator teres and the quadratus.

DORSAL-LATERAL MUSCLES. Muscles on the dorsal aspect of the forearm and the lateral side of the elbow are supinators of the forearm and extensors of the wrist and the fingers. They are arranged in 2 layers: (1) superficial layer—brachioradialis, extensor carpi radialis longus, extensor carpi radialis brevis, extensor digitorum communis, extensor digiti quinti proprius, extensor carpi ulnaris and anconeus; and (2) deep layer—supinator, abductor pollicis longus, extensor pollicis longus, extensor pollicis brevis and extensor indicis proprius.

The muscles of the superficial layer, with the exception of the brachioradialis, the extensor carpi radialis longus and the anconeus, share a common tendon of origin from the front of the lateral epicondyle of the humerus.

The brachioradialis (Fig. 107) is the principal muscle on the radial side of the forearm. It lies on the lateral side of the hollow of the elbow and extends across the elbow joint. It arises from the humerus and inserts on the proximal part of the styloid process of the radius.

The extensor carpi radialis longus (Fig. 101) extends from the humerus to the base of the second metacarpal bone.

The extensor carpi radialis brevis (Fig. 101) extends to the base of the second and the third metacarpal bones.

The extensor digitorum communis (Fig. 101) divides into 4 tendons that insert on the middle and the distal phalanges of the fingers.

The extensor carpi ulnaris (Fig. 101) inserts on the base of the fifth metacarpal bone.

The anconeus (meaning "elbow") (Fig. 101) is a small triangular muscle that arises from the lateral epicondyle of the humerus and inserts on the olecranon and the dorsal surface of the ulna.

The supinator, as indicated by the name, supinates the forearm or helps to pull the radius into a position parallel with the ulna, with palm upward. It arises from the lateral epicondyle of the humerus and the proximal part of the ulna and inserts on the radius (Fig. 101), after curving around the upper third of this bone.

The abductor pollicis longus (Fig. 101) arises from the ulna and the radius and inserts on the base of the first metacarpal bone.

The extensor pollicis brevis (Fig. 101) extends from the radius to the base of the first phalanx of the thumb.

The extensor pollicis longus (Fig. 101) extends from the ulna to the base of the second phalanx of the thumb.

The muscles on the dorsal aspect of the forearm and the lateral side of the elbow may be divided into 4 functional groups, as illustrated in Figure 103. The muscles that extend the fingers are the extensor digitorum communis, the extensor indicis proprius (acting chiefly on the first finger) and the extensor digiti quinti proprius, (acting chiefly in independent movement of the little finger). The muscles that act on the thumb are the abductor pollicis longus and the extensor pollicis longus and brevis. The muscles that extend the wrist are the extensor carpi radialis longus and brevis and the extensor carpi ulnaris. The muscles that act on the forearm are the brachioradialis (flexes and supinates the forearm), the supinator and the anconeus, which assists in extension of the forearm at the elbow joint.

Numerous tendons are visible or palpable at the wrist. On the front of the wrist, starting on the thumb side, one can feel the lower end of the radius. The tendon that passes directly from the end of the radius out to the thumb is that of the abductor pollicis longus. Pass the finger across the front of the wrist, feel the radial artery, then the tendons of the flexor carpi radialis, the palmaris longus and, on the ulnar side, the flexor carpi ulnaris. The last tendon can be followed down to its insertion on the pisiform bone. On the back of the wrist one can feel the tendon of the extensor pollicis longus as it passes to the distal phalanx of the thumb. On the back of the hand the tendons of the extensor digitorum communis can be felt.

Muscles of the Hand. The *thenar eminence* (thumb side of the palm) is made up of muscles that arise from the carpus and the metacarpus and insert on the metacarpal and first phalanx of the thumb. A similar group about the little finger makes up the *hypothenar eminence.* These muscles of the hand act on the first and the fifth metacarpal bones and bring the thumb and the little finger into contact with each other. The free movements of the thumb are of great importance in the human hand and are characteristic of man.

Between the metacarpals are the *dorsal* and the *palmar inter- osseous muscles,* which are inserted on the first row of phalanges and into the extensor tendons and are important for movements of the second and the third phalanges. They spread and approxi- mate the fingers. The *lumbricales* extend from the tendons of the flexors to the tendons of the extensors and flex the first phalanx and extend the distal phalanges of the fingers. Observe all the intricate movements that you can perform with your thumb and fingers; keep in mind that many of these are peculiar to the hand of man.

MUSCLES OF THE LOWER EXTREMITY

The muscles of the lower extremity are used chiefly to support the body in the standing position and are specialized for locomo- tion. The movements of the pelvic girdle are greatly restricted; the only movements possible here are those that take place at the lumbosacral joint and at the joints between the lumbar vertebrae. Limited flexion, extension, abduction, adduction and rotation are possible. When sitting, the pelvis is flexed, and the weight of the body is transmitted through the sacrum and the hip bones to the ischial tuberosities. When standing, the pelvis is extended, and the weight of the body is transmitted to the femoral bones through the acetabula. When walking, the pelvis is rotated forward toward the limb that is being moved forward.

The hip joint is a synovial joint (diarthrosis) that permits free movements, except as limited by muscles around it. The head of the femur fits into the acetabulum; and flexion and extension, as

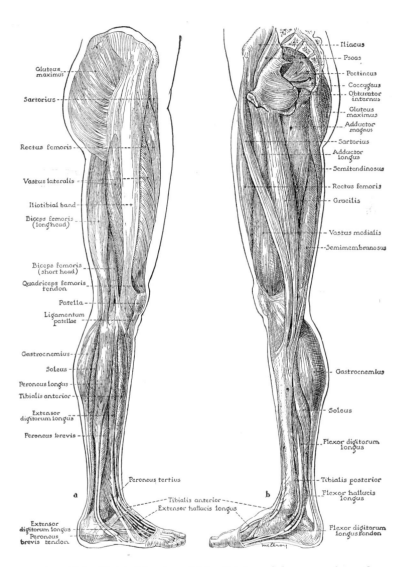

FIG. 104. (*Left*) Muscles of hip, thigh and leg, seen from the lateral view. The relations of the patella to the tendons is indicated. (*Right*) Muscles of hip, thigh and leg seen from the medial view. The muscles which originate from the walls of the pelvis are shown. The relations of tendons to the ankle and digits are shown.

in walking and running, are possible. Abduction, adduction, circumduction and rotation occur and are important in balancing the body.

The muscles of the lower extremity are divided into the following 4 groups: (1) muscles of the gluteal region or buttock; (2) muscles of the thigh; (3) muscles of the leg; and (4) muscles of the foot.

Muscles of the Gluteal Region or Buttock. These are the gluteus maximus, the gluteus medius, the gluteus minimus, the tensor fasciae latae, the piriformis, the obturator internus, the quadratus femoris and the gemelli. The gluteal muscles arise from the ilium and the sacrum and insert on the great trochanter and the shaft of the femur and into the iliotibial band. (The fascia lata is the dense fascia surrounding the muscles of the thigh, and the iliotibial band is a thickened portion of this fascia that extends from the outer tuberosity of the tibia to the iliac crest.)

THE GLUTEUS MAXIMUS (Figs. 98, 99 and 104, *left*) is a broad, thick, fleshy, quadrilateral muscle that forms much of the buttock. Its fibers are very coarse. The large size of the gluteus maximus is characteristic of man and is associated with walking in the upright position. When the pelvis is fixed the gluteus maximus is a very powerful extensor of the thigh. When the femur is fixed, the gluteus maximus supports the pelvis and the trunk on the femur, as in standing on one leg. When you rise to a standing position, after stooping over, you can feel the powerful action of the gluteal muscles. The gluteus maximus helps to rotate the lower extremity outward. It is used in walking up stairs and in climbing hills, and you may notice soreness after undue climbing. During standing the gluteus maximus steadies the femur on the articular surfaces of the tibia. Frequently, this muscle is used for intramuscular injections.

THE GLUTEUS MEDIUS (Fig. 105, *left*) and the GLUTEUS MINIMUS (Fig. 105, *right*) abduct the thigh when the limb is extended. They are called into action chiefly in supporting the body on one limb and, therefore, are used in every step that you take.

THE TENSOR FASCIAE LATAE (Figs. 97 and 99) arises from the anterior part of the iliac crest and is inserted between the layers of the fascia lata. Its contraction pulls the fascia lata tight, and it aids in abduction and inward rotation of the thigh.

THE PIRIFORMIS (Fig. 105, *left*), the OBTURATOR INTERNUS (Fig. 101) the QUADRATUS FEMORIS (Fig. 105, *right*) and the GEMELLI

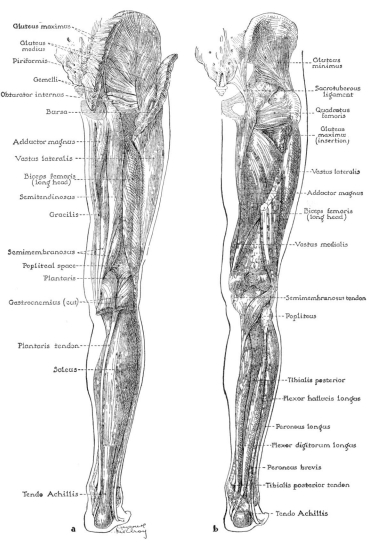

Gluteus maximus

Gluteus medius

Piriformis

Gemelli

Obturator internus

Bursa

Adductor magnus

Vastus lateralis

Biceps femoris (long head)

Semitendinosus

Gracilis

Semimembranosus

Popliteal space

Plantaris

Gastrocnemius (cut)

Plantaris tendon

Soleus

Tendo Achillis

Gluteus minimus

Sacrotuberous ligament

Quadratus femoris

Gluteus maximus (insertion)

Vastus lateralis

Adductor magnus

Biceps femoris (long head)

Vastus medialis

Semimembranosus tendon

Popliteus

Tibialis posterior

Flexor hallucis longus

Peroneus longus

Flexor digitorum longus

Peroneus brevis

Tibialis posterior tendon

Tendo Achillis

a   b

FIG. 105. (*Left*) Superficial muscles of the posterior aspect of hip, thigh and leg. Gluteus maximus cut and turned aside and belly of gastrocnemius removed to show deeper muscles. (*Right*) Deep muscles of hip, thigh and leg. Certain muscles have been removed and others cut to expose the various bones.

(Fig. 105, *left*) extend transversely from the pelvis to the upper end of the femur and are chiefly lateral rotators of the thigh.

Muscles of the Thigh. The muscles of the thigh may be divided into 3 groups: (1) anterior or extensor, (2) medial or adductor and (3) posterior or flexor.

THE ANTERIOR thigh muscles are the sartorius (meaning "tailor"), the quadriceps femoris, the iliopsoas and the pectineus (meaning "comb") muscles.

The sartorius (Fig. 106) is a long muscle, narrow and ribbonlike. It arises from the anterior superior spine of the ilium, extends obliquely across the upper part of the thigh from the lateral to the medial side and is inserted on the upper part of the medial surface of the tibia. It is used in crossing the legs, as tailors of old used to sit cross-legged on the floor or the table (which explains the origin of the name). It flexes, abducts and rotates the thigh laterally; also, it flexes and rotates the leg medially.

The quadriceps femoris (Figs. 97 and 106) is the large fleshy mass covering the front and the sides of the femur. It is composed of 4 parts: the rectus femoris, which arises from the ilium, and the vasti (lateralis, medialis and intermedius), which arise from the femur, as shown in Figures 105 and 106. There is a common tendon of insertion for the 4 parts, and in this tendon, which is closely applied to the capsule of the knee joint, is the patella. The tendon is inserted on the tubercle of the tibia. The chief action is extension of the leg, but it also helps to keep the femur erect on the tibia; this means that the quadriceps is important in both walking and standing. The rectus femoris portion of the muscle flexes the thigh.

The iliopsoas is a compound muscle. Its parts, the psoas major and the iliacus, are illustrated in Figure 106. The iliac portion arises from the iliac fossa, and the psoas major arises from the lumbar vertebrae. The fibers combine and pass along the brim of the pelvis to the front of the thigh, where they wind around the neck of the femur and insert on the lesser trochanter of the femur. This muscle is a powerful flexor of the thigh. When standing, it helps to hold the trunk erect by keeping it from falling backward. When the femur is fixed, the iliopsoas bends the lumbar portion of the vertebral column forward and tilts the pelvis forward. It is used in raising the trunk from the recumbent position.

The psoas minor muscle is present in about 60 per cent of individuals. It is a small, flat muscle that lies on the medial surface of the psoas major, and aids in flexing the pelvis.

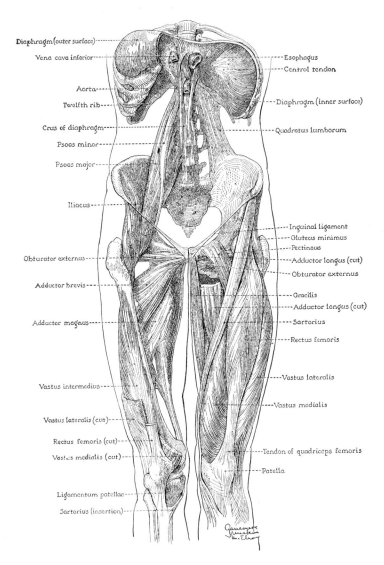

Diaphragm (outer surface)
Vena cava inferior
Aorta
Twelfth rib
Crus of diaphragm
Psoas minor
Psoas major
Iliacus
Obturator externus
Adductor brevis
Adductor magnus
Vastus intermedius
Vastus lateralis (cut)
Rectus femoris (cut)
Vastus medialis (cut)
Ligamentum patellae
Sartorius (insertion)

Esophagus
Central tendon
Diaphragm (inner surface)
Quadratus lumborum
Inguinal ligament
Gluteus minimus
Pectineus
Adductor longus (cut)
Obturator externus
Gracilis
Adductor longus (cut)
Sartorius
Rectus femoris
Vastus lateralis
Vastus medialis
Tendon of quadriceps femoris
Patella

FIG. 106. Diaphragm, anterior view, with a portion removed to
show the inner surface, with central tendon and openings. Most of
the muscles of the abdomen and upper right thigh have been removed to show the relations of the deeper muscles to the skeleton.
The superficial muscles are shown on the left thigh.

The pectineus (Fig. 106) assists in flexing and adducting the thigh, as in crossing the legs or in riding horseback. This muscle, together with others, grasps the sides of the saddle between the knees.

THE MEDIAL thigh muscles are the gracilis, the adductors (longus, brevis and magnus) and the obturator externus.

The gracilis (Figs. 104, *right* and 106) is the most superficial muscle on the medial aspect of the thigh. It is ribbonlike, as it extends from the pubis along the medial side of the thigh to the medial side of the upper portion of the tibia. It adducts the thigh, flexes the leg and rotates it medially.

The adductors are the most important muscles on the medial aspect of the thigh. They arise from the pubis and the ischium and are inserted on the linea aspera and the adductor tubercle of the femur. The 3 components of the adductor muscles are illustrated in Figures 105 and 106. They adduct and flex the thigh and aid in grasping the saddle between the knees when riding horseback.

The obturator externus (Fig. 106) arises from the rim of the obturator foramen and the outer surface of the obturator membrane. It is inserted on the femur at the base of the great trochanter. It rotates the femur laterally.

In walking, the above muscles of the medial aspect of the thigh assist in drawing the lower extremity forward.

THE POSTERIOR or hamstring muscles are the biceps femoris, the semitendinosus and the semimembranosus.

The biceps femoris (Fig. 105) lies on the posterior and lateral aspects of the thigh. It arises by two heads: the long head arises from the tuber of the ischium, and the short head from the linea aspera. The fibers of the two portions join and are inserted on the head of the fibula.

The semitendinosus (Figs. 104, *right* and 105, *left*) lies on the posterior and medial aspects of the thigh. It arises from the ischial tuberosity and inserts by a long tendon on the medial side of the tibia.

The semimembranosus (Fig. 104, *right*) arises from the ischial tuberosity and inserts on the medial condyle of the tibia.

You can feel the tendons of the hamstring muscles as ridges behind the knee; they form the lateral boundaries of the popliteal space, which is the diamond-shaped space at the back of the knee and the thigh. It is bounded above by the biceps femoris (laterally) and the semitendinosus and the semimembranosus (medially) and below by the two heads of the gastrocnemius muscle. In flexion the hollow is present, and in extension of the leg the hollow is obliterated. The roof is formed by the popliteal fascia, and the floor by the femur above and the fascia of the popliteus muscle below. The chief contents are the popliteal vessels, the termination of the small saphenous vein, the tibial and the common peroneal nerves and some popliteal lymph nodes, all embedded in a mass of fatty tissue. The tendon of the biceps femoris is on the lateral side, and the tendons of the semitendinosus and the semimembranosus are on the medial side. The action of the hamstring muscles is to flex the leg upon the thigh. If the tibia is fixed, they support the pelvis on the femur. They can be used to draw the trunk backward and are the muscles used when one performs the feat of throwing the body backward in the form of an arch. Extreme relaxation of these short muscles is required for the high kick and for touching the toes without bending the knees.

Muscles of the Leg. Since the muscles of the leg are responsible for the movements of the foot and the toes, it is important to have the movements clearly in mind before describing the muscles. In the foot, upward movement at the ankle joint is called *dorsal flexion* of the foot, and downward movement at the ankle joint is called *plantar flexion* of the foot. Upward movement of the toes is called *extension* and downward movement is called *flexion* of the toes. In other words, upward and downward movements at the ankle and the metatarsophalangeal joints are described by different terms. Turning the sole of the foot inward is called *inversion* and turning it outward is called *eversion.*

The muscles of the leg are divided into 3 groups: anterior, lateral and posterior.

ANTERIOR MUSCLES. The muscles of the anterior group are the tibialis anterior, the extensor digitorum longus, the peroneus tertius, the extensor hallucis longus and the extensor digitorum brevis (Fig. 104, *left*). These muscles arise in part from the distal end of the femur but mainly from the tibia and the fibula.

The tendon of the *tibialis anterior* crosses over the front of the tibia to the first metatarsal and the first cuneiform bones.

The tendons of the *extensor digitorum longus* extend to the terminal phalanges of all except the great toe.

The peroneus tertius, which is really part of the extensor digitorum longus, is inserted by a tendon on the fifth metatarsal bone.

The extensor hallucis longus crosses over the ankle to the great toe.

The actions of the anterior group of leg muscles are to (1) dorsiflex the foot at the ankle joint, (2) evert the foot and (3) extend the toes. If the insertions are fixed, all of these muscles serve to hold the bones of the leg in the perpendicular position and give increased strength to the ankle joint when one stands.

LATERAL MUSCLES. The muscles of the lateral group are the peroneus longus and brevis.

The tendon of the *peroneus longus* (Fig. 104, *left*) passes around the lateral malleolus, crosses the sole of the foot obliquely and is inserted on the first cuneiform and base of the first metatarsal bone.

The tendon of the *peroneus brevis* also passes around the lateral malleolus but is inserted on the tuberosity of the fifth metatarsal bone.

Both are antagonists of the tibialis anterior and the peroneus tertius; they plantar flex and evert the foot. The peroneus longus helps to maintain the transverse arch. If the insertions are fixed, these muscles help to steady the leg on the foot, especially in standing on one leg.

POSTERIOR MUSCLES. The muscles of the posterior group are subdivided into superficial and deep groups. The superficial muscles are the gastrocnemius, the plantaris and the soleus. The deep muscles are the popliteus, the flexor digitorum longus, the flexor hallucis longus and the tibialis posterior.

The superficial muscles form the powerful muscular mass called the calf of the leg. The large size of this muscle group is one of the most characteristic features of the muscular system of man, and it is due to the erect posture and walking on 2 extremities instead of all 4.

The 2 heads of the *gastrocnemius* (Figs. 98, 99 and 104, *left*) arise from the medial and the lateral condyles of the femur. The muscle fibers extend to the middle of the back of the leg where they insert into the tendon of Achilles; this long tendon inserts on the calcaneus.

The soleus (Fig. 105, *left*) also inserts into the tendon of Achilles, which is the thickest and strongest tendon in the body. The superficial muscles of the posterior group are the chief plantar flexors of the foot at the ankle joint. They are used in standing, walking, toe-dancing and leaping. In walking, they raise the heel from the ground; the body is supported on that foot, and the opposite limb is free to be carried forward. If the soleus is fixed below, it steadies the leg upon the foot and helps to prevent the body from falling forward.

When the gastrocnemius is fixed below, it bends the knee or flexes the femur upon the tibia. These muscles enable one to stand on the tips of one's toes; consequently, they are greatly overdeveloped in toe dancers. Conversely, if these muscles are paralyzed it is impossible for the patient to stand on the tips of his toes.

The popliteus (Fig. 105, *right*) is a thin, flat, triangular muscle that forms the lower part of the floor of the popliteal fossa. It assists in flexing the leg upon the thigh, and when the leg is flexed the popliteus rotates the tibia inward. It is called into action at the beginning of the act of bending the knee.

The tendons of the *flexor digitorum longus* (Figs. 104, *right* and 105, *right*) are inserted on the base of the last phalanx of each toe except the great one.

The tendon of the *flexor hallucis longus* inserts on the base of the last phalanx of the great toe. These muscles are the flexors of the toes, and they assist also in plantar flexing the foot, in which act they assist the gastrocnemius and the soleus.

The tibialis posterior (Fig. 105, *right*) is inserted on the tuberosity of the navicular bone and on the calcaneus, the cuneiform, the cuboid and the base of the second, the third and the fourth metatarsal bones. It is a direct plantar flexor of the foot at the ankle joint. When it acts with the tibialis anterior, it inverts the foot.

The tendon of the tibialis posterior is an important factor in the maintenance of the medial longitudinal arch of the foot. If the insertions are fixed, these muscles help to maintain the upright posture by steadying the tibia and the fibula upon the talus.

You can easily locate the medial and the lateral malleoli, and on the front of the ankle you can see or palpate the tendons of the tibialis anterior, the extensor hallucis longus and the extensor digitorum longus by passing from the medial to the lateral side of the ankle. Just behind the medial malleolus, the tendon of the tibialis posterior enters the sole of the foot. On the outer side of the foot, the tendon of the peroneus brevis muscle passes around the lateral malleolus to be inserted on the base of the fifth metatarsal bone.

Muscles of the Foot. Deep in the sole of the foot, there are numerous muscles that act on the toes.

Interosseous and *lumbricales* are present, as in the hand.

The flexor digitorum brevis, which arises from the calcaneus, lies in the middle of the sole of the foot and inserts on the middle phalanx of the 4 lateral toes.

The quadratus plantae is peculiar to the foot; it extends from the calcaneus to the tendons of the long flexor and pulls them toward the mid-line of the foot.

THE ARCHES OF THE FOOT increase its strength and elasticity and provide protected places for the soft structures of the sole, such as blood vessels and nerves. The feet constitute a firm basis of support for the rest of the body.

The bones of the arch are arranged longitudinally, supported by a posterior (calcaneal) and an anterior (metatarsal) base. There are two segments in the anterior portion of the arch. The medial segment is made up of the first 3 metatarsals, 3 cuneiforms, the navicular and the talus bones. The lateral segment is composed of the last 2 metatarsals, the cuboid and the calcaneus bones. The medial division is especially important in the act of jumping; the lateral is more important as a basis of support in the upright position. A transverse arch is formed by the metatarsal bones in front and the distal row of the tarsus behind.

Ligaments of the Arch. The following ligaments aid in the support of the arch of the foot:

1. Inferior Calcaneonavicular. This fills the long gap left in the inner arch of the foot between the navicular and the calcaneus; the tendon of the tibialis posterior runs under this ligament and supports it.

2. Long Plantar. This makes a canal for the peroneus longus tendon, which runs beneath it.

Muscles that Support the Arch. The following muscles support the tarsal arch:

1. Tibialis Anterior, Peroneus Brevis and Peroneus Tertius. These are inserted practically into the convexity of the tarsal arch and they tend to support it by pulling it upward. The tibialis anterior braces up the keystone of the arch.

2. Flexor Digitorum Longus and Peroneus Longus. These meet and cross on the sole of the foot and form a sling on which the arch rests when the muscles contract. The tibialis posterior braces together the tarsal bones and prevents their separation in treading. It helps to support the head of the talus and to maintain the arch when the weight of the body is thrown forward on the instep. The peroneus longus steadies the lateral side of the arch.

AXIAL MUSCLES

As stated previously, the axial muscles are those of the trunk, the head and the neck. The muscles of the trunk comprise the following groups: (1) the muscles of the abdominal wall, (2) the

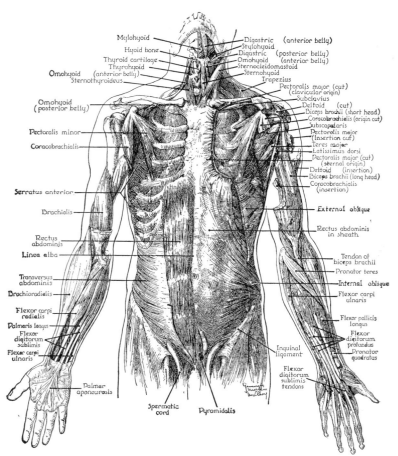

Mylohyoid
Hyoid bone
Thyroid cartilage
Thyrohyoid
Omohyoid (anterior belly)
Sternothyroideus
Omohyoid (posterior belly)
Pectoralis minor
Coracobrachialis
Serratus anterior
Brachialis
Rectus abdominis
Linea alba
Transversus abdominis
Brachioradialis
Flexor carpi radialis
Palmaris longus
Flexor digitorum sublimis
Flexor carpi ulnaris
Palmar aponeurosis

Digastric (anterior belly)
Stylohyoid
Digastric (posterior belly)
Omohyoid (anterior belly)
Sternocleidomastoid
Sternohyoid
Trapezius
Pectoralis major (cut) (clavicular origin)
Subclavius
Deltoid (cut)
Biceps brachii (short head)
Coracobrachialis (origin cut)
Subscapularis
Pectoralis major (insertion cut)
Teres major
Latissimus dorsi
Pectoralis major (cut) (sternal origin)
Deltoid (insertion)
Biceps brachii (long head)
Coracobrachialis (insertion)
External oblique
Rectus abdominis in sheath
Tendon of biceps brachii
Pronator teres
Internal oblique
Flexor carpi ulnaris
Flexor pollicis longus
Flexor digitorum profundus
Pronator quadratus
Flexor digitorum sublimis tendons

Inguinal ligament
Spermatic cord
Pyramidalis

FIG. 107. Muscles of neck, thorax, abdomen and upper extremity, anterior view. Certain muscles which are shown in Fig. 97 have been removed to show those of a deeper level. Many muscles have been removed on one side; other muscles have been cut. Certain bones are exposed.

diaphragm, (3) the muscles of the thoracic wall, (4) the muscles of the pelvic floor, (5) the perineal muscles and (6) the deep muscles of the back.

MUSCLES OF THE TRUNK

The muscles of the abdominal wall are arranged in 3 groups: the muscles of the lateral, the anterior and the posterior walls.

LATERAL. The muscles of the lateral abdominal wall comprise 3 pairs, the external oblique, the internal oblique and the transversus abdominis muscles.

The external oblique is the strongest and most superficial muscle of the lateral abdominal wall. It is a broad, thin, muscular sheet, as shown in Figures 107 and 108. It is composed of muscular tissue on the lateral wall and an aponeurosis on the anterior wall of the abdomen. It arises from the sides of the lower 8 ribs by slips that interlace with those of the serratus anterior. The fibers extend downward and forward to be inserted on the iliac crest, the anterior superior iliac spine and the pubic tubercle. Between the iliac spine and the pubic tubercle, the lower border of the muscle has no bony attachment but folds back on itself to form a thick band called the *inguinal ligament* (Figs. 106 and 108).

The large, triangular aponeurosis of the external oblique muscle forms part of the anterior abdominal wall. This aponeurosis unites with the aponeuroses of other muscles of the abdominal wall and helps to form the sheath of the rectus abdominis muscles. The aponeurosis is attached to the anterior-superior iliac spine and the pubic bone below, the xiphoid process of the sternum above, and combined with that from the external oblique of the opposite side into a sort of seam in the mid-line called the *linea alba* (meaning "white line"). There is a slit in the aponeurosis of the external oblique muscle, just above the pubic bone, called the *subcutaneous inguinal ring*. The posterior portions of the external oblique muscles are overlapped by the latissimus dorsi muscles.

The internal oblique muscle (Fig. 107) also is a broad, thin sheet of muscular tissue. It is located between the external oblique and the transversus abdominis muscles. It arises from the lumbar fascia, part of the iliac crest and lateral two thirds of the inguinal ligament. The fibers extend upward and forward. Some are inserted on the cartilages of the seventh, the eighth and the ninth ribs; the remainder of the fibers spread out like a fan and become an aponeurosis, which inserts into the linea alba. The lower part of the aponeurosis inserts on the pubic bone; the upper part splits to enclose the rectus abdominis before it reaches the linea alba.

The transversus abdominis (Fig. 107) is deeply placed in the lateral abdominal wall. It arises from the iliac crest, the inguinal ligament, the deep fascia of the back and the lower ribs. The fibers pass directly forward around the abdominal wall to form what has been called a "living girdle." They end in an aponeurosis which has a double insertion. The first takes place in the following man-

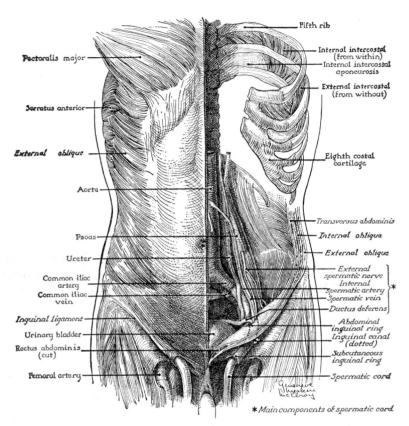

Pectoralis major

Serratus anterior

External oblique

Aorta

Psoas

Ureter

Common iliac artery

Common iliac vein

Inguinal ligament

Urinary bladder

Rectus abdominis (cut)

Femoral artery

Fifth rib

Internal intercostal (from within)

Internal intercostal aponeurosis

External intercostal (from without)

Eighth costal cartilage

Transversus abdominis

Internal oblique

External oblique

External spermatic nerve

Internal spermatic artery

Spermatic vein

Ductus deferens

Abdominal inguinal ring

Inguinal canal (dotted)

Subcutaneous inguinal ring

Spermatic cord

*Main components of spermatic cord

FIG. 108. Inguinal canal, spermatic cord and contents. Greater part of abdominal wall removed on left side to expose these structures. Intercostal muscles shown in their relationship to ribs from within and from without. Superficial muscles of abdomen and thorax shown on right side.

ner: After helping to form the sheath of the rectus abdominis, the aponeurosis is attached to the xiphoid process, the linea alba and the pubic bone. The second portion joins the aponeurosis of the internal oblique muscle and inserts into the linea alba and on the pubic bone. There is a slit in the aponeurosis of the transversus abdominis halfway between the anterior superior iliac spine and the pubis. This slit is called the *abdominal inguinal ring* (Fig. 108). The fibrous sheet internal to the transversus abdominis muscle is called the transversus fascia, and internal to this fascia is the serous membrane known as the peritoneum (p. 585).

The external oblique, the internal oblique and the transversus muscles, with their aponeuroses, form a triple wall for the abdomen. The muscle fibers run in 3 directions and greatly strengthen the wall.

ANTERIOR. The muscles of the anterior abdominal wall are the rectus abdominis and the pyramidalis.

The rectus abdominis muscle (Fig. 107) is a long, straplike muscle that arises from the pubic bone and its ligaments. It widens as it extends upward to be inserted on the anterior surface of the xiphoid process and the costal cartilages of the fifth, the sixth and the seventh ribs. It is entirely enclosed in the sheath formed by the aponeuroses of the muscles of the lateral wall of the abdomen.

Inguinal Canal. The inguinal canal is an oblique canal about 4 cm. long which passes through the lower abdominal wall parallel with, and a little above, the inguinal ligament. The inguinal canal extends from the abdominal inguinal ring to the subcutaneous inguinal ring, as shown in Figure 108. The inguinal canal transmits the spermatic cord (p. 761) in the male from the testis into the abdominal cavity. In the female, the inguinal canal transmits the round ligament (p. 769) which is attached to the uterus.

Weak Places in the Abdominal Wall. Owing to the upright position of man, the pressure of the weight of the abdominal viscera falls on the ventral part of the abdominal wall. As one stands, any weak places in this portion of the wall will be put under added strain. The weak places are the abdominal inguinal ring, the subcutaneous inguinal ring, the umbilicus and the femoral ring (abdominal opening of the femoral canal). The umbilicus lies just below the mid-point of the linea alba, opposite the disk between the third and the fourth lumbar vertebrae. It is a puckered scar that marks the closure of the umbilical opening of the fetus (p. 464). These weak places in the wall are likely to be the site of hernia.

Action of the Muscles of the Lateral and Anterior Walls of the Abdomen. These muscles protect the abdominal viscera, assist in respiration, defecation, emesis (vomiting) and parturition (delivery of infant). They assist in bending the body forward or flexing the vertebral column. They act powerfully in the exercise of raising both lower extremities when lying on the back. In this act they are quickly exhausted, since they serve as fixation muscles for the pelvis and the vertebral column.

POSTERIOR. The muscles of the posterior abdominal wall are the quadratus lumborum and the psoas portion of the iliopsoas (p. 172).

The quadratus lumborum lies in the posterior abdominal wall, lateral to the vertebral column (Fig. 106). It extends from the last rib to the iliac crest. The kidneys lie in close relationship to the quadratus lumborum muscles. If the two quadratus lumborum muscles act together they flex the trunk. If the thorax and the vertebral column are fixed, the muscle raises the pelvis toward its own side. The two muscles may act together as muscles of inspiration by drawing the last ribs downward and thereby enlarging the thoracic cavity.

The Diaphragm. The diaphragm forms a muscular partition between the thoracic and the abdominal portions of the ventral cavity. It is arranged in the form of 2 domes, the upper surface of which forms the floor of the thoracic cavity and the lower surface the roof of the abdominal cavity (Figs. 6 and 106). The central portion is composed of fibrous tissue and is called the *central tendon;* the peripheral portions are composed of muscular tissue. The liver lies under the right dome, and the stomach under the left dome. The heart rests on the upper surface of the diaphragm between the two domes, and the lungs rest on the upper surface of the diaphragm on either side of the heart.

The muscular portion of the diaphragm arises from the xiphoid process of the sternum, the costal margins of the lower 6 ribs and the vertebral column. The fibers converge to be inserted into the central tendon. There are 3 large openings in the central tendon: one transmits the vagus nerves and the esophagus; the second transmits the aorta and the thoracic duct, and the third transmits the inferior vena cava.

When the muscular fibers of the diaphragm contract, the central portion is pulled downward, and thus the thoracic cavity above is enlarged from top to bottom. Because of this, the diaphragm is the principal muscle of respiration. The level of the domes is changing constantly during respiratory movements. Also, its level varies with the amount of distention of the stomach and the intestines. The diaphragm is higher when a person is lying on his back than when he is standing.

Muscles of the Thoracic Wall. The muscles of the thoracic wall are the external intercostals, the internal intercostals, the levatores costarum, the serratus posterior superior, the serratus posterior inferior and the transversus thoracis (Figs. 101 and 108). Many of these muscles are covered by the muscles that extend from the trunk to the shoulder girdle and the arm.

The external intercostals fill in the spaces between the ribs. They arise from the lower portions of the first 11 ribs, and the fibers extend downward and forward to be inserted on the upper borders of the ribs below. These muscles play an important part in respiration by enlarging the thoracic cavity from side to side and from front to back.

The internal intercostals lie under cover of the external intercostals and are similar to them, except in the direction of their fibers, which pass downward and backward.

Muscles of the Pelvic Floor. To refresh your memory the following description of the pelvis is presented. The pelvis is the complete bony ring formed by the two hip bones in front and on the sides and by the sacrum and the coccyx in the back (Fig. 47). The cavity enclosed by the bony ring or pelvis is divided into two portions, a smaller, inferior cavity called the *true pelvis* and a larger, superior one called the *false pelvis*. The side walls of the true pelvis are formed largely by the pubic bones and the ischia, and the side walls of the false pelvis are formed by the ilia.

The true pelvis consists of the inlet, the outlet and the cavity. The space included within the brim (between the upper margin of the symphysis pubis and the prominence of the sacrum) is the *inlet*. The *outlet* is the space between the tip of the coccyx, the ischial tuberosities and the pubis. The pelvic *cavity* is the short curved canal between the inlet and the outlet. The outlet is closed by the muscles that form the pelvic floor (Fig. 109).

The musculature of the pelvic floor is divisible into 3 groups of muscles and fasciae: (1) the levator ani muscles and fascia, which form the pelvic diaphragm; (2) the deep transverse perineal muscles and fasciae, which form the urogenital diaphragm; and (3) the muscles of the external genitalia. The pelvic floor and associated structures that occupy the pelvic outlet constitute the perineum. Some of these may be torn during childbirth.

The muscles of the pelvic floor are an exceedingly important group, for on them rests part of the weight of both the abdominal and the pelvic viscera. They consist of the *levator ani* and the *coccygeus* muscles on each side. The levator ani muscles arise

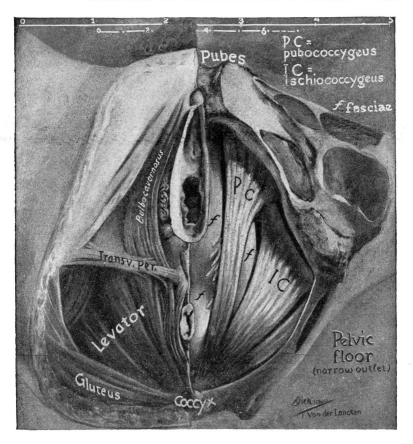

FIG. 109. Muscles of the pelvic floor. (Dickinson, R. L.: Atlas of Human Sex Anatomy, ed. 2, Baltimore, Williams & Wilkins)

from the body of the pubis, the spine of the ischium and the obturator fascia along the lateral pelvic wall. The fibers extend downward, backward and toward the mid-line. The posterior fibers are inserted on the coccyx; the anterior fibers unite with those from the opposite side in a raphe or seam. There is a slit in the seam between the rectum and the symphysis pubis. In the male, the lower part of the prostate gland (p. 762) and part of the urethra (p. 672) lie in this slit; in the female, the vagina (p. 776) and the urethra (p. 671) occupy the slit.

The levator ani (and coccygeal) muscles of the two sides form

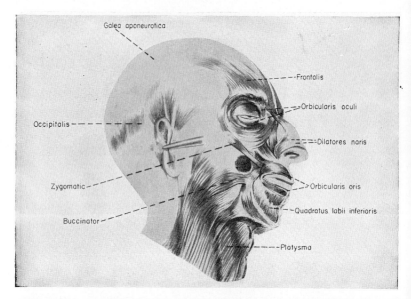

Galea aponeurotica

Frontalis

Orbicularis oculi

Occipitalis

Dilatores naris

Orbicularis oris

Zygomatic

Quadratus labii inferioris

Buccinator

Platysma

FIG. 110. Superficial dissection of the head, showing the muscles of facial expression and the platysma.

a support for the pelvic viscera and resist the pressure that is transmitted to the pelvic floor when the diaphragm descends during inspiration. The levator ani muscles constrict the lower part of the rectum and pull it forward, thus aiding in defecation.

Perineal Muscles. The pelvic wall is strengthened by a triangular muscular and fibrous membrane that extends between the rami of the ischial and the pubic bones; this membrane is called the urogenital diaphragm. The deep transverse perineal muscles are the most important ones in this region. They are flat bands of muscle that arise from the rami of the ischial and the pubic bones. The fibers intertwine in the mid-line and form a raphe or seam.

Deep Muscles of the Back. The deep muscles of the back lie on either side of the vertebral column and form a complex group. They are attached to the sacrum, to the ilium, to the spines, the transverse and the articular processes and the laminae of the lumbar, the thoracic and the cervical vertebrae and to the posterior aspects of the ribs and the base of the skull. They are the splenius capitis and cervicis, the sacrospinalis, the semispinalis, the multifidus, the rotatores, the interspinales and the intertransversarii muscles. Only the sacrospinalis and the semispinalis will be described.

THE SACROSPINALIS is the longest muscle in the body. It is an elongated muscular mass, consisting of separate slips, which extends from the sacrum to the skull (Fig. 101). It arises from the lower and posterior part of the sacrum, the posterior portion of the iliac crests and the spines of the lumbar and the lower two thoracic vertebrae. It "climbs" the back in a series of columns and extends as high as the cervical vertebrae and the temporal bone. The lateral muscular column is called the *iliocostalis* muscle; and the medial is called the *longissimus* muscle. The sacrospinalis muscle is attached on the ribs and the vertebrae all the way up the back to the mastoid process of the temporal bone.

The sacrospinalis helps to maintain the vertebral column in the erect posture. At certain times these muscles bend the trunk backward. This occurs when it is necessary to counterbalance the effect of weight at the front of the body, such as in pregnancy. Since the vertebral column is drawn backward in pregnancy, the gait is peculiar and very characteristic.

If the sacrospinalis of one side acts alone, it bends the vertebral column to that side. You can note the great flexibility of the vertebral column if you extend, flex, abduct and adduct it. The cervical and the lumbar regions possess the greatest freedom of movement.

THE SEMISPINALIS muscles extend from the loin (lateral and posterior region of the body between the ribs and the pelvis) to the skull. Each may be divided into 3 parts: (1) semispinalis capitis (Fig. 101), (2) semispinalis cervicis and (3) semispinalis dorsi. If the 2 semispinalis muscles act together they help to extend the vertebral column. When the cervicis and the dorsi muscles of one side act, they rotate the thoracic and the cervical portions of the column and turn the body to the opposite side. The 2 semispinalis capitis muscles draw the head backward when they act together. If one acts alone it draws the head to that side and rotates it so that the face is turned to the opposite side.

MUSCLES OF THE HEAD

The muscles of the scalp, of the face, of mastication and of the tongue comprise the muscles of the head.

Muscles of the Scalp. *The epicranius* is the scalp muscle; it is composed of the *frontalis* and the *occipitalis* (Fig. 110). The frontalis lies over the frontal bone and the occipitalis over the occipital bone. The two muscular portions are connected by a fibrous sheet called the *galea aponeurotica*, which extends over and covers the

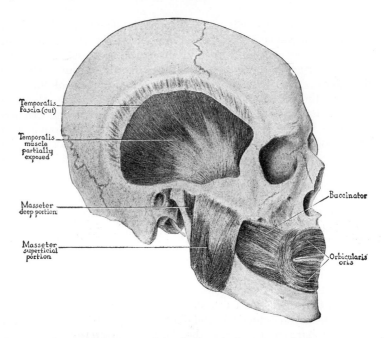

Temporalis
fascia (cut)

Temporalis
muscle
partially
exposed

Masseter
deep portion

Masseter
superficial
portion

Buccinator

Orbicularis
oris

Fig. 111. Lateral aspect of the skull with the temporal, the masseter, the buccinator, and the orbicularis oris muscles in place.

whole of the upper part of the cranium. The frontalis, which arises from the galea and inserts into the skin in the region of the eyebrows, raises the eyebrows and wrinkles the skin of the forehead. It is used in expressing both attention and surprise; if its action is exaggerated it gives rise to the expression of fright or horror. The occipitalis arises from the occipital bone and the mastoid process and inserts into the galea; it draws the scalp backward.

Muscles of the Face. The muscles of the face are divided into two groups—those of the orbit and the eyelids and those of the lips. These take origin from bone or skin and insert into skin or mucous membrane.

Muscles of the Orbit and the Eyelids. The muscles that encircle the orbit constrict the entrance of the orbit, shut out light and protect the eye against the entrance of foreign bodies.

The orbicularis oculi is a large, flat, elliptical muscle that lies in the eyelids and over the bone surrounding the orbit (Fig. 110).

It consists of 3 parts, the *palpebral,* the *orbital* and the *lacrimal.*
The orbicularis oculi arises from the nasal portion of the frontal
bone, the frontal process of the maxilla and the medial palpebral
ligament. The fibers extend laterally, occupy the eyelid, surround
the circumference of the orbit and spread over the temple and
downward over the cheek.

The palpebral portion closes the eyelids gently. It acts involun-
tarily, as in sleeping and blinking, and also dilates the lacrimal
sac and permits tears to flow away readily.

The orbital portion is under the control of the will. The upper
half contracts and depresses the tissue that overhangs the orbit.
The lower half raises the skin of the cheek and causes the wrinkles
that radiate from the corner of the eye. The lacrimal portion probably compresses the lacrimal sac, thereby forcing tears into the
nasolacrimal duct.

The levator palpebrae superioris is the antagonist of the orbicularis oculi. This muscle, together with the 4 recti and the 2 oblique
muscles of the orbit, is described on pages 353 to 354, with the
anatomy of the eye.

MUSCLES OF THE LIPS. The only two that will be described are
the obicularis oris and the buccinator.

The orbicularis oris consists of numerous layers of muscle fibers
that surround the opening of the mouth and extend in different
directions (Fig. 110). It is composed partly of fibers derived from
other facial muscles, which are inserted into the lips, and partly
of fibers proper to the lips. This muscle causes closure of the lips
by tightening the lips over the teeth, contracting them or causing
the protrusion of one over the other.

The buccinator (Figs. 110 and 111) is the muscle coat of the
cheeks. It arises from the maxilla and the mandible and extends
forward to be inserted into the sides of the mouth. It draws the
corner of the mouth laterally, pulls the lips against the teeth and
flattens the cheek. It aids in mastication, swallowing, whistling
and blowing wind instruments. It prevents food from being pock-
eted between the teeth and the cheek. When the cheeks have been
distended with air, the buccinator muscles expel it between the
lips, as in blowing the trumpet, from which the muscle derived
its name. All of the muscles of the eyelids, the lips, the cheeks
and the forehead are used in expressing various emotions and in
emphasizing spoken words. If you watch the facial expressions of
your classmates you will see how frequently the expression changes
due to the varying activity of these muscles. Look in the mirror

and assume various facial expressions, such as smiling, frowning and doubting, and note which muscles you use.

Muscles of Mastication. The masseter, the temporal, the internal pterygoid and the external pterygoid muscles are the muscles of mastication. They all are inserted on the mandible and act across the mandibular joint (Fig. 79, *bottom*).

The masseter (Fig. 111) arises from the zygomatic arch and is inserted on the lateral surface of the ramus and the angle of the mandible. If you close your jaws tightly you can feel this muscle while it is in action; it appears as a bulging mass near the angle of the jaw.

The temporal muscle (Fig. 111) is a fan-shaped muscle that arises from the temporal fossa, extends downward beneath the

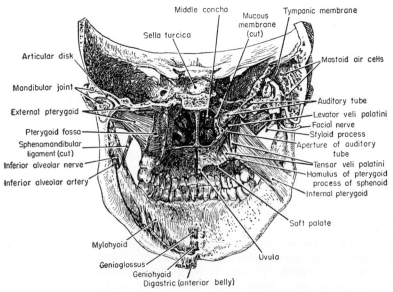

FIG. 112. Coronal section of head, showing the nasal cavity, the roof of mouth and the lower jaw. The external pterygoid and internal pterygoid muscles are shown passing from their origin to their insertion. The levator veli palatini and tensor veli palatini are shown. The attachment of the mylohyoid and other muscles to mandible are indicated. The mandibular foramen and the nerves and blood vessels entering are shown. The auditory tube passing from the pharynx to the middle ear, the tympanic membrane and the mastoid air cells are shown.

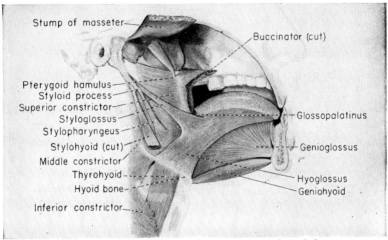

Stump of masseter
Buccinator (cut)
Pterygoid hamulus
Styloid process
Superior constrictor
Styloglossus
Stylopharyngeus
Stylohyoid (cut)
Middle constrictor
Thyrohyoid
Hyoid bone
Inferior constrictor
Glossopalatinus
Genioglossus
Hyoglossus
Geniohyoid

FIG. 113.   Pharyngeal muscles and extrinsic muscles of the tongue.

zygomatic arch and inserts on the coronoid process of the mandible. If the jaws are closed firmly, the temporal muscle bulges out in the temple.

The pterygoids (Figs. 112 and 148) are deeply placed and extend from the under aspect of the skull to the medial surface of the ramus of the mandible. The external pterygoid muscle assists in opening the mouth. The side-to-side movements, such as occur in grinding the teeth, are produced by the pterygoid muscles of the two sides acting in alternation. If the external pterygoids of the two sides act together, they protrude the jaw.

The muscles of mastication enable one to close the mouth and clench the teeth. Normally, we keep the mouth closed; it is remarkable how the expression can change by merely opening the mouth. When the muscles are relaxed, the mandible drops, due to the pull of gravity.

Muscles of the Tongue. The most characteristic feature of the tongue is its flexibility. It is composed of muscles covered with mucous membrane. There are two groups of muscles in the tongue, the *intrinsic* and the *extrinsic*.

The intrinsic muscles lie entirely within the tongue and are responsible for its mobility and changes in general shape. The intrinsic muscles are important in speaking, mastication and swallowing.

The extrinsic muscles arise outside the tongue and insert into it: the genioglossus, the styloglossus and the hyoglossus (Fig. 113).

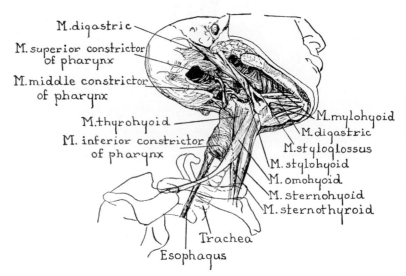

M.digastric

M. superior constrictor
of pharynx

M. middle constrictor
of pharynx

M. thyrohyoid

M. inferior constrictor
of pharynx

M. mylohyoid
M. digastric
M. styloglossus
M. stylohyoid
M. omohyoid
M. sternohyoid
M. sternothyroid

Trachea

Esophagus

FIG. 114. Muscles attached to the hyoid bone. (After Braus)

The genioglossus forms the main part of the body of the tongue. It arises from the mandible, behind the point of the chin, and spreads out in a fanlike manner to be inserted along the whole length of the undersurface of the tongue. It performs various functions according to the part of it that contracts. The anterior fibers withdraw the tongue into the mouth and depress its tip; the middle fibers draw the base of the tongue forward, depress the middle portion and protrude it from the mouth; the inferior fibers elevate the hyoid bone and carry it forward. If the 2 genioglossus muscles act along their entire length, they draw the tongue downward. When this is done, the superior surface of the tongue becomes concave, like a channel. Fluids readily pass along this channel toward the pharynx during the act of sucking.

The styloglossus (Fig. 113) arises from the styloid process of the temporal bone and is inserted into the whole length of the side and the underpart of the tongue. The styloglossus muscles retract the tongue, elevate the margins and raise the hyoid bone and the base of the tongue.

The hyoglossus (Fig. 113) arises from the sides of the body and the whole length of the greater cornu of the hyoid bone and extends almost vertically upward to enter the side of the tongue.

The hyoglossus muscles depress the tongue, retract it and draw its sides down.

MUSCLES OF THE NECK

The muscles of the anterolateral region of the neck are (1) the superficial cervical, (2) the lateral, (3) the suprahyoid and the infrahyoid, (4) the anterior vertebral and (5) the lateral vertebral.

Superficial Cervical. *The platysma* (Fig. 110) is the principal muscle of this region. It is a long, broad sheet of muscle that arises from the fascia covering the upper parts of the pectoralis major and the deltoid muscles. The fibers extend across the clavicle and obliquely upward and medially along the side of the neck to be inserted on the mandible and into the skin around the mouth. The platysma is a muscle of expression; it acts particularly on the skin of the lower lip and the neck. It wrinkles the skin of the neck, depresses the corner of the mouth and expresses melancholy, sadness, fright and suffering. It also relieves the pressure on the veins that lie under it and thus aids the circulation of the blood.

Lateral. The trapezius and the sternocleidomastoid muscles compose this group.

The trapezius is described on page 160.

The sternocleidomastoid (Figs. 97, 98, 99 and 107) is a strong, bandlike muscle that lies superficially across the side of the neck. It can be palpated in its entire length if you resist the pressure of one hand under your chin. It arises from the upper border of the sternum and the clavicle and extends obliquely upward and backward to be inserted on the mastoid process of the temporal bone. The sternocleidomastoid draws the head toward the shoulder of the same side and rotates the head so as to carry the face toward the opposite side. If the 2 muscles act together, they flex the cervical part of the vertebral column and bend the head forward. If the head is fixed, these muscles elevate the thorax and, in this way, aid in forced inspiration.

Suprahyoid and Infrahyoid Muscles. THE SUPRAHYOID muscles extend from the hyoid bone to the base of the skull. This group comprises the *digastric,* the *stylohyoid,* the *mylohyoid* and the *geniohyoid* muscles (Figs. 113 and 114). The suprahyoid muscles raise the larynx, the hyoid bone and the base of the tongue during swallowing. After the food has passed through the pharynx, the hyoid bone is carried upward and backward, which assists in preventing the return of food to the mouth. If the hyoid bone is fixed, the suprahyoid muscles depress the mandible.

THE INFRAHYOID muscles extend downward from the hyoid bone to the clavicle and the scapula. The *sternohyoid*, the *sternothyroid*, the *thyrohyoid* and the *omohyoid* muscles comprise this group (Fig. 107). The infrahyoid muscles depress the larynx and the hyoid bone after they have been drawn up with the larynx and the tongue during the act of swallowing. Both the suprahyoid and the infrahyoid muscles aid in speaking.

Anterior Vertebral. These are the *longus colli*, the *longus capitis*, the *rectus capitis anterior* and the lateralis muscles. The longus capitis and the rectus capitis anterior are the antagonists of the muscles at the back of the neck and restore the head to its natural position after it has been drawn backward by other muscles. The entire group flexes and rotates the head.

Lateral Vertebral. These are the *scalenus anterior*, the *medius* and the *posterior*, which cover the apex of the pleural cavity laterally. The scalene muscles extend from the cervical vertebrae to the ribs, as illustrated in Figure 244. When the scalene muscles act from above they elevate the first and the second ribs and, in this way, aid respiration. When they act from below they bend the vertebral column to one side or the other. If the muscles of both sides act together, they flex the vertebral column slightly.

PRACTICAL CONSIDERATIONS

Flatfoot. If one does a great deal of walking and standing, the muscles that support the arches of the feet may be unable to meet the demands placed upon them. Likewise, the ligaments may give way and fail to lend the proper support to the arches. When the arch is not supported, it falls, and the result is flatfoot (Fig. 115).

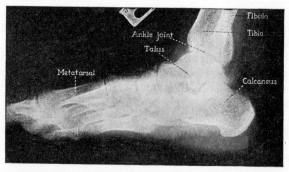

FIG. 115. Roentgenogram of bones of the foot; flatfoot.

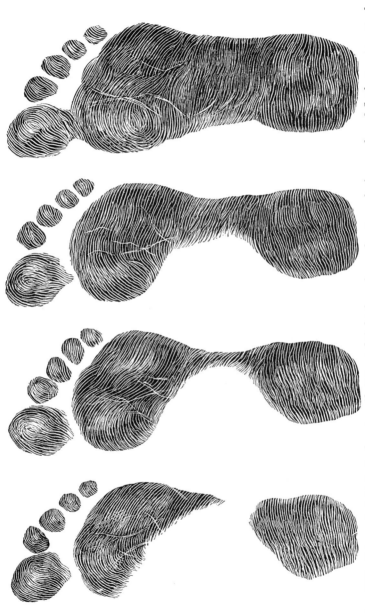

FIG. 116. Prints of right foot, showing (*left to right*) high arch. moderate arch, low arch and flatfoot, respectively.

The strength of the muscles supporting the arches should be increased by proper exercises and massage. If this is not sufficient to maintain the arches, electrical stimulation of the muscles may be used. Nurses are prone to have difficulty with their arches and many suffer from flatfoot. In flatfoot the head of the talus is carried downward and inward by the body weight. It is associated with abduction of the foot, and the arch may disappear entirely. Figure 116 shows prints of the right foot with high, normal and low arches, and flatfoot.

Tendon Sheaths. The volar and the dorsal carpal ligaments at the wrist are of importance in their relation to the tendons and their sheaths. Injuries of the hand may easily sever the tendons of the muscles of the forearm. Repair after such lacerations must be exact in order for normal movements to be restored. When such repairs are attempted in outpatient clinics, sometimes wrong ten-

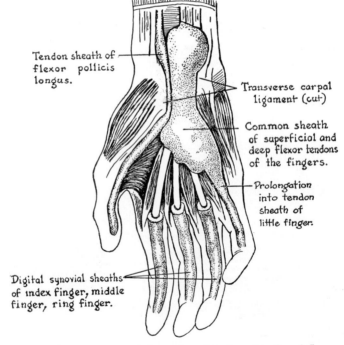

Tendon sheath of flexor pollicis longus.

Transverse carpal ligament (cut)

Common sheath of superficial and deep flexor tendons of the fingers.

Prolongation into tendon sheath of little finger.

Digital synovial sheaths of index finger, middle finger, ring finger.

FIG. 117. Dissection of the palm, showing sheaths of flexor tendons artificially distended.

dons have been sutured together. Generally it is realized that it is imperative to do such repairs on tendons of the wrist and the hand in the operating room where better facilities are available. Infection in the hand may travel along the tendon sheaths. The artificially distended sheaths of the flexor tendons of the right hand are illustrated in Figure 117.

Weak Places in the Abdominal Wall with Possible Hernia. The abdominal inguinal ring, the subcutaneous inguinal ring, an abnormal umbilicus and the femoral ring (just below the inguinal ligament) are weak places in the abdominal wall. A hernia or rupture may occur in these places.

Hernia refers to the protrusion of an organ or part of an organ or other structure through the wall of the cavity that normally contains it. The hernia takes the name of the ring through which it protrudes, such as inguinal, umbilical, diaphragmatic, obturator or scrotal. In inguinal hernia, which is the most frequent type, there is a loss of tone in the abdominal muscles, and such acts as coughing, heavy lifting or straining, which increase the pressure in the abdominal cavity, make possible the production of hernia.

Tenosynovitis (meaning "tendon" and "inflammation") is an inflammation of a tendon and its sheath.

Dangers from Fractures. One of the most common and most serious of the sequelae of fracture of the lower end of the radius is stiffness of the wrist and fingers from adhesions of the extensor tendons and their sheaths to the bone, to each other or to the surrounding structures.

Torticollis or wryneck may be due to spasm of the sternocleidomastoid muscle, either alone or in association with a similar condition of the trapezius.

Stiff neck may be due to inflammation of the trapezius.

Furuncles or Boils. The buttock is the gluteal prominence or breech. The skin over this region is thick, and it is a common site of furuncles or boils. These are apt to be painful, since the nerve supply is abundant. Intramuscular injections are given in the muscles of the buttock.

The Perineum. The structures of the perineum may be torn during childbirth. To prevent this the obstetrician often cuts through them just before delivery of the head. This procedure is called an *episiotomy*. The advantage of an episiotomy is that there is a clean cut instead of an irregular laceration, and the former is much easier to repair and it heals more readily. Repair is performed before the mother leaves the delivery table.

SUMMARY

1. Types of muscular tissue
   A. Microscopic structure
      a. skeletal
      b. smooth
      c. cardiac
   B. Gross structure
      a. skeletal
      b. smooth
      c. cardiac
   C. Location of each type
   D. Blood and lymph supply
2. Control of muscular tissue
   A. Skeletal—afferent and efferent nerves; motor unit
   B. Smooth—afferent and double efferent
   C. Cardiac—afferent and double efferent
3. Individual skeletal muscles
   A. Manner of naming—six ways
   B. Parts of a skeletal muscle
      a. Origin, insertion, body or belly
      b. Attachments
   C. Action—prime movers, antagonists, synergistic muscles
   D. Groups of skeletal muscles
      a. Appendicular muscles
         (1) Muscles of the upper extremity
            (A) Connecting upper extremity to trunk
               (a) Dorsal or superficial muscles of the back
—trapezius, latissimus dorsi, levator scapulae, rhomboid minor and rhomboid major
               (b) Ventral or muscles of the pectoral region
—pectoralis major, pectoralis minor, subclavius and serratus anterior
            (B) Muscles of the shoulder—deltoid, supraspinatus, teres major, teres minor and subscapularis
            (C) Muscles of the arm—biceps brachii, coracobrachialis, brachialis and triceps brachii
            (D) Muscles of the forearm
               (a) anterior-medial, which are pronators and flexors of the wrist and the fingers, arranged in superficial, intermediate and deep layers

(b) dorsal-lateral, which are supinators of the forearm and extensors of the wrist and the fingers, arranged in superficial and deep layers

(E) Muscles of the hand—muscles of the thenar and the hypothenar eminences; interosseous muscles; lumbricales.

(2) Muscles of the lower extremity

(A) Muscles of the gluteal region or buttock—gluteus maximus, gluteus medius, gluteus minimus, tensor fasciae latae, piriformis, obturator internus, quadratus femoris and the gemelli

(B) Muscles of the thigh

(a) Anterior—sartorius, quadriceps femoris, iliopsoas and pectineus muscles

(b) Medial or adductor group—gracilis, adductors (longus, brevis, magnus) and obturator externus

(c) Posterior or hamstring muscles—biceps femoris, semitendinosus and semimembranosus

(C) Muscles of the leg

(a) Anterior—tibialis anterior, extensor digitorum longus, peroneus tertius, extensor hallucis longus and extensor digitorum brevis

(b) Lateral—peroneus longus and brevis

(c) Posterior

(AA) Superficial group — gastrocnemius, plantaris and soleus

(BB) Deep group—popliteus, flexor digitorum longus, flexor hallucis longus and tibialis posterior

(D) Muscles of the foot—interosseous, lumbricales, flexor digitorum brevis and quadratus plantae

b. Axial muscles

(1) Muscles of the trunk

(A) Muscles of the abdominal wall — external oblique, internal oblique, transversus abdominis, rectus abdominis and quadratus lumborum

(B) Diaphragm

(C) Muscles of the thoracic wall—external intercostals, internal intercostals, levatores costarum, serratus posterior superior, serratus posterior inferior and transversus thoracic

(D) Muscles of the pelvic floor—levator ani and coccygeal muscles

(E) Perineal muscles—deep transverse perineal

(F) Deep muscles of the back—splenius capitis,

splenius cervicis, sacrospinalis, semispinalis, multifidus, rotatores, interspinales and intertransversarii muscles.

      (2) Muscles of the head
          (A) Muscles of the scalp—epicranius
          (B) Muscles of the face:
              (a) Muscles of the orbit and the eyelids—orbicularis oculi
              (b) Muscles of the lips—orbicularis oris and buccinator
          (C) Muscles of mastication—masseter, temporal, internal pterygoid and external pterygoid
          (D) Muscles of the tongue
              (a) Intrinsic
              (b) Extrinsic—genioglossus, styloglossus and hyoglossus
      (3) Muscles of the neck
          (A) Superficial cervical—platysma
          (B) Lateral—trapezius and sternocleidomastoid
          (C) Suprahyoid and infrahyoid muscles
          (D) Anterior vertebral
          (E) Lateral vertebral—scalene muscles

TABLE OF MUSCLES

In the table are given the name of each muscle, its origin, insertion, innervation and action.

APPENDICULAR MUSCLES

I. MUSCLES OF THE UPPER EXTREMITY

1. Muscles Connecting the Upper Limb to the Trunk

A. DORSAL, OR SUPERFICIAL MUSCLES OF THE BACK

Muscle	Origin	Insertion	Innervation and Action
Trapezius	Occipital bone, nuchal ligament, seventh cervical and all thoracic vertebrae	Lateral third of clavicle, acromion, and lateral part of spine of scapula	Spinal accessory, second, third and fourth cervical nerves. Upper part raises shoulder, extends head, bends head toward shoulder, and turns head toward opposite side. Lower part draws scapula downward and inward, rotating the inferior angle laterally. The whole muscle rotates the scapula so that the lateral angle points upward.

Muscle	Origin	Insertion	Innervation and Action
Latissimus dorsi	Spines of last six thoracic and upper lumbar vertebrae, lumbodorsal fascia, and crest of ilium	Anterior surface of upper part of humerus	Thoracodorsal nerve. Adducts, extends, and rotates arm medially. Depresses shoulder.
Levator scapulae	Transverse processes of first four cervical vertebrae	Upper part of vertebral border of scapula	Third and fourth cervical nerves. Draws scapula upward.
Minor rhomboid	Nuchal ligament, last cervical, and first thoracic vertebrae	Vertebral border of scapula	Dorsal scapular nerve. Draw scapula upward and medially. Rotate it so as to depress the tip of the shoulder.
Major rhomboid	Upper four thoracic vertebrae	Vertebral border of scapula	

B. VENTRAL, OR MUSCLES OF THE PECTORAL REGION

Muscle	Origin	Insertion	Innervation and Action
Pectoralis major	Cartilages of second to sixth ribs, sternum, and medial half of clavicle	Humerus, on a line extending downward from the greater tubercle	Anterior thoracic nerves (medial and lateral). Adducts, flexes and rotates arm medially.
Pectoralis minor	Second to fifth ribs, near their cartilages	Coracoid process of scapula	Medial anterior thoracic nerve. Pulls scapula forward.
Subclavius	First rib near its cartilage	Lower surface of clavicle	Fifth cervical nerve. Depresses scapula and shoulder.
Serratus anterior	Lateral surfaces of upper eight or nine ribs	Vertebral border of scapula	Long thoracic nerve. Draws scapula forward and laterally; rotates it so as to raise the tip of the shoulder.

2. MUSCLES OF THE SHOULDER

Muscle	Origin	Insertion	Innervation and Action
Deltoid	Spine of scapula, acromion, and lateral part of clavicle	Deltoid tubercle of humerus	Axillary nerve. Abducts arm; anterior part flexes and rotates arm medially; posterior part extends and rotates arm laterally.
Supraspinatus	Supraspinous fossa of scapula	Greater tubercle of humerus	Suprascapular nerve. Abducts arm.
Infraspinatus	Infraspinous fossa of scapula	Greater tubercle of humerus	Suprascapular nerve. Rotates arm laterally.
Teres major	Axillary border of scapula	Anterior surface of upper part of humerus	Lower subscapular nerve. Adducts, extends, and rotates arm medially.
Teres minor	Axillary border of scapula	Greater tubercle of humerus	Axillary nerve. Rotates arm laterally.
Subscapularis	Subscapular fossa of scapula	Lesser tubercle of humerus	Subscapular nerves. Rotates arm medially; holds humerus in glenoid cavity.

3. Muscles of the Arm

Muscle	Origin	Insertion	Innervation and Action
Biceps brachii	Short head from coracoid process; long head from scapula above glenoid fossa	Tubercle on proximal end of radius	Musculocutaneous nerve. Flexes and supinates forearm; flexes and rotates arm medially; long head abducts, short head adducts the arm.
Coraco-brachialis	Coracoid process of scapula	Middle third of humerus	Musculocutaneous nerve. Adducts and flexes arm. Aids in medial rotation of the arm.
Brachialis	Ventral surface of distal half of humerus	Tubercle on proximal end of ulna	Musculocutaneous nerve. Flexes forearm.
Triceps brachii	Long head from infraglenoid tubercle of scapula. Lateral and medial heads on posterior surface of humerus	Olecranon of ulna	Radial nerve. Extends forearm. Long head also extends and adducts the arm.

4. Muscles of the Forearm

A. ANTERIOR AND MEDIAL ASPECTS

Muscle	Origin	Insertion	Innervation and Action
Pronator teres	Medial epicondyle of humerus and coronoid process of ulna	Middle third of lateral surface of radius	Median nerve. Pronates and flexes forearm.
Flexor carpi radialis	Medial epicondyle of humerus	Base of second metacarpal	Median nerve. Flexes wrist and forearm.
Palmaris longus	Medial epicondyle of humerus	Fascia of palm	Median nerve. Flexes the wrist.
Flexor carpi ulnaris	Medial epicondyle of humerus and proximal two-thirds of ulna	Pisiform bone and third, fourth, and fifth metacarpals	Ulnar nerve. Flexes and adducts the hand.
Flexor digitorum sublimis	Medial epicondyle of humerus, coronoid process of ulna, and proximal part of radius	Volar surfaces of second phalanges of fingers	Median nerve. Flexes fingers and hand.
Flexor digitorum profundus	Proximal three-fourths of ulna and interosseous membrane	Volar surfaces of third phalanges of fingers	Median and ulnar nerves. Flexes fingers and hand.
Flexor pollicis longus	Volar surface of radius and interosseous membrane	Terminal phalanx of thumb	Median nerve. Flexes thumb and hand.
Pronator quadratus	Distal fourth of volar surface of ulna	Distal fourth of volar surface of radius	Median nerve. Pronates the forearm.

B. POSTERIOR AND LATERAL ASPECTS

Muscle	Origin	Insertion	Innervation and Action
Brachio-radialis	Ridge above lateral epicondyle of humerus	Proximal part of styloid process of radius	Radial nerve. Flexes and supinates forearm.
Extensor carpi radialis longus	Ridge above lateral epicondyle of humerus	Base of second metacarpal	Radial nerve. Extends and abducts hand. Flexes forearm.
Extensor carpi radialis brevis	Lateral epicondyle of humerus	Bases of second and third metacarpals	Radial nerve. Extends hand.
Extensor digitorum communis	Lateral epicondyle of humerus	By four tendons into phalanges of fingers	Radial nerve. Extends wrist and fingers.
Extensor digiti quinti proprius	Septum separating it from extensor digitorum communis	Phalanges of little finger	Radial nerve. Extends little finger.
Extensor carpi ulnaris	Lateral epicondyle of humerus; proximal three-fourths of ulna	Base of fifth metacarpal	Radial nerve. Extends and adducts hand and fifth metacarpal.
Supinator	Lateral epicondyle of humerus; proximal fifth of ulna	Proximal third of radius	Radial nerve. Supinates forearm.
Anconeus	Lateral epicondyle of humerus	Proximal part of ulna	Radial nerve. Extends forearm.
Abductor pollicis longus	Dorsal surface of ulna, radius, and interosseous membrane	Base of first metacarpal	Radial nerve. Abducts the first metacarpal.
Extensor pollicis brevis	Middle part of dorsal surface of radius and interosseous membrane	Base of first phalanx of thumb	Radial nerve. Extends thumb and abducts first metacarpal.
Extensor pollicis longus	Middle third of dorsal surface of ulna and interosseous membrane	Base of second phalanx of thumb	Radial nerve. Extends both phalanges of thumb.
Extensor indicis proprius	Distal third of dorsal surface of ulna and interosseous membrane	Aponeurosis on dorsal surface of index finger	Radial nerve. Extends index finger.

5. MUSCLES OF THE HAND

Abductor pollicis brevis	Transverse carpal ligament and lateral part of carpus	Base of first phalanx of thumb	Median nerve. Abducts thumb; flexes the first and extends the second phalanx.

Muscle	Origin	Insertion	Innervation and Action
Flexor pollicis brevis	Transverse carpal ligament; distal row of carpal bones	Base of first phalanx of thumb	Median nerve. Flexes, adducts, and rotates thumb medially.
Opponens pollicis	Transverse carpal ligament and greater multangular bone	Lateral border of metacarpal of thumb	Median nerve. Flexes, adducts, and rotates thumb medially.
Adductor pollicis	Second and third metacarpals, capitate, and ligaments	Base of first phalanx of thumb	Ulnar nerve. Adducts and flexes the thumb.
Palmaris brevis	Palmar aponeurosis	Skin of medial side of palm	Ulnar nerve. Draws skin of medial side of hand toward center.
Abductor digiti quinti	Pisiform bone and ligaments	First phalanx of little finger	Ulnar nerve. Abducts little finger; flexes the first phalanx of little finger.
Flexor digiti quinti brevis	Transverse carpal ligament and hamate bone	First phalanx of little finger	Ulnar nerve. Flexes first phalanx of little finger.
Opponens digiti quinti	Transverse carpal ligament and hamate bone	Fifth metacarpal	Ulnar nerve. Flexes and adducts little finger.
Lumbricales (4)	Tendons of flexor digitorum profundus	Tendons of extensor digitorum communis	Ulnar nerve, except the lateral two lumbricales, which are supplied by the median nerve. All flex the first and extend the second and third phalanges. Lumbricales draw fingers toward thumb. Volar interossei draw fingers toward middle finger, and dorsal interossei draw fingers away from middle finger.
Interossei volares (4)	First, second, fourth, and fifth metacarpals	First phalanx of thumb, index, ring, and little fingers	
Interossei dorsales (4)	Adjacent sides of metacarpal bones	First phalanx of middle three fingers, two muscles inserting on middle finger	

II. MUSCLES OF THE LOWER EXTREMITY

1. MUSCLES OF THE GLUTEAL REGION OR BUTTOCK

Gluteus maximus	Iliac crest, lateral surface of ilium, sacrum, coccyx, and sacrotuberous ligament	Iliotibial band and gluteal tuberosity of femur	Inferior gluteal nerve. Extends thigh; rotates thigh laterally.
Gluteus medius	Lateral surface of ilium	Great trochanter of femur	Superior gluteal nerve. Abducts thigh; aids in rotation.
Gluteus minimis	Lateral surface of ilium; capsule of hip joint	Great trochanter of femur	Superior gluteal nerve. Abducts and rotates thigh medially.
Tensor fasciae latae	Anterior part of iliac crest	Iliotibial band	Superior gluteal nerve. Tenses fascia lata; flexes, abducts, and rotates thigh medially.

Muscle	Origin	Insertion	Innervation and Action
Piriformis	Ventral surface of sacrum and sacrotuberous ligament	Great trochanter of femur	First or second sacral nerve, or both. Extends, abducts, and rotates thigh laterally.
Obturator internus	Pelvic surface of pubis, ischium, and obturator membrane	Trochanteric fossa of femur	Fourth lumbar to second sacral nerves. Rotates thigh laterally.
Quadratus femoris	Ischial tuberosity	Line below great trochanter of femur	Fourth lumbar to first sacral nerves. Rotates thigh laterally.
Gemellus superior	Ischial spine	With obturator internus	Nerve to obturator internus — Rotate thigh laterally.
Gemellus inferior	Ischial tuberosity	With obturator internus	Nerve to quadratus femoris —

2. MUSCLES OF THE THIGH

A. ANTERIOR ASPECT

Muscle	Origin	Insertion	Innervation and Action
Sartorius	Anterior superior iliac spine	Medial surface of proximal end of tibia	Femoral nerve. Flexes thigh and leg; rotates thigh laterally.
Quadriceps femoris	Arises by four heads from ilium and femur	Tuberosity of tibia, through a common tendon	Femoral nerve. All parts extend leg. Rectus femoris flexes thigh.
Rectus femoris	Anterior inferior iliac spine	Common tendon	
Vastus medialis	Medial lip of linea aspera	Common tendon	
Vastus lateralis	Lateral lip of linea aspera	Common tendon	
Vastus intermedius	Anterior surface of femur	Common tendon	
Psoas major	Bodies of twelfth thoracic to fifth lumbar vertebrae and intervertebral disks	Small trochanter of femur	Second to fourth lumbar nerves. Flexes thigh; adducts and rotates it medially.
Iliacus	Iliac fossa of ilium	Small trochanter of femur	Femoral nerve. Flexes thigh; adducts and rotates it medially.
Iliopsoas	The iliacus and psoas major muscles are often considered together as the iliopsoas.		
Psoas minor	Twelfth thoracic and first lumbar vertebrae	Iliopectineal eminence of coxal bone	First and second lumbar nerves. Flexes the pelvis.
Pectineus	Crest of pubis	Pectineal line of femur, below small trochanter	Femoral nerve. Flexes and adducts thigh.

B. MEDIAL ASPECT

Muscle	Origin	Insertion	Innervation and Action
Gracilis	Rami of pubis and ischium	Tibia, below medial condyle	Obturator nerve. Adducts and flexes thigh; rotates thigh laterally; flexes leg.
Adductor longus	Superior ramus of pubis	Middle third of linea aspera of femur	Obturator nerve. Adducts, flexes and rotates thigh laterally.
Adductor brevis	Inferior ramus of pubis	Upper third of linea aspera of femur	Obturator nerve. Adducts thigh.

Muscle	Origin	Insertion	Innervation and Action
Adductor magnus	Rami of pubis and ischium, and ischial tuberosity	Linea aspera of femur; tubercle above medial condyle	Obturator and sciatic nerves. Adducts thigh; aids in flexion, extension, and lateral rotation.
Obturator externus	Lateral surface of pubis, ischium, and obturator membrane	Trochanteric fossa of femur	Obturator nerve. Rotates thigh laterally; aids in adduction.

C. POSTERIOR ASPECT

Muscle	Origin	Insertion	Innervation and Action
Biceps femoris	Long head from ischial tuberosity; short head from middle third of linea aspera	Head of fibula; lateral condyle of tibia	Sciatic nerve. Flexes leg and rotates it laterally; long head also extends and adducts thigh.
Semitendinosus	Ischial tuberosity	Proximal part of medial surface of tibia	Sciatic nerve. Flexes leg and rotates it medially; extends and adducts thigh and rotates it medially.
Semimembranosus	Ischial tuberosity	Medial condyle of tibia	Sciatic nerve. Flexes leg and rotates it medially; extends and adducts thigh and rotates it medially.

3. MUSCLES OF THE LEG

A. ANTERIOR ASPECT

Muscle	Origin	Insertion	Innervation and Action
Anterior tibial	Lateral condyle and proximal part of tibia and interosseous membrane	First cuneiform and base of first metatarsal	Common and deep peroneal nerves. Dorsal flexes foot and inverts sole.
Extensor digitorum longus	Lateral condyle of tibia, interosseous membrane, and shaft of fibula	Phalanges of four lateral toes	Deep peroneal nerve. Dorsal flexes foot; everts foot and extends toes.
Peroneus tertius	Distal third of fibula and interosseous membrane	Base of fifth metatarsal (and fourth)	Deep peroneal nerve. Dorsal flexes foot and everts it.
Extensor hallucis longus	Middle half of fibula; distal half of interosseous membrane	Second phalanx of big toe	Deep peroneal nerve. Extends big toe, dorsal flexes foot and inverts sole.

B. LATERAL ASPECT

Muscle	Origin	Insertion	Innervation and Action
Peroneus longus	Lateral condyle of tibia, head and shaft of fibula, and intermuscular septum	First cuneiform and base of first metatarsal	Common peroneal nerve. Plantar flexes, abducts, and everts foot. Supports arch of foot.
Peroneus brevis	Middle third of fibula, and intermuscular septa	Tuberosity of fifth metatarsal	Superficial peroneal nerve. Everts foot; aids in extension.

C. POSTERIOR ASPECT

Muscle	Origin	Insertion	Innervation and Action
Gastroc-nemius	Medial and lateral condyles of femur	Calcaneus, through tendon of Achilles	Tibial nerve. Flexes leg; plantar flexes, adducts, and inverts foot.
Soleus	Head and proximal third of fibula, and middle third of tibia	Calcaneus, through tendon of Achilles	Tibial nerve. Plantar flexes, adducts, and inverts foot.
Plantaris	Line above lateral condyle of femur	Through a slender tendon terminating in the fibrous tissue of the heel	Tibial nerve. Flexes leg and plantar flexes foot. Its action is very weak.
Popliteus	Lateral condyle of femur	Proximal fourth of tibia	Tibial nerve. Flexes leg and rotates it medially.
Flexor digitorum longus	Dorsal surface of tibia and fascia covering tibialis posterior	Phalanges of lateral four toes	Tibial nerve. Flexes digits; plantar flexes and inverts foot.
Flexor hallucis longus	Distal two-thirds of fibula and fascia covering tibialis posterior	Terminal phalanx of big toe	Tibial nerve. Flexes big toe; plantar flexes and inverts foot.
Posterior tibial	Posterior surfaces of tibia, fibula, and interosseous membrane	Navicular, cuboid, and all cuneiform bones; second and fourth metatarsals	Tibial nerve. Adducts, plantar flexes, and inverts foot.

4. MUSCLES OF THE FOOT

Extensor digitorum brevis	Calcaneus and cruciate ligament	Phalanges of medial four toes	Deep peroneal nerve. Extends medial four toes.
Quadratus plantae	Calcaneus and ligaments	Tendon of flexor digitorum longus	Lateral plantar nerve. Aids flexor digitorum longus.
Flexor digitorum brevis	Calcaneus, plantar aponeurosis, and septa	Phalanges of lateral four toes	Medial plantar nerve. Flexes toes.
Abductor hallucis	Calcaneus and ligaments	First phalanx of big toe	Medial plantar nerve. Abducts big toe; flexes first and extends second phalanx of big toe.
Flexor hallucis brevis	Cuneiform bones and ligaments	First phalanx of big toe	Medial plantar nerve. Flexes first and extends second phalanx of big toe.
Adductor hallucis Oblique head	Cuboid, third cuneiform, second and third metatarsals, and ligaments	First phalanx of big toe	Lateral plantar nerve. Adduct big toe; aid in flexion of big toe. Transverse head holds heads of metatarsal bones together.
Transverse head	Capsules of metatarsophalangeal joints	Sheath of tendon of flexor hallucis longus	
Abductor digiti quinti	Calcaneus and fascia of sole	First phalanx of little toe	Lateral plantar nerve. Abducts and flexes little toe.

Muscle	Origin	Insertion	Innervation and Action
Flexor digiti quinti brevis	Cuboid and first metatarsal	First phalanx of little toe	Lateral plantar nerve. Abducts and flexes little toe.
Opponens digiti quinti	Cuboid	Fifth metatarsal	Lateral plantar nerve. Draws little toe medially and plantarward.
Lumbricales (4)	Tendons of flexor digitorum longus	Phalanges of lateral four toes	⎫ Medial plantar nerve to most medial lumbrical. Others by lateral plantar nerve. These muscles flex the first phalanx. Dorsal interossei abduct from, plantar interossei adduct toward, second toe. Lumbricales extend second phalanges.
Interossei dorsales (4)	Metatarsal bones and ligaments	Phalanges of middle three toes	⎬
Interossei plantares (4)	Metatarsal bones and ligaments	Medial side of phalanges of digits	⎭

AXIAL MUSCLES

I. MUSCLES OF THE ABDOMINAL WALL

Muscle	Origin	Insertion	Innervation and Action
External oblique	Lower eight ribs	Iliac crest, inguinal ligament and linea alba	Lower seven intercostal nerves and iliohypogastric nerve. Compresses abdomen; flexes and rotates vertebral column.
Internal oblique	Inguinal ligament, iliac crest, and lumbodorsal fascia	Lower three ribs, linea alba, and pubic bone	Iliohypogastric, ilio-inguinal, and last three intercostal nerves. Compresses abdomen; flexes and rotates vertebral column.
Cremaster	Upper border of inguinal ligament	Pubic tubercle	Genital nerve. Lifts testis toward subcutaneous inguinal ring.
Transversus abdominis	Lower six ribs, lumbodorsal fascia, iliac crest, and inguinal ligament	Linea alba and pubic tubercle	Iliohypogastric, ilio-inguinal, genitofemoral, and last five intercostal nerves. Compresses abdomen.
Rectus abdominis	Symphysis pubis and body of pubis	Fifth to seventh costal cartilages; xiphoid process	Lower six intercostal nerves. Depresses thorax; flexes vertebral column and pelvis.
Pyramidalis	Body of pubis	Linea alba	Last thoracic nerve. Tenses linea alba.
Quadratus lumborum	Iliac crest, lower three lumbar vertebrae	Upper three lumbar vertebrae, twelfth rib	First three or four lumbar nerves. Flexes vertebral column laterally; extends vertebral column.

II. DIAPHRAGM

Muscle	Origin	Insertion	Innervation and Action
Diaphragm	Xiphoid process, lower six ribs and their cartilages, lumbar vertebrae	Central tendon of diaphragm	Phrenic nerve. Expands thorax; compresses contents of abdominal cavity.

III. MUSCLES OF THE THORACIC WALL

Muscle	Origin	Insertion	Innervation and Action
External intercostal	Lower border of each rib	Upper border of next rib	Intercostal nerves. Elevate ribs and enlarge thorax.
Internal intercostal	Lower border of each rib	Upper border of next rib	Intercostal nerves. Contract thorax (probably).

Muscle	Origin	Insertion	Innervation and Action
Levatores costarum	Transverse processes of thoracic vertebrae	Next lower rib	Intercostal nerves. Bend vertebral column laterally; extend and rotate it.
Transversus thoracis	Dorsal surface of lower half of sternum	Cartilages of second to sixth ribs	Second to sixth intercostal nerves. Depresses ribs (in expiration).
Serratus posterior superior	Nuchal ligament and upper three thoracic vertebrae	Second to fifth ribs	Upper four intercostal nerves. Raises ribs, in this way enlarges thorax.
Serratus posterior inferior	Last three thoracic and first two lumbar vertebrae	Last four ribs	Ninth to eleventh intercostal nerves. Draws lower ribs outward; enlarges thorax.

IV. MUSCLES OF THE PELVIC FLOOR

Muscle	Origin	Insertion	Innervation and Action
Levator ani	Body of pubis, ischial spine, and obturator fascia	Coccyx and raphe joining coccyx to rectum	Fourth sacral nerve. Flexes coccyx; raises anus; resists downward pressure of abdominal viscera.
Coccygeus	Ischial spine	Fourth and fifth sacral vertebrae and coccyx	Third and fourth sacral nerves. Flexes and abducts coccyx.
External anal sphincter	Fibers of this muscle surround the anus and are attached to the skin and to the coccyx		Inferior hemorrhoidal nerves. Keeps anus closed.

V. MUSCLES OF THE PERINEUM

Muscle	Origin	Insertion	Innervation and Action
Transversus perinei profundus	Inferior ischial ramus	Fibers interdigitate in midline	Perineal nerve. Draws back central tendon of perineum.
Sphincter urogenitalis	Pubic ramus	Fibers interdigitate in midline, some encircle urethra	Perineal nerve. Compresses the urethra; compresses vagina or Cowper's glands.
Ischiocavernosus	Ischial tuberosity and inferior ischial ramus	Crus penis (in male) Crus clitoridis (female)	Perineal nerve. Constricts crus penis (or clitoridis).
Bulbocavernosus	Dense tissue covering root of penis	Median raphe on ventral side of bulb; central tendon of perineum	Perineal nerve. Compresses bulb of urethra.
Transversus perinei superficialis	Inferior ischial ramus	Central tendon of perineum	Perineal nerve. Fixes central tendon of perineum.

VI. DEEP MUSCLES OF THE BACK

Muscle	Origin	Insertion	Innervation and Action
Splenius cervicis	Third to sixth thoracic vertebrae	Upper two or three cervical vertebrae	Posterior rami of second, third, and fourth cervical nerves. Bend and rotate head toward the side of the muscle which is acting.
Splenius capitis	Nuchal ligament and upper thoracic vertebrae	Mastoid process and occipital bone	
Sacrospinalis (iliocostalis, longissimus, spinalis)	Ilium, sacrum, lumbar, thoracic, and last four cervical vertebrae, posterior parts of ribs	Lumbar, thoracic, and cervical vertebrae; posterior parts of all ribs; mastoid process	Posterior rami of spinal nerves from first cervical to fifth lumbar. Bends head and vertebral column to side. Extends head and vertebral column.

Muscle	Origin	Insertion	Innervation and Action
Semispinalis capitis	Last five cervical and upper five thoracic vertebrae	Occipital bone, between inferior and superior nuchal lines	Posterior rami of upper five cervical nerves. Extends head and bends it laterally.
Semispinalis cervicis and dorsi	All thoracic vertebrae	Lower six cervical and upper five thoracic vertebrae	Posterior rami of third to sixth cervical and third to sixth thoracic nerves. Extend and rotate the vertebral column.
Multifidus	Iliac crest, sacrum, and all vertebrae below fourth cervical	Spines of vertebrae up to second cervical	Posterior rami of spinal nerves. Extends and rotates the vertebral column.
Rotatores	Transverse processes of vertebrae	Next vertebrae above	Posterior rami of spinal nerves. Extend and rotate vertebral column.
Interspinales	Spines of vertebrae	Spines of next vertebrae above	Posterior rami of spinal nerves. Extend vertebral column.
Intertransversarii	Transverse processes of vertebrae	Transverse processes of next vertebrae	Posterior rami of spinal nerves. Bend vertebral column to side.

VII. MUSCLES OF THE SCALP, FACE, MASTICATION, TONGUE AND NECK

1. MUSCLES OF THE SCALP AND EAR

Occipitalis	Supreme nuchal line of occipital bone	Epicranial aponeurosis	Facial nerve. Tenses epicranial aponeurosis and draws scalp backward.
Frontalis	Epicranial aponeurosis	Skin of eyebrow and of root of nose	Facial nerve. Elevates eyebrow; wrinkles forehead.
Auricularis anterior	Epicranial aponeurosis, in front of auricle	Cartilage of auricle	Facial nerve. Draws auricle forward.
Auricularis superior	Epicranial aponeurosis, above auricle	Cartilage of auricle	Facial nerve. Draws auricle upward.
Auricularis posterior	Epicranial aponeurosis, behind auricle	Cartilage of auricle	Facial nerve. Draws auricle backward.

2. MUSCLES OF THE FACE

A. ORBIT AND EYELIDS

Superior rectus	Margin of optic foramen	Eyeball, above pupil	Oculomotor nerve. Turns eyeball upward.
Medial rectus	Margin of optic foramen	Eyeball, medial to pupil	Oculomotor nerve. Turns eyeball medially.
Inferior rectus	Margin of optic foramen	Eyeball, below pupil	Oculomotor nerve. Turns eyeball downward.
Lateral rectus	Margin of optic foramen	Eyeball, lateral to pupil	Abducens nerve. Turns eyeball laterally.
Superior oblique	Margin of optic foramen	Lateral side of eyeball	Trochlear nerve. Turns eyeball downward and laterally. Rotates medially.
Inferior oblique	Medial part of floor of orbit	Lateral side of eyeball	Oculomotor nerve. Turns eyeball upward and laterally. Rotates laterally.

Muscle	Origin	Insertion	Innervation and Action
Levator palpebrae superioris	Margin of optic foramen	Upper eyelid	Oculomotor nerve. Raises upper lid.
Orbicularis oculi	Medial palpebral ligament, frontal bone, and maxilla	Lateral and medial palpebral ligaments; some fibers encircle eye	Facial nerve. Closes eyelids; stretches skin of forehead.
Corrugator	Frontal bone	Skin of eyebrow	Facial nerve. Draws skin of brow downward and medially, as in frowning.
Procerus	Cartilages of nose	Skin over root of nose	Facial nerve. Draws skin of forehead down.
Nasalis	Maxilla above incisor and canine teeth; dorsum of nose	Skin of nasolabial groove and margin of nostril	Facial nerve. Draws wings of nose laterally and upward; constricts nostrils.

B. MUSCLES OF THE LIPS

Muscle	Origin	Insertion	Innervation and Action
Orbicularis oris	Various muscles running into lip	Fibers surround oral opening, forming a sphincter	Facial nerve. Draws lips together.
Quadratus labii superioris			
Angular head	Root of nose	Alar cartilage; upper lip	Facial nerve. The whole muscle raises the upper lip. The angular head also lifts the wings of the nose.
Infra-orbital head	Maxilla below orbit	Upper lip	
Zygomatic head	Zygomatic bone	Upper lip	
Quadratus labii inferioris	Mandible below canine and premolar teeth	Lower lip	Facial nerve. Draws lower lip downward.
Incisivus labii (inferior and superior)	Maxilla and mandible, near canine and lateral incisor teeth	Orbicularis oris muscle	Facial nerve. Draws corners of lips medially.
Zygomatic	Zygomatic bone	Orbicularis oris muscle	Facial nerve. Raises corner of mouth and draws it laterally.
Canine	Canine fossa of maxilla	Orbicularis oris muscle	Facial nerve. Raises corner of mouth and draws it medially.
Risorius	Subcutaneous tissue over parotid gland	Skin and mucous membrane at corner of mouth	Facial nerve. Draws corner of mouth laterally.
Triangularis	Mandible below canine, premolar and first molar teeth	Orbicularis oris muscle	Facial nerve. Draws corner of mouth downward.
Buccinator	Maxilla, mandible, and pterygomandibular raphe	Orbicularis oris muscle and skin of lips	Facial nerve. Draws corner of mouth laterally; pulls lips and cheek against teeth.
Mentalis	Mandible, below lower lateral incisor	Skin of chin	Facial nerve. Draws up skin of chin.

3. Muscles of Mastication

Muscle	Origin	Insertion	Innervation and Action
Masseter	Zygomatic arch	Lateral surface of ramus of mandible	Masticator or motor root of trigeminal nerve. Raises mandible and draws it forward.
Temporal	Temporal fossa of temporal bone	Coronoid process of mandible	Masticator or motor root of trigeminal nerve. Raises mandible.
External pterygoid	Lateral pterygoid plate, sphenoid and palate bones	Neck of condyle of mandible	Masticator or motor root of trigeminal nerve. Draws mandible forward and sideward; aids in opening mouth.
Internal pterygoid	Maxilla and palate bone	Medial surface of ramus of mandible	Masticator or motor root of trigeminal nerve. Draws mandible upward and sideward.

4. Muscles of the Tongue, Pharynx and Soft Palate

Genioglossus	Spine of mandible, near midline	Fascia of tongue; hyoid bone	Hypoglossal nerve. Anterior fibers retract tongue; remainder draws it forward and depresses its tip. Draws hyoid bone upward and forward.
Hyoglossus	Body and great cornu of hyoid bone	Fascia of tongue	Hypoglossal nerve. Depresses side of tongue and retracts it.
Styloglossus	Styloid process of temporal bone	Side of tongue	Hypoglossal nerve. Draws tongue backward.
Glossopalatinus	Aponeurosis of soft palate	Side and under surface of tongue	Pharyngeal plexus (vagus nerve). Draws side of tongue upward and soft palate downward. Constricts faucial isthmus.
Inferior constrictor of pharynx	Lateral surfaces of thyroid and cricoid cartilages	Dorsal part of pharynx	Pharyngeal plexus. Constricts pharynx; aids in swallowing.
Middle constrictor of pharynx	Greater and lesser cornua of hyoid bone; stylohyoid ligament	Dorsal part of pharynx; occipital bone	Pharyngeal plexus. Constricts pharynx; aids in swallowing.
Superior constrictor of pharynx	Pterygoid process, pterygomandibular raphe, and mylohyoid ridge of mandible	Dorsal part of pharynx; occipital bone	Pharyngeal plexus. Constricts pharynx; aids in swallowing.
Stylopharyngeus	Styloid process of temporal bone	Thyroid cartilage and lateral wall of pharynx	Glossopharyngeal nerve. Lift pharynx in act of swallowing.
Pharyngopalatine	Aponeurosis of soft palate and cartilage of auditory tube	Thyroid cartilage and lateral wall of pharynx	Pharyngeal plexus (vagus nerve). Closes opening between nasa and oral pharynx; depresse soft palate.
Levator veli palatini	Under surface of temporal bone and cartilage of auditory tube	Aponeurosis of soft palate	Pharyngeal plexus (vagus nerve). Raises soft palate; narrow pharyngeal opening of auditor tube.

Muscle	Origin	Insertion	Innervation and Action
Tensor veli palatini	Scaphoid fossa of sphenoid bone and cartilage of auditory tube	Palate bone and aponeurosis of soft palate	Masticator or motor root of trigeminal nerve. Tightens soft palate; opens auditory tube.
Uvulae	Aponeurosis of soft palate	Uvula	Pharyngeal plexus (vagus nerve). Draw up the uvula.

5. MUSCLES OF THE ANTERO-LATERAL REGION OF THE NECK

A. SUPERFICIAL CERVICAL

Muscle	Origin	Insertion	Innervation and Action
Platysma	Subcutaneous tissue of neck	Lower border of mandible; skin of lower part of cheek and corner of mouth	Facial nerve. Wrinkles skin of neck; depresses corner of mouth.

B. LATERAL

Muscle	Origin	Insertion	Innervation and Action
Sternocleidomastoid	Manubrium of sternum and medial third of clavicle	Mastoid process and occipital bone	Spinal accessory, second and third cervical nerves. Bends head and neck toward shoulder; rotates head toward opposite side. Both sides acting together flex the neck and extend the head.

C. SUPRA- AND INFRAHYOID MUSCLES

Muscle	Origin	Insertion	Innervation and Action
Stylohyoid	Styloid process of temporal bone	Body of hyoid bone	Facial nerve. Draws hyoid bone upward and backward.
Digastric Posterior belly	Temporal bone, medial to mastoid process	Intermediate tendon	Facial nerve. Both bellies raise hyoid bone. Anterior belly also draws it forward.
Anterior belly	Intermediate tendon	Digastric fossa of mandible	Mylohyoid nerve.
Mylohyoid	Medial surface of body of mandible	Hyoid bone and median raphe extending to mandible	Mylohyoid nerve. Draws hyoid bone toward mandible.
Geniohyoid	Mental spine of mandible	Body of hyoid bone	Hypoglossal nerve. Draws hyoid bone upward and forward.
Sternohyoid	Sternum and medial end of clavicle	Body of hyoid bone	Ansa cervicalis. Depresses hyoid bone.
Omohyoid	Superior margin of scapula	Body of hyoid bone	Ansa cervicalis. Depresses hyoid bone and draws it laterally.
Sternothyroid	Manubrium of sternum and cartilage of first rib	Thyroid cartilage	Ansa cervicalis. Depresses thyroid cartilage.
Thyrohyoid	Thyroid cartilage	Body and great cornu of hyoid bone	1st and 2nd cervical nerves. Draws thyroid cartilage and hyoid bone together.

D. ANTERIOR VERTEBRAL

Muscle	Origin	Insertion	Innervation and Action
Longus colli	Lower five cervical and first three thoracic vertebrae	Upper six cervical vertebrae	Second to sixth cervical nerves. Flexes neck.

Muscle	Origin	Insertion	Innervation and Action
Longus capitis	Transverse processes of third to sixth cervical vertebrae	Basilar part of occipital bone	First four cervical nerves. Flexes head and rotates it toward same side.
Rectus capitis anterior	Lateral part of atlas	Basilar part of occipital bone	First cervical nerve. Flexes head and rotates it toward same side.
Rectus capitis lateralis	Transverse process of atlas	Lateral part of occipital bone	First cervical nerve. Bends head to side.
Rectus capitis posterior major	Spine of epistropheus	Inferior nuchal line of occipital bone	Suboccipital nerve. Extends and rotates head.
Rectus capitis posterior minor	Posterior tubercle of atlas	Inferior nuchal line of occipital bone	Suboccipital nerve. Extends head.
Obliquus capitis inferior	Spine of epistropheus	Transverse process of atlas	Suboccipital nerve. Rotates head.
Obliquus capitis superior	Transverse process of atlas	Inferior nuchal line of occipital bone	Suboccipital nerve. Extends head.

E. LATERAL VERTEBRAL

Muscle	Origin	Insertion	Innervation and Action
Anterior scalene	Transverse processes of fourth to sixth cervical vertebrae	First rib	Fifth, sixth, and seventh cervical nerves. Raises first rib and bends neck to same side.
Middle scalene	Transverse processes of third to seventh cervical vertebrae	First and second ribs	Fourth to eighth cervical nerves. Raises first and second ribs; bends neck to same side.
Posterior scalene	Transverse processes of fifth and sixth cervical vertebrae	Second rib	Seventh or eighth cervical nerves. Action is the same as that of the scalenus medius. All scalene muscles aid in forced inspiration.

SITUATION AND QUESTIONS

A. Name the type of movement.

B. Name the muscle whose contraction accomplishes the action.

UNIT 2. THE ERECT AND MOVING BODY

5. Physiology of Muscular Tissue

SKELETAL MUSCLE

Tonus

In the waking state, even at rest, the skeletal muscles are in a state of partial contraction which we call *tonus.* The partial contraction is a sign of health; when it is lacking we know that one's health, both mental and physical, is below par.

Tonus in skeletal muscle is due to the stretch reflex (p. 288). The skeletal muscles are so arranged in the body that they are held in slight stretch over the joints. This is particularly true of the "extensor" muscles or those that enable us to stand erect; in these an excellent tonus is maintained. When muscle fibers are stretched, sensitive nerve endings or receptors are stimulated. Such receptors are located in muscle spindles, and when they are stimulated impulses are sent in to the central nervous system. The impulses that reach the central nervous system produce changes there which, in turn, cause impulses to be sent back to the part of the muscle that is being stretched and thus, produce contraction of its fibers. During the maintenance of tonus, groups of motor units work in relays or shifts. This means that one group of motor units is active for a short period of time; then this group relaxes, and another group becomes active.

Physicians always are interested in the muscle tonus of their patients. If tonus is normal, it indicates that the muscles themselves, the nerve fibers which carry impulses to the central nervous system, the reflex centers of the central nervous system and the nerve fibers which carry impulses from the central nervous system to the muscles are all working properly. If tonus is below normal, it is the duty of physicians to determine which part of the "stretch reflex" is failing in its function.

Response to Stimulation

In the intact body, skeletal muscles undergo contraction only when they are stimulated by nerve impulses. If no nerve impulses reach them, they will be relaxed. During a surgical operation it is essential to have the skeletal muscles relaxed, and this is accomplished in various ways. The most frequent manner of producing muscular relaxation is to administer a general anesthetic that abolishes stretch reflexes as one of its effects. A second manner of producing muscular relaxation is to administer a spinal anesthetic that abolishes the stretch reflexes of the muscles of the abdominal wall

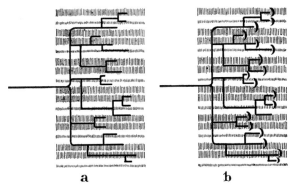

a   **b**

Fig. 118. Diagram showing blocking of nerve impulse at the neuromuscular junction by curare: (*Left*) normal; (*Right*) curarized muscle.

Fig. 119. Simple muscle twitch. Average latent period of frog's gastrocnemius muscle (*top*) 1/100 second; average period of contraction, 4/100 second; average period of relaxation, 5/100 second. The tuning fork rate is 100 double vibrations per second (*bottom*).

and the lower extremities. In both of these methods, the central nervous system is the part affected; muscles are relaxed because no impulses reach the central nervous system from them and no impulses are sent to them from the central nervous system.

It is possible to produce muscular relaxation in a third way. This is by the use of a drug called *curare,* which blocks the impulses at the neuromuscular junction. Figure 118 is a diagram of the effect of curare at the neuromuscular junction.

All of our voluntary movements and reflex movements, as well as tonus, are due to impulses that reach the muscles from the central nervous system.

Changes During Contraction

Molecular Changes. If you watched a single muscle fiber contract under an ordinary microscope, you would not gain much information about the contraction process. Investigators using more penetrating methods of study, such as the electron microscope and x-ray diffraction, have learned that the structural changes that characterize contraction are inside of the molecules of protein in the muscle fibrillae. The protein that undergoes a change is called *actomyosin.* It is composed of long chains of molecules that fold up into shorter chains when the fiber contracts. Although the process of contraction is still a mystery, it is known that it involves a reversible folding and unfolding of long chains of actomyosin molecules.

Gross Changes During Contraction. The gross change which you can see without the aid of any microscope is the shortening and the thickening of a muscle when it contracts. You can feel this change, also, if you flex your forearm while keeping your opposite palm over the biceps brachii.

Many facts can be learned by experimenting with an isolated

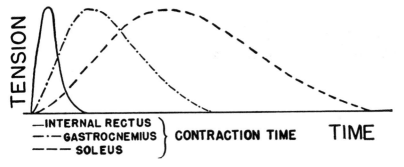

TENSION

—INTERNAL RECTUS
—·—GASTROCNEMIUS } CONTRACTION TIME   TIME
—— — SOLEUS

FIG. 120. Relative durations of simple twitches of different types of skeletal muscles. The internal rectus of the eye is a white muscle; it is rapid in its responses. The soleus is a red muscle, and its twitch is of long duration. The gastrocnemius is intermediate. (Redrawn from Fulton, J. F.: Textbook of Physiology (Howell), Philadelphia, Saunders)

frog's muscle in the laboratory. The gastrocnemius muscles of frogs are the most convenient ones to study. Such muscles will respond to many types of stimulation, such as the application of a hot wire, a pinch, a crystal of salt and a strong salt solution, but the stimulus of preference is an electric shock. Electrical stimuli are least harmful, most easily regulated and most like nerve impulses which stimulate muscles in the intact body. Consequently, the discussion that follows is based on the results of electrical stimulation.

After a gastrocnemius muscle is isolated, its proximal end is fixed by placing the femur, some of which has been left attached, in a clamp. The distal end passes into the tendon of Achilles. It is easy to tie the tendon to a lever, and the lever, tipped with a stylus, writes a graphic record of the contraction of the muscle.

If a single electric shock is sent through the muscle, it responds by giving one contraction, which we call a *simple twitch*. Such a record is shown in Figure 119. If the recording surface is not moving, the muscle moves the lever straight up and down as it contracts and then relaxes, and the record is a straight line. If the recording surface is moving, a very different picture is obtained. It is noted that a short period of time elapses after the stimulus is applied and before the muscle contracts; then the lever describes a curve. The period of time between the application of the stim-

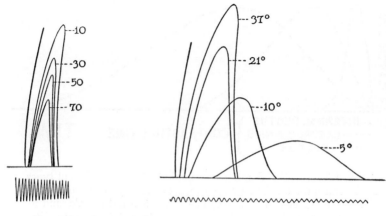

FIG. 121. (*Left*) Effect of load on simple muscle twitch. The figures indicate the load in grams. The tuning fork is vibrating at the rate of 100/sec.

FIG. 122. (*Right*) Effect of altering the temperature on simple muscle twitch. Temperature expressed in degrees Centigrade. The tuning fork is vibrating at the rate of 100/sec.

ulus and the beginning of the contraction is called the *latent period*. The time during which the muscle is shortening is called the *contraction period* and that during which the muscle is lengthening is called the *relaxation period*. The duration of each of these periods varies with the muscle studied. The comparative times in an extrinsic muscle of the eye, the soleus and the gastrocnemius are shown in Figure 120. You will note that the eye muscle is the most rapid, and the soleus the slowest, in accordance with the functions which each performs in the intact body.

Many extrinsic factors can alter the form of the simple twitch; some of these will be mentioned.

The weight that the muscle lifts alters the form of the twitch. As the load is increased the latent period becomes longer, the height of contraction lower, and the relaxation faster. These changes are illustrated in Figure 121.

The temperature of the fluid that bathes the muscle influences the form of the twitch. As the muscle is warmed the latent period becomes shorter, the height of contraction greater, and the relaxation more rapid. Cooling the muscle has the opposite effect. The form of the curve at different temperatures is shown in Figure 122.

If you continue to stimulate a frog's muscle after removing it from the body, you will fatigue it. It is not being supplied with oxygen and food, and its waste products are not being removed.

As fatigue progresses, the latent period becomes longer, the height of contraction less, and relaxation slower. You can tell by the shape of the curve if a muscle is fresh or fatigued (Fig. 123). As fatigue begins, the first apparent change is a failure to relax completely; later the other changes appear. In fact, human beings find it difficult to relax if they permit themselves to become "too tired."

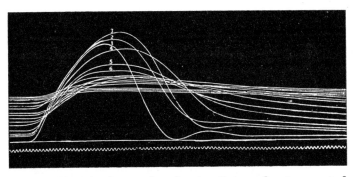

Fig. 123. Muscle twitches showing fatigue due to repeated stimulation. The first six contractions are numbered. (Evans, C. L.: Starling's Principles of Human Physiology, London, Churchill)

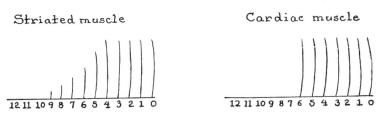

Fig. 124. All or none law in skeletal or striated and cardiac muscles. In skeletal, with increasing strength of stimulus, the contractions are higher and higher, due to more motor units being brought into action, until finally all the units are active. In cardiac muscle, every contraction is maximal, regardless of the strength of the stimulus, due to the branching and interlacing of fibers. The figures indicate the distance between the secondary and primary coils of the inductorium; the smaller the distance, the stronger the current.

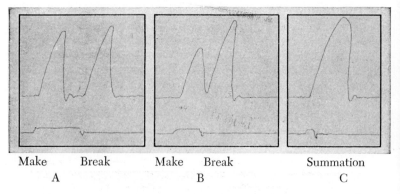

Make   Break   Make   Break   Summation
    A   B   C

FIG. 125. Summation of skeletal muscle contractions. (*Left*)
Stimuli far apart; two single twitches. (*Center*) Stimuli closer together; beginning summation. (*Right*) Stimuli very close together;
complete summation.

The strength of the stimulus can alter the height of contraction.
With the weakest effective or minimal stimulus, the contraction is
small. As the strength of the stimulus is increased, the height of
contraction becomes greater and greater until the maximal response
is obtained. This change in the height of contraction of skeletal
muscle with increasing strength of stimulation is due to the fact
that more and more motor units are brought into action as the
stimulus is increased. It must be kept in mind that this is true
only for skeletal muscle. If the same experiment is carried out
on an isolated quiescent ventricle (one that is no longer beating
spontaneously), it will be noted that the height of contraction is
the same whether minimal or maximal stimuli are used. Since
cardiac muscle fibers branch, and there are no motor units as in
skeletal muscle, the entire muscle mass behaves as a unit. The
responses of skeletal and cardiac muscle obtained by increasing
strengths of stimuli, on a stationary surface, are shown in Figure
124.

In the intact body we can execute contractions of different
strengths by using varying numbers of motor units. In other words,
we can grade our muscle contractions; we use few units in weak
contractions and more units in strong contractions.

We shall now leave the simple twitch and consider the results
that follow the application of two stimuli in quick succession. If
the second stimulus follows the first too quickly, the muscle will
not respond to the second one. We know from this fact that there

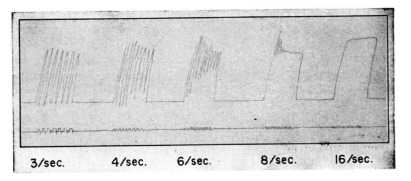

3/sec.   4/sec.   6/sec.   8/sec.   16/sec.

Fig. 126. Tetanic contractions of skeletal muscles. Break shocks only; make shocks subminimal. (*Left* to *right*) Shocks at the rate of 3 per second produce individual twitches. There are incomplete tetanic contractions when shocks come at the rate of 4, 6 and 8 per second. Complete tetanic contraction results when shocks occur at the rate of 16 per second.

is a short refractory period following stimulation of skeletal muscle, during which it will not respond to a second stimulus, no matter how strong that stimulus is.

If a little more time is allowed to elapse between the first and the second stimulus (that is, if time for recovery of excitability is allowed, or if we wait until the refractory period is over), the muscle responds to both the first and the second stimulus, and the second response is added to the first, producing a higher contraction called a *summation* (Fig. 125).

If more than two stimuli are sent into the muscle, it fails to relax completely between contractions, and the response is called an *incomplete tetanic contraction*. If the stimuli are sent in sufficiently rapidly, there is no indication of relaxation, and the response is called a *complete tetanic contraction*. Incomplete and complete tetanic contractions are illustrated in Figure 126.

The rate at which stimuli need to be applied to produce complete contractions varies in different muscles. In the soleus muscle of a mammal, complete tetanic contractions are produced when the rate of stimulation is about 30 per second; in the extrinsic eye muscles about 350 stimuli per second are required to produce complete tetanic contractions.

NATURE OF VOLUNTARY CONTRACTIONS

It has been determined by recording electrical changes in **human** skeletal muscles during activity that contractions are tetanic in nature, and no simple twitches occur. This means that voluntary contractions are short, sustained contractions, with no sign of relaxation until the contraction is over. The rate of stimulation, as measured by action currents in a single motor nerve fiber, increases from 5 to 50 per second as voluntary contractions progress from weak to strong. Therefore, a second means of grading our voluntary contractions is by varying the rate of discharge of impulses in motor units.

This means of gradation, together with gradation due to using varying numbers of active motor units, offers unlimited possibilities for altering the strength of our voluntary contractions. During both reflex and voluntary contractions, the rate of discharge varies in different motor units—one may discharge at 8 per second, a second at 10, a third at 12, and so on, up to 50 per second. This results in *asynchronism*, the net result of which is a smooth contraction. If all of the motor units in use contracted and relaxed at the same rate, the result would be a series of jerks, instead of a smooth contraction. In pathologic cases this condition does exist and is called *clonus*.

When impulses reach a muscle, they must cross the neuromuscular junction and then reach the muscle fibers. Two processes are involved. The first process consists of a spreading or conduction of an electrical change over the entire surface of the particular muscle fiber affected by the impulse. The second process consists of a molecular change which constitutes contraction or shortening of the fiber. We do not know yet just what happens when an impulse in a nerve fiber reaches a muscle fiber and causes the latter to contract. Perhaps a chemical substance (acetylcholine) is released as the impulse reaches the junction. Another possibility is that the electrical change that accompanies activity in the nerve fiber (p. 253) stimulates the junction and sets up an electrical change over the surface of the muscle fiber, and this, in turn, produces the contraction of the fiber. The first idea is called the "chemical or humoral" theory of transmission, and the second is the "electrical" theory.

According to the chemical theory, acetylcholine is produced to "ferry" the impulse across the gap in (1) autonomic ganglia (p. 270), (2) between postganglionic craniosacral fibers and effectors (p. 275), (3) between postganglionic thoracolumbar fibers (p. 274) and sweat glands and (4) between somatic nerve fibers and skeletal muscles fibers (at neuromuscular junctions). A second chemical substance or mediator called "sympathin" is thought to assist in

FIG. 127. The arrangement of two nerve-muscle preparations for demonstration of action current is shown.

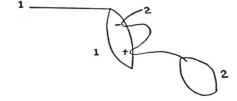

ferrying impulses across the gap between postganglionic thoracolumbar fibers (p. 274) and the effectors which they supply (except sweat glands).

ELECTRICAL CHANGES

The electrical changes that accompany activity in any tissue are so fundamental that they must be discussed. These changes accompany muscular contraction, the conduction of impulses in nerves, the secretion of juices by glands and all other types of activity in the body. Electrical changes are recorded and studied daily in hospitals. Some examples will be given.

The changes in heart muscle are recorded most frequently. Every heart beat is accompanied by electrical changes; these "action currents of the heart" are recorded as electrocardiograms. Physicians can learn a great amount about the heart's activity from such records. The electrocardiograms indicate whether or not the heart is receiving sufficient oxygen, if the beats are beginning in the normal place (p. 489), if the blood bathing the heart contains sufficient potassium, and so on.

The knowledge of the electrical changes that accompany activity in skeletal muscles is used in the study of muscle damage and recovery after poliomyelitis and after peripheral nerve injury.

The electrical changes that characterize activity in the brain are recorded and are of special interest in such conditions as epilepsy (p. 325).

The same principles are involved in all of the above examples. You can study the elementary principles in an isolated frog muscle. When a muscle fiber contracts it becomes a microscopic battery. If the ends of the fiber are connected by a wire it can be shown that each time the fiber contracts, a current flows through it. This current is called an action current or electric potential. It is like the current between the poles of any battery. The instrument used most often to demonstrate action currents is a galvanometer of some kind.

However, you do not need a galvanometer to demonstrate action currents. If you make 2 frog nerve-muscle preparations and arrange them as indicated in Figure 127, you can see the effects of the action current. Each time the nerve of the first preparation is stimulated, its muscle contracts and momentarily becomes a battery. The action current which it generates is sufficient to stimulate the nerve of the second preparation, and the second muscle contracts. No matter how complicated an instrument is used, the fundamental principles are the same as those you can show so easily by 2 nerve-muscle preparations.

COMPOSITION OF MUSCLE

Muscle contains about 75 per cent water, 20 per cent protein, and the remaining 5 per cent is made up of carbohydrates, lipids, inorganic salts and extractives. The composition differs widely in different species and in different muscles in the same animal. The carbohydrate in muscle is glycogen; it forms from 0.5 to 1.0 per cent of the muscle. Phosphocreatine and adenosine triphosphate (abbreviated as ATP) are present in small amounts but are exceedingly important.

Chemical Changes During Muscular Contraction. These changes are very complicated and are not fully understood, but a summary of what is known follows. The kinetic energy (that used to perform work) and heat that are released by muscular contraction come from the potential chemical energy of food substances which are brought to the muscles by the blood stream. Consequently, muscles require a good blood supply so that they may be furnished with a constant supply of fuel and oxygen, and that the heat may be dissipated and the waste removed. Adenosine triphosphate (ATP) possesses ready energy and is used to set off changes in the molecules of protein which result in the folding up of the chains or in the shortening of the myofibrils. The ready energy of ATP is replaced at once by the splitting of phosphocreatine. Then glycogen is broken down to furnish energy to rebuild phosphocreatine. In the process of the breakdown of glycogen, pyruvic acid is produced.

Adenosine triphosphate may be likened to money in your pocket; it is available for spending at any time. But as soon as you spend your pocket money it is wise to replace it with money from the bank, which may be likened to phosphocreatine. Funds in the bank are exhaustible, so we must work to earn money to replace that taken from the bank. Glycogen in the muscle is likened to our ability to work and earn money, according to one author.

To return to the chemical changes in muscle during activity, the course of events from pyruvic acid on depends on whether or not oxygen is available in sufficient quantities for the work being done at the time. If you are exercising at a moderate rate, some pyruvic acid is burned to carbon dioxide and water, and this supplies enough energy to restore the remainder of pyruvic acid back to glycogen.

If you perform a short spurt of severe exercise, and if not enough oxygen can be breathed in at the moment that it is required, pyruvic acid is changed to lactic acid which accumulates. The accumulation of lactic acid really is the same as running up an oxygen debt. When you sleep late and make a dash up the steps to get to class before the lecture begins, you run into debt for oxygen. But nature has decreed that you must pay back that oxygen debt before you can take notes on the lecture, so you will be "out of breath" until that debt is paid in full. What is happening in chemical terms is that you are changing some lactic acid back to pyruvic and oxidizing it to furnish energy to rebuild the remainder of lactic acid into glycogen. The food you eat supplies building stones for glycogen, adenosine triphosphate and phosphocreatine. Oxygen is essential in the use of these materials for muscular contraction.

Heat Production in Muscle. Most of the energy liberated during muscle contraction appears as heat. However, only a small part can be converted to work. If muscles are compared with steam engines, their efficiency, like that of engines, is between 20 and 30 per cent. This means that only this percentage of the energy that muscles expend can be used to perform mechanical work, and all the rest goes to maintain body temperature.

Heat is produced in two phases during muscular contraction— initial and delayed phases. Heat is produced in the initial phase by the breakdown of ATP and phosphocreatine, and it does not depend on the use of oxygen. Heat is produced in the delayed phase by the breakdown of glycogen and the restoration of part of it by burning pyruvic acid to supply the essential energy. The delayed or recovery heat depends on the presence of oxygen.

Muscular activity furnishes most of the heat produced in the body. Heat is produced also at night by the activity of muscles of respiration, contractions of heart muscle and the smooth muscle in the walls of blood vessels and the gastro-intestinal tract. If you

cannot put on more clothes when you are exposed to a low environmental temperature you are likely to move about to generate more
heat in your body. If you cannot do this, nature takes a hand in
your affairs and increases your heat production by making you
shiver.

Control of Skeletal Muscular Activity

Practically all parts of the nervous system enter into the control
of muscular activity. We wish to call this to your attention now,
even if the nervous system remains to be studied, since the movements that we all take so for granted are really under a most complex control. There are 8 requirements for normal movements of
skeletal muscles.

The first requirement for normal voluntary contraction of skeletal muscles is intact receptors in the muscles and the afferent fibers
to carry impulses from the muscles to the central nervous system.
These impulses from the muscles inform the brain of the degree
of contraction of active muscles. This information is essential in
accurately grading and timing the ensuing contractions. We must
know what our muscles are doing in order to control our movements.

The second requirement is a normal cerebral cortex (p. 309).
This is the region of the brain in which we "will" to move. If the
seat of highest motor control is damaged, our muscles are paralyzed and stiff (spastic).

The third requirement is normally functioning basal ganglia
(p. 307). This region of the brain controls the so-called associated
movements and gives steadiness to our muscular contractions. This
means that we show a great deal of facial expression when we talk,
we swing our arms when we walk, we cross our legs when we
sit down, and our movements are free from tremor (that is, the
hands do not tremble).

The fourth requirement is a normal cerebellum (p. 299). This
region of the brain permits us to gauge our voluntary movements
correctly. We pick up objects we reach for, and our movements
are direct, smooth and accurate.

The fifth requirement is a normal spinal cord (p. 287). Impulses that start in the cerebral cortex, the basal ganglia or the
cerebellum travel downward to the spinal cord and are relayed on
from there by other neurons. If there is something wrong with the
cells in the spinal cord, no impulses can be sent out to muscles.
In this case the muscles will be paralyzed and limp or flaccid.

The sixth requirement is intact efferent nerve fibers to carry

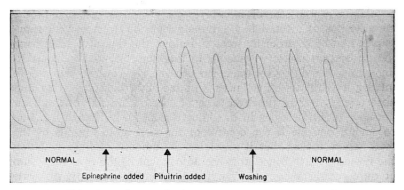

NORMAL   ↑   ↑   ↑   NORMAL

Epinephrine added   Pituitrin added   Washing

Fig. 128. Smooth muscle from a strip of rat uterus. Three normal, spontaneous contractions are shown at the left. When epinephrine was added, complete inhibition resulted. With the addition of pituitrin, the contractions began again with an increase in tonus. When this was washed out (*right*), the normal contractions began.

impulses from the cells in the central nervous system out to skeletal muscles. If peripheral nerve fibers are damaged, impulses cannot reach the muscles.

The seventh requirement is healthy skeletal muscles. If the muscles themselves are diseased the impulses that reach them have no effect, and voluntary and reflex contractions cannot occur.

The eighth and final requirement for normal voluntary movement is a psychic factor, known as *psychic elaboration.* There may be no organic disorder in the central nervous system, peripheral nerves or muscles, yet the individual may not be able to perform voluntary movements. This situation is due to a psychic disturbance or mental abnormality and is said to be "functional." This term is used to describe disorders for which no anatomic change is responsible.

Occasionally, you should stop long enough to meditate upon all the requirements for normal muscular contractions as you use your skeletal muscles for thousands of activities during the day. We are indeed "fearfully and wonderfully made."

SMOOTH MUSCLE

Functions

Because of the widespread distribution of smooth muscular tissue, it has many varied functions to perform. One of these is the regulation of the size of blood vessels, which is essential to the maintenance of arterial blood pressure (p. 500). A second function is that of transporting material along the digestive tract from the upper part of the esophagus to the anus. While food is passing along the digestive tract, smooth muscle contractions aid in mixing it with digestive juices and facilitate both digestion and absorption. A third function is regulation of the size of small air passages or bronchioles in the lungs (p. 537). A fourth function of smooth muscle is the control of the size of the pupils of the eyes, which means that it regulates the amount of light reaching the retina. A fifth function is the adjustment of the eyes for vision at different distances. A sixth function is the transport of urine from the kidneys through the ureters to the bladder, and from the bladder through the urethra to the exterior. A seventh function is assisting the movement of lymph through the large lymphatic vessels to its destination in the venous system (p. 469). An eighth function is the role it plays in both impregnation and parturition; thus smooth muscle is indispensable in reproduction.

PROPERTIES

Tonus in smooth muscle differs widely from that in skeletal muscle. In skeletal muscle the stretch reflex is responsible for tonus, which means that the central nervous system is essential for its maintenance. In smooth muscle, tonus is entirely independent of the nervous system. An isolated strip of smooth muscle shows widely fluctuating tonus waves, upon which are superimposed individual contractions. The tonus is influenced markedly by the presence of drugs in the fluid bathing the smooth muscle. Figure 128 illustrates the spontaneous contractions of a strip of rat uterine muscle and the effect of epinephrine and pituitrin on its tonus.

If you wish to record contractions of strips of smooth muscle, much greater care is needed than with gastrocnemius muscles of frogs. Smooth muscle is taken from warm-blooded animals; it is necessary to immerse it in warm salt solution, which has the same composition as the blood plasma of the animal, and to supply it with oxygen and glucose. When the smooth muscle strip is properly prepared and maintained, it undergoes spontaneous tonus changes which probably indicate that intact smooth muscle in the body undergoes fluctuations in its tonus constantly.

Excitability, or the ability to be affected by changes in the environment, is very evident in smooth muscle. It responds to a great variety of stimuli, such as stretch or distention, temperature changes and electric shocks. So far as temperature is concerned, the application of cold increases the activity of smooth muscles. In fact, an ice pack can have detrimental effects if it stimulates activity in the intestine when an inflamed and swollen appendix is at the point of bursting. The effect of heat varies with the speed of application. If smooth muscle is heated rapidly, it contracts, but if heated slowly, the muscle relaxes. Thus the response of smooth muscle to heat depends not only on the elevation of temperature but also on the rapidity with which the temperature is raised.

In addition to the stimuli listed above, smooth muscle is sensitive to changes in the composition of the blood or the tissue fluid that bathes it. Hormones, vitamins, drugs, salts, acids and alkalies affect the activity of smooth muscle, either inside the body or outside. Curare, in addition to its paralyzing effects on skeletal muscle, leads to a temporary loss of tone and activity in the intestinal tract, the blood vessels and the smooth muscle generally. It is evident from the above statements that smooth muscle is extremely sensitive to the chemical composition of its environment. The response to any particular substance may be rhythmic contraction, an increase in tonus or a decrease in tonus (relaxation). In fact, a given stimulus which produces contraction under some circumstances may produce relaxation under other circumstances, depending on the condition of the muscle itself and its environment.

Conductivity. Another property of some smooth muscles is conductivity. A wave of contraction spreads throughout a strip of muscle due to intercellular bridges (called fibrils) between the cells. The arrangement of cells in smooth muscles is variable; the cells may occur singly, in bundles or in sheets in different organs.

Contractility. All smooth muscles possess the property of contractility, but some are spontaneously rhythmic. The smooth muscle that forms the walls of the hollow viscera possesses the property of rhythmic contractility. It contracts spontaneously in the body and also after removal from the body, if properly prepared. The spontaneous rhythmic contractions of this type of smooth muscle are illustrated in Figure 128.

A second type of smooth muscle is found in the walls of blood vessels and in the intrinsic muscles of the eyeball. This type does not contract spontaneously either inside or outside the body, and the contraction wave that is produced by nerve impulses does not spread from one muscle cell to another. This means that there are no anatomic connections between adjacent fibers as in the visceral type. A single contraction of the second type of smooth muscle lasts from 10 to 15 times as long as a simple twitch of skeletal muscle.

Extensibility. The extensibility (ability to stretch when force is applied) of smooth muscle is truly remarkable. This property makes possible the increase in size of the urinary bladder as urine accumulates. If the bladder could not distend, there would be a constant dribbling of urine instead of a periodic emptying of the bladder. Figure 129 illustrates the bladder in an empty and in a markedly distended condition. Distention of such a degree as illustrated is serious and occurs only under abnormal circumstances. Normally, as the bladder is moderately distended the sense of fullness in the bladder merges into pain, and the bladder is emptied long before it is stretched to a dangerous extent. Abnormal distention occurs in an unconscious patient if the bladder is not emptied by catheterization at intervals (p. 675).

It was stated on page 27 that transitional epithelium is found in the urinary bladder and that the appearance of it varies with the state of emptiness or fullness of the bladder. Figure 130 illustrates the epithelial cells of the mucosa in an empty and in a full bladder.

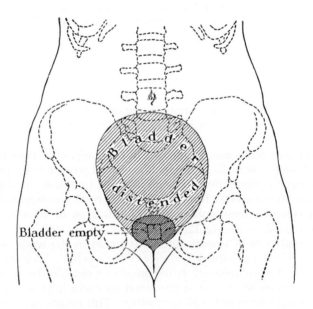

Fig. 129. Urinary bladder, empty and distended.

The extensibility of the smooth muscle of the stomach is well known to all of us. We can eat a fairly large quantity of food at one meal, and the stomach stretches to accommodate it, without an increase of pressure. The difference in size before and after a meal is illustrated in Figure 131. Smooth muscle, like skeletal muscle, contracts more forcibly when it is slightly stretched. Smooth muscle is elastic, which means that it returns to its original length after the stretching force has been removed.

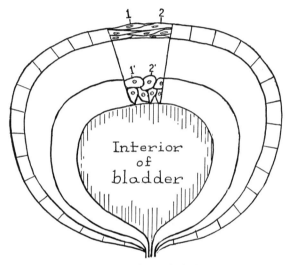

FIG. 130. Transitional epithelial cells in empty and distended bladder. The cells flatten out, as in 1 and 2, when the bladder is distended; they are spherical, as in 1′ and 2′, when the bladder is not distended.

FIG. 131. Stomach (*left*) before and (*right*) after a meal.

Control

There are wide differences in the degree of dependence of smooth muscle on its innervation: at one extreme is the uterine musculature over which the nerves exert no essential control; at the other extreme is the ciliary muscle of the eye (p. 360) whose finely graded and frequently altered degree of activity is wholly dependent on its nerve supply. In the visceral type of smooth muscle, the extrinsic nerves do not excite activity but merely increase or decrease the spontaneous activity that is already in progress and thus serve in a regulatory capacity.

The afferent nerves that transmit impulses from smooth muscle to the central nervous system are concerned with pain. If the intestine is distended with gas that cannot escape by the rectum, pain results, and, as many of you know, gas pains can be very severe. The pain disappears when the gas escapes, either spontaneously or after the insertion of a rectal tube. An overfilled bladder, also, can lead to pain in a conscious patient.

Menstruation may be accompanied by pain; *dysmenorrhea* is the term applied to painful menstruation. In some cases strong contractions of the uterine muscle occur, and these give rise to pain. In some patients the cause of the pain is due to other factors that are poorly understood at the present time.

Chemical Changes

The chemical changes that accompany activity in smooth muscle are of the same type as those that occur in skeletal muscle (p. 226).

PRACTICAL CONSIDERATIONS

Uses of Curare

Curare is used in conjunction with various types of anesthetics to produce muscular relaxation; this is important to the surgeon when he is ready to "close the abdomen." This is the time when the intestine must be kept within the abdominal cavity, and the abdominal walls sewed together in layers. It is difficult to pull the muscles, the fascia and the skin together unless the muscles are completely relaxed. If curare is not used, the anesthesia usually has to be "deepened" just at these critical last few minutes of an operation.

Another important use of curare is in electric and insulin "shock therapy," in which the brain is stimulated excessively, and generalized convulsions of the skeletal muscles occur unless they are kept from receiving impulses from the central nervous system.

Curare is invaluable in the treatment of convulsions that accompany tetanus (an infectious disease commonly know as *lockjaw*), rabies *(hydrophobia)* and strychnine poisoning.

Perhaps you have been wondering about the respiratory muscles as you read about curare. For some unknown reason, the muscles of the abdominal wall and the extremities respond to smaller doses of curare than do the muscles of respiration. However, if larger doses of curare are administered, the muscles of respiration will be paralyzed also, and in such cases artificial respiration must be given until the effects of curare wear off, in about 30 minutes. It should be a fixed requirement to be prepared to administer artificial respiration following a dose of curare given to any patient, in case there should be paralysis of the muscles of respiration.

PATHOLOGIC TYPES OF MUSCULAR CONTRACTIONS

A spasm is a sudden involuntary contraction of a skeletal muscle. If the contraction is persistent, it is called a tonic spasm or *cramp*. If the spasm is characterized by alternate contraction and relaxation, it is called a clonic spasm or *clonus*. In this condition the motor units involved discharge synchronously, instead of asynchronously, as under normal conditions. Spasms may occur in smooth muscle, also. In this case, the spasm is evident as a transitory constriction of a passage, a duct or an orifice, an example of this being the spasm during the passage of a gallstone or a kidney stone. Spasmodic contractions are accompanied by pain.

A contracture is a localized tetanic contraction in a part of a skeletal muscle. It is due to a direct stimulation of the contractile substance of the muscle and is not conducted to other parts of the muscle. The 3 most frequent sites of contracture are the pectoral, the gastrocnemius and the hamstring muscles.

Fasciculation is the contraction of some motor units whose nerve cells are undergoing pathologic changes; it resembles localized shivering in some respects and is evident in superficial muscles just under the skin.

Fibrillation. After injury to the nerve supply, the fibers of a skeletal muscle may show individual spontaneous contractions called fibrillation. This cannot be seen in the muscles under the skin, but if it happens to involve the tongue muscles it can be seen as a quivering of parts of the protruded tongue.

Electromyography

The study of action currents in skeletal muscles of man is of great clinical importance. The electrical responses give a measure of the functional impairment that results from a lesion in (1) the central nervous system, (2) peripheral nerve or (3) the neuromuscular junction.

Muscular Paralyses and Disturbances of Contraction

Skeletal muscles are unable to contract if their nerve supply is destroyed, which means that they receive no impulses from the central nervous system. Such muscles are said to be paralyzed. If the cerebral cortex is the site of injury the muscles show the spastic type of paralysis; that is, they are stiff. This type of paralysis in the young most commonly is due to birth injury. The application of forceps during delivery may damage the underlying motor cortex through the skull bones on both sides of the head. There are now many clinics and schools in which spastics are taught to gain some control of their muscles, and they may improve sufficiently to become self-supporting. There may be no impairment of intelligence. The training is long and hard, and these individuals are never as sure of their movements as are normal individuals.

There is a spastic type of paralysis in older individuals following a stroke or hemorrhage in the brain. It is limited to one side of the body and shows up as a stiffness in the upper and the lower extremities.

If there is damage to the basal ganglia the muscles are not paralyzed but are quite rigid, and there is a tremor of the hands when at rest. This is called a pill-rolling movement because of the peculiar rubbing of the thumb and the fingertips. Sometimes there is also a nodding of the head, which is another manifestation of the tremor. There is no change in facial expression, the arms do not swing when walking, the legs are not crossed when sitting down, the hands never are used when talking, and the entire body is bent forward. The condition which has been described is known as Parkinson's disease or paralysis agitans.

Two other types of disorder characterize lesions of the basal ganglia. One of these is chorea or St. Vitus' dance. The movements in this condition are quick and uncontrolled, and grimaces of the face occur constantly. The individual seems never to be still.

The third condition that characterizes lesions of the basal ganglia is called athetosis (meaning "not fixed") in which slow, squirming movements of the hands and the feet occur constantly.

Which of the 3 conditions occurs in any patient depends on the location of the lesion in the basal ganglia and other circumstances which are not understood at the present time. You will note that in spite of the fact that the center which controls voluntary movements is intact, the individual is subject to a variety of movements over which he has no control and he becomes more or less incapacitated, although the mind still functions perfectly.

If there is a lesion in the part of the cerebellum concerned with control of voluntary movements, the movements are poorly measured (dysmetria). The individual cannot touch the tip of his nose or ear or perform other voluntary acts efficiently. When he attempts a voluntary movement the muscles tremble.

If the cells of the spinal cord are damaged, as is the case in poliomyelitis, impulses cannot be sent out to the muscles. The muscles are paralyzed but limp, instead of stiff as with damage to the cerebral cortex. Since the muscles cannot be used voluntarily they undergo atrophy (wasting or decrease in size) unless properly treated. Much of the training and the treatment of poliomyelitis patients is directed at the prevention of atrophy of the involved muscles. In most of the involved muscles only a portion of the motor units is affected, and with training the surviving units can be made to contract at will. Sometimes a nerve supply to a group of muscles is divided; some nerve fibers from a good muscle are transplanted into a paralyzed muscle and, by training, the patient can learn to use the affected muscle correctly. Sister Kenny contributed valuable suggestions for the early treatment of poliomyelitis.

The incoming impulses from the muscles are lacking in tabes dorsalis (syphilis of the spinal cord), and as a result the movements are poorly controlled or ataxic. The patient does not really know what his muscles are doing; he uses his eyes to give information about the muscles of the lower extremities. Consequently, he cannot walk in the dark, since his eyes cannot help him. He cannot stand upright with his eyes closed; if he attempts to do so he will fall.

MUSCULAR DISORDERS

Progressive Muscular Atrophy. Skeletal muscles may undergo atrophy from unknown causes. This type of atrophy begins first in the lower extremities and then progresses to other muscles. Eventually, it becomes disabling.

Myasthenia Gravis. This condition is characterized by weakness and fatigability of skeletal muscles. It begins first in the muscles innervated by the cranial nerves and then spreads to other muscles, eventually incapacitating the patient. The difficulty seems to be at the neuromuscular junction. Electrical studies indicate that the impulses leave the central nervous system in a normal manner but are blocked at the neuromuscular junction. It is somewhat like the situation that occurs after the injection of curare. Administration of Prostigmin Bromide restores muscular activity to normal for a time by allowing acetylcholine to act for a longer time. The muscular weakness that characterizes myasthenia gravis is relieved by rest but returns on effort. It may occur at any age. The extraocular muscles and the muscles of the eyelids are involved first; there are ptosis (drooping of the upper lid) and diplopia (double vision, due to lack of control of the extrinsic muscles). Respiratory infections are particularly bad in these patients, since they cannot cough because of the weakness of their muscles.

Paralysis of Smooth Muscle. Paralysis of the smooth muscle of the small intestine may occur, especially after abdominal operations. It is not due to difficulty with the nerve supply. Some investigators think that it may be due to too low a concentration of potassium salts in the blood. The condition is called *paralytic ileus.* The inactive portion of bowel acts as an actual obstruction, and the condition may prove to be fatal.

TREATMENT OF PARALYZED SKELETAL MUSCLES. Atrophy will occur in paralyzed muscles if they are untreated. Atrophy will occur, likewise, in muscles rendered immobile by splints or casts, or if their tendons are cut. When muscles cannot be contracted voluntarily, they should be massaged, exercised by passive movements or stimulated to contract by electrical methods. This is a part of the field called physical medicine or physiotherapy, which is a relatively new science. Remarkable progress has been made, especially in the treatment of poliomyelitis and the spastic paralyses following birth injuries.

SUMMARY

1. Skeletal muscles
   A. Tonus
   B. Response to stimulation; relaxation and curare

    C. Molecular changes during contraction
    D. Gross changes during contraction
       a. Simple twitch; alterations of form due to load, temperature, fatigue and strength of stimulation
       b. Summation
       c. Tetanic contractions
    E. Nature of voluntary contraction; neuromuscular junction
    F. Electrical changes
    G. Composition of muscle
       a. Chemical changes during muscular contraction
       b. Heat production in muscle
    H. Control of skeletal muscular activity
       a. Receptors in muscle and afferent fibers to transmit information to central nervous system from muscles
       b. Cerebral cortex; voluntary control
       c. Basal ganglia; associated movements
       d. Cerebellum; direction, measure and co-ordination of muscle groups
       e. Spinal cord; relay station for impulses from cortex
       f. Peripheral nerve fibers; efferent fibers to transmit impulses from central nervous system to skeletal muscles
       g. Intact muscles
       h. Psychic elaboration

  2. Smooth muscle
    A. Functions
    B. Properties
       a. Tonus
       b. Excitability
       c. Conductivity
       d. Contractility
       e. Extensibility
    C. Control
       a. Efferent; regulatory
       b. Afferent; pain
    D. Chemical changes

  3. Practical considerations

SITUATION AND QUESTIONS

After a strenuous game on the football field, Bob Crole was happy to get back to the dressing room for his usual shower and massage.

Massage is beneficial after such strenuous exercise because it relieves the sensations of fatigue and cramps which are caused by: _____(a) accumulation of carbon dioxide within the muscles; _____(b) accumulation of lactic acid within the muscles; _____(c) increased blood supply to the muscles; _____ (d) increase in the amount of heat produced in muscles.

The first sign of fatigue as it affects muscular contraction is: _____(a) shorter latent period; _____(b) the height of contraction is increased; _____(c) muscular spasm; _____ (d) prolonged period of relaxation.

Athletes, because of their exercise and training, have good muscle tone. Tonus may be defined as: _____(a) a quick muscular contraction; _____(b) a sustained muscular contraction; _____(c) a state of continued partial contraction; _____ (d) the ability to return to its original size and shape after being stretched.

Our player is considered an outstanding athlete because of his excellent control and co-ordination of muscles. This control is integrated at the level of: _____(a) the cerebral cortex; _____ (b) the basal ganglia; _____(c) cerebellum; _____(d) spinal cord.

UNIT 3

INTEGRATION AND CONTROL OF THE BODY BY THE NERVOUS SYSTEM

6. Anatomy and Physiology of the Peripheral Nervous System

INTRODUCTION

The following sequence of events illustrates the functions of the nervous system. A friend gives you a piece of candy, and as you chew it you suddenly become aware of a very severe toothache. This is the fourth time that you have noted a toothache upon eating something sweet. You realize that there must be a cavity in a tooth, and that you must not ignore it any longer. You telephone a nearby dentist, and he says that if you can be in his office within the next half hour he can take care of the tooth. As you start to walk to his office, worrying about the expense of filling the tooth, and the possibility of losing it, you step off the curb to cross the street, without your usual vigilance.

There is an immediate screech of brakes, and you are back on the sidewalk in a flash, trembling, your knees shaking, and your heart pounding "like a trip-hammer." You feel so weak that you cannot stand up, so you sit down on a step until you get "hold of yourself." A few minutes elapse before you remember that you were on your way to the dentist's office, and a few more minutes pass before you feel that you can continue on your way.

In terms of functions of the nervous system, the sweet saliva penetrated a crack in the enamel of a tooth and reached the nerve endings. This constituted a change in the environment of the nerve endings (receptors), and, since they were excitable (capable of being affected by a change in the environment or a stimulus), they sent messages (nerve impulses) to the brain over afferent nerve fibers. This means that the first function of the nervous system is the arousal of impulses in afferent nerves due to stimulation of their sensitive endings or receptors.

When the impulses reached the brain they produced a sensation of pain. The recognition of pain, together with the memory of the three previous similar experiences, and your knowledge of the consequences of neglected cavities, lead to the decision to attend to the situation without further delay. This illustrates the second function of the nervous system, the interpretation of incoming impulses and making decisions about them on the basis of memory. The brain also "sorts out" incoming impulses; unimportant ones are ignored; and important ones are given attention; and the type of adjustment to the stimulus is decided upon.

You decided to "do something" about that tooth, so you telephoned the dentist and started on your way. You were so "wrapped in thought" about the consequences of the toothache that you were heedless of what you were doing. The screech of brakes was a startling change in the external environment, and the impulses flashed to your brain, your brain made its decision and flashed impulses back to your muscles, and you were back on the sidewalk before you were really aware of what had happened. The third function of the nervous system is illustrated by 2 examples: (1) you telephoned the dentist and started on your way and (2) you returned to the sidewalk in a hurry. In other words, once the brain has made its decision, impulses are sent over efferent nerve fibers to "effectors" which carry out the orders of the brain. The effectors of the body are skeletal muscles, smooth muscle, cardiac muscle and glands. The third function of the nervous system is to notify the effectors of the responses which they are to make to any stimulus. Your responses to the toothache consisted of telephoning the dentist and walking toward his office, which involved chiefly the skeletal muscles. Your responses to the screech of brakes consisted of getting back on the sidewalk, which involved skeletal muscles but also other effectors, as evidenced by the trembling and pounding heart.

The final scene in the drama of response to a stimulus consists of the transmission of impulses from the active effectors back to the brain, informing it that the assignment is being carried out. You know that your skeletal muscles are contracting and that your heart is pounding. And while you continue to tremble, as you sit on the step to recover, this experience is stored in your memory in a vivid manner and it will be a long time before you again step off the curb without giving it some thought.

GENERAL PLAN OF THE NERVOUS SYSTEM

The nervous system is the most highly organized system of the body, since it is responsible for all the complicated processes that make up one's adjustment to one's external and internal environment. It accomplishes its function by means of conduction pathways or nerve fibers and centers, which have been compared with the wires and the switchboards of the telephone system. The nervous system consists of 2 main divisions—a peripheral and a central.

The peripheral nervous system is composed of nerves that carry messages to and from the central nervous system. The nerves that carry impulses to and from the brain are called *cranial* nerves; those that carry impulses to and from the spinal cord are called *spinal* nerves. With respect to function, peripheral nerves are divided into 4 types: somatic afferent, somatic efferent, visceral afferent and visceral efferent.

SOMATIC AFFERENT nerves carry impulses from the skin, the skeletal muscles, tendons and joints to the central nervous system.

SOMATIC EFFERENT nerves carry impulses from the central nervous system to the skeletal muscles.

VISCERAL AFFERENT fibers carry impulses from the viscera to the central nervous system.

VISCERAL EFFERENT fibers (which are called the "autonomic division," also) carry impulses from the central nervous system to smooth muscle, cardiac muscle and glands.

The central nervous system consists of the brain and the spinal cord; each is made up of nerve cells and their processes or nerve fibers. The brain, which lies inside the cranial cavity, may be sub-divided into three parts.

THE FOREBRAIN is the largest part and fills most of the cranial cavity. Extending caudally from the forebrain is the midbrain. The fore-brain and the midbrain comprise the cerebrum. Beyond this is the hindbrain, which comprises the cerebellum, the pons and the medulla.

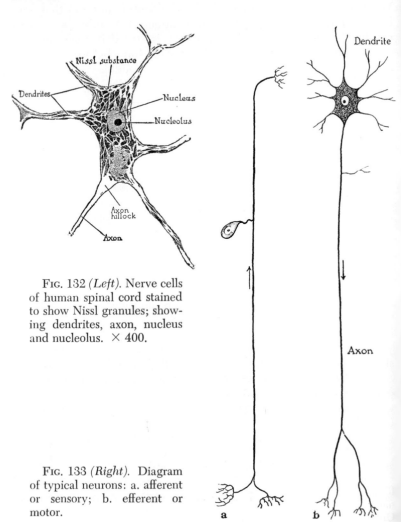

FIG. 132 (Left). Nerve cells of human spinal cord stained to show Nissl granules; show-ing dendrites, axon, nucleus and nucleolus. × 400.

FIG. 133 (Right). Diagram of typical neurons: a. afferent or sensory; b. efferent or motor.

THE SPINAL CORD lies in the vertebral canal. It connects with the medulla above, and it terminates below at the level of the disk between the first and the second lumbar vertebrae.

The accompanying chart indicates the general plan of the nervous system:

1. Peripheral nervous system: somatic afferent, somatic efferent, visceral afferent, visceral efferent (autonomic) components

    A. Cranial nerves

    B. Spinal nerves

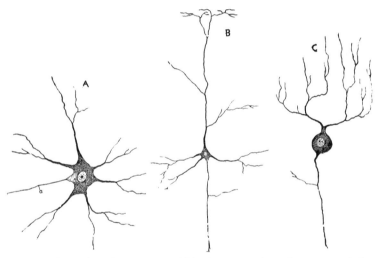

FIG. 134. Multipolar neurons. (A) From spinal cord, a. axon. (B) From cerebral cortex. (C) From cerebellar cortex.

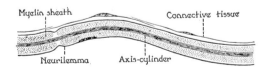

FIG. 135. Nerve fibers. *(Top)* Myelinated fiber. *(Bottom)* Unmyelinated fibers.

2. Central nervous system:
   A. Brain: forebrain, midbrain and hindbrain
   B. Spinal cord

PERIPHERAL NERVOUS SYSTEM

Microscopic Structure

The nervous system is made up of nervous tissue; this consists of nerve cells and supporting tissue called *neuroglia,* which has the same function as connective tissue in other organs.

Nerve cells are called *neurons.* Each neuron consists of a nucleus and cytoplasm. The cytoplasm of neurons differs from that of other cells in that it is prolonged into processes which extend long or short distances (from more than a meter to a fraction of a milli-meter) from the cell body. The part of the neuron that contains the nucleus is called the *cell body.*

The cell body of a neuron contains a large spherical nucleus, a small nucleolus and cytoplasm. The cytoplasm contains charac-teristic granules which are called *Nissl granules* after the investi-gator who first described them (Fig. 132). Nissl granules are thought to be concerned with nutrition of neurons, since they dis-appear when nerve cells are exhausted. Fine fibrils which are

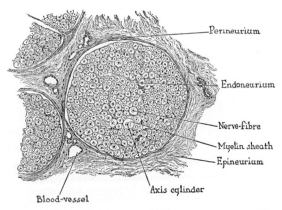

FIG. 136. Transverse section of nerve bundle, composed of nerve fibers, held together and sur-rounded by connective tissue fibers which constitute the endoneurium and perineurium, respectively. × 175.

called *neurofibrils* are present in the cytoplasm of the cell body and in the processes. These are organelles (p. 20).

The processes that extend from nerve cell bodies are called *dendrites* and *axons*. Dendrites (meaning "treelike") are the fibers that carry impulses to the cell body; axons carry impulses away from the cell body. Dendrites vary greatly in different neurons; some are long and branch only at the end, as illustrated in Figure 133 a. Other dendrites are short and branch freely (Figs. 133 b and 134). Each neuron has only one axon, and the branches are less numerous than in dendrites. When impulses pass from one neuron to another they come from the axon of the first neuron to the dendrite of the second neuron.

The conducting core or center of axons and dendrites is called the *axis cylinder*. Neurofibrils from the cell body continue through the axis cylinder and constitute the actual conducting mechanism. Axis cylinders of peripheral nerves are covered with a membrane called the *neurilemma,* which is a delicate structure containing many nuclei. The processes of neurons that lie entirely within the central nervous system have no typical neurilemma covering them. Many axis cylinders are enclosed in sheaths of myelin (meaning "marrow"), which probably acts as an insulator to prevent the spread of action currents to adjacent fibers. Those axis cylinders that are supplied with myelin sheaths are called *myelinated;* those lacking a myelin sheath are called *unmyelinated* fibers (Fig. 135).

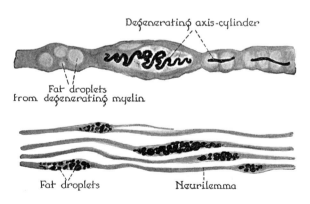

FIG. 137. Degeneration of nerve fibers. The lower illustration shows a more advanced stage than the upper. Osmic acid was used. With this method the nuclei of the neurilemma do not show.

Components of Nerves

Peripheral nerves, such as the sciatic, are composed of an infinite number of nerve fibers. Individual nerve fibers (axons and dendrites of various neurons) are bound to one another by delicate connective tissue called *endoneurium*. Nerve fibers are grouped into bundles, which are surrounded by connective tissue called *perineurium*. A "nerve" is made up of a large number of bundles of nerve fibers which are held together, and the entire structure is bound together by *epineurium,* as illustrated in Figure 136.

If nerve fibers are injured or separated from their cell bodies, they die, as does cytoplasm of any other cell when separated from its nucleus. The death of a nerve fiber is called "degeneration." In myelinated fibers, the myelin sheath and the axis cylinder break up into fragments (Fig. 137). Sometime later on, repair or regeneration begins. The first sign of this is an increase in the nuclei of the neurilemma. The old neurilemma seems to guide and protect the growing neurofibrils which now begin to grow out from

Fat droplets from degenerated myelin

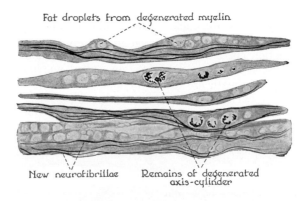

New neurofibrillae   Remains of degenerated
                                        axis-cylinder

Spiral arrangement of new neurofibrillae

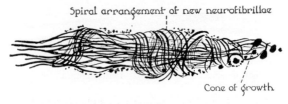

Cone of growth

FIG. 138. Regeneration of nerve fibers. *(Top)* Low power. *(Bottom)* Detail seen under high power. New neurofibrillae are shown.

the central end of the dead fiber (Fig. 138). Regeneration is a slow process, and it takes months or perhaps years to grow a new nerve fiber and establish former connections and functions. Within the central nervous system, where there is no typical neurilemma, there is no regeneration of axis cylinders after injury or separation from their cell bodies.

CLASSIFICATION OF NEURONS

Neurons may be classified on the basis of structure or on the basis of function.

On the basis of **structure,** neurons are bipolar (in which there is a single dendrite and a single axon) or multipolar (in which there are several dendrites and one axon). Bipolar neurons are illustrated in Figures 133 a and 139; multipolar neurons are illustrated in Figures 133 b and 134.

On the basis of **function** there are 3 classes of neurons: afferent, efferent and internuncial.

AFFERENT (or sensory) neurons are characterized by having the distal end of the dendrite specialized to receive stimuli (Fig. 133 a). These neurons transmit impulses to the central nervous system.

EFFERENT neurons transmit impulses from the central nervous system to some organ (effector). The impulses to effectors may lead to different types of activity, such as movement, secretion, speeding and strengthening (augmentation) of activity or slowing up and weakening of activity (inhibition), according to the organ which they reach and the effect that they exert on the activity of that organ. *Motor* neurons carry impulses that lead to contraction of skel-

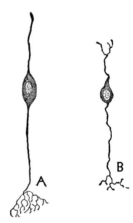

FIG. 139. Bipolar neurons: A. from olfactory mucous membrane; B. from retina.

etal muscles. *Secretory* neurons transmit impulses that lead to secretion by glands. *Augmentative* and *inhibitory* neurons supply smooth muscle and cardiac muscle with impulses that alter the activity as indicated by the names. An efferent neuron of the motor type is shown in Figure 133 b.

INTERNUNCIAL (meaning "messenger between") neurons transmit impulses from one part of the brain or the spinal cord to another. Consequently, their processes do not leave the central nervous system.

The entire nervous system is composed of chains of neurons, but there is no anatomic continuity between them. This means that neurofibrillae do not extend from one neuron into the next. Each neuron is a separate unit but it is in contact with other neurons. The points of contact are called *synapses* (meaning "clasp" or "touch together"). Since impulses are transmitted to cell bodies over dendrites and away from cell bodies over axons, a synapse is necessarily an area of contact between the axon of one neuron and the dendrite of the next; the impulse can pass only from axon to dendrite across a synapse.

CHARACTERISTICS OF NERVOUS TISSUE

The two oustanding characteristics of nervous tissue are excitability and conductivity.

Excitability refers to the sensitivity of living beings to changes in their environment; the ability to be affected by such changes constitutes excitability. This property is highly developed in afferent nerve endings or receptors. If these lose their excitability life soon ends, as the body is unaware of harmful surroundings. Consequently, excitability is one's most valuable asset so far as preservation of life is concerned.

Conductivity is the property of nerve fibers by which the brain is informed of changes in the environment and by which it can assign duties to various effectors.

No change is visible in a nerve fiber as it conducts an impulse, but, by many types of investigation, certain facts are known about conduction.

1. The impulse is self-propagating. This means that each section of nerve fiber is affected in such a way, as it conducts an impulse, that it acts as a stimulus for the next section and also furnishes the energy to transmit the impulse along.

2. The impulse travels at a definite speed which depends on the

size of the nerve fiber over which it passes. Larger fibers conduct faster than smaller ones. In man the impulses travel a fraction of a millimeter in the smallest nerve fibers and 120 meters per second in the largest nerve fibers. This is a slower rate than that at which sound waves travel, but even in a man who is 6 feet tall, the impulses could travel in large afferent nerve fibers from toes to brain and back to the toes over large efferent fibers in less than one twentieth of a second.

3. Chemical changes occur in nerve fibers while they are conducting impulses. There is a larger use of oxygen and greater production of carbon dioxide than when they are not conducting. Glucose is used during conduction, and some ammonia is produced. However, explanations of chemical changes that accompany activity in nerve fibers are not nearly as well worked out as for skeletal muscle. For normal activity, the brain is as dependent on glucose as on oxygen, but the details of oxidation remain to be solved.

4. Thermal changes accompany conduction of impulses in nerves. The amount of heat produced is very small; it is less than one ten-thousandth of that produced in an equal weight of muscle by one contraction. Another way of stating this fact is that you never will become overheated from thinking, as you might from vigorous exercise.

5. Electrical changes accompany the passage of nerve impulses. If each tiny section of nerve fiber may be considered as a battery, there is an infinite number of batteries discharging as an impulse passes along a nerve fiber. We do not know all that happens, but we do know that there is a leakage of potassium ions from the inside to the outside of the axis cylinder and a movement of sodium ions in the opposite direction during conduction of impulses.

The study of the electrical changes that accompany the transmission of impulses in nervous tissue is a valuable method of investigation. Records of action currents or action potentials in nerve fibers are made frequently. Records of the so-called "brain waves" are really records of electrical changes in the brain. Such records are called *electro-encephalograms.* They are of great diagnostic importance in the study of brain disorders.

From the study of thousands of electrical changes accompanying the conduction of nerve impulses, it has been concluded that all impulses are alike in afferent and efferent nerve fibers. The reason we have a sensation of pain from an impulse in one fiber and a contraction of a muscle in another is because of the location of the ending of the two fibers. It is possible to have sensations of pain

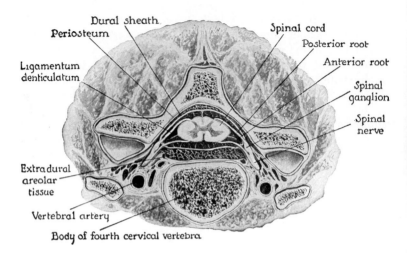

FIG. 140. Cross section of vertebral column at the level of the the fourth cervical vertebra, showing spinal cord in position. The H-shaped gray matter, surrounded by the white matter, is seen.

only in one particular area of the brain, and to have contraction only, in a muscle. Impulses may be compared with electric currents flowing through wires. In one case the current will produce heat and toast bread; in a second case it will ring a doorbell; in a third, it will run a motor. The electric current is the same in each wire; the difference is in the ending to which it is conducted.

6. After a nerve fiber conducts one impulse, a short interval of time must pass before it can conduct another. This period is called the *refractory period*. No stimulus, however strong, can force the nerve fiber to conduct a second impulse before it has recovered from the effects of the first.

Perhaps this time is essential for the potassium ions to re-enter the axis cylinder and the sodium ions to leave. In any case, each impulse is a separate or distinct event; there is no fusion of impulses and, therefore, there is nothing comparable with tetanic contractions in skeletal muscle. The recovery period is short but nonetheless essential.

A nerve fiber never seems to be "pushed to its limit," so far as conduction of impulses is concerned. If a weak constant stimulus is applied to a nerve fiber it may conduct 2 impulses per second; if a very strong constant stimulus is applied, the nerve may conduct

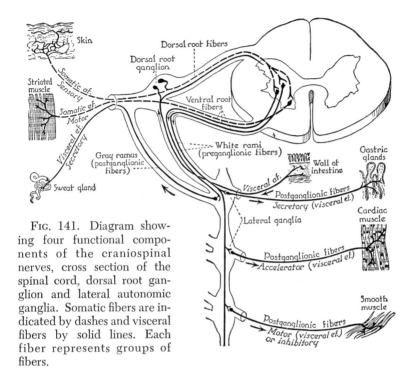

FIG. 141. Diagram showing four functional components of the craniospinal nerves, cross section of the spinal cord, dorsal root ganglion and lateral autonomic ganglia. Somatic fibers are indicated by dashes and visceral fibers by solid lines. Each fiber represents groups of fibers.

as many as 50 impulses per second. However, since the recovery period is very short, it is calculated that a nerve fiber could conduct between 1,000 and 2,000 impulses per second, but we seem unable to force it to carry the maximal number.

In some unknown manner the shift of potassium ions and sodium ions plays a part in setting up the electrical change in the active section of nerve fiber which serves as a stimulus for the next section. The change in permeability of the axis cylinder, which permits the movement of ions, and the electric change which ensues, progress along the nerve fiber at a definite speed, and the wave of recovery follows rapidly in the wake of the impulse. The above idea of the sequence of events is called the "membrane hypothesis" of nerve conduction.

DIVISIONS OF THE PERIPHERAL NERVOUS SYSTEM

Spinal Nerves. There are 31 pairs of spinal nerves: 8 pairs of cervical, 12 pairs of thoracic, 5 pairs of lumbar, 5 pairs of sacral and 1 pair of coccygeal nerves. Each spinal nerve arises as dorsal (sensory, afferent, posterior) and ventral (motor, efferent, anterior) roots from the spinal cord, as shown in Figures 140 and 141. There is a ganglion (collection of nerve cell bodies outside of the central nervous system) on each dorsal root; this is called a *dorsal root ganglion.* The dendrites of these neurons (whose cell bodies are in the dorsal root ganglia) are incoming afferent fibers, and their axons extend from the cell bodies into the spinal cord. The fibers that make up each anterior root are axons of nerve cell bodies located within the spinal cord.

Both the posterior and the anterior roots of one side of the spinal cord extend to the corresponding intervertebral foramen (Figs. 58, 59 and 60). Since the spinal cord ends in the upper lumbar region of the vertebral column, the lower lumbar, the sacral and the coccygeal nerve roots must descend further and further to reach their respective intervertebral foramina before they leave the dorsal cavity (vertebral canal). Each successive pair of roots is longer than the one before, and as the roots descend they form a fairly large bundle of nerve fibers which is called the *cauda equina* (meaning "tail of a horse"), as shown in Figure 142.

As an anterior and posterior root reach their intervertebral foramen they unite to form a spinal nerve, as shown in Figure 140. The spinal nerve then passes through the foramen, and as it emerges from the outer aspect of the foramen it immediately divides into 2 branches called *anterior* and *posterior rami.* These are not to be confused with *anterior* and *posterior roots.* When the roots join to form the spinal nerve there is a rearrangement of the component fibers, so that each ramus contains fibers from both the anterior and the posterior roots. The fibers that make up the posterior ramus supply all the structures of the skin, the fascia and the longitudinal muscles of the back. The fibers that make up the anterior ramus supply all the structures of the lateral and the anterior portions of the body and the limbs.

In the cervical, the lumbar, the sacral and the coccygeal regions of the spinal cord, the anterior rami (not anterior roots) combine to form networks of nerve fibers called *plexuses.*

CERVICAL PLEXUS. The anterior rami of the first 4 cervical spinal nerves combine to form the cervical plexus (Fig. 143). From this plexus there are cutaneous branches which supply all the structures of the head, the neck and the shoulders. Motor fibers from this plexus supply the trapezius and the sternocleidomastoid muscles. One of the most important motor branches of the cervical

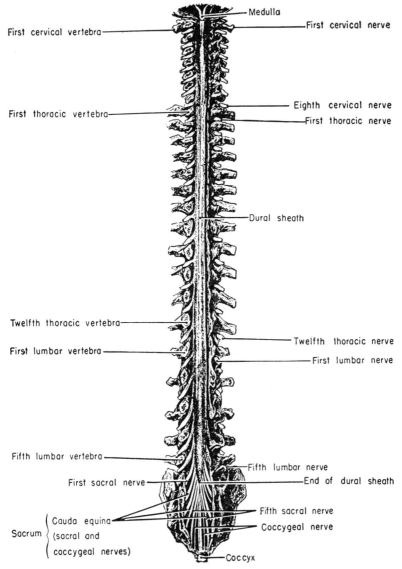

Medulla

First cervical vertebra

First cervical nerve

Eighth cervical nerve

First thoracic vertebra

First thoracic nerve

Dural sheath

Twelfth thoracic vertebra

First lumbar vertebra

Twelfth thoracic nerve

First lumbar nerve

Fifth lumbar vertebra

Fifth lumbar nerve

First sacral nerve

End of dural sheath

Fifth sacral nerve

Coccygeal nerve

Sacrum { Cauda equina (sacral and coccygeal nerves)

Coccyx

FIG. 142. Spinal cord enclosed in unopened dural sheath, lying within the vertebral canal. The neural arches are completely removed on the right side, partially on the left, to expose the dorsal surface of the dura. The first and last nerves of the cervical, the thoracic, the lumbar and the sacral groups are indicated; the corresponding vertebrae are indicated. The bundle of nerve roots below the dural sac forms the cauda equina.

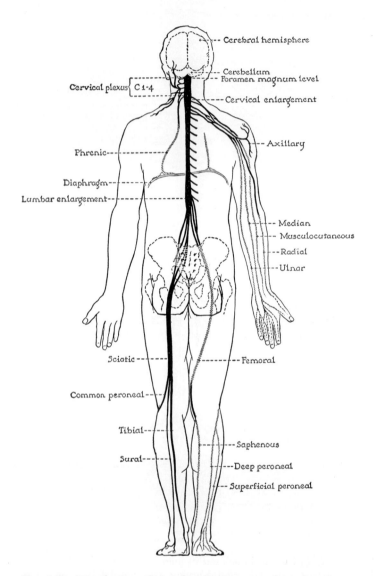

FIG. 143. Distribution of peripheral nerves seen from dorsal view. Brain, spinal cord, cervical plexus and phrenic nerve are shown also.

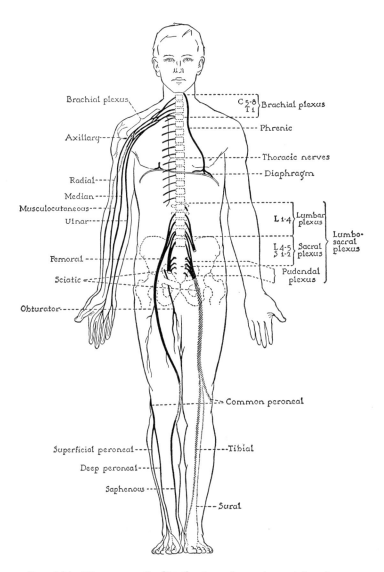

Brachial plexus
Axillary
Radial
Median
Musculocutaneous
Ulnar
Femoral
Sciatic
Obturator

C 5-8
T 1 } Brachial plexus
Phrenic
Thoracic nerves
Diaphragm
L 1-4 } Lumbar plexus
L 4-5
S 1-2 } Sacral plexus
Pudendal plexus
} Lumbo-sacral plexus

Common peroneal
Superficial peroneal
Deep peroneal
Saphenous
Tibial
Sural

FIG. 144. Diagrammatic distribution of certain peripheral nerves projected on the ventral surface. The components of the brachial and the lumbosacral plexuses are shown.

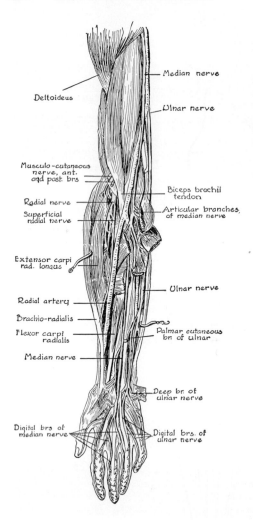

Deltoideus

Median nerve

Ulnar nerve

Musculo-cutaneous nerve, ant. and post. brs

Radial nerve

Superficial radial nerve

Biceps brachii tendon

Articular branches of median nerve

Extensor carpi rad. longus

Ulnar nerve

Radial artery

Brachio-radialis

Flexor carpi radialis

Palmar cutaneous br. of ulnar

Median nerve

Deep br. of ulnar nerve

Digital brs of median nerve

Digital brs. of ulnar nerve

Fig. 145. Dissection of anterior surface of right upper extremity, showing course and distribution of parts of radial, ulnar and median nerves.

plexus is the phrenic nerve, which supplies the diaphragm. Consequently, respiration is very dependent on the phrenic nerves.

BRACHIAL PLEXUS. The anterior rami of the last 4 cervical and the first thoracic spinal nerves combine to form the brachial plexus (Fig. 144), which supplies all the structures of the upper extremity. The chief nerves that emerge from this plexus, on each side, are the (1) musculocutaneous, part of which supplies the biceps brachii muscle; (2) the median nerve, which supplies motor fibers

Fig. 146. Deep dissection of posterior surface of right thigh, showing sciatic nerve dividing into peroneal and tibial nerves.

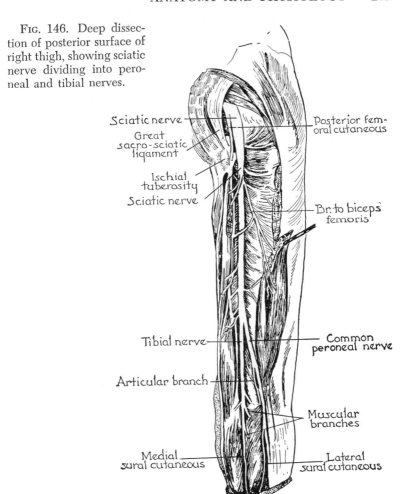

Sciatic nerve

Great sacro-sciatic ligament

Ischial tuberosity

Sciatic nerve

Posterior femoral cutaneous

Br. to biceps femoris

Tibial nerve

Articular branch

Common peroneal nerve

Muscular branches

Medial sural cutaneous

Lateral sural cutaneous

to some of the muscles on the anterior aspect of the forearm and sensory fibers to the radial half of the palm; (3) the ulnar nerve, which passes back of the medial epicondyle of the humerus, carries motor fibers to some of the muscles of the anterior aspect of the forearm and the hand and sensory fibers from the ulnar aspect of the same region; and (4) the radial nerve, which is the largest branch, supplies motor fibers to the triceps brachii and sensory fibers to parts of the posterior aspect of the forearm and the hand.

The distribution of these nerves is shown in Figure 145. When you strike your elbow and feel the tingling and the pain in the forearm you say that you have hit your "crazy bone," but you really have given a mechanical stimulus or blow to the ulnar nerve beside the olecranon.

The 12 thoracic spinal nerves are called the *intercostal nerves,* and the anterior rami of these nerves do not form plexuses. The intercostal nerves supply somatic efferent fibers to the muscles of the wall of the abdomen and sensory and visceral efferent fibers to the skin of the same region.

LUMBAR PLEXUS. The anterior rami of the first 4 lumbar spinal nerves unite to form the lumbar plexus. They supply motor fibers to the muscles of the abdominal wall, the muscles of the loin and a part of the lower extremity (Fig. 144). The femoral nerve is the most important branch; it supplies motor fibers to the quadriceps femoris muscle and has a long sensory branch called the *saphenous nerve.* The latter carries afferent impulses from the medial side of the leg, the knee and the thigh to the central nervous system. The obturator nerve supplies most of the adductor muscles of the thigh with motor and sensory fibers.

SACRAL PLEXUS. The sacral plexus is formed by the combination of the anterior rami of the fourth and the fifth lumbar and the first (and sometimes the second) sacral spinal nerves (Fig. 144). Branches from this plexus supply part of the thigh, the leg, the perineum (area between anus and external genitalia) and the gluteal muscles. The main branch is the sciatic nerve, which is the largest and longest nerve in the body. It is shown in Figures 143 and 146. The sciatic nerve supplies the skin of almost the entire leg with somatic, sensory and visceral efferent fibers and also supplies motor fibers to the hamstring muscles and the muscles of the leg and the foot. Near the distal end of the thigh, the sciatic nerve divides into the tibial and the common peroneal (meaning "the shape of a pin") nerves. The tibial nerve supplies the gastrocnemius muscle, the posterior part of the leg and the sole of the foot. The common peroneal nerve supplies the peroneal region of the leg near the fibula and the dorsum of the foot.

PUDENDAL PLEXUS. The anterior rami of the third and the fourth (and sometimes the second) sacral spinal nerves form the pudendal plexus. The pudendal nerve is the largest branch, and it supplies the levator ani muscle, the skin and other structures of the perineum of its own side.

COCCYGEAL PLEXUS. The coccygeal plexus is formed by the an-

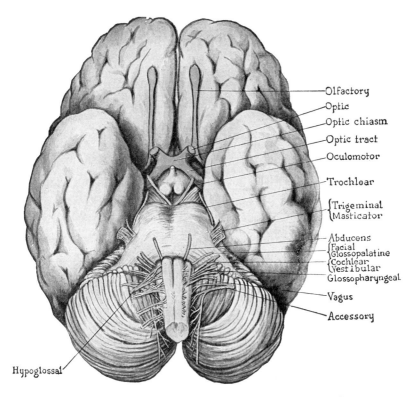

Olfactory
Optic
Optic chiasm
Optic tract
Oculomotor
Trochlear
{Trigeminal
{Masticator
Abducens
{Facial
{Glossopalatine
{Cochlear
{Vestibular
Glossopharyngeal
Vagus
Accessory
Hypoglossal

FIG. 147. Base of brain showing entrance or exit of cranial nerves: olfactory; optic; oculomotor; trochlear; trigeminal with its motor root, the masticator; abducens; facial, with the intermediate nerve of Wrisberg, which is labeled the glossopalatine; cochlear and vestibular branches of acoustic; glossopharyngeal; vagus; accessory; and hypoglossal.

terior rami of the fifth sacral and the coccygeal nerves. Its branches supply the skin and the ligaments in the region of the coccyx.

Cranial Nerves. There are 12 pairs of cranial nerves, the origins of which are shown in Figure 147. In those cranial nerves that have somatic and visceral sensory functions to perform, the afferent fibers arise from cell bodies outside the central nervous system, in ganglia that correspond to the ganglia on the dorsal roots of the spinal nerves. Such ganglia have special names in the case of the cranial nerves, but these are not given in this text. The somatic

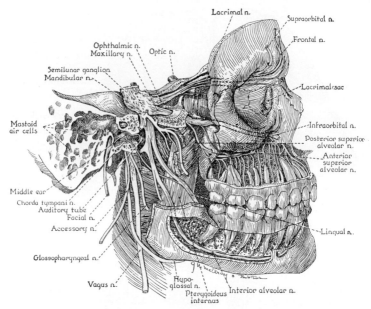

FIG. 148. Dissection of the lateral side of cranium and face. Ramus of mandible is removed. Shown are the divisions of the trigeminal nerve, branches from teeth (shown by opening bone), semilunar ganglion, motor root of trigeminal or masticator nerve and its branches, chorda tympani (branch of facial), optic nerve, facial, glossopharyngeal, vagus, accessory and hypoglossal nerves. Internal pterygoid and external pterygoid (cut) muscles are shown. Opening of auditory tube to middle ear and the connection of middle ear with mastoid air cells also are shown.

and visceral efferent fibers arise from cell bodies within the brain.

1. OLFACTORY. This is the nerve of smell. Its fibers arise from cell bodies in the olfactory membrane (p. 350) and carry impulses to the brain. The two olfactory nerves are purely somatic sensory nerves.

2. OPTIC. This is the nerve of sight. Each optic nerve arises from cell bodies in the retina of the eye on its side and is composed of about 1,250,000 individual fibers. The fibers from the medial half of each retina cross in the optic chiasm (Fig. 201) on the way to the opposite side of the brain. The group of nerve fibers beyond the optic chiasm is called the *optic tract,* and the fibers from the left half of each eye travel in the left optic tract,

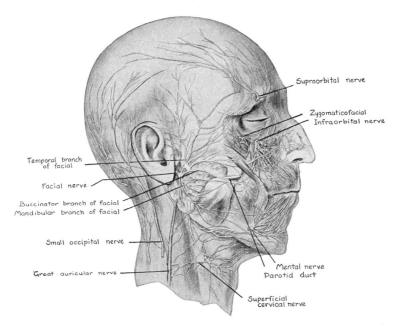

Supraorbital nerve

Zygomaticofacial
Infraorbital nerve

Temporal branch
of facial

Facial nerve

Buccinator branch of facial
Mandibular branch of facial

Small occipital nerve

Great auricular nerve

Mental nerve
Parotid duct

Superficial
cervical nerve

FIG. 149. Superficial dissection of head and neck, showing facial and terminal branches of trigeminal nerve and branches of the cervical plexus.

those from the right half of each eye in the right optic tract. The optic nerves are purely somatic sensory nerves.

3. OCULOMOTOR. The name indicates that this nerve is concerned with eye movements. It also transmits impulses from eye muscles to the brain; consequently, it is a "mixed" nerve; that is, it contains both afferent and efferent fibers. The oculomotor nerves supply all of the extrinsic muscles of the eyeballs except the superior oblique and the lateral rectus muscles. They also supply the levator palpebrae superioris muscles. Visceral efferent fibers supply the muscles of the iris and the ciliary muscles.

4. TROCHLEAR NERVE. These are the smallest of the cranial nerves. Each supplies the superior oblique muscle of its own side with both somatic motor and sensory fibers.

5. TRIGEMINAL NERVE. This is the largest cranial nerve. It is the great somatic sensory nerve of the head and the face and supplies somatic motor fibers to the muscles of mastication. The

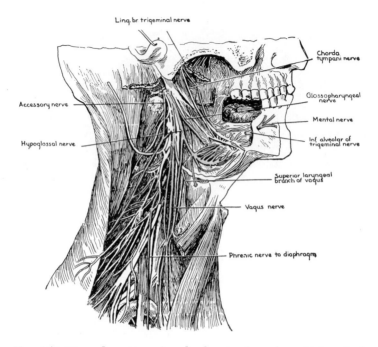

Ling. br. trigeminal nerve

Chorda tympani nerve

Glossopharyngeal nerve

Accessory nerve

Mental nerve

Hypoglossal nerve

Inf. alveolar of trigeminal nerve

Superior laryngeal branch of vagus

Vagus nerve

Phrenic nerve to diaphragm

FIG. 150. Deep dissection of neck, showing branches of trigeminal, facial, glossopharyngeal, vagus, accessory and hypoglossal nerves.

afferent or sensory portion consists of 3 large divisions: ophthalmic, maxillary and mandibular branches. Somatic sensory fibers are supplied to the front part of the head, the face, part of the external ear, the orbit, the nose, the palate, part of the nasopharynx, the tonsils, the mouth, the tongue and the teeth. The distribution of the trigeminal nerve is shown in Figures 148 and 149.

6. ABDUCENS NERVE. This is a small cranial nerve; it supplies both somatic motor and sensory fibers to the lateral rectus muscle of its own side.

7. FACIAL NERVE. The facial nerve is somatic motor and sensory to the facial muscles and the platysma. Its distribution is shown in Figures 149 and 333. It is the nerve of taste to the anterior two thirds of the tongue. It supplies secretory and vasodilator fibers to some salivary glands.

8. ACOUSTIC NERVE. This nerve is composed of 2 sets of fibers

which differ in their peripheral endings, central connections and functions. The *cochlear* division, which arises from cell bodies in the cochlea of the internal ear (p. 370), is a somatic sensory nerve concerned with hearing. The *vestibular* division arises from cell bodies in a ganglion near the semicircular canals (p. 371) of the internal ear. It carries somatic sensory impulses which are aroused by the movement of the body through space and by the position of the head in space and in relation to the rest of the body.

9. GLOSSOPHARYNGEAL NERVE. As indicated by the name, this nerve is distributed to the tongue and the pharynx. It is the somatic sensory nerve of the pharynx and the nerve of taste for the posterior third of the tongue. Some of its fibers transmit impulses from the carotid sinus (p. 508) and the carotid body (p. 558). These visceral afferent impulses are essential in the control of circulation (p. 513) and respiration (p. 558). The glossopharyngeal nerve is very important in the act of swallowing, because of the impulses it carries to the central nervous system from the pharynx. The distribution of the glossopharyngeal nerve is shown in Figures 148 and 150. It supplies secretory and vasodilator fibers to the parotid gland.

10. VAGUS NERVE. The name *vagus* means "wanderer," and the root is the same as that in *vagabond*. In other words, this is the only cranial nerve that wanders away from the head and the neck region. It transmits visceral and somatic afferent impulses to the central nervous system from the external ear, the aortic body (p. 558), the aortic sinus (p. 508), the right atrium, the great veins, the walls of the alveolar ducts of the lungs, (p. 557), the mucous membrane of the respiratory passages, the pharynx, the esophagus and the thoracic and abdominal viscera. It transmits somatic and visceral efferent impulses from the central nervous system to the muscles of the larynx, the pharynx and to all of the thoracic and abdominal viscera. The vagus nerves will be encountered throughout the study of physiology. They are especially important in connection with the control of respiration (p. 558) and circulation (p. 513). Part of the distribution of the vagus nerves is shown in Figures 148 and 150.

11. ACCESSORY NERVE. This nerve arises from both the brain and the spinal cord and formerly was called "spinal accessory" because of the latter component. It supplies somatic motor and sensory fibers to the sternocleidomastoid and part of the trapezius muscles, as do some of the branches of the cervical plexus (p. 256). It also shares some of the functions of the vagus nerves.

FUNCTIONS OF CRANIAL NERVES

Number	Name	Structures Innervated by Efferent Components	Structures Innervated by Afferent Components	Functions
I	Olfactory	None	Olfactory mucous membrane	Nerve of smell
II	Optic	None	Retina of eye	Nerve of vision
III	Oculomotor	Superior, medial, inferior recti; inferior oblique; levator palpebrae superioris; ciliary; sphincter of iris	Same muscles (muscle sense)	Raises upper lid; motor and muscle sense to various muscles listed; accommodation to different distances; regulates the amount of light reaching retina. Most important nerve in eye movements
IV	Trochlear	Superior oblique	Same	Motor and muscle sense to superior oblique. Eye movements
V	Trigeminal (motor root called masticator)	Muscles of mastication	Skin and mucous membranes in head; teeth. Same muscles	Nerve of pain, touch, heat, cold to skin and mucous membranes listed; same for teeth; movements of mastication and muscle sense
VI	Abducens	Lateral rectus	Same	Motor and muscle sense to lateral rectus. Eye movements
VII	Facial (and intermediate nerve of Wrisberg or glossopalatine)	Submaxillary and sublingual glands; muscles of face, scalp and a few others	Same muscles; taste buds of anterior two thirds of tongue	Taste to anterior two thirds of tongue; secretory and vasodilator to two salivary glands; motor and muscle sense to facial and a few other muscles. Nerve of facial expression
VIII	Acoustic (cochlear and vestibular portions)	None	Cochlear-organ of Corti. Vestibular-semicircular canals, utricle and saccule	Cochlear division is nerve of hearing. Vestibular division is concerned with registering movement of the body through space and with the position of the head
IX	Glossopharyngeal	Stylopharyngeus muscle; parotid gland	Taste buds of posterior one third of tongue; parts of pharynx; carotid sinus and body; stylopharyngeus muscle	Taste to posterior one third of tongue and adjacent regions; secretory and vasodilator to parotid gland; motor and muscle sense to stylopharyngeus; pain, touch, heat and cold to pharynx; afferent in circulatory and respiratory reflexes
X	Vagus	Muscles of pharynx, larynx, esophagus, thoracic and abdominal viscera; coronary arteries; walls of bronchi; pancreas; gastric glands	Same muscles; skin of external ear; mucous membranes of larynx, trachea, esophagus; thoracic and abdominal viscera; arch of aorta; carotid sinus	Secretory to gastric glands and pancreas; inhibitory to heart; motor to alimentary tract; motor and muscle sense to muscles of larynx and pharynx; constrictor to coronaries; motor to muscle in walls of bronchi; afferent for alimentary tract; afferent to walls of pulmonary alveoli and mucous membrane of respiratory passages; afferent for aortic arch, atria and great veins and carotid sinus; important in respiratory, cardiac and circulatory reflexes
XI	Accessory	Sternocleidomastoid and trapezius muscles; with vagus	Distributed with vagus	Motor and muscle sense to muscles listed; shares functions of vagus
XII	Hypoglossal	Muscles of tongue	Same	Motor and muscle sense to muscles of tongue; important in speech, mastication and deglutition

12. HYPOGLOSSAL NERVE. The hypoglossal nerves supply somatic motor and sensory fibers to the muscles of the tongue. The distribution is shown in Figures 148 and 150.

The accompanying table gives the number, the name, the efferent and afferent distribution and the general functions of each pair of cranial nerves.

AUTONOMIC OR VISCERAL EFFERENT NERVES

It was stated previously that peripheral nerves contain 4 types of fibers with respect to function. Visceral efferent fibers, also called the autonomic division of the nervous system, usually are treated apart from the remainder of the nervous system. Anatomists, physiologists and pharmacologists are responsible for this "artificial" division. The reasons for considering the usual separate treatment as "artificial" are:

(1) There are visceral efferent fibers in all spinal nerves and in many cranial nerves; (2) most responses of the body to both external and internal stimuli involve skeletal muscles (somatic efferent) on the one hand and smooth muscle, cardiac muscle and glands (visceral efferent) on the other. It has been assumed that somatic structures relate an organism to its environment, since when stimuli are received from the outside world, the response in skeletal muscles can be seen readily. However, there are generally simultaneous changes in visceral effectors (smooth muscle, heart muscle and glands) which cannot be seen but can be detected by appropriate observations.

In accordance with custom, this one functional component of peripheral nerves will be given special attention in this text, although it is inseparably integrated with the other functional components.

Autonomic or visceral efferent fibers are those which transmit impulses from the central nervous system to smooth muscle, cardiac muscle and glands. Such fibers differ from somatic efferent fibers (which supply skeletal muscles) in that there are two neurons in the pathway from the central nervous system to visceral effectors while the somatic efferent pathway consists of only one neuron. It seems as though the cerebral cortex (p. 309) is the master switchboard, and it shunts many calls to an auxiliary switchboard (the hypothalamus, p. 304). The latter relieves many of the demands on the controlling center by taking care of routine adjustments in smooth muscle, cardiac muscle and glands. In this manner the cerebral cortex is free to devote its efforts to regulating the activities in skeletal muscles directly.

The first neuron in the autonomic or visceral efferent pathway has a cell body in the brain or spinal cord, from which an axon extends to a ganglion of the autonomic group. In such a ganglion the axon comes in contact with the dendrites of a second neuron at a synapse. The axons of the second neuron transmit impulses on to the effectors (smooth muscle, cardiac muscle and glands). By means of the synapses in the autonomic ganglia, visceral activities are removed from voluntary control. The general arrangement is illustrated in Figure 141.

Preganglionic fibers, which are the axons of cell bodies in the brain or the spinal cord, are small, myelinated nerve fibers and transmit impulses to autonomic ganglia. The axons that transmit impulses from nerve cells in autonomic ganglia to visceral effectors are called *postganglionic fibers* and are unmyelinated.

Preganglionic fibers have a less extensive origin than somatic efferent fibers. The former are limited to 3 regions of outflow from the central nervous system.

The first region is cranial. Preganglionic fibers accompany somatic efferent fibers in the oculomotor (third), facial (seventh), glossopharyngeal (ninth) and vagus (tenth) cranial nerves and are called the *cranial autonomics.*

The second outflow of autonomic fibers is in the thoracolumbar region of the spinal cord. These preganglionic fibers, which form part of the anterior roots of the spinal nerves from the eighth cervical to the fourth lumbar, are called the *thoracolumbar autonomics.* This group of fibers passes through the intervertebral foramina as part of the respective spinal nerves, then leaves the spinal nerve as a "white ramus" and continues on to an autonomic ganglion, as shown in Figure 141. The postganglionic fibers of the thoracolumbar outflow travel by two pathways; some pass directly to abdominal and pelvic viscera while others return as gray rami to join every spinal nerve and travel in company with somatic afferent and somatic efferent fibers to peripheral structures (sweat glands, smooth muscle around hair follicles and smooth muscles of blood vessels).

The third outflow is in the sacral region. Preganglionic fibers, which are present in the anterior roots of the second, the third and the fourth sacral spinal nerves, are called *sacral autonomics.*

Autonomic ganglia are divided into 3 groups—lateral, collateral and terminal.

Fig. 151. Anterior dissection of the spinal cord showing relationship of the spinal nerves with sympathetic trunk.

(1) Cranial pia mater covering frontal lobe of the brain; (2) cranial pia mater covering temporal lobe of the brain; (3) Cranial pia mater covering pons; (4) Cranial pia mater covering medulla; (13) Spinal pia mater; (both 16s) Anterior roots of spinal nerves covered by sheath of pia mater; (upper 23) Superior cervical sympathetic ganglia; (lower 23) Inferior cervical sympathetic ganglia; (25) Thoracic portion of sympathetic trunk; (lower 26) communication between thoracic nerve and sympathetic ganglia; (upper 27) Lumbar sympathetic chain; (lower 27) Sacral sympathetic chain; (19) Cervical plexus; (both 24s) Communication between cervical and brachial plexus and cervical sympathetic trunk; (both 18s) Dorsal root ganglia; (both 17s) Anterior rami of spinal nerves; (20) Brachial plexus; (28) Communication between lumbar and sacral ganglia and lumbar and sacral nerves; (After Hirschfeld) (Southworth, J. L., Hingson, R. A., and Pitkin, W. M.: Conduction Anesthesia, ed. 2, Philadelphia, Lippincott).

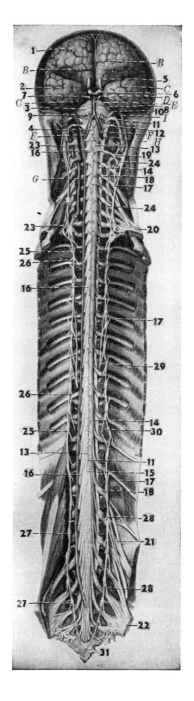

The lateral ganglia lie in 2 chains, one on either side of the vertebral column, and extend vertically through the neck, the thorax and the abdomen (Fig. 151). There are 22 ganglia in each chain: 3, cervical; 11, thoracic; 4, lumbar; and 4, sacral.

The collateral ganglia lie along the front of the abdominal aorta and the celiac artery, and postganglionic fibers follow arteries to abdominal and pelvic viscera. Preganglionic, postganglionic fibers and ganglia are intertwined into autonomic plexuses. One of the largest of these plexuses is called the *celiac plexus* (commonly called the *solar plexus*). The preganglionic fibers from the fifth to the ninth thoracic spinal nerves form the greater splanchnic nerve, and those from the ninth and the tenth thoracic nerves form the lesser splanchnic nerve.

The third group of autonomic ganglia lies close to or within the walls of the organs which the postganglionic fibers supply and are called *terminal ganglia*.

The preganglionic fibers from any one white ramus of the thoracolumbar region establish connections with as many as 9 lateral ganglia. A single axon may connect with 30 or more neurons in the autonomic ganglia of the lateral chains. One such axon is shown in Figure 141; it connects with 3 ganglia. This arrangement for "divergence" makes possible a diffuse discharge of impulses and an extensive distribution of postganglionic thoracolumbar fibers in contrast with the limited distribution of the postganglionic fibers of the cranial and the sacral outflows.

The visceral efferent fibers that arise from the cranial and the sacral regions comprise the craniosacral or parasympathetic division of the autonomic system. Those which arise from the thoracic and the lumbar regions of the spinal cord comprise the thoracolumbar or sympathetic division of the autonomic system.

There are several reasons for dividing the autonomic portion of the nervous system into two. The first reason is that many visceral effectors have a double nerve supply, one from the craniosacral and the other from the thoracolumbar division. The two are sometimes antagonistic in action. For example, the cranial autonomic supply to the heart inhibits it, and the thoracic supply accelerates it. A second reason is that the craniosacral fibers have their synapses only in terminal ganglia, while the thoracolumbar fibers have their synapses in lateral or collateral ganglia. A third reason is based on the response to drugs; one drug will stimulate the craniosacral division, and another will stimulate the thoracolumbar division (p. 280).

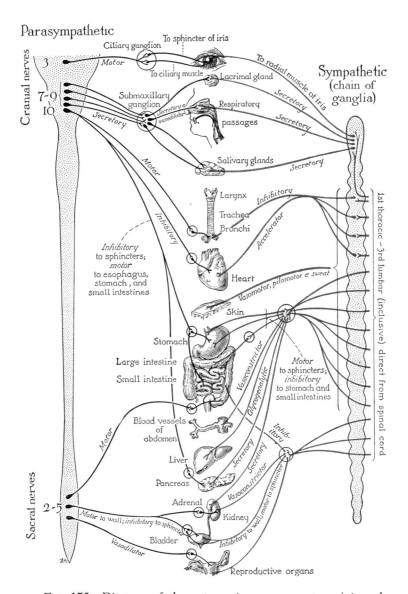

Parasympathetic

Cranial nerves

3

7-9

10

Ciliary ganglion

To sphincter of iris

Motor

To ciliary muscle

Submaxillary ganglion

Secretory

To radial muscle of iris

Sympathetic
(chain of
ganglia)

Lacrimal gland

Secretory

Secretory

Respiratory

passages

Secretory e vasodilator

Motor

Salivary glands

Secretory

Inhibitory
to sphincters;
motor
to esophagus,
stomach, and
small intestines

Inhibitory

Larynx

Trachea

Bronchi

Inhibitory

Accelerator

Heart

Skin

Vasomotor, pilomotor e sweat

Stomach

Large intestine

Small intestine

Vasoconstrictor

Glycogenolytic

Motor
to sphincters;
inhibitory
to stomach and
small intestines

Motor

Blood vessels
of
abdomen

Secretory

Secretory

Inhibitory

Vasoconstrictor

Liver

Pancreas

Sacral nerves

2-5

Adrenal

Kidney

Motor to wall; inhibitory to sphincter

Bladder

Vasodilator

Inhibitory to wall; motor to sphincter

Inhibitory to wall; motor to sphincter

Reproductive organs

1st thoracic ~ 3rd lumbar (inclusive) direct from spinal cord

FIG. 152. Diagram of the autonomic nervous system (visceral
efferent). The craniosacral (parasympathetic) division is shown in
black; the origin, relay station and functions are indicated. The
thoracolumbar (sympathetic) division is shown in red; the origin
in the spinal cord is not shown; the fibers as they emerge from the
spinal cord and enter the chain of lateral ganglia are indicated, together with the relay stations and the functions.

There are a few visceral effectors which receive only one autonomic supply. The sweat glands, the smooth muscles around the hair follicles (pilomotor muscles) and the smooth muscle of the blood vessels of the digestive tract are supplied by nerves from only one autonomic division, and that is the thoracolumbar division.

The functions of the thoracolumbar division of the autonomic system are illustrated in Figure 152, in red, on the right side of the diagram. A list of the functions follows:

1. **Motor or Augmentative Functions.** This division causes *contraction* of the following: the radial muscle of the iris, which means dilatation of the pupil of the eye (p. 357); the pilomotor muscles, which make the hair stand on end or cause "gooseflesh"; the smooth muscle in the capsule of the spleen; the smooth muscle of the uterus; and the smooth muscle in the sphincters of the gastro-intestinal tract and the urinary bladder. Since the heart beats independently of nerve impulses, when the thoracolumbar fibers to the heart are stimulated they cause it to beat faster and more forcibly. When impulses reach the smooth muscle of the blood vessels in the skin and the viscera, they cause the muscle to contract to a greater extent, and this is called *vasoconstriction*, since the blood vessels become constricted or smaller.

2. **Inhibitory Functions.** This means that when impulses reach certain effectors by way of the thoracolumbar autonomic fibers, the smooth muscle relaxes. The smooth muscle which is so affected is that in the blood vessels of skeletal muscles (leading to dilatation of these vessels), the coronaries (which supply the heart), the muscle in the walls of the gastro-intestinal tract (which stops contracting), the wall of the urinary bladder and the walls of the bronchioles (p. 537), which makes it easier for air to get into and out of the lungs.

3. **Secretory Functions.** Thoracolumbar fibers carry impulses to sweat glands, to the medulla of the adrenal gland, the lacrimal glands (p. 355), and to the salivary glands. In the last instance a thick, viscid saliva is produced, which leads to a feeling of dryness in the mouth.

4. **Glycogenolytic Function.** This means that when impulses reach the cells of the liver by way of the thoracolumbar nerves, glycogen of the liver is broken down to glucose, which is released to the blood and raises the level of sugar in the blood.

The thoracolumbar division of the autonomic system is constantly active and helps to maintain homeostasis or constancy of the internal environment. It acts as a unit in times of stress, such as during severe exercise, after hemorrhage or loss of blood, in severe pain, during emotional excitement, during exposure to extreme heat or cold, during periods when the blood sugar is low (hypoglycemia) and in asphyxia. It prepares an individual to meet emergencies, whether he remains and "fights it out" or takes to his heels in flight.

The functions of the craniosacral division are illustrated in Figure 152, in black, on the left side of the diagram. A list of the functions follows:

1. **Motor or Augmentative Functions.** This division causes contraction of the sphincter muscle of the iris, which makes the pupil of the eye smaller; of the ciliary muscle (p. 360) of the eye, which adjusts the lens system for vision at different distances; of the smooth muscle of the bronchioles, which makes them smaller, and air is moved in and out of the lungs with more difficulty; of the smooth muscle of the walls of the stomach, the intestine and the urinary bladder, which causes these organs to become more active.

2. **Inhibitory Functions.** The impulses that reach certain effectors by way of the craniosacral division lead to a decrease in the activity or the relaxation of smooth muscle. The smooth muscle in the walls of blood vessels of the salivary glands, the mucous membrane of the mouth and the external genitalia is relaxed, which means that these blood vessels dilate. Impulses that reach the heart by way of the cranial autonomic (in the vagus nerves) fibers cause it to beat more slowly and weakly. The sphincters of the gastro-intestinal tract and the urinary bladder are relaxed by this division.

3. **Secretory Functions.** Impulses that reach the glands of the mucous membrane in the respiratory passages stimulate them to produce more secretion. Impulses that reach the salivary glands lead to the production of a thin, watery saliva.

The craniosacral division has a limited distribution, and one organ at a time may be involved. There is no widespread action as in the case of the thoracolumbar division. Activity in the craniosacral division is initiated primarily by internal changes in the viscera themselves. The cranial portion is protective in function; it slows the action of the heart and protects the eyes from strong light. The sacral portion is the nerve of emptying; it empties the urinary bladder and the large bowel.

The functions of the visceral efferent or autonomic division are presented in tabular form for ease of study.

TABLE OF AUTONOMIC FUNCTIONS

Structure	Action of thoracolumbar fibers	Action of craniosacral fibers
Radial muscle of iris	Contraction; dilatation of pupil	
Sphincter muscle of iris		Contraction; constriction of pupil
Ciliary muscle of eye		Contraction; adjusting thickness of lens; accommodation
Salivary glands	Secretory to mucous cells; thick, viscid saliva	Secretory to serous cells; thin, watery saliva; vasodilatation
Heart	Augmentor; faster and more forceful beat	Inhibitory; slower and weaker atrial beat
Smooth muscle of bronchi	Relaxation; dilatation of bronchi	Contraction; narrowing of bronchi
Glands along respiratory passages		Secretory; production of mucus
Smooth muscle in walls of alimentary tract	Relaxation; dilatation of gut	Contraction; increased activity
Glands of alimentary tract (stomach and pancreas)		Secretory; increased secretion
Liver	Glycogenolysis; increase in blood sugar	
Sphincters of alimentary tract	Contraction	Relaxation
Wall of urinary bladder	Relaxation; retention	Contraction; emptying
Sphincters of urinary bladder	Contraction	Relaxation
Uterine muscle	Contraction under some conditions; varies with time of cycle and pregnancy	Inhibition; variable
Smooth muscle in spleen	Contraction	
Pilomotor muscles	Contraction; gooseflesh	
Smooth muscle of blood vessels of skin	Contraction; vasoconstriction	
Smooth muscle of blood vessels of abdominal viscera	Contraction; vasoconstriction	
Smooth muscle of blood vessels of salivary glands, external genitalia		Inhibition; vasodilatation
Smooth muscle of coronaries and vessels of skeletal muscles	Relaxation or inhibition; vasodilatation	
Sweat glands	Secretory; production of sweat	
Medulla of adrenal gland	Secretory; production of epinephrine	

PRACTICAL CONSIDERATIONS

Nerve Injuries

Nerve injuries lead to loss of sensation and paralysis of muscles. We speak of an injured nerve as a "paralyzed" nerve, although this usage really is incorrect, since it is the muscles supplied by the nerve that are paralyzed.

Injuries of the Cervical Plexus. The phrenic nerve is the most important branch of the cervical plexus and is damaged by injury to the plexus. Damage to the phrenic nerves is associated with spasm or paralysis of the diaphragm. Irritation of the phrenic nerves leads to hiccoughs (hiccups) which are spasmodic contractions of the diaphragm causing inspiration, followed by a sudden closure of the glottis (opening between the vocal cords). The phrenic nerve may be compressed by tumors or abscesses of the neck or be injured by wounds of the neck.

Injuries of the Brachial Plexus. A pure paralysis of only the median nerve is rare but may follow injury to this nerve. The paralysis is more often a part of an extended involvement of the brachial plexus.

When the *median nerve* alone is damaged, there is inability to pronate the forearm or to flex the wrist properly, since the pronators and most of the flexors are supplied by it. The second phalanges of the middle and the index fingers cannot be flexed. The thumb cannot be flexed and abducted, which is one of the most characteristic features of the normal hand. The ability to appose the thumb to any one of the fingers, as is done in picking up very small objects, is lost.

After damage to the *ulnar nerve,* flexion and adduction of the wrist are impaired. There is difficulty in spreading the fingers; the hand is clawed. This nerve is involved particularly in those persons whose occupations require them to press their elbows against hard objects or to strike blows with the ulnar border of the hand. The ulnar nerve is most frequently involved in forearm and wrist injuries.

The *axillary nerve* is often paralyzed as a result of injuries to the shoulder, as in birth injuries when undue pressure is made in the axilla.

The *axillary nerve* may be involved when there are dislocations of the shoulder. The most prominent sign of paralysis of the axillary nerve is the loss of roundness of the shoulder due to atrophy of the deltoid muscle after its nerve supply is damaged.

The *radial nerve* is paralyzed more frequently than any other branch of the brachial plexus. It is damaged in the axillary region due to crutch pressure. If the arm is used for a pillow during sleep, the radial nerve is exposed to pressure where it passes between the triceps brachii muscle and the humerus. When one throws an object with violence, the radial nerve may be injured by the excessive contraction of the triceps muscle. The most characteristic sign and most common form of radial nerve paralysis is the inability to extend the hand at the wrist; this is called "wrist drop."

Injuries of the Lumbar Plexus. The femoral nerve may be paralyzed by the pressure of tumors in the pelvis, by an abscess of the psoas muscle or by fracture of the pubic bone. If this nerve is paralyzed the hip cannot be flexed or the knee extended. There is a loss of feeling in the thigh, along the anterior and the inner surfaces of the leg, the inner border of the foot and the ball of the big toe.

Injuries of the Sacral Plexus. Paralysis of the *sciatic nerve* may result from fracture of the lumbar vertebrae, the sacrum or the coccyx, from pressure of tumors in the pelvis, from pressure due to the fetal head during labor or from the improper use of forceps at the time of delivery. The leg hangs in a flail-like manner, with loss of power of flexion at the knee.

Injury to the *peroneal nerve* causes foot drop, with a loss of the arch of the foot.

Injury to the *tibial nerve* is followed by loss of the ability to plantar flex the foot at the ankle joint.

Prevention of Damage to Nerves During Intramuscular Injections. As nurses frequently are asked to give intramuscular injections, it is essential to know the location of the nerves, in order to prevent injury during injection. While one nurse was giving an injection of penicillin to a mechanic she struck the radial nerve. The patient told her that it felt queer, but she persisted, and the entire amount of the drug was placed in contact with the nerve, and the nerve was damaged. As a result, the mechanic lost the use of some of the muscles of his right forearm and hand for a long time and was unable to follow his occupation until new neurofibrillae had grown out to replace the damaged ones.

SCIATICA

Sciatica is the condition in which there is constant pain along the course of the sciatic nerve, due to inflammation. There is tenderness, numbness and tingling, in addition to pain. The muscles supplied by the sciatic nerve undergo atrophy or "wasting," since they are not used.

NEURITIS

Neuritis is the condition in which there is pain, paralysis, hyper-sensitivity, loss of reflexes and atrophy of muscles, due to degenerative or inflammatory changes in a nerve. Sciatica is one type of neuritis.

NEURALGIA

Neuralgia is the condition in which there are severe paroxysmal pains along the course of a nerve; there is no structural change in the nerve, as in neuritis. The pain is sharp and stabbing in type.

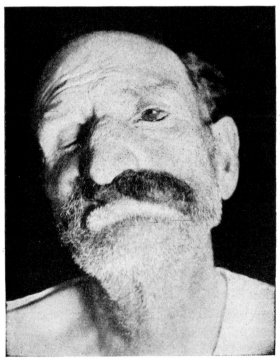

Fig. 153. Left-sided facial paralysis of the central type. (Minneapolis General Hospital)

A ruptured intervertebral disk may lead to pain by pressure on various nerves.

CRANIAL NERVE INJURIES

The effects of injury to cranial nerves are: olfactory, loss of smell; optic, blindness; oculomotor, drooping (ptosis) of the upper eyelid, the eyeball turned downward and outward and the pupil dilated; trochlear, abnormal position of eyeball; trigeminal, loss of sensation of face, mouth and scalp; paralysis of muscles of mastication; tic douloureux, paroxysmal neuralgia of the trigeminal nerve; abducens, abnormal position of the eyeball; facial, paralysis of the muscles of the facial expression with a "masklike" expression, as shown in Figure 153 (known as Bell's palsy), inability to whistle and wrinkle the forehead, interference with the secretion of the submaxillary and sublingual glands, loss of taste in the anterior two thirds of the tongue; acoustic, cochlear portion—deafness, vestibular portion—disorientation accompanied by dizziness and nystagmus (p. 372); glossopharyngeal, loss of sensation in pharynx with accompanying difficulty in swallowing, loss of taste in posterior third of tongue; vagus, difficulty in breathing and swallowing, changes in voice, widespread minor disturbances due to the extensive distribution of these nerves; accessory, inability to turn the head and to raise the shoulder due to paralysis of the sternocleidomastoid and the trapezius muscles; hypoglossal, difficulty in speaking, chewing and swallowing, (if the paralysis is unilateral, the tip will be deflected to the paralyzed side as the patient protrudes the tongue).

ACTION OF DRUGS ON THE AUTONOMIC DIVISION

Atropine inhibits the activities of the craniosacral division. The pupils are dilated, the bronchioles dilated, secretion of glands along the respiratory passages inhibited and movements of stomach and intestine inhibited. The most common uses of atropine are in eye examinations, with morphine, before a general anesthetic is administered and in acute colds.

Pilocarpine has the same effects as normal stimulation of the craniosacral division. One of the chief effects is to constrict the pupils. Consequently, this drug is used in the treatment of glaucoma.

Epinephrine has the same effects as normal stimulation of the thoracolumbar division. The effects of epinephrine are: relaxation of bronchioles in asthma, stimulation of the heart in cardiac collapse, constriction of blood vessels with rise in blood pressure and delay in the absorption of a local anesthetic by constriction of the blood vessels.

INJURY TO THE SYMPATHETIC TRUNK

The cervical portion of the chain of lateral ganglia may be injured by deep wounds of the neck or compressed by tumors, abscesses or aneurysm of the aorta. The changes noted on that side of the face are: redness of the conjunctiva, constriction of the pupil, sinking in of the eyeball (enophthalmos) and a warm, flushed, dry skin. This condition is called *Horner's syndrome*.

DISORDERS OF THE AUTONOMIC DIVISION

There may be spasmodic constrictions of the blood vessels of the fingers and the toes in a condition called *Raynaud's disease*. The spasms are induced by exposure to cold. The digits appear blue or purple, then pale and, finally, they become numb. After the spasm the digits are red, and there is a burning pain in them. The condition is made worse by smoking. As the condition progresses, there may be ulcerations of the tips of the fingers.

Prolonged periods of emotional tension eventually lead to hemorrhagic erosions or ulcers of the gastric mucous membrane, associated with hypermotility and hypersecretion of the stomach.

Hypertension (high arterial blood pressure) is due to unknown causes but is accompanied by constriction of small arteries (arterioles). Sympathectomy is performed to relieve the vasoconstriction and to lower the blood pressure.

BODILY CHANGES IN EMOTIONAL CRISES

Let us consider the chain of events that occur in a cat when a dog approaches. Afferent impulses from the eyes and the nose reach the cat's cortex and in some way affect the centers for vision and smell, and the orbitofrontal area. Outgoing impulses are sent to the hypothalamus and are relayed on to the lower levels, which prepare the cat to meet the emergency.

The whole thoracolumbar division goes into action. As a result, the heart beats faster, the blood vessels of the skin and the viscera are constricted, the coronary vessels and the blood vessels in the skeletal muscles are dilated, the bronchi are dilated, the musculature of the stomach and the intestine is inhibited, the pilomotor muscles contract to make the hair stand on end, the spleen contracts and forces stored red blood corpuscles out into the circula-

Fig. 154. Appearance of a cat in an emotional crisis.

tion. Since the cat is going to fight or take flight, the above changes in the body are such as to supply more blood to the skeletal muscles and the heart muscle and to decrease the blood supply to the skin and the intestine. Air can be moved in and out of the lungs more easily. The raised hair makes the cat look larger and may help to frighten the dog.

The glycogen in the liver is changed to glucose and put into circulation to supply more energy for activity. The adrenal medullae are stimulated to produce more epinephrine, and this intensifies the activity of the thoracolumbar division and prolongs it. Figure 154 depicts a cat in an emotional crisis.

You can recognize many of these same responses in your own body in emotional crises. In view of the inhibition of the gastro-intestinal activities, it is inadvisable to permit yourself to be upset emotionally during a meal or shortly thereafter.

SUMMARY

1. General plan of the nervous system: peripheral and central; peripheral nerves carry impulses to and from the central nervous system. Four groups with respect to function: somatic afferent, somatic efferent, visceral afferent and visceral efferent (also called the autonomic system). Central: brain and spinal cord; cells and fibers

2. Peripheral nervous system

A. Microscopic structure; neurons; cell bodies; dendrites and axons. Axis cylinder; myelin sheath; neurilemma

B. Components of nerves; axons and dendrites, with connective tissue. Degeneration and regeneration

C. Classification of neurons

a. On basis of structure: bipolar and multipolar

b. On basis of function: afferent, efferent and internuncial
D. Neuron theory; chains of neurons, with synapses between individual neurons
E. Characteristics of nervous tissue
  a. Excitability
  b. Conductivity; impulses self-propagating, travel at a definite speed, accompanied by chemical changes, heat produced during activity, passage of impulses accompanied by electrical changes; refractory periods
3. Divisions of the peripheral nervous system
A. Spinal nerves; 31 pairs; dorsal and ventral roots; spinal nerve; anterior and posterior rami
B. Plexuses: cervical—phrenic; brachial—musculocutaneous, median, ulnar and radial. Lumbar: femoral. Sacral: sciatic. Pudendal: pudendal nerve. Coccygeal: to region of coccyx
C. Cranial nerves: 12 pairs: olfactory, optic, oculomotor, trochlear, trigeminal, abducens, facial, acoustic, glossopharyngeal, vagus, accessory and hypoglossal
4. Visceral efferent nerves (autonomic)
A. Anatomical arrangement
  a. Preganglionic fibers: origin
    (1) Cranial; 3, 7, 9 and 10 cranial nerves
    (2) Thoracolumbar
    (3) Sacral
  b. Autonomic ganglia
    (1) Lateral
    (2) Collateral
    (3) Terminal
B. Divisions
  a. Craniosacral
  b. Thoracolumbar
C. Functions
  a. Thoracolumbar division
    (1) Motor or augmentative functions
    (2) Inhibitory functions
    (3) Secretory functions
    (4) Glycogenolytic function
  b. Craniosacral division
    (1) Motor or augmentative functions
    (2) Inhibitory functions
    (3) Secretory functions

SITUATION AND QUESTIONS

It is vital for student nurses to learn well the exact technic for giving injections and to know the exact location in which to insert the needles.

1. The inner aspect of the upper outer quadrant of the buttock is the site for intramuscular injections. This specific site is used to avoid injury to the nerve which supplies the posterior thigh, the leg and the foot. The name of this nerve is: _____(a) femoral; _____(b) dorsalis pedis; _____(c) sciatic; _____(d) tibial.

2. There are sensory fibers located in the sciatic nerve. Neurons, which conduct impulses giving rise to sensations, can also be called: _____(a) afferent neurons; _____(b) internuncial neurons; _____(c) efferent neurons; _____(d) neuroglia.

3. The part of the neuron which first receives and transmits an impulse is: _____(a) the axon; _____(b) the Nissl granules; _____(c) the dendrite; _____(d) the nucleus.

4. In learning a procedure well and making it a habit, _____ (a) resistance must be lowered in certain synapses; _____(b) resistance must be built up at synapses; _____(c) excitability of receptors must be increased; _____(d) conductivity in nerve fibers must be abolished.

5. Dentists are equally careful with their injections as there is a possibility of damage to the trigeminal nerve. Damage to this nerve would result in: _____(a) loss of facial expression; _____(b) loss of taste; _____(c) loss of sensation in face and mouth; _____(d) paralysis of muscles of face and forehead.

A patient received a fairly large dose of epinephrine intravenously. This drug, when injected, acts similar to stimulation of the thoracolumbar division of the autonomic nervous system. A nurse observing this patient could expect the following changes:

1. Heart rate: _____(a) more rapid; _____(b) slower; _____(c) no change.

2. Respiration: _____(a) more rapid; _____(b) slower; _____(c) no change.

3. Blood pressure: _____(a) increased; _____(b) decreased; _____(c) no change.

4. Intestinal activity: _____(a) increased; _____(b) decreased; _____(c) no change.

5. Secretion of saliva and other digestive juices: _____(a) increased; _____(b) decreased; _____(c) no change.

6. Pupils of eyes: _____(a) constricted; _____(b) dilated; _____(c) no change.

7. Secretion of sweat: _____(a) increased; _____(b) decreased; _____(c) no change.

8. Blood vessels in skeletal muscles: _____(a) constricted; _____(b) dilated; _____(c) no change.

UNIT 3. INTEGRATION AND CONTROL OF
THE BODY BY THE NERVOUS SYSTEM

7. Central Nervous System

The central nervous system consists of the brain and the spinal cord.

THE SPINAL CORD

ANATOMY

The spinal cord is attached to the medulla at the level of the foramen magnum, and at the caudal end it tapers into a point called the *conus medullaris*. There are 2 enlargements of the spinal cord, the cervical and the lumbar, in the regions where the brachial and the lumbosacral plexuses arise.

In cross section the spinal cord is round or oval, depending on the level examined. There is a small canal called the *central canal* near the center. There is a deep fissure called the *ventral fissure* which extends almost to the central canal (Fig. 155). The posterior median septum is located between the right and the left halves of the dorsal portion of the spinal cord. The gray matter, as is evident in Figures 155 and 140, is H-shaped. There are 2 anterior columns or horns and 2 posterior columns or horns of gray matter. In the thoracic region, a lateral column or horn of gray matter is present. Cell bodies of neurons are located in the gray matter and are responsible for its darker color.

286

The white matter lies superficial to the gray matter in the spinal cord. It is divided by projecting columns of gray matter into 3 *funiculi* (meaning "a little cord")—anterior, lateral and posterior. White matter is composed of large numbers of nerve fibers which are myelinated. The nerve fibers are arranged in groups called *tracts*. Each funiculus is composed of a large number of tracts. There is a white commissure located between a gray commissure and the ventral median fissure (Fig. 155). In the white commissure nerve fibers cross from one side of the spinal cord to the other. The roots of spinal nerves are shown in Figure 140.

FUNCTIONS

The spinal cord serves 2 functions: as a reflex center and as a conduction pathway to and from the brain.

Reflex arcs are functional units of the nervous system. Each arc consists of 3 parts: (1) an afferent neuron to transmit impulses from a receptor to the central nervous system, (2) a center and (3) an efferent neuron to transmit impulses from the central nervous system to an effector. A reflex path is shown by diagram in Figure 156, from a receptor in the skin to the spinal cord, over an inter-

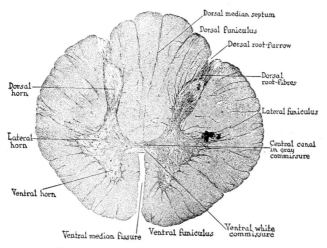

FIG. 155. Cross section of the spinal cord in the thoracic region, showing the H-shaped gray matter, surrounded by white matter. The latter is divided into ventral, lateral and dorsal funiculi. × 13.

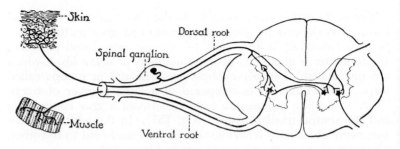

FIG. 156. Diagrammatic section through the spinal cord to illustrate a simple reflex arc. Dendrites of the afferent neuron transmit impulses from the skin to the cell body in the ganglion on the dorsal root of a spinal nerve. The axon transmits impulses on to the spinal cord in which they are transferred over synapses to internuncial neurons (and commissural neurons). From the internuncial neuron the impulses are relayed to the efferent neuron, by means of which they reach the effector muscle. (Based on Ranson)

nuncial neuron to a cell body in the ventral horn of gray matter and out over the axon to skeletal muscle.

The number of neurons in a reflex arc varies from 2 to many; great variation is possible between simple and complex reflexes. Any part of the central nervous system may be used in reflexes. The activity that results from the passage of impulses over a reflex arc is called a *reflex act* or simply a *reflex*. A reflex is defined as an involuntary response to a stimulus.

Examples of spinal reflexes are the stretch reflexes and the flexor reflexes, which will be described. The knee jerk is a stretch reflex; to demonstrate this reflex the tendon of the quadriceps femoris muscle is struck lightly, and the leg extends. By striking the tendon the muscle is stretched slightly, and the spindles (receptors) are stimulated. Impulses travel from the receptors in the muscle over dendrites in the femoral nerve to cell bodies in the dorsal root ganglion and then on over the axon to the synapse in the ventral horn of gray matter. The impulses cross the synapses to the dendrites of cell bodies in the ventral horn, pass over the dendrites and the cell bodies and on to the axons and to the muscle fibers of the quadriceps femoris muscle, causing contraction. Probably 3 segments of the spinal cord in the lumbar region and hundreds of incoming and outgoing fibers are involved in this reflex.

It is a local reflex, and the contraction is limited to the part of the muscle stretched. It really is due to stretch reflexes in our extensor muscles (those that oppose gravity) that we are able to maintain the standing position.

Not all spinal reflexes are so simple as the knee jerk, as will be noted in the following illustration. Suppose that as you step out of bed expecting to put your feet into your bedroom slippers you encounter a sharp object with one foot. You withdraw that foot, put your weight on the other leg and grab something to keep from falling, and you note that your heart is beating faster and more forcibly than usual. In this case there was a stimulation of the receptors in one foot, and the impulses passed to the spinal cord. Some impulses were transferred directly to efferent neurons and sent back immediately to the skeletal muscles to cause that foot to be withdrawn from the harmful object. This is a "flexor reflex." Other impulses were sent to the muscles of the opposite leg, to enable you to maintain your balance, and to the upper extremities, to enable you to hold on to something to prevent a fall. The entire spinal cord from the sacral to the cervical region is involved in this response. Even cell bodies of autonomic neurons received impulses which caused the heart to beat faster. While all of this was going on in the spinal cord, impulses were arriving at the brain which made you conscious of the pain in the foot after it had been withdrawn from the stimulus. Flexor reflexes are protective in nature and help to guard us from harm; they are fundamental to preservation of life. They are widespread, and the responses outlast the stimulus.

Spinal reflexes may be brought about as a result of stimuli outside of the body or inside the body, and they may involve skeletal muscle, smooth muscle, heart muscle and glands.

Conduction Pathway. In its function as a conduction pathway to and from the brain, the spinal cord makes use of tracts. Ascending tracts transmit impulses to the brain, and descending tracts transmit impulses from the brain to various levels of the spinal cord. In many cases, the tracts of the spinal cord are given names that indicate the origin and the destination of the constituent fibers.

ASCENDING TRACTS. There are 3 ascending tracts in each side of the spinal cord: posterior columns, spinocerebellar and spinothalamic tracts. The axons of some cell bodies in the dorsal root ganglia compose the *posterior columns.*

They ascend up to the medulla and eventually reach the highest centers of the brain. The impulses that travel in the posterior

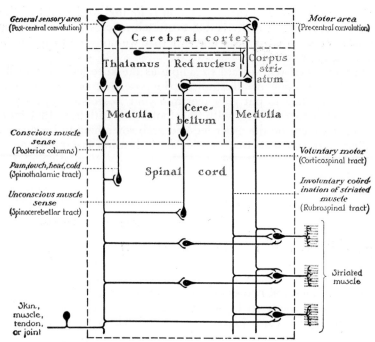

FIG. 157. Diagram representing conduction pathways through the mammalian nervous system. An impulse which arises in skin, muscle, tendon or joint has many pathways open to it: it may be transferred to an efferent neuron in the spinal cord, at the same or a slightly higher level; it may reach the medulla, the cerebellum, the thalamus or the cortex of the cerebral hemisphere. Regardless of the pathway taken, the impulse (in this diagram) eventually reaches the nerve cells in the ventral horn of the spinal cord, from which it passes to striated muscular tissue. (Modified from Bayliss)

columns come from receptors (muscle spindles) in skeletal muscles, receptors in tendons and in capsules around joints. They are impulses of "conscious muscle sense," which means that when they reach the brain they give us information about the degree of contraction of our skeletal muscles and the position of the bones at joints. There are also impulses concerned with direct touch traveling in the posterior columns on their way to the brain. These come from the skin, and they reach the same side of the brain as the skin that was stimulated. The pathway is shown by diagram in Figures 157 and 158.

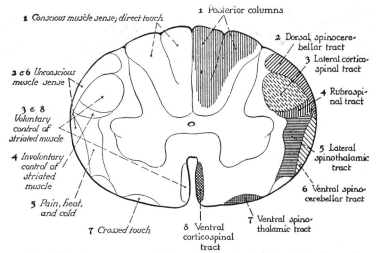

FIG. 158. Cross section of the spinal cord. On the right, the principal conduction pathways are shown; of these, 1, 2, 5, 6 and 7 are ascending, and 3, 4 and 8 are descending tracts. On the left, the functions of the various tracts are indicated. Diagrammatic. All tracts are bilateral.

The fibers that compose both the dorsal and the ventral *spinocerebellar tracts* are axons, which arise from cell bodies in the spinal cord and end in the cerebellum.

The first neuron carries impulses from the receptors to the spinal cord, and the second neuron carries impulses from the spinal cord to the cerebellum. It is the second neurons which give the tracts their name. The impulses which travel in the spinocerebellar tracts originate in receptors in skeletal muscles, tendons and joints, as do those which travel in the posterior columns. However, the destination differs, and the former do not reach the conscious centers of the brain but play an important part in reflex adjustments of posture. The spinocerebellar tracts convey impulses concerned with "unconscious muscle sense." The location of these tracts is shown in Figures 157 and 158.

The axons that compose the *spinothalamic tracts* arise from cell bodies in the spinal cord and terminate in the part of the brain called the thalamus (p. 304). The first neuron transmits impulses from receptors in the skin to the spinal cord, and the second neuron transmits impulses on to the thalamus. There are 2 spinothalamic tracts—ventral and lateral. The fibers in the ventral spinothalamic tract transmit impulses concerned with indirect touch. These impulses arise from receptors in the skin and are sent eventually to the opposite side of the brain. The lateral spinothalamic tract transmits impulses concerned with pain, heat and cold. The impulses in this tract arise from receptors in the skin and eventually reach the opposite side of the brain. The pathway is shown in Figures 157 and 158. The lateral spinothalamic tracts of the spinal cord are cut by surgical procedure to make life bearable for some patients who suffer from intractable pain (meaning pain that is not relieved by the usual drugs) as a result of cancer. There is no sensation of pain if the pathway which transmits impulses from the diseased area is cut.

DESCENDING TRACTS. There are two groups of descending tracts in each side of the spinal cord:

1. The first is the *corticospinal* or *pyramidal* tracts. These originate in the cortex of the brain and end in the spinal cord. The name "pyramidal" was given to these tracts because some of the axons arise from pyramid-shaped cells in the brain. The corticospinal tracts (lateral and ventral) cross to the opposite side of the spinal cord. Thus, the left side of the brain controls the skeletal muscles on the right side of the body, and the right side of the brain controls the left side of the body. The corticospinal tracts transmit impulses from the brain to dendrites of cell bodies in the spinal cord, and these impulses are concerned with voluntary motion. The corticospinal tracts are shown in Figures 157 and 158 and are labeled *F* in Figure 159.

2. The second group of descending tracts is called the *extrapyramidal* group; this means all "outside" of the pyramidal. The fibers that compose these tracts arise from various parts of the brain and have a relay station in the brain before an axon of a third neuron transmits them to the spinal cord. They make it possible for impulses from various parts of the brain to exert an influence on the neurons of the spinal cord. The convergence of many pathways on the last motor neuron, called the *final common path,* is illustrated in Figure 159.

Internuncial neurons transmit impulses from one level of the spinal cord to another. They are exceedingly important in bringing about properly co-ordinated activity in various segments of the spinal cord.

COVERINGS OF THE SPINAL CORD

The outer covering of the spinal cord is bony and consists of the vertebrae. The inner covering is membranous, and it lies just beneath the bony covering.

Fig. 159. Diagram of principal types of descending pathways which converge on nerve cells in the spinal cord. (A) Internuncial or associational neuron from one level of the spinal cord to another. (B) Vestibulospinal tract from vestibular nucleus in the medulla. (C) Rubrospinal tract from red nucleus in the midbrain. (D) Tectospinal tract from roof of midbrain. (E) Reticulospinal tract from reticular formation. (F) Corticospinal (frequently called *pyramidal*) tract from cerebral cortex to lower motor neurons (the fibers which compose

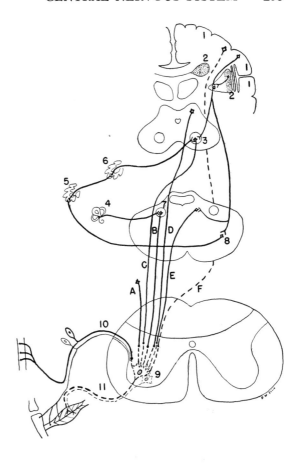

this tract arise primarily from cells in the precentral cortex). B, C, D and E represent extrapyramidal tracts. They arise from practically all parts of the cerebral cortex and synapse at various subcortical levels such as the basal ganglia, the reticular formation, the red nucleus, the pons and the cerebellum, before converging on lower motor neurons. The pyramidal and extrapyramidal tracts converge on lower motor neurons directly or by way of internuncial neurons.

(1) cerebral cortex; (2) basal ganglia; (3) red nucleus of midbrain; (4) semi-circular canals of inner ear; (5) cerebellar cortex; (6) dentate nucleus of cerebellum; (7) Deiter's nucleus (vestibular); (8) nucleus in gray matter of pons; (9) anterior horn cell (representing lower motor neurons); (10) posterior root of spinal nerve; (11) anterior root of spinal nerve, innervating skeletal muscles. This is the "final common path."

Meninges. The membranous covering is composed of 3 *meninges* (meaning "membranes").

THE OUTER MEMBRANE is the *dura mater* (meaning "hard mother"). It is composed of dense fibrous connective tissue. The dura mater extends below the spinal cord and ends as a blind sac at the level of the lower border of the second component of the sacrum and is anchored to the coccyx by a threadlike strand of pia called the *filum terminale*. The dura mater covers the spinal nerve roots as they leave the spinal cord and extend to the intervertebral foramina.

THE MIDDLE LAYER of the meninges is called the *arachnoid* (meaning "like a spider web"). It is very thin and it follows the dura mater to the end of the dural sac below the spinal cord and covers the spinal nerve roots.

THE INNER LAYER of the meninges is called the *pia mater* (meaning "gentle mother"). It is delicate and filled with blood vessels, firmly adherent to the spinal cord and ends as the filum terminale below the end of the spinal cord.

Spinal Fluid. The space between the walls of the vertebral canal and the spinal dura mater is called the *epidural space* or *extradural space*. The space between the dura mater and the arachnoid is called the *subdural space*. It likewise is small and contains a minute amount of fluid. The space between the arachnoid and the pia mater is called the *subarachnoid space*. It is very roomy and is filled with a fluid called the *spinal fluid* (really cerebrospinal fluid, since there is fluid in the cranial subarachnoid space, also). There is no communication between the subdural and the subarachnoid spaces.

Between the end of the spinal cord in the upper lumbar region and the end of the dural sac in the sacral region, there is a large amount of spinal fluid which can be withdrawn for diagnostic purposes (p. 322).

THE BRAIN

There are 3 primary divisions of the brain, based on embryologic development (p. 316). These are the forebrain, the midbrain and the hindbrain, and each of these is subdivided further, as shown in the accompanying breakdown.

Brain

    1. Forebrain (prosencephalon)

        A. Cerebral hemispheres (telencephalon), enclosing lateral ventricles. Each hemisphere comprises:

   a. Cerebral cortex
   b. Basal ganglia
   c. Rhinencephalon or olfactory portion
  B. Diencephalon; connects cerebral hemispheres with midbrain and comprises most of the parts that form the walls of the third ventricle
   a. Dorsal portion comprises thalamus and epithalamus
   b. Ventral portion comprises hypothalamus and subthalamus

  2. Midbrain (mesencephalon); connects forebrain with hindbrain and surrounds cerebral aqueduct
  A. Ventral portion comprises cerebral peduncles. These are a pair of large ropelike structures that emerge from the anterior border of the pons and diverge from each other as they extend toward the under surface of the cerebral hemispheres
  B. Dorsal portion comprises the corpora quadrigemina (also called the *superior* and *inferior colliculi*)

  3. Hindbrain (rhombencephalon, made up of metencephalon and myelencephalon); surrounds fourth ventricle
  A. Metencephalon
   a. Cerebellum
   b. Pons
  B. Myelencephalon or medulla oblongata

STRUCTURE AND FUNCTIONS

  The primary divisions are illustrated in Figure 160. When the cerebral hemispheres and the cerebellum are removed, the remaining basal portions of the brain constitute the "brain stem."
  The outer part of the brain is composed of gray matter, and here and there within the underlying white matter in the brain there are collections of nerve cell bodies. These masses of gray matter within the white matter are called *nuclei* (or, incorrectly, ganglia).
  The myelinated nerve fibers which make up the white matter of the brain form 3 groups: projection, commissural and associational fibers.
  Projection fibers are those which transmit impulses from one level of the central nervous system to another.
  Commissural fibers transmit impulses from one cerebral hemisphere to the other.
  Associational fibers are those which transmit impulses from one part of the cerebral cortex to another on the same side. They do not cross from one side to the other or pass to lower levels of the central nervous system.
  The original cavity of the primitive neural tube (Fig. 173) per-

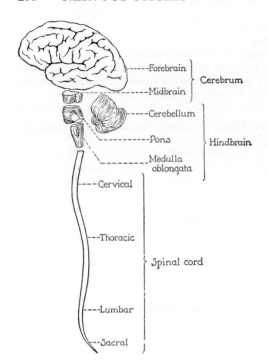

Forebrain
Midbrain
} Cerebrum

Cerebellum
Pons
Medulla oblongata
} Hindbrain

Cervical

Thoracic

Spinal cord

Lumbar

Sacral

FIG. 160. Diagram of the central nervous system. Various parts of the brain and the spinal cord have been separated from one another. The term "cerebrum" includes the forebrain and the midbrain. If the cerebral hemispheres of the forebrain and the cerebellum of the hindbrain are removed, the remaining parts comprise the brain stem (diencephalon, midbrain, pons and medulla). (Adapted from Morris)

sists and eventually comes to form the 4 *ventricles* of the brain, their communicating channels and the central cavity of the spinal cord. The first and the second ventricles are the *lateral* ventricles. They lie within the cerebral hemispheres and are shown as they appear by x-rays in an encephalogram (Fig. 161). Each lateral ventricle consists of a body and 2 horns; one horn extends into the frontal lobe (p. 309) and another into the temporal lobe (p. 309). The interventricular foramina are communicating channels between the 2 lateral ventricles and the third ventricle, as shown in Figure 162. The third ventricle is a narrow cleft which communicates with the fourth ventricle by way of the cerebral aqueduct. From the fourth ventricle there are 3 openings into the cranial subarachnoid space; the 2 lateral openings are called the *foramina of Luschka,* and the medial one is called the *foramen of Magendie.* These openings from the fourth ventricle are indicated by arrows in Figure 162. The fourth ventricle connects with the central canal of the spinal cord.

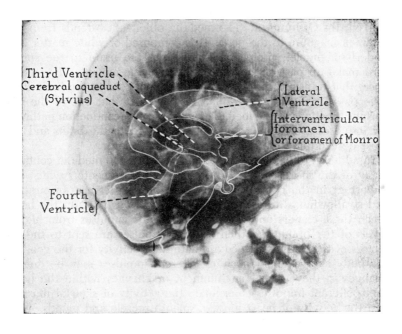

FIG. 161. Encephalogram, showing the ventricles of the brain and their connecting channels. (From Dr. Kuhlenbeck)

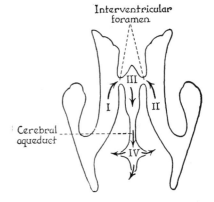

FIG. 162. Outline of the ventricles of the brain. Arrows indicate direction of flow of cerebrospinal fluid.

Hindbrain

Medulla Oblongata. The medulla oblongata extends from the foramen magnum to the pons. It is composed of white matter and underlying nuclei; projection fibers from the brain to the spinal cord make up part of the white matter of the medulla. Projection fibers that transmit impulses from the spinal cord to the brain likewise pass through the medulla. It is evident that one of the important functions of the medulla is to serve as a conduction pathway for impulses ascending from the spinal cord to the brain and for those descending from the brain to the spinal cord.

In addition to being a conduction pathway, the medulla contains many of the so-called "vital centers." These are centers which are important in the control of the heart, blood pressure, respiration and swallowing. Afferent impulses from various parts of the body reach these centers and are integrated with impulses from higher levels of the brain, and then efferent impulses are sent to the effectors of the body which co-ordinate their activity for the good of the body as a whole. Incoming afferent impulses may be due to changes in the external environment or changes within the body itself; efferent impulses co-ordinate the activity of skeletal muscles and the activity of heart muscle, smooth muscle and glands. This means that the medulla is a reflex center of prime importance. One example of a reflex which is handled at the level of the medulla is swallowing; this is aroused when the mucosa of the oral pharynx is stimulated. A mass of food (or an applicator) arouses afferent impulses when it touches the mucosa of the pharynx. These impulses reach the medulla, are shunted to the swallowing center, and the act of swallowing ensues. This not only means contraction of the muscles in the wall of the pharynx and the esophagus but also means inhibition of respiration while the food passes through the pharynx to the esophagus and the elevation of the larynx to close the respiratory passages. Place your fingers on your larynx and swallow, and you will feel the elevation of the larynx. The act of swallowing is even more complex, since it involves movement of the tongue, closure of the nasopharynx, relaxation of the sphincter at the lower end of the esophagus and a change in the tone of the muscles of the stomach wall. Yet a new-born babe can perform this complicated reflex act if something is placed in his mouth.

Pons. The term *pons* means "bridge." The pons extends from the medulla to the midbrain. It is composed of white matter with scattered nuclei of gray matter. The pons is an important part of

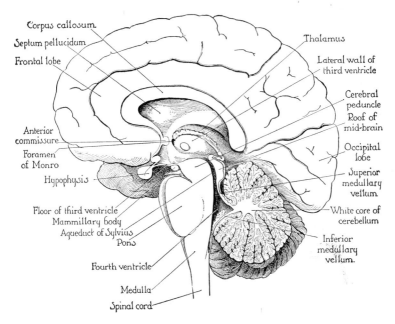

Corpus callosum
Septum pellucidum
Frontal lobe
Anterior commissure
Foramen of Monro
Hypophysis
Floor of third ventricle
Mammillary body
Aqueduct of Sylvius
Pons
Fourth ventricle
Medulla
Spinal cord

Thalamus
Lateral wall of third ventricle
Cerebral peduncle
Roof of mid-brain
Occipital lobe
Superior medullary vellum
White core of cerebellum
Inferior medullary vellum.

FIG. 163. Human brain seen in midsagittal section, showing relations of forebrain, midbrain, hindbrain, ventricles and hypophysis or pituitary gland.

the conduction pathway between the cerebral cortex and the cerebellum. The pons is also a reflex center; some of the reflexes of respiration are handled at the level of the pons.

Cerebellum. The term cerebellum means "little brain." The cerebellum is the largest part of the hindbrain. It overlaps the pons and the medulla, and in turn is overlapped by the occipital lobe of the cerebral cortex as shown in Figure 163. The cerebellum is attached to the midbrain and other parts of the hindbrain by 3 cerebellar peduncles (bundles of nerve fibers), called the *superior,* the *middle* and the *inferior* cerebellar peduncles.

In man, the superior peduncle is the smallest of the three. It transmits some afferent impulses from the spinal cord to the cerebellar cortex. It transmits efferent impulses from cerebellar nuclei to the spinal cord, by way of the red nucleus and reticular formation, and to the cerebral cortex by way of the red nucleus and the thalamus. The middle peduncle is the largest of the three: it transmits impulses to the cerebellar cortex from the cerebral cortex by way of the pons. The inferior peduncle transmits afferent impulses from the spinal cord, the medulla and some cranial nerves to the cerebellar cortex. It also transmits some efferent impulses from the cerebellar nuclei to the vestibular nuclei in the medulla.

The outer portion of the cerebellum is composed of gray matter; beneath this there is white matter which is composed of nerve fibers. Deep within the white matter are masses of gray matter which are called the *cerebellar nuclei*. The cut surface of the cerebellum looks like the leaves of a tree (Fig. 163).

The 2 major divisions of the cerebellum are the flocculonodular lobe (meaning "little tuft of wool" and "nodular") and the corpus cerebelli, which are separated by the posterolateral fissure. The corpus cerebelli is subdivided into anterior and posterior lobes by the fissura prima. The parts of the cerebellum are shown in Figure 164.

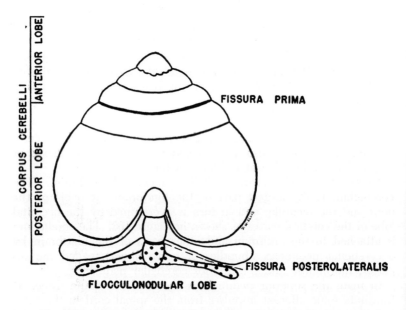

Fig. 164. The cerebellum. The fissura prima separates the corpus cerebelli into anterior and posterior lobes; the fissura posterolateralis separates the corpus cerebelli from the flocculonodular lobe. (Modified from Larsell, O.: Arch. Neurol. & Psychiat. **38**:580)

THE FLOCCULONODULAR LOBE is the vestibular portion of the cerebellum; it receives fibers from the vestibular nuclei which are closely connected with the internal ear (p. 369), and outgoing fibers connect it with midbrain, medulla and spinal cord. It is concerned with the maintenance of equilibrium or balance and the proper orientation in space. The flocculonodular lobe is concerned with motion sickness. The receptors in the semicircular canals (p. 371) are stimulated by swinging or some other form of motion, and the afferent impulses are transmitted to the flocculonodular lobe. From this reflex center impulses are discharged to the medulla, and excessive secretion of saliva (salivation) and vomiting ensue. Glands, skeletal muscle and smooth muscle are involved in the reponse to motion sickness.

THE ANTERIOR LOBE of the cerebellum receives fibers from, and sends fibers to, the midbrain, the medulla and the spinal cord. This portion of the cerebellum is concerned with the adjustment of tone in skeletal muscles. It influences the stretch reflexes which are handled in the spinal cord by way of its connections with the nuclei in the midbrain, and these in turn send impulses to the neurons whose cell bodies are located in the anterior horn of gray matter in the spinal cord.

THE POSTERIOR LOBE of the cerebellum receives fibers from, and sends fibers to, the cerebral cortex of the opposite side. It is responsible for the final delicate adjustments by which various muscle groups act smoothly and harmoniously in carrying out co-ordinated movements. Impulses from the cerebellum in some way regulate the inhibition of antagonistic muscles and stimulate synergistic muscles to just the proper degree. The posterior lobe of the cerebellum thus permits a perfect gradation and amount of skeletal muscular activity as is essential in accurate voluntary movements. The cerebellum is not concerned with sensation.

Midbrain

The midbrain is a short, narrow segment of nervous tissue which connects the forebrain with the hindbrain. It comprises the structures that enclose the cerebral aqueduct. They are the cerebral peduncles on the ventral surface (Fig. 163) and the corpora quadrigemina (also called the *superior* and the *inferior colliculi*) on the dorsal surface or roof of the midbrain. The cerebral peduncles, which connect the forebrain with the hindbrain, are projection fibers, and they unite the cerebral cortex with other levels of the central nervous system. The peduncles are composed of white matter, and the corpora quadrigemina of gray matter. The corpora quadrigemina are concerned with visual and auditory reflexes. They connect with the nuclei of the cranial nerves (oculomotor, trochlear and abducens) which move the eyeball in accordance with changes in the position of the head. They are responsible also for turning the head to hear sounds on one side of us.

There are many centers for postural and righting reflexes in the midbrain. Postural reflexes are concerned with the position of the head in relation to the trunk and with the adjustments of the extremities (Fig. 165) and the eyes to the position of the head. The

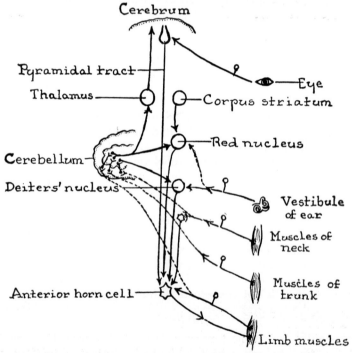

FIG. 165. Regulation of posture. Impulses pass to various parts of the central nervous system from the eyes, the vestibules of the ears and the neck, the trunk and the limb muscles. Impulses from the cortex, the cerebellum (by way of the red nucleus and vestibular or Deiter's nucleus), the red nucleus, Deiter's nucleus and a few other regions converge to the anterior horn cell. Impulses pass from this cell to the limb muscles and regulate tone and posture. (Modified from Wright)

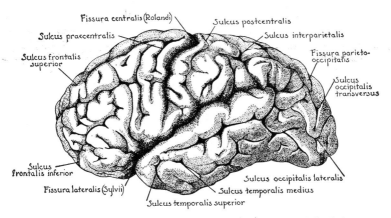

Fissura centralis (Rolandi)

Sulcus postcentralis

Sulcus praecentralis

Sulcus interparietalis

Sulcus frontalis superior

Fissura parieto-occipitalis

Sulcus occipitalis transversus

Sulcus frontalis inferior

Sulcus occipitalis lateralis

Fissura lateralis (Sylvii)

Sulcus temporalis medius

Sulcus temporalis superior

FIG. 166. Fissures and sulci of the lateral aspect of the left cerebral hemisphere.

righting reflexes are concerned with the orientation of the head in space; men and animals are alike in wishing to keep the head right side up. This is made possible by the eyes, the inner ear (p. 369) and the skeletal muscles of the neck and the trunk. When an animal is placed on its back a chain of reflexes is initiated to put it right side up again. The cerebral cortex, the midbrain, the medulla, the cerebellum and the spinal cord are involved. Impulses which reach the midbrain from many sources are grouped in such centers as the red nucleus and are sent to the cell bodies in the anterior horn of gray matter of the spinal cord, over extra-pyramidal pathways, and to the nuclei of several of the cranial nerves from which efferent impulses are discharged to effectors to complete the reflex acts required to put the animal right side up with the universe. The impulses from the eyes are of greatest importance in keeping human beings right side up.

In summary, it is evident that the midbrain is both a conduction pathway and a reflex center of great importance, as are all the levels of the central nervous system below it.

Forebrain

The forebrain is the largest division of the brain. It consists of the telencephalon or cerebral hemispheres and the diencephalon (Figs. 163 and 166).

The diencephalon lies under cover of the cerebral hemispheres and is hidden by them except on the ventral aspect of the brain. The only portions of the diencephalon that will be discussed are the hypothalamus and the thalamus.

THE HYPOTHALAMUS is the chief subcortical center for the regulation of visceral activities. Craniosacral activities are integrated in the anterior portion of the hypothalamus, and thoracolumbar activities are integrated in the lateral and the posterior portions. The hypothalamus has extensive connections with the cerebral cortex, the thalamus, the midbrain, the hindbrain and the cell bodies of the cranial and the spinal nerves that contain preganglionic fibers concerned with visceral efferent activities. Visceral and somatic functions are integrated in the hypothalamus for the purpose of maintaining homeostasis. Examples of this are the constriction of blood vessels and shivering in response to cold, and the dilatation of blood vessels and panting (in dogs) in response to heat.

Many centers of control are located in the hypothalamus; these are for regulation of temperature, water balance, sleep and emotional expression. The last is shown in animals after removal of the cerebral cortex. Such "decorticated" animals show signs of rage when they are stimulated, but the rage is undirected. It is called *sham rage,* since the animal never attacks an enemy. Human beings who permit themselves to indulge in "blind rages" seem to be decorticated functionally during such episodes, since, temporarily, they are not using the cortical level of the brain.

THE THALAMUS (Figs. 167 and 168) receives impulses from all parts of the body. These afferent impulses are sorted out and rearranged, and those having to do with similar functions are grouped together and then relayed to a definite area in the cerebral cortex. Consequently, the thalamus is a sensory integrating organ of great complexity, and its activities are related to consciousness. It is not concerned with discrimination, but with the "affective" side of sensation, such as pain, agreeableness or disagreeableness. The thalamus not only relays impulses to the cerebral cortex but also receives impulses from the cerebral cortex through its connections with the frontal lobe. The thalamus has extensive connections with other parts of the brain. By means of its connections with the hypothalamus it can exert an influence on visceral and somatic effectors.

Before closing the discussion of the diencephalon, we wish to mention the "reticular formation." This refers to a sort of background material of the central nervous system that is composed of small islands of gray matter (cell bodies) separated by fine bundles

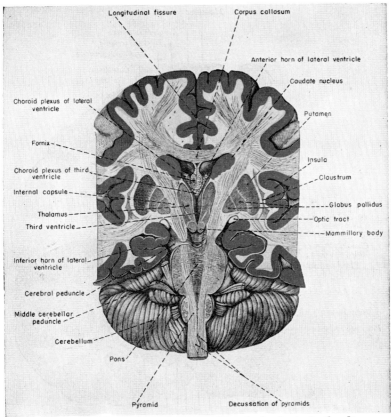

Longitudinal fissure

Corpus callosum

Anterior horn of lateral ventricle

Caudate nucleus

Choroid plexus of lateral ventricle

Putamen

Fornix

Insula

Choroid plexus of third ventricle

Claustrum

Internal capsule

Globus pallidus

Thalamus

Optic tract

Third ventricle

Mammillary body

Inferior horn of lateral ventricle

Cerebral peduncle

Middle cerebellar peduncle

Cerebellum

Pons

Pyramid

Decussation of pyramids

Fig. 167. Oblique frontal section through the brain in the direction of the cerebral peduncles and the pyramids, as seen from in front. (After Toldt) (From Schaeffer, J. P.: Morris' Human Anatomy, ed. 11, New York, Blakiston Division of McGraw-Hill)

of nerve fibers that run in every direction. It extends from the upper portion of the spinal cord forward through the medulla, the pons and the midbrain to the diencephalon. The reticular formation has widespread afferent connections and, in turn, sends efferent impulses to both the lower and the higher levels of the central nervous system. It augments both reflex and voluntary movements and helps to make possible optimum motor activity. Also it is capable of inhibiting certain activities; in other words, it can regulate the background activities of the rest of the nervous system by excitation of some and inhibition of other activities.

The reticular formation is thought to have a cephalic influence

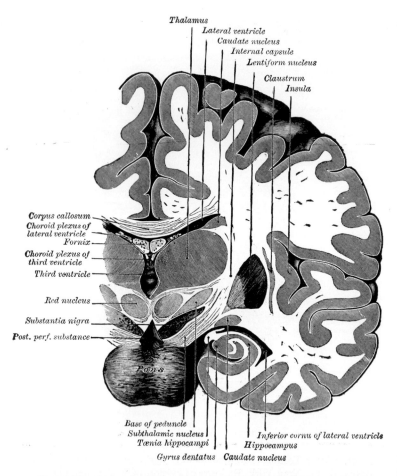

Thalamus
Lateral ventricle
Caudate nucleus
Internal capsule
Lentiform nucleus
Claustrum
Insula

Corpus callosum
Choroid plexus of lateral ventricle
Fornix
Choroid plexus of third ventricle
Third ventricle

Red nucleus

Substantia nigra
Post. perf. substance

Pons

Base of peduncle
Subthalamic nucleus
Tœnia hippocampi
Gyrus dentatus   Caudate nucleus
Inferior cornu of lateral ventricle
Hippocampus

FIG. 168. Coronal section of brain immediately in front of pons. Some of the basal ganglia of the cerebral hemisphere, the thalamus of the diencephalon, the red nucleus of the midbrain and the pons are shown. (From Lewis, W. H.: Gray's Anatomy, ed. 26, Philadelphia, Lea and Febiger)

that activates and regulates cortical activities that underlie the state of wakefulness or alertness, on which the highest functions of the cerebral cortex depend. The functions of the reticular formation are being studied extensively, and its great importance is just beginning to be appreciated.

Telencephalon or Cerebral Hemispheres. The cerebral hemispheres (rhinencephalon, basal ganglia and cerebral cortex) extend posteriorly and overlap other portions of the brain (Fig. 163). The space between them is called the *longitudinal fissure* (Fig. 167). At the bottom of this fissure, the hemispheres are connected by the *corpus callosum* (meaning a "firm" or "tough body"), as shown in Figure 167.

THE RHINENCEPHALON comprises the olfactory portions of the cerebral hemispheres. This portion of the brain receives and integrates olfactory impulses. It establishes reflex connections with visceral activities, by way of the hypothalamus, and with somatic activities, by way of the midbrain and the medulla. It establishes cortical connections in the hippocampus (Fig. 168) in the floor of the inferior horn of the lateral ventricle; this is the olfactory center of the highest order. The hippocampus sends out both commissural and projection fibers. By means of the latter the olfactory sense can influence many activities.

THE BASAL GANGLIA comprise 4 masses of gray matter or nuclei deep within the white matter of the cerebral hemispheres. They are the caudate nucleus, the lentiform (or lenticular) nucleus, the amygdala and the claustrum (Fig. 167). The lentiform nucleus is subdivided into the putamen and the globus pallidus. The caudate nucleus and the lentiform nucleus, together with that portion of the internal capsule that lies between them, comprise the corpus striatum. The corpus striatum is an important link in the extrapyramidal motor pathways.

In man, the basal ganglia aid the activity of the motor area of the cerebral cortex in many ways. For example, when one "wills" to walk, impulses are sent from the motor cortex to the spinal cord and then are relayed out to the proper skeletal muscles of the lower extremities. Meanwhile, impulses are sent from another part of the cerebral cortex to the basal ganglia and then are relayed to lower levels of the central nervous system where they eventually bring about the swinging of the arms as one walks. A second example is talking, during which the cerebral cortex directs the muscles of lips, tongue, cheeks, larynx and diaphragm. In this case, the impulses from another part of the cerebral cortex reach the basal ganglia and then are forwarded to lower levels to bring about the changes in facial expression and the gesticulations that accompany speech.

The accessory movements that accompany voluntary activity are called *associated movements* and are dependent on the premotor area of the cerebral cortex and the basal ganglia. Impulses over these pathways exert effects on many of the same neurons which are supplied also by the corticospinal or pyramidal tracts. Another way of stating this is that impulses from motor and premotor areas (by way of the basal ganglia) converge on the same motor neurons in the spinal cord (final common path).

The internal capsule is one of the most important groups of projection fibers; it is shown in Figures 167 and 168. It continues on to form part of the cerebral peduncle on its own side.

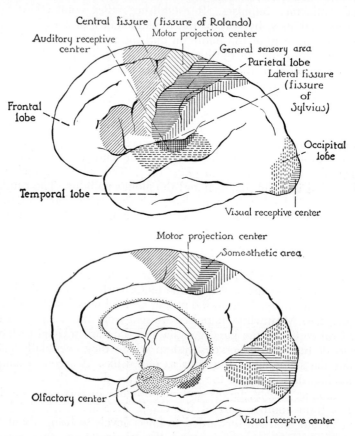

FIG. 169. Diagram of the localization of function in the cerebral hemisphere. The various functional areas are shown in relation to the lobes and the fissures: (*top*) lateral view; (*bottom*) medial view. (The somesthetic area is the same as the general sensory area.)

The cerebral cortex is the convoluted layer of gray matter upon the surface of each cerebral hemisphere. The ridges or hills are called *gyri* or *convolutions,* and the grooves or valleys are called *sulci* (Fig. 166). There are 2 very deep grooves on the lateral aspect of each cerebral cortex. The upper one is called the *central fissure* (fissure of Rolando), and the lower is called the *lateral fissure* (fissure of Sylvius); these are shown in Figure 166.

The cerebral cortex of each hemisphere is divided into 4 lobes: frontal, parietal, temporal and occipital. Each lobe takes the name of the cranial bone that covers it. The frontal lobe is anterior to the central fissure. The parietal lobe is posterior to the central fissure. Both are separated from the temporal lobe below by the lateral fissure. The temporal lobe is below the lateral fissure, and the occipital lobe forms the posterior pole of the cerebral cortex.

The insula or island of Reil is a part of the cortex which lies buried in the lateral fissure and can be seen only when the lips of that fissure are drawn apart. The lobes and the fissures are illustrated in Figure 169, *top.*

Beneath the gray matter of the cerebral cortex there is white matter composed of projection, association and commissural fibers. The largest group of commissural fibers is the corpus callosum, shown in Figures 163, 167 and 168. Other groups of commissural fibers are the anterior commissure, the middle commissure and the posterior commissure, the optic chiasma and the *fornix* (meaning an "arch"). The anterior commissure is shown in Figure 163, and the optic chiasma in Figure 147.

The cerebral cortex is the organ of sensation. It is concerned with the discriminative aspect of sensation. This means that sensations are compared as to intensity, place of stimulation and relative positions in space and time. Sensations are integrated into perceptions of form, size and texture; movements are judged as to extent, direction and sequence. Sensations are the foundation of knowledge and the means by which we acquire information about the external and internal environments. Abstract thought is made possible by the activity of the cerebral cortex. It is estimated that there are about 14 billion nerve cells in the cerebral cortex of man.

THE FRONTAL LOBE is subdivided into precentral, premotor, orbito-frontal and speech areas.

The precentral area is just anterior to the central fissure. It is the motor area which controls voluntary movement and from which projection fibers transmit impulses to lower brain levels (nuclei of cranial nerves and other masses of subcortical gray matter) and spinal cord (nuclei of spinal nerves). These projection fibers constitute the corticospinal or pyramidal tracts which cross to the opposite side of the body before they end. Because of this, each half of the cerebral cortex controls the skeletal muscles of the opposite side of the body.

The premotor area lies just anterior to the precentral area in the frontal lobe. Its projection fibers transmit impulses to the basal ganglia. Between the precentral and the premotor areas there is a narrow strip of cerebral cortex which is called a *suppressor strip*. In animals, stimulation of this strip stops the activity in skeletal muscles due to impulses coming from the motor area, indicating an inhibitory function. This suppressor strip connects with the inhibitory portion of the reticular formation in the medulla. As yet its function in man is unknown.

All of the activities of the body which are regulated through visceral efferent or autonomic nerves are influenced, to some degree, by impulses from the cerebral cortex, especially the motor and the premotor areas. There is an extensive overlapping of the areas involved in somatic and visceral efferent functions which makes possible an excellent correlation between such functions. In other words, the areas that are chiefly concerned in the cortical regulation of definite visceral functions (such as vasodilatation of arterioles of skeletal muscles) are thought to be located near the cortical areas which control the voluntary contractions of such skeletal muscles.

The orbitofrontal area lies anterior to the premotor area and comprises all of the frontal pole of the cerebral cortex. This is concerned with the autonomic system and has extensive connections with the hypothalamus. This area is of great clinical importance since this part of the brain is involved in frontal lobotomy (severing the connections of this region from underlying parts of the central nervous system). This operation is done to relieve patients who are victims of unbearable pain due to a spreading cancer. Also, it is performed in patients who have various types of neuroses, depressions and psychoses. Loss of intelligence is not conspicuous after lobotomy, although there may be some decrease in general intelligence. Such postoperative patients cannot analyze situations and cannot plan. They have no foresight and cannot anticipate future events on the basis of past experiences. They fail to grasp the seriousness of any situation and are highly distractible, turning from one activity to another without completing anything. There are regressive changes in conduct and ethical standards.

In summary, it seems that the function of this portion of the brain is the integration of behavior and emotional life; it is not the seat of intelligence.

The speech area lies at the base of the motor area and a little anterior to it. It is called *Broca's area.* The speech center is in the left cerebral cortex in right-handed individuals and in the right cerebral cortex in left-handed individuals. If a child who is naturally left-handed is made to write with his right hand he may develop a speech and reading difficulty. It seems as if "handedness" is linked with cerebral dominance; the left hemisphere dominates in right-handed persons.

THE PARIETAL LOBE. The great general sensory area is located in the parietal lobe. The sensations of pain, heat, cold, touch, muscle sense, spatial relationships and recognition of size, shape and texture of objects depend upon the activities of this lobe. The left hemisphere receives impulses from the right side of the body, and vice versa.

THE TEMPORAL LOBE. The center for hearing lies in the temporal lobe; each hemisphere receives impulses from both ears.

THE OCCIPITAL LOBE. The center for vision lies in the occipital lobe (Fig. 169, *bottom*). The right occipital cortex receives impulses from the right half of each eye, and the left cortex receives impulses from the left half of each eye.

The remaining areas in the adjoining portions of the parietal, the occipital and the temporal lobes are concerned with the understanding of spoken and written language. They are called associational areas. It is not known where memory, reasoning and abstract thinking are carried out, but it is probable that the cerebral cortex as a whole is involved in these processes.

Cortical Effects on Reflex Activities of Lower Centers. The cerebral cortex modifies reflex activities of lower centers. The situation may be compared with that of a student nurse; what she is permitted to do for a certain patient depends on the senior nurse in the same ward, the floor supervisor and the superintendent of nurses. The student nurse has freedom within limits; just so, the spinal reflexes are really subject to control by the higher centers. In the body when the higher level is removed by disease the activities of the spinal cord are modified in 2 ways: (1) some activities are not carried out at all, and (2) others are exaggerated. The absence of some activities is expressed as a deficiency phenomenon, and it can be illustrated by the absence of movement in paralyzed muscles or the absence of sensation in parts of the body unable to send impulses to the brain. The exaggeration of other activities is expressed as a release phenomenon, and it can be illustrated by an exaggerated knee jerk when the cerebral cortex is damaged.

Conditioned Reflexes. The cerebral cortex is important in the formation of conditioned reflexes. These are acquired and are peculiar to the individual. They differ markedly from the unconditioned reflexes, such as the knee jerk, which are inborn, predictable and alike in all of us. Conditioned reflexes enter largely into human behavior, and we have conditioned reflexes in connection with most of our activities, as shown by the following examples. One person puts on both stockings and then both shoes; another puts on the left stocking, the left shoe, then the right. One puts on the stockings and shoes before the dress, another puts them on last. We also have many conditioned reflexes in connection with meals. One polishes the silver with her napkin before she eats, another wants her salad first, another wants her coffee with her dinner, and so on.

What are your conditioned reflexes in connection with study? Do you want the radio blaring? Do you want the room to be quiet? Do you get down to work promptly or do you put it off and do everything else you can think of before you get at your lessons? Do you study before you get ready for bed? Or do you prefer to undress and lounge in a comfortable chair while you study? Do you spend a large part of your study time complaining about the long assignment in anatomy and physiology before you settle down to tackle it?

If you observe your own conditioned reflexes for a day you will be surprised at the number you have and how they influence your behavior. It is no wonder that people have difficulty in adjusting to each other when each individual is so controlled by her own particular conditioned reflexes that she becomes intolerant of those of the people about her.

Sleep. Sleep is the condition in which the cerebral cortex is relatively inactive and consciousness is lost. Yet most of us can be brought back to a state of wakefulness with relative ease. A feeling of lassitude precedes sleep; the eyelids droop; the eyes feel dry; and the lids may itch. When we retire we have a characteristic pattern of going to sleep. The deepest sleep occurs about 1½ hours after going to sleep. We change position frequently during the night, due to overheating some parts of the body, stretching of some muscles, cramping of joints, pressure of the bed clothing on part of the body, and so on.

The degree of exhaustion bears no relation to the depth of sleep;

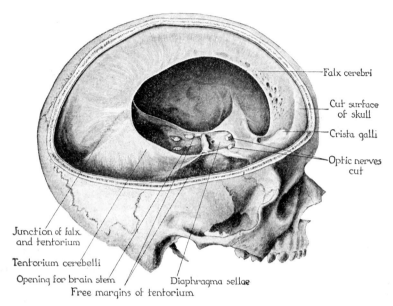

Falx cerebri

Cut surface
of skull

Crista galli

Optic nerves
cut

Junction of falx
and tentorium

Tentorium cerebelli

Opening for brain stem

Diaphragma sellae

Free margins of tentorium

FIG. 170. Dura mater. Side of skull removed, showing falx cerebri and tentorium cerebelli. These are extensions of the dura mater between the two cerebral hemispheres, and between the cerebrum and the cerebellum, respectively.

in fact, one may be too tired to sleep. Worries are reflected in sleep; they make one sleep lightly. For those who find it difficult to drop off to sleep when they retire, the following suggestions may be of help. Freedom from pain is essential; one does not go to sleep readily if in pain. Darkness and quiet make it easier for most individuals to go to sleep, although there are exceptions to this. We have seen students go to sleep in class with bright lights shining and the teacher talking. The temperature of the bedroom should be agreeable, and the amount of bed clothing satisfactory. Some young people like to eat (usually some highly undigestible food) before going to bed; it is more difficult to go to sleep if one is hungry. Dull stories usually help one to get to sleep. A warm bath relaxes some individuals; it stimulates others. Muscular relaxation usually makes it easier to get to sleep. Drugs should be used only as a last resort, after all other measures have proved to be ineffective, and only on the recommendation of a physician.

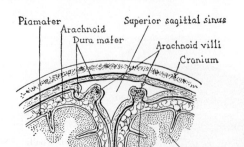

Piamater
Arachnoid
Dura mater
Superior sagittal sinus
Arachnoid villi
Cranium
Brain substance

FIG. 171. Meninges. Arachnoid villi or pacchionian bodies within superior sagittal sinus; one site of passage of the cerebrospinal fluid into the blood. (After Weed)

COVERINGS OF THE BRAIN

Meninges

The cranial bones cover the brain and protect it. The inner covering is membranous and is composed of the 3 meninges.

Dura Mater. The cranial portion of the dura mater consists of 2 layers. It not only covers the brain but also lines the interior of the skull and serves as the internal periosteum of the cranial bones. The two layers of the dura mater are in contact with each other in some places, and in other places they are separated, and the spaces or channels between them are filled with blood. These blood-filled channels of the dura mater are called the *cranial venous sinuses* and are not to be confused with the air sinuses of the cranial bones (p. 124).

Extensions from the dura mater project as protecting partitions between parts of the brain. The projection of dura mater which separates the right and the left halves of the brain is called the *falx cerebri;* it is shown in Figure 170. The superior sagittal or longitudinal venous sinus lies in the upper margin, and the inferior sagittal or longitudinal venous sinus lies in the lower margin of the falx cerebri. These are shown in Figure 255. A second projection of the dura mater extends between the occipital lobes of the cerebrum and the cerebellum; this is called the *tentorium cerebelli* (Fig. 170). The transverse or lateral and superior petrosal venous sinuses are contained in this projection (Fig. 255). The straight venous sinus lies in the line of junction of the falx cerebri and the tentorium cerebelli.

Arachnoid. The middle layer of the meninges or arachnoid sends little extensions (called *villi*) into the dura mater in the region of the superior sagittal or longitudinal venous sinus. The

FIG. 172. Schematic diagram to show the relations of the pia mater, the arachnoid, the blood vessels and the brain. The perineuronal and perivascular spaces are in communication with the subarachnoid space. (Weed, L. H.: Am. J. Anat. 31:202)

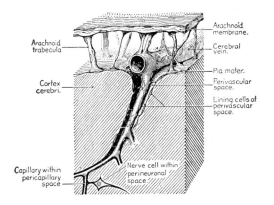

Arachnoid membrane.

Cerebral vein.

Pia mater.

Perivascular space.

Lining cells of perivascular space.

Arachnoid trabecula

Cortex cerebri.

Capillary within pericapillary space

Nerve cell within perineuronal space

rounded ends of these villi appear like granules and are called *pacchionian* bodies after the man who described them first. The villi are shown in Figure 171.

Pia Mater. The inner layer of the meninges or pia mater covers the brain very closely and follows all of the "hills and valleys" of the brain surface. The larger blood vessels of the brain lie in the subarachnoid space, and branches from these pass through the pia mater and enter the brain substance, as shown in Figure 172. In certain places the pia mater is caught in the folds of the developing brain (p. 316) and bits of it remain there and become the choroid plexuses of the ventricles. The pia mater and the arachnoid are connected by a network of fine threadlike structures; in some areas over the brain it is difficult to separate them.

Cerebrospinal fluid

The cerebrospinal fluid is a clear, watery fluid that fills the ventricles of the brain, the perivascular (around the blood vessels) spaces, the perineuronal (around nerve cell bodies) spaces and the subarachnoid space. Some of it is formed by the choroid plexuses of the ventricles, and the remainder is formed by filtration from the capillaries just as is tissue fluid elsewhere (p. 401). The communication of the perivascular and the perineuronal spaces with the subarachnoid space is illustrated in Figure 172. Cerebrospinal fluid is absorbed by 2 pathways: (1) it enters the blood of the venous sinuses from the arachnoid villi and the blood capillaries throughout the extent of the central nervous system and (2) it passes along the tissue spaces of the sheaths of all the cranial and the spinal nerves and enters lymphatic capillaries. Ventricles, perivascular spaces, perineuronal spaces, subarachnoid space and tissue spaces along the cranial and the spinal nerve sheaths are continuous.

The cerebrospinal fluid protects the central nervous system from mechanical injuries by acting as a shock absorber or fluid buffer. It serves as a reservoir to help regulate the contents of the cranium and is a pathway of exchange of nutrient material and waste between the blood and the cells of the central nervous system. It varies in amount from 100 to 200 cc. in an adult. It is formed and drained continuously as is tissue fluid elsewhere. The average specific gravity is 1.006. The average pressure of the fluid in the cranial and the spinal subarachnoid spaces is between 70 and 200 mm. of water in the lateral recumbent position. If the flow of blood from the venous sinuses into the internal jugular veins is shut off temporarily by pressure, the intracranial pressure rises; this is the basis of the Queckenstedt test. In the upright position the intracranial pressure falls to zero, and the pressure of the fluid in the lumbar region of the subarachnoid space rises to between 400 and 500 mm. of water. During convulsions the intracranial pressure may rise to about 50 mm. of mercury (13.6 times greater than water).

EMBRYOLOGY OF THE NERVOUS SYSTEM

The embryonic disk from which the embryo develops is shown in Figure 416. The ectoderm of the disk folds up into 2 longitudinal ridges which are called *neural folds;* the space between them is called the *neural groove.* All these structures are shown in Figure 417. The neural groove deepens, and the folds become elevated until they meet and fuse in the mid-line and convert the groove into a tube called the *neural tube.* These various stages are shown in Figure 173.

As the neural tube closes, some masses of cells separate but continue to lie by the tube; these are called cells of the *ganglionic crest.* The neural tube develops into the brain and the spinal cord. The cranial end of the tube develops several expansions or dilatations, which form 4 vesicles, as shown in Figure 173. The cavities of the vesicles form the ventricles of the brain and their connecting channels. The walls of the vesicles form the nervous tissue of the brain. The remainder of the tube forms the spinal cord. The cavity becomes the central canal of the spinal cord, and the walls form the nervous tissue of the spinal cord.

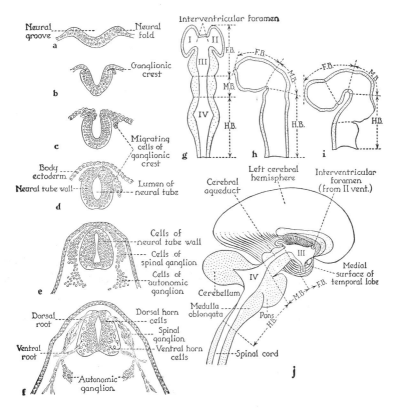

FIG. 173. Embryology of nervous system. (*a* to *f*.) Transverse sections of neural tube: a, neural groove and fold; b, c, and d, closing neural fold to form neural tube; b, ganglionic crest; c, d, and e, migration of ganglionic cells to form spinal ganglion and autonomic ganglion; f, neural tube in spinal cord region. Cells of tube, cells of ganglia growing nerve fibers: g, h, and i, brain region of neural tube showing foldings and thickenings of wall; g, four vesicles are shown: walls about I, II, and III constitute the forebrain; the walls about the duct connecting III and IV constitute the midbrain; the walls about IV constitute the hindbrain. h and i, the same brain vesicles and walls in later development; j, advanced development of walls of ventricles, showing forebrain, midbrain and hindbrain with some of the principal structures.

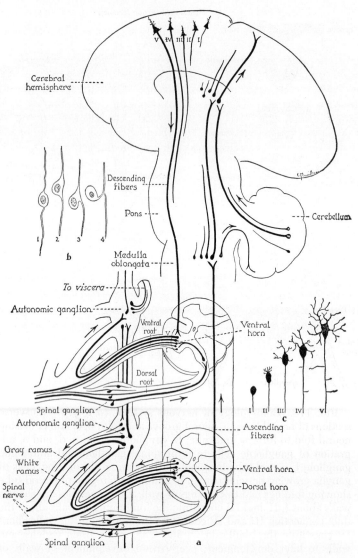

Fig. 174. Diagram of growth of neurons in the development of
the nervous system. (c) I, II, III, IV and V represent the growth of
the fibers from one efferent neuron at different ages. (b) 1, 2, 3
and 4 successive stages in the development of afferent neuron; fusion

(Continued on facing page)

The cells that split off as the ganglionic crest are the beginning of the cranial and the spinal dorsal root ganglia and the autonomic ganglia. The primitive ganglia migrate ventrally along the sides of the neural tube and form the cranial and the spinal ganglia. As the migration is going on, some cells split off from the ventral ends and become the autonomic ganglia. The various stages of this are shown in Figure 173.

The neurons of the nervous system develop from the neuroblasts or embryonic nerve cells in the walls of the neural tube and the ganglionic crest. The processes appear as outgrowths from the pointed ends of the developing nerve cells, as shown in Figure 174. The first outgrowth forms the axon; later outgrowths form the dendrites. The neurilemma appears later. The myelin sheath is the last to be laid down. The outgrowths continue to grow until they establish connections with receptors, effectors or other neurons, as shown in Figure 174.

From the cells in the ventral portion of the spinal cord nerve fibers begin to grow out, as shown in Figure 174. These are the axons which eventually form the anterior roots of the spinal nerves. The dendrites establish connections with axons of other neurons within the spinal cord.

From the cells in the spinal ganglia, axons grow into the posterior portion of the spinal cord and form the posterior roots, as

Fig. 174 (*Continued*)

of processes of bipolar neuron to form T-shaped structures. (a) Illustrates method by which cells located in the neural-tube wall and in the spinal ganglia and in the autonomic ganglia grow fibers in the formation of conducting paths. In the upper spinal ganglion, cells are represented at four different ages; it is seen that the axon grows into the spinal cord through the dorsal root, and the dendrite grows out to the periphery. In the lower spinal ganglion 1, 2, 3 and 4 are cells growing axons which pass up the spinal cord as ascending fibers to reach the higher centers. The upper ventral horn is shown growing axons to the periphery through the ventral root and dendrites which remain within the spinal cord. The ventral horn in the lower spinal segment is shown growing axons through the white ramus to the autonomic ganglion. The lower autonomic ganglion is shown growing fibers through the gray ramus to the spinal nerve. The upper autonomic ganglion is shown growing fibers to the viscera. Nerve fibers are shown growing between the autonomic ganglia. Cells of various parts of the brain wall are shown growing fibers to other parts of the brain. Cells of the cerebral cortex are shown growing descending fibers to the spinal cord.

shown in Figure 174. The dendrites grow toward the periphery, after joining the ventral roots, with which they form the spinal nerves.

The development of the brain consists essentially of folds and thickenings of the walls of the vesicles; 2 steps in the process are shown in Figure 173.

PRACTICAL CONSIDERATIONS
INJURY TO THE SPINAL CORD

If the spinal cord is severed due to injury to the vertebral column, it is referred to as a "broken back." The results of an injury below the level of the cervical plexus will be described. So long as the cervical plexus is not damaged the phrenic nerves to the diaphragm permit the patient to breathe. The entire body below the level of injury is paralyzed, and sensation is abolished in the same region. All spinal reflexes are absent. After a period of several weeks a flexor reflex appears. If the sole of the foot is stroked, there is slight flexion of the leg. As time goes on, a "mass reflex" appears; this means that stroking the sole of the foot leads to flexion of both legs, an outburst of sweating and the emptying of bowel and bladder.

The nursing care of such a patient presents great difficulties; the patient can breathe and talk, the heart beats, and the blood circulates, but he cannot feed himself, scratch his nose when it itches or do anything for himself. Until a few years ago patients with broken backs died of bladder and kidney infections, since the "cord" bladder does not empty completely, and bacterial organisms flourish in the residual urine. Infection spreads rapidly from the bladder upward through the ureters and into the kidney. The advent of chemotherapy and antibiotics has completely changed the picture, and spinal cord damage no longer means early death. If excellent nursing care is given during the period of spinal shock (period during which reflexes are absent), the patient may survive for long periods of time. Use is made of the returning flexor reflex to establish bowel and bladder control. Local nerves take over the emptying of the bowel, and the bladder may be controlled largely by the amount of liquids taken. Due to the persistent efforts of many splendid physicians and nurses, a large percentage of patients who have spinal cord injuries below the midthoracic region have been taught to do many things by the use of braces and crutches. Many of them have been rehabilitated and made self-supporting; this is indeed a triumph for medicine and nursing.

INJURY TO VARIOUS TRACTS OF THE SPINAL CORD

Posterior Columns. Ataxic movements result from injury to the posterior columns since the afferent impulses from the muscles are unable to reach the brain. There is also astereognosis, which means that the individual loses the ability to recognize the size, the shape and the texture of objects. Syphilis of the spinal cord (locomotor ataxia or tabes dorsalis) leads to damage to the posterior columns.

Lateral Spinothalamic Tract. Injury to this tract is accompanied by loss of sensitivity to pain, warmth and cold. The first is called *analgesia,* and the last 2 *thermo-anesthesia.* Nurses must be especially alert if the latter condition exists, as the patient can be burned by hot water bottles and heating pads unless great care is exercised.

Ventral Spinothalamic Tract. Injury to this tract leads to an impairment of the sense of touch.

Spinocerebellar Tracts. Injury to these tracts leads to inco-ordinated voluntary movements, chiefly because of abnormal tone in the skeletal muscles.

Corticospinal Tracts. Injury to the corticospinal tracts leads to paralysis of skeletal muscles, the muscles being stiff or spastic.

MENINGITIS

Inflammation of the meninges is called meningitis. It may involve the dura only or it may involve the arachnoid and the pia mater. It may be due to a variety of infectious agents, such as the tubercle bacillus, meningococcus, streptococcus or staphylococcus.

MENINGOCELE, ENCEPHALOCELE AND SPINA BIFIDA

There may be congenital defects in the ossification of the cranial bones. In this condition a portion of the meninges protrudes in the form of a sac containing fluid, and this constitutes a *meningocele.* In addition to the meninges the protrusion may consist of brain tissue; this condition is called an *encephalocele. Spina bifida* is due to the failure of the laminae of the vertebrae to unite, and the contents of the spinal canal protrude through the gap.

EPIDURAL HEMORRHAGE

An epidural (or extradural) hemorrhage may occur in the vertebral canal. It is a collection of blood between the internal periosteum of the walls of the vertebral canal and the dura mater, due to injury of the vertebral column. It exerts pressure on the delicate spinal cord and damages it.

CEREBROSPINAL FLUID

When a spinal tap or lumbar puncture is made, the pressure of the spinal fluid is measured; it is above normal in meningitis, brain tumor and when there is any interference with drainage. As the fluid is collected the color (clearness or cloudiness) and the general appearance are noted. Cell counts are made; normally there are about 10 white blood cells per cu. mm. of spinal fluid. The chemical composition varies with disease, so it is necessary to make a chemical analysis for diagnostic purposes. Traces of protein are present normally; the amount increases in diseases of the spinal cord or meninges. Bacterial examinations are important also, in order to decide upon proper therapy.

Drugs are introduced into the spinal fluid for the treatment of some infections of the meninges. Spinal anesthetics are introduced into the spinal fluid; this is a frequently used type of anesthesia.

The technic of making a spinal tap or lumbar puncture is as follows. A long spinal needle is inserted in the mid-line between the third and the fourth or between the fourth and the fifth lumbar spines and is directed forward and slightly upward. By flexing the vertebral column as fully as possible, the interspinous spaces are widened. The needle is inserted to a depth of 5 cm. in an adult and 1.8 cm. in an infant. Fluid is withdrawn slowly into a syringe or is allowed to drop into a collecting tube.

Certain precautions are to be observed after a lumbar puncture, and they require nursing care. If some fluid has been removed for diagnostic purposes and none replaced, the patient is not allowed in the upright position for several hours. If this precaution is not observed, the medulla may tend to slip down into the foramen magnum because of the lowered pressure in the spinal subarachnoid space. If this happens, the pressure on the medulla, by the walls of the foramen, may lead to death. After several hours the upright position may be assumed without headache due to the tug on the meninges.

Hydrocephalus. If the channels between the ventricles (Figs. 161 and 162) or the foramina between the fourth ventricle and the subarachnoid space are blocked, the cerebrospinal fluid accumulates in the ventricles of the brain and distends them. This condition is called internal hydrocephalus. Hydrocephalus in a child of 11 years is illustrated in Figure 87.

Injury to the Medulla. This leads to death due to interference with the activity of the vital centers which control respiration, heart and blood pressure.

INJURY TO THE CEREBELLUM

The disturbances that follow injury to the cerebellum vary with the part of the cerebellum involved. If the *flocculonodular lobe* alone is involved, there is a loss of equilibrium, a reeling walk and nystagmus. If the *anterior lobe* alone is involved, the postural reflexes are abnormal. If the *posterior lobe* alone is involved, there is a disturbance in voluntary movements. The movements are inaccurate; there are errors in range, direction and force of all movements. There may be tremors in the muscles when one attempts to make voluntary movements. If all parts of the cerebellum are involved, the result will be a composite picture of all of the above disorders.

INJURY TO THE HYPOTHALAMUS

Injury to the hypothalamus leads to: (1) a disturbance in water balance which is called *diabetes insipidus.* This condition is accompanied by the output of exceedingly large amounts of urine which is very dilute and contains no sugar. (2) There may be disturbances in the regulation of body temperature. If the lesion is in one part of the hypothalamus there is an unusually high temperature, but if it is in another part the temperature is several degrees below normal. (3) Some cases of injury to the hypothalamus are characterized by pathologic sleep during which the patients may sleep for months or even years, waking up only long enough to be fed.

INJURY TO THE CORPORA STRIATA OF THE BASAL GANGLIA

Injury to the corpora striata may lead to one of 3 conditions. The first is called *Parkinson's disease* or *paralysis agitans.* This is characterized by tremor of muscles, weakness of contraction, delay in starting voluntary movements, a peculiar running gait and loss of associated movements, such as swinging the arms when walking, and gesticulating when talking. The second condition is called *chorea* or *St. Vitus' dance.* This is a convulsive nervous disease with involuntary and irregular jerking movements and mental impairment. The third condition is called *athetosis* and it is characterized by constantly recurring, slow, wormlike movements of hands and feet.

Injury to the Cerebral Hemispheres

Injury to the *motor area* of the frontal lobe leads to paralysis of the skeletal muscles on the opposite side of the body. This may be the result of birth injury or of a brain tumor. The same result occurs when there is a cerebral hemorrhage and the blood clot presses on the internal capsule and injures the fibers from the motor area as they pass through this region.

Injury to the *parietal lobe* in the postcentral region leads to an impairment of the senses of touch, pain, temperature and muscle sense. Injury to the *occipital lobe* leads to blindness. Injury to the *temporal lobe* leads to impairment in hearing.

A disturbance in the language sense is called *aphasia*. This may be motor in type. The individual knows what he wishes to say but is unable to say it, although there is no paralysis of the muscles used in speaking. The inability to write what one wishes is called *agraphia*. There may be word-blindness; the individual is unable to interpret written words, although he can see them. There may be word-deafness, in which the individual can hear but cannot interpret what he hears. Aphasia is a manifestation of a functional or organic disturbance in the higher functions of the cerebral cortex which give meaning to sensations and integrate information into useful knowledge.

Cerebral Hemorrhage

Hemorrhage into the brain substance is very common; this condition is called *apoplexy* or *stroke*. Usually it is due to hardening of the arteries. The artery which is most likely to rupture is the lenticulostriate, which supplies blood to the internal capsule. In fact, this is called the artery of cerebral hemorrhage. The resulting paralysis is due to damage of nerve fibers in the internal capsule. The term *hemiplegia* refers to the one-sided paralysis of the body, which is the end result of cerebral hemorrhage.

Concussion

Concussion of the brain is a condition noted after violent blows on the head; it is accompanied by unconsciousness, a weak pulse and slow respiration.

Changes in Reflexes in Disease

An injury to any part of a reflex arc leads to a change in the reflex handled by that arc. Injury to the *upper motor neuron* or *corticospinal tract* is followed by a spastic or stiff type of paralysis, and the spinal reflexes such as the knee jerk are increased, since they are released from cortical control. If there is injury to the *lower motor neuron* in the spinal cord (final common path) there is a flaccid or limp type of paralysis, and the reflexes disappear. The absence of such reflexes as the knee jerk is a deficiency phenomenon. If the knee jerk is tested in a patient with a cerebellar lesion, the leg keeps swinging after the patellar tendon is struck instead of extending just once.

Normally, if the sole of the foot is stroked the toes turn downward or flex. If there is upper motor neuron damage the great toe turns upward instead of downward; this response is called a *positive Babinski reflex* (Babinski first described it).

Pupillary reflexes are important. The pupils become smaller when light is flashed into the eyes and also when the gaze is shifted from a distant to a near object. The former is called the *light reflex* and the latter the *accommodation reflex.* If there is syphilis of the central nervous system the light reflex disappears, but the accommodation reflex remains; this condition is called an *Argyll Robertson "pupil."*

The ankle jerk is tested by having the subject kneel on a chair, with the legs stretched out behind; a sharp tap on the tendon of Achilles causes a quick contraction of the calf muscles. This is a stretch reflex. If there is damage to the corticospinal tracts so that the spinal reflex arc is abnormally excitable (released), a rapid rhythmical series of twitches of the calf muscles occurs and is called *ankle clonus.* In such patients a tap on the quadriceps tendon produces a patellar clonus, which is due to a series of twitches of the quadriceps femoris muscle.

The reflexes listed above are the ones most commonly tested in a routine physical examination.

ELECTRO-ENCEPHALOGRAM

An electro-encephalogram is a record of "brain waves" or the electric currents accompanying activity in the brain; the electrodes are applied to the scalp. Such records are of value in localizing brain damage, tumors and abscesses of the brain and in the diagnosis of epilepsy.

EPILEPSY

Epilepsy is a functional disease which manifests itself by attacks of unconsciousness and convulsions. The patient falls as consciousness is lost; the strong contractions of the jaw muscles during the

convulsions may injure the tongue. Involuntary emptying of the
bladder and the bowel may accompany the attacks. Often there
is frothing at the mouth. The patient usually has a warning before the attack, as smelling a particular odor, seeing a certain color,
hearing a sound or feeling a tingling in some region of the body.
After the attack the patient falls into a deep sleep. The attacks
are thought to be due to some irritation of the brain. Drugs that
depress excitability of the nervous system are administered to
epileptic patients to prevent attacks.

Subdural Hemorrhage

A subdural hemorrhage refers to a collection of blood between
the cranial dura mater and the arachnoid membrane. It is due to
the rupture of a number of small blood vessels under a depressed
fracture, or the hemorrhage may come from a large vessel, particularly the middle cerebral artery. It causes damage to various brain
structures by pressing on them.

Ventriculogram

A ventriculogram is an x-ray picture of the brain after the withdrawal of fluid and the injection of air or an opaque medium into
the cerebral ventricles through a trephine opening in the cranial
bones. It is used as a diagnostic test for brain tumors. A trephine
is a circular instrument which is used to saw or cut out buttons
of bone from the cranial bones.

Shock Therapy and Psychosurgery

Electric shock therapy makes use of convulsive seizures, after
which the patient loses the memory for recent events. Insulin
shock therapy is used for the same purpose; the blood sugar falls
to such a low level that functions of the cerebral cortex are suspended and generalized convulsions occur. In shock therapy the
convulsions are so severe that patients may sustain injuries of the
back and fractures of bones. Curare is given to prevent the contractions of muscles, but this does not affect the changes in the
brain which bring about loss of memory. Shock therapy is used in
certain types of psychoses.

Psychosurgery refers to operations on the brain for the purpose
of relieving mental abnormalities. Frontal lobotomy may be carried out, or thalmotomy (cutting bundles of nerve fibers between
the thalamus and the frontal lobe) may be preferred in some psy-
chotic patients.

Multiple Sclerosis

Multiple sclerosis is a condition characterized by scattered patches of hardening (due to replacement of nervous tissue by connective tissue) throughout the brain or the spinal cord, or both. Weakness, in-co-ordinated movements and strong jerking movements of the arms and the legs are present. It is not curable and may last for years. There is atrophy of nervous tissue and increase in the interstitial tissue or neuroglia.

Facial Neuralgia

Facial neuralgia refers to severe and intractable pain over the region supplied by the trigeminal nerve. The pain occurs in paroxysms and may be accompanied by reflex spasms of the facial muscles. Sometimes injections of alcohol are made into the nerve. In some patients the maxillary and the mandibular branches of the trigeminal nerve are cut to relieve the pain.

Delirium

Delirium is a mental disturbance in which there are hallucinations and cerebral excitement, with physical restlessness. It occurs in insanity, or as a result of fever, disease or injury. *Delirium tremens* is such a condition and is usually associated with alcoholic poisoning.

Nursing Care

Special nursing problems accompany the care of patients who are paralyzed, who have sensory disturbances or are unconscious (in coma). Paralyzed patients cannot perform the voluntary movements necessary for daily care. The nurse has to do a great many things for them. It requires skill and tact on her part to keep them from feeling useless and depressed. Patients with sensory disturbances need special protection, since their warning signals are absent; harmful stimuli arouse no impulses which bring about responses of self-preservation. Unconscious patients are even more helpless than newborn babies; the latter can cry when something disturbs them, but the unconscious patient is quite unaware of everything. Such patients must be fed, given fluids and kept warm, and the emptying of the bladder and the bowel must be taken care of. The only things that do not depend on the nurse are circulation and respiration. All of the other activities require her aid.

MENTAL HYGIENE

Some individuals who have the capacity for intelligent living, allow the emotions to influence their behavior in such a way that they deviate from the standards set by society. The way an individual reacts to situations is assumed to be indicative of character and intelligence. One may live on one of two levels, so to speak.

Subcortical. One level is subcortical. When living on this level the individual tries to escape the difficult situations of life instead of meeting them "head on." He resorts to all kinds of devices to escape facing reality. He may indulge in alcoholism, under the influence of which he may forget his troubles temporarily; but the difficulties are still there when he sobers up, so he has to get drunk again. He may become a drug addict. In this situation nothing is important except to get the next dose of the drug, and crimes will be committed, if necessary, to obtain more of the drug. All semblance of human dignity is lost in drug addiction.

A less drastic means of escape is hysteria; many individuals take refuge in this. Some folks put the blame on others and have an explanation for everything that keeps them from living a satisfactory life. Other apparently intelligent individuals rationalize. This means they do whatever they wish and then find excuses for having done so. Rationalization differs from reasoning in that in the latter all the arguments for and against a particular act are brought to mind and sensibly evaluated and the decision is then made whether to do the act or to refrain from it. Some folks daydream; they never put their ideas or plans into action, but always are talking about what they are *going* to do. Unless we are constantly on guard, we may find ourselves on the subcortical level in some things.

Cortical. The other level may be called the cortical level. To live on this level requires courage and strength of character. One must face facts squarely and with honesty and sincerity. Mistakes must be acknowledged. Plans must be carried out. Sportsmanship is essential. Grudges must not be held; it is advisable to "get them off your chest" promptly. One cannot afford to sulk; one must retain "poise" under all circumstances. Perspective must be kept in meeting each day's problems. An objective attitude is excellent. Confession, which has been called catharsis of the mind, is good for each of us. One's work, whatever it may be, should be done to the best of one's ability. Nothing else can bring quite the same satisfaction as work that has been well done. Play is essential now and then, and its main objective is to make us eager to return to work. Make the most of whatever talent you have been given. Only by living up to your best, on the cortical level, can you find happiness. It lies within you and it is up to you to realize that material possessions cannot give you happiness.

PERSONAL ADJUSTMENT. No one but yourself can make the adjustments required of you. You alone must decide whether you will live on the cortical level or the subcortical level. You must live with yourself as long as life continues, so you might as well be the kind of person you like to have around. Every once in awhile, just look in the mirror and say to yourself, "Well, you certainly behaved in a feeble-minded manner in that situation! Now come on, snap out of it and get back where you belong and do better next time."

If you live on the cortical level you always should enjoy good mental health. You can do your work well and enjoy doing it. If you live on the subcortical level you will go from one position to another, from one physician to another, from one marriage venture to another, and the "cards always will be stacked against you" in your own opinion. A sick mind is as much in need of help as a sick body, but many individuals seem to be unable to realize that such a condition as mental illness exists. Anything that can be done to help the mentally ill to live useful and happy lives instead of being misfits in every human relationship is well worth the doing.

SUMMARY

1. The spinal cord
   A. Structure: extent, cross section: gray and white matter
   B. Functions
      a. As a reflex center
         (1) Parts of a reflex arc
         (2) Examples of spinal reflexes
            (A) Stretch reflex; knee jerk
            (B) Flexor reflexes; withdrawal
      b. As a conduction pathway to and from the brain
         (1) Ascending tracts
            (A) Posterior columns
            (B) Spinocerebellar tracts
            (C) Spinothalamic tracts
         (2) Descending tracts
            (A) Corticospinal or pyramidal
            (B) Extrapyramidal
   C. Coverings: meninges; spinal fluid

2. The brain

A. Primary divisions: forebrain, midbrain and hindbrain, and subdivisions

    B. General structure

        a. Gray matter outside and in underlying nuclei

        b. White matter inside; nerve fibers

            (1) Projection fibers

            (2) Commissural fibers

            (3) Associational fibers

        c. Ventricles and connecting channels

    C. Hindbrain

        a. Medulla oblongata

            (1) Anatomy

            (2) Functions

                (A) As a conduction pathway

                (B) Contains vital centers; reflex center of prime importance

        b. Pons

            (1) Anatomy

            (2) Functions; conduction pathway and reflex center

        c. Cerebellum

            (1) Anatomy; location; attachments to other parts of brain; gray matter outside and in nuclei; white matter inside

            (2) Divisions

                (A) Flocculonodular lobe; vestibular portion; concerned with equilibrium

                (B) Corpus cerebelli

                      (a) Anterior lobe; concerned with adjustment of tone in skeletal muscles

                      (b) Posterior lobe; concerned with delicate adjustments of voluntary movements

    D. Midbrain

        a. Anatomy

        b. Center for postural and righting reflexes

    E. Forebrain

        a. Cerebral hemispheres; rhinencephalon, basal ganglia and cerebral cortex.

        b. Diencephalon; hypothalamus and thalamus.

    F. Coverings: meninges (dura mater, arachnoid and pia mater); cerebrospinal fluid

3. Embryology of the nervous system

SITUATIONS AND QUESTIONS

A spinal tap is a procedure which is frequently performed in a hospital.

1. Which of the following is *not* a purpose of a spinal tap? _____(a) Removing fluid for analysis and diagnosis; _____ (b) Removing fluid for the purpose of relieving increased intracranial pressure; _____(c) Introduction of fluids in order to treat general bodily dehydration; _____(d) Introduction of drugs for the treatment of certain disease processes.

2. At what level is the needle introduced in a spinal tap? _____(a) Between the third and the fourth lumbar vertebrae; _____(b) Between the first and the second lumbar vertebrae; _____(c) Below the last lumbar vertebra; _____(d) Between the fifth and the sixth thoracic vertebrae.

3. An anatomic fact important in withdrawing fluid from around the spinal cord is its relationship to the meninges. Where do the meninges terminate with reference to the spinal cord? _____ (a) Above the spinal cord; _____(b) Below the spinal cord; _____(c) At the same level as the spinal cord; _____(d) At the foramen magnum.

Students in the neurology clinic attempted to determine the sites of lesions or destruction of parts of nervous system by observing the symptoms of the various patients.

1. A patient with visual disturbances may have a tumor of the: _____(a) temporal lobe; _____(b) frontal lobe; _____ (c) parietal lobe; _____(d) occipital lobe.

2. They observed a patient who walked without swinging his arms. They also noticed that other associated movements were lacking. The students suspected that the lesion was in the region of the: _____(a) basal ganglia; _____(b) motor cortex; _____(c) cerebellum; _____(d) medulla.

3. If a patient has a lesion of the temporal lobe, he may show signs of: _____(a) blindness; _____(b) deafness; _____ (c) loss of general sensation; _____(d) difficulty in speaking.

4. Death would most probably result from a lesion of the: _____(a) medulla; _____(b) cerebellum; _____(c) cerebral cortex; _____(d) midbrain.

5. Following a cerebral vascular accident, one patient suffered damage to the fibers of the pyramidal (corticospinal) tract. Which of the following symptoms would result? _____(a) Loss of muscle sense on one side of the body; _____(b) Loss of temperature, touch and pain sensations; _____(c) Loss of muscle tone; _____(d) Loss of voluntary muscular movement.

~~~~~~

8. Anatomy and Physiology of the Senses

~~~~~~

SENSORY MECHANISMS

A sensory mechanism is a group of structures by means of which a change in the environment gives rise to a sensation. The 3 components of such a mechanism are: a sense organ or receptor, which is like a special receiving instrument; a pathway to the brain; and a sensory area in the cerebral cortex which is definite for each sense. The parts of a sensory mechanism are shown by diagram in Figure 175.

SENSE ORGANS

Sense organs or receptors are the peripheral endings of dendrites of afferent neurons. In these endings the property of excitability reaches its peak of development. The threshold or minimal stimulus (least change necessary to affect the receptor) is very low. Each receptor, except those for pain, is specialized for the reception of a particular type of stimulus which is called its *adequate*

332

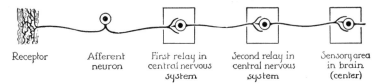

Receptor — Afferent neuron — First relay in central nervous system — Second relay in central nervous system — Sensory area in brain (center)

FIG. 175. Parts of a sensory mechanism: receptor or sense organ, afferent (lower) and internuncial (intermediate and higher) neurons, center or sensory area in brain.

stimulus. For example, light is the adequate stimulus for the receptors of vision, and sound waves for those of hearing.

There is no satisfactory classification of receptors, but the following one is useful. Those receptors which are affected by changes in the external environment are called *exteroceptors* and are concerned with touch, cutaneous pain, heat, cold, smell, vision and hearing. Those receptors which respond to changes in skeletal muscles, tendons, joints and the labyrinth of the inner ear (semicircular canals and utricle, p. 371) are called *proprioceptors* and are concerned with muscle sense, sense of position and movement of the body in space. Those receptors which respond to changes in the viscera are called *interoceptors* and are concerned with visceral pain, hunger and thirst.

Receptors are located in skin, connective tissue, muscles, tendons, taste buds, olfactory epithelium, retina of eye, cochlea of ear, labyrinth of ear, mucous membranes, serous membranes, walls of blood vessels, lungs, heart and walls of abdominal and pelvic viscera.

AFFERENT PATHWAY TO BRAIN

The first neuron in a cranial or spinal nerve in the pathway is the afferent neuron whose dendrites are specialized to serve as receptors. In addition to this, there may be one or more neurons in the pathway from the axons of the cranial and spinal nerves to the sensory areas in the cerebral cortex.

SENSORY AREAS IN CEREBRAL CORTEX

The sensory area for touch, heat, cold and muscle sense is in the postcentral region of the parietal lobe. The auditory area is in the temporal lobe. It is assumed that the sensory area for impulses from the labyrinth of the inner ear likewise is in the temporal lobe, but this awaits further investigation. The visual area is in the occipital lobe.

Each sensory unit ends in a sensory area in the cerebral cortex, and the end result of the stimulus applied to a receptor is a sensation aroused in consciousness. However, activity does not stop here. Sensations are interpreted, analyzed, combined with sensations from other sensory units and synthesized into perceptions. As sensations take on meaning, there may be voluntary or reflex movements, visceral reflexes or storing of sensations in memory to be used in the future. Thus, various sensations contribute to the general fund of information about the outside world and to the knowledge of normal or pathologic activities within the body itself.

All parts of a particular sensory unit must be functioning in order to give rise to its characteristic sensations. If one sense is lost, other senses may be developed more highly. Such a condition exists in blindness, in which the patient learns to read and write through touch and muscle sense by the Braille method. Children who are deaf cannot learn to speak by hearing others speak; they learn through sight, by watching others speak, and by muscle sense, as they feel the throat, the tongue and the lips. Helen Keller, who was both blind and deaf, learned to speak through touch and muscle sense, by noting the position of tongue, cheeks, lips and larynx when her teacher was speaking. The way in which some handicapped individuals meet their problems seems to be miraculous, and it should make those of us who have the use of all of our special senses wish to make more of our lives than we do. We take so many things in our lives for granted without stopping often to show a deep appreciation for the wonders of the human body and that divine spark which we called the "spirit."

CHARACTERISTICS OF SENSATIONS

Projection. Although the brain is the seat of sensation we can scarcely realize that this is the case, since we have the habit of projecting the sensation to the source of stimulation. For example, we say "Sugar is sweet," when we really mean that it arouses in our brains a sensation which we call "sweetness." We say that a light is bright, but the sensation of brightness is in the brain. This habit of projection accounts for the fact that if an afferent nerve is stimulated anywhere along its course other than at its end (receptor), the impulses that reach the brain set up the sensation as usual, and it is projected to the receptor as usual. There is nothing in consciousness to differentiate impulses aroused by stimulation along the course of afferent nerves from those aroused by stimulation at the ends of afferent fibers or receptors.

After-images. Sensations tend to persist in consciousness after the cessation of stimulation. This lingering sensation is called an *after-image.*

Adaptation. When a stimulus continues to act, one gets used to it or ignores it. This phenomenon is called *adaptation.*

Local Sign. The ability to recognize the point of stimulation is called the local sign of a sensation. This ability is acquired by experience.

Contrast. Any sensation is affected by events which have just preceded it (successive contrast) or accompany it (simultaneous contrast).

Intensity. Sensations are more intense on some occasions than others. The intensity depends on the number of receptors stimulated and on the number of impulses that each afferent fiber transmits per second. With a stronger stimulus more receptors are stimulated, and the afferent fiber of each carries a greater number of impulses per second than when a weaker stimulus is applied.

CLASSIFICATION OF SENSES

Senses may be classified as cutaneous, muscle sense, hunger, thirst, smell, taste, vision, hearing and the sense of position or orientation of the head with the universe and movement of the body through space.

CUTANEOUS SENSES

Touch, heat, cold and pain comprise the cutaneous senses.

Distribution. The receptors for the cutaneous senses are widely

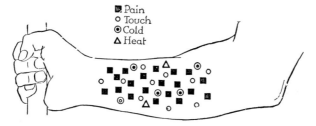

Fig. 176. Punctiform or point distribution of the cutaneous sense organs on the forearm. Touch and light pressure are treated as one.

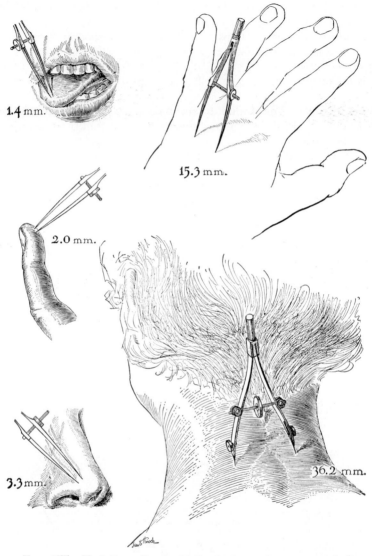

FIG. 177. Variations in sensitivity in two-point or spatial discrimination. The distance between the compass points indicates the sensitivity in different regions. The tip of the tongue is most sensitive, the back of the neck least sensitive. These are the actual averages found on a group of 25 medical students.

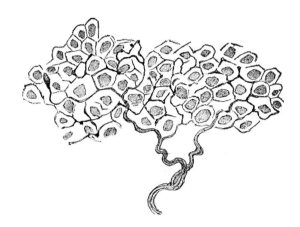

Fig. 178. Free nerve endings in epithelial tissue of a rabbit. Expanded ends (not to be confused with nuclei) can be made out between epithelial cells.

distributed in the skin and the connective tissues. The skin of the forearm can be tested for the distribution of each type of receptor. Figure 176 shows the location of each type of receptor in such an area. The receptors for the different senses vary in number; those for pain are most numerous and for heat least numerous.

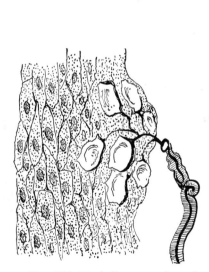

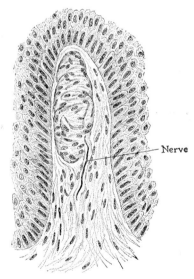

Fig. 179. Merkel's corpuscle and stratified squamous epithelium of the skin of pig's snout.

Fig. 180. Corpuscle of Meissner in papilla of corium; skin of finger. × 270.

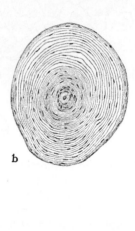

Fig. 181. Corpuscles of Vater-Pacini (lamellated) from skin of finger: (a) longitudinal and (b) cross section. × 145.

b

—Nerve

a

Receptors are distributed in points. This arrangement is called a *punctiform* (meaning "shaped like a point") distribution. Each sensitive spot marks the location of one or more receptors.

Sensitivity. Since the number of receptors varies in different areas, not all parts of the body are equally sensitive. An area that has few receptors is relatively insensitive, while sensitive areas have large numbers of receptors. The variation in sensitivity to touch can be shown by the two-point discrimination test. A compass is used, and the distance between its points is varied. The subject tells whether he feels the compass points separately or as one. The more sensitive the area, the closer together the points of the compass may be and still be felt as 2 separate points. Figure 177 shows the tip of the tongue to be the most sensitive and the back of the neck the least sensitive of the many areas tested. In other words, the points can be very close together on the tongue and be felt separately since the receptors are so numerous in this area. The scarcity of the receptors on the back of the neck requires that the distance between the points be great in order to feel them as separate.

Receptors for Cutaneous Senses. There are 2 types of receptors in epithelial tissues; these are the free nerve endings in skin

Fig. 182. End-bulbs of Krause (corpuscles of Golgi-Mazzoni) from conjunctiva.

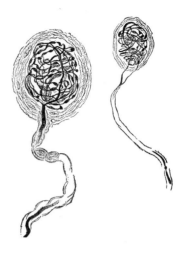

and mucous membranes, for touch and pain (Fig. 178), and
Merkel's corpuscles in the deeper layers of the skin, for touch
(Fig. 179).

The receptors in connective tissue (derma of skin, supporting
tissues of mucous, serous and synovial membranes) may be free
nerve endings or encapsulated structures. The free nerve endings
vary from simple endings to very complex networks. There are 3
types of encapsulated receptors: (1) corpuscles of Meissner (Fig.
180), (2) Vater-Pacini corpuscles (Fig. 181) and (3) Golgi-Mazzoni corpuscles, also called *end-bulbs of Krause*, (Fig. 182).

Touch

Types of Receptors. The 4 types of receptors for the sense
of touch and pressure are: (1) free nerve endings around hair
follicles, (2) corpuscles of Meissner in the connective tissue papillae of the skin, (3) Merkel's corpuscles on the borders of the
tongue and (4) corpuscles of Vater-Pacini deep in the subcutaneous tissue beneath mucous and serous membranes, in the mesentery, the perimysium and near tendons and joints.

Afferent Pathway for Impulses Concerned with Touch. Impulses travel from touch receptors over large myelinated dendrites,
in spinal and cranial nerves, to cell bodies in dorsal root ganglia
of spinal nerves and corresponding ganglia on cranial nerves, and
then on over axons into the central nervous system. Those impulses that reach the spinal cord travel in ascending tracts to the

thalamus and are relayed to the cerebral cortex. The pathways for touch impulses in the spinal cord (posterior columns and anterior spinothalamic) are shown in Figures 157 and 158. The impulses that travel over cranial nerves likewise reach the thalamus before they are relayed to the cerebral cortex.

Sensory Area for Touch. The sensory area for touch is in the parietal lobe of the cerebral cortex, just posterior to the central fissure (Fig. 169).

Characteristics. THE ADEQUATE STIMULUS for touch receptors is pressure which dents or deforms the skin. Receptors are especially numerous around hair follicles, and the sensitivity of a hairy area is greatly reduced after shaving.

AFTER-IMAGES are short in the sense of touch. Adaptation is rapid, and we get used to clothes very quickly unless they cause pain or discomfort. We soon become used to the pressure of a seat against the skin of the buttocks and only realize that the seat is hard if we sit still for a long time.

THE LOCAL SIGN is very accurate for the sense of touch. If one is blindfolded and a spot on the skin is touched, the subject can put his finger on the very spot with accuracy.

The sense of touch is exceedingly important in acquiring information about the outside world; children and adults alike desire to take objects in their hands when observing them for the first time.

TEMPERATURE SENSE

Receptors. The receptors for cold are the Golgi-Mazzoni corpuscles or end-bulbs of Krause, which lie near the surface of the skin. The receptors for heat are the corpuscles of Ruffini, which lie deep in the skin or even in the subcutaneous tissues.

Afferent Pathway. Impulses travel to the central nervous system from temperature receptors over small myelinated fibers in cranial and spinal nerves. They are relayed on by other neurons to the thalamus, and from here to the cerebal cortex. The ascending tracts (lateral spinothalamic) over which temperature impulses travel in the spinal cord are illustrated in Figures 157 and 158.

Sensory Area. Temperature impulses reach the general sensory area in the parietal lobe of the cerebral cortex, just posterior to the central fissure (Fig. 169).

Characteristics. SUCCESSIVE CONTRAST is particularly important in the temperature sense, as shown by the following experiment. Place one hand in a basin of hot water and the other in a basin of cold water, for 30 seconds. Then place both hands in a basin of tepid water; it will feel cold to the one which has been in hot water and hot to the one which has been in cold water previously. In other words, the sensation of temperature aroused in each hand when placed in tepid water is greatly influenced by preceding events.

THE LOCAL SIGN is poorly developed in the temperature sense.

ADAPTATION. On entering a room it may seem too warm or too cold, but you soon forget about the temperature as your receptors undergo adaptation.

AFTER-IMAGES are long in the temperature sense, as can be shown by the following trick. If you blindfold a person and press a cold coin on his forehead and tell him to shake his head until the coin falls off he will shake his head about 3 times if he does not hear the coin fall the first time he shakes his head. He continues to shake his head until the after-image disappears.

The skin of the face and the hands is less sensitive to temperature changes than the parts of the body covered by clothing. In general, the mucous membranes, except in the mouth and the rectum, are insensitive to temperature. One can drink a hot liquid at a temperature that would be painful to the hands. If hot food burns the mouth, the individual usually swallows it quickly since he cannot feel it burn the esophagus and the stomach. But it damages the mucous membrane, even if he is unaware of it.

PAIN

Receptors. The receptors for pain are free nerve endings. They are scattered throughout the body, and it is estimated that there are several million of them. These receptors respond to more than one variety of stimulus. An intense stimulus of any type, such as a hot object, can affect them, especially if it threatens harm to the body.

Types of Pain. Three types of pain are recognized: (1) superficial or cutaneous pain, (2) deep pain, from muscles, tendons, joints and fasciae and (3) visceral pain, from the viscera.

Afferent Pathway. Impulses concerned with pain travel over fine myelinated and unmyelinated fibers in cranial and spinal nerves and in company with visceral efferent fibers. The ascending tracts (lateral spinothalamic) in the spinal cord are shown in Figures 157 and 158. By various relays, pain impulses reach the thalamus.

Sensory Areas. It is thought that pain sensations are aroused in the general sensory area of the parietal lobe, although when this region is stimulated in conscious patients during brain operations they never report a sensation of pain as one of the results. It is possible that the orbitofrontal cortex is the center for visceral pain, since if this region is removed functionally by frontal lobotomy (p. 310) the pain of a spreading cancer, for example, disappears. Further studies must be carried out before we can state that the above areas are the cortical centers for the sensation of pain.

Adaptation does not exist in the sense of pain. This is especially important, since pain is a warning signal of danger, and if we became used to it and ignored it, damage to the body would follow. It is important in protecting us, and it is the harmful nature of the stimulus that is noted rather than its specific quality.

Visceral Afferent System

It is appropriate to digress from the discussion of special senses at this time in order to give essential consideration to the visceral afferent system.

Adequate stimuli for visceral receptors fall into 3 groups: (1) dilatation or distention of a viscus, (2) spasms or strong contractions (such as colic) and (3) chemical irritants.

Impulses from visceral receptors travel over one of the following pathways: (1) afferent fibers which travel in company with craniosacral nerves but are quite independent of them, (2) afferent fibers which travel in company with thoracolumbar nerves but are quite independent of them, and (3) afferent fibers which travel with somatic afferent nerves from the body wall and diaphragm.

The dendrites that make up all 3 pathways belong to cell bodies in dorsal root ganglia of spinal nerves or comparable ganglia of cranial nerves. Visceral afferent fibers have no cell bodies or synapses in autonomic ganglia and must not be confused with visceral efferent fibers in whose company they travel for a part of their journey to the central nervous system.

Visceral afferent impulses may be divided into 3 groups with respect to their central connections: (1) impulses which are concerned with the reflex control of vital visceral phenomena, (2) impulses concerned with organic sensations and (3) impulses which give rise to visceral pain.

Reflex Control. The impulses of the first group are conducted by afferent fibers which travel in the company of craniosacral autonomic or visceral efferent fibers, and they do not reach consciousness. They are concerned with the reflex control of the heart, the size of blood vessels, respiratory reflexes and micturition (emptying of the urinary bladder). They are regulatory in function and active at all times.

Organic Sensations. The impulses of the second group are conducted by afferent fibers which likewise travel in the company of craniosacral nerves. They give rise to the so-called organic sensations of hunger, thirst, nausea, distention of the bladder and bowel and sexual sensations. The sensory areas in the brain have not yet been identified.

Visceral Pain. The impulses of the third group are conducted by afferent fibers which travel in the company of thoracolumbar nerves. They reach the brain and give rise to somatic reflexes which involve skeletal muscle, visceral reflexes or sensations of pain. An example of the first is the reflex muscular rigidity of the abdominal wall which accompanies appendicitis. An example of the second is the reflex secretion of mucus when the large intestine is distended. An example of the third is pain due to an irritating substance in the stomach.

The impulses that give rise to the sensation of pain require further consideration. The afferent neurons that conduct such impulses from receptors in the viscera to the spinal cord come in contact with second neurons in the spinal cord whose axons form the lateral spinothalamic tracts. Some of these impulses (such as those from serous membranes) have a private pathway to the brain, somewhat like a private telephone line. Other impulses are not so fortunate as on a party telephone line, they must share the second neurons with impulses from cutaneous areas. Thus the axons of the second neurons do double duty by conducting impulses from visceral pain receptors and from cutaneous pain receptors to the same areas in the thalamus and the cerebral cortex. This arrangement is called convergence, and sometimes it can lead to confusion as you will see.

In the first case, in which there is a private wire to the cerebral cortex, the pain can be localized accurately as it is projected to the point of stimulation with ease. As an example of this, the patient with pleurisy can point to a certain spot where he experiences a sensation of pain on the chest, and the physician will hear a "friction rub" over this area, which means that the pleural membrane is inflamed in this particular spot.

In the second case, in which there is a party line, the sensation of pain is aroused in the brain as usual. However, it is projected to the cutaneous area from which impulses come to the same area in the brain. This happens since cutaneous pain is of more frequent

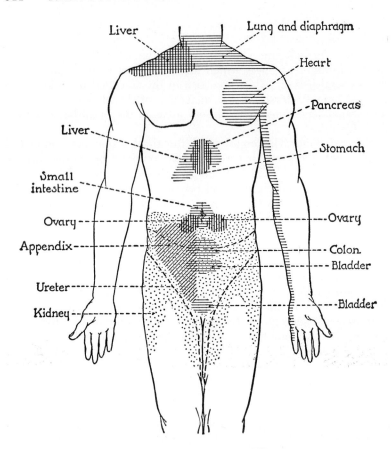

FIG. 183. Referred pain, anterior view. The cutaneous areas to which pain in the various organs is referred are indicated. (Adapted from Pottenger)

occurrence than visceral pain, and the brain projects over the well-trod path. This phenomenon is called *referred pain,* which means that pain from a viscus is referred to a related cutaneous area.

The cutaneous areas to which visceral pains are referred are of great diagnostic importance. In angina pectoris (due to spasm of the smooth muscle in the walls of the coronary arteries) the pain is referred to the left shoulder and down the left arm, instead of to the heart, in which the difficulty really lies. In pneumonia the

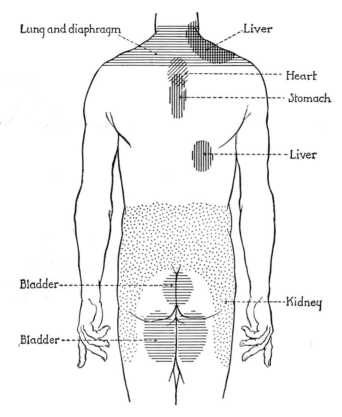

Lung and diaphragm

Liver

Heart

Stomach

Liver

Bladder

Kidney

Bladder

FIG. 184. Referred pain, posterior view. (Adapted from Pottenger)

pain often is referred to the abdomen, and some patients have been subjected to an appendectomy because of the referred pain in the abdomen, when time was not taken for a complete physical examination and history. Figures 183 and 184 illustrate the cutaneous areas to which pain from the various viscera is referred. Referred pain always must be taken into account by physicians; the theory of convergence-projection helps to understand referred pain.

From the studies on regeneration of cutaneous nerves after experimental cutting, some investigators have thought that cutaneous senses may be divided into 2 groups, which are called *protopathic* and *epicritic*.

In the protopathic group, pain and extremes of temperature are

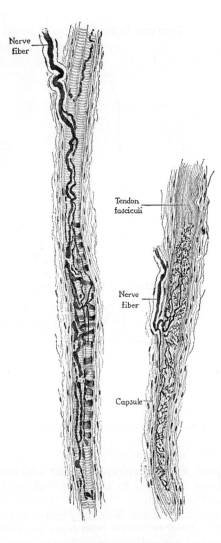

FIG. 185. Sensory nerve ending enveloping a fiber of an ocular muscle.

FIG. 186. Longitudinal section of receptor in muscular tissue (muscle spindle, *left*) and in tendon (*right*).

found; such sensations are diffuse, poorly localized and probably appreciated in the thalamus rather than the cerebral cortex.

The 2 epicritic senses are: accurately localized pain and fine discriminations of temperature. These are appreciated at the level of the cerebral cortex.

MUSCLE SENSE

Receptors. The receptors for skeletal muscle may be localized in muscular tissue, in tendons or at the junctions of muscle and tendon. The receptors may be simple or complex endings, such as muscle spindles. Receptors for skeletal muscle are illustrated in Figures 185, 186 and 187. The receptors for smooth muscle may be located between muscle bundles or in the fibers; a receptor for smooth muscle is shown in Figure 188.

Afferent Pathway. Impulses from receptors in muscles and tendons travel to the central nervous system over large myelinated

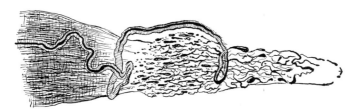

FIG. 187. Receptors at junction of muscle fiber with tendon.

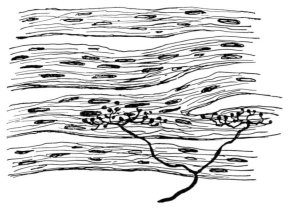

FIG. 188. Receptors in smooth muscle of bronchi.

nerve fibers in cranial and spinal nerves. Those muscle sense impulses destined to reach consciousness travel in ascending tracts (posterior columns) first to the thalamus and then on to the cerebral cortex, while those destined for reflex adjustments travel to the cerebellum over spinocerebellar tracts (Figs. 157 and 158).

Sensory Area. Conscious muscle sense impulses are relayed in the thalamus to the general sensory area in the parietal lobe of the cerebral cortex, just posterior to the central fissure (Fig. 169).

Importance. Because conscious muscle sense impulses inform us of the degree to which our skeletal muscles are contracted and the tendons tensed, it is possible for us to adjust our muscular efforts to the work to be done. This sense also is called the *proprioceptive* or *kinesthetic* sense and it enables us to know the position of various parts of our bodies without the aid of vision. It is indispensable for the proper control of voluntary movements and for the correlation of various muscle groups, as in walking. There must be co-ordination in both time and space. When this sense is lacking the movements become ataxic.

Muscle sense and touch combined enable us to judge the texture of cloth, the weight of objects and the shape of objects even if we are blindfolded. The ability to judge the above properties is called *stereognosis* (meaning "solid knowledge"). A lack of this ability is called *astereognosis*.

Some examples of skills in which muscle sense is all-important are typing, piano playing and violin playing.

HUNGER

Hunger is one of the organic sensations. It is projected to the stomach and is associated with powerful rhythmic contractions of the stomach musculature. Hunger occurs periodically, if food is not eaten. You can be very hungry, and after a little while you forget that you are hungry. Then contractions begin again and you feel hungry again, and so it goes until the next meal is eaten.

Hunger is a disagreeable sensation. In some individuals it is accompanied by a feeling of weakness, trembling, nausea and headache. The nervous system seems to be hyperexcitable, and one feels more and more miserable. When you have a particularly difficult or trying task to perform, tackle it with a comfortably filled stomach. Make no important decisions when you are hungry. If you have favors to ask you will receive a more impartial reply from the donor after he has had a good dinner.

Fig. 189. Section of olfactory epithelium. Two olfactory cells are shown, with the axon of one extending toward the brain.

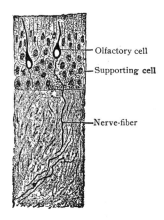

Olfactory cell

Supporting cell

Nerve-fiber

Prolonged starvation is not accompanied by acute suffering; after about 3 days hunger pangs are less pronounced, although weakness increases.

The receptors that are stimulated during hunger contractions have not been located. Perhaps the spindles in the stomach musculature serve this function.

Appetite is an agreeable desire for food and pleasure in thinking about it, seeing it or smelling it. The senses of taste and smell contribute to one's appetite. You can have an appetite for your favorite dessert even at the end of a full meal. When a person is mentally depressed or ill there is "no appetite," or if one has an unpleasant experience just before a meal the appetite disappears.

THIRST

The sensation of thirst is projected to the pharynx. It is a protective signal and warns of the need for the intake of fluid. It may be unquenchable after vomiting, diarrhea or hemorrhage in which large amounts of fluids are lost. Thirst may be extreme in untreated diabetes mellitus (p. 741) and in diabetes insipidus (p. 725), because large amounts of urine are excreted and the patients are dehydrated.

If fluid is not available when one desires it, thirst becomes more and more acute and leads to mental anguish. In fact, prisoners and suspected criminals used to be tortured by depriving them of water and letting them hear the sound of dripping or running water. Insanity may develop under such conditions.

SMELL

The receptors for the sense of smell are located in the olfactory epithelium which lines the upper part of the wall of the nasal cavities and the septum. Cell bodies of neurons are located in the membrane, and this peripheral position, unusual as it is, exposes them to injury. The olfactory cells are surrounded by supporting cells and glands. The latter secrete fluid which absorbs and dissolves gaseous particles of volatile, odorous substances. Only volatile substances in solution can stimulate the receptors of smell. A section of olfactory epithelium is shown in Figure 189.

The afferent pathway is the olfactory or first cranial nerve.

The center for olfaction is thought to be in the hippocampus, which is located in the floor of the inferior horn of the lateral ventricle.

The sense of smell is less important in man than in animals. Many of their activities are regulated by this sense. The keenness of smell varies greatly in different individuals; in many sufferers of severe sinus infections the olfactory epithelium is badly damaged.

Adaptation is rapid in the sense of smell. Receptors are fatigued rapidly by persistent odors, but new odors may be detected at once. There are probably different receptors for different odors. The sensations of smell which are aroused during ordinary breathing depend on diffusion from the moving air in the respiratory path into the still air of the upper portion of the nasal cavity. For a really good "whiff," one must sniff to bring the air with its odorous particles into the upper nasal cavity to stimulate the receptors. The amount of volatile substance required to stimulate the receptors of smell is very small; one part of odorous substance in 10 million parts of air is sufficient for some substances to stimulate the receptors.

Irritating substances, such as ammonium salts (smelling salts), stimulate the endings of the trigeminal or fifth cranial nerve and give rise to pain. Respiratory reflexes are initiated by such substances; therefore, they were used to revive delicate ladies who were subject to the art of fainting, before the age of "emancipation of women."

If two odors are presented, you smell first one and then the other. This occurs if both lilacs and lilies of the valley are present in a room; there is no blending of the two odors, but rivalry between them.

The memory for odors is very keen; we can recall odors that we have smelled only once. Some physicians and nurses think that

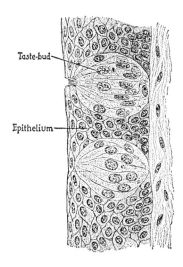
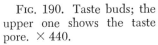
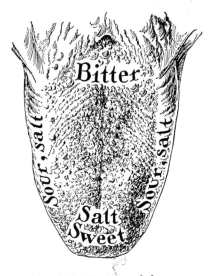

FIG. 190. Taste buds; the upper one shows the taste pore. × 440.

FIG. 191. Regions of the tongue which are most sensitive to the various tastes.

certain diseases give rise to definite odors. For example, they say that they can diagnose pneumonia or cancer by the odor noted on entering the room of the patient.

Hallucinations (vivid sensations when no stimulus is present) of smell are of common occurrence in insane patients.

TASTE

The receptors for the sense of taste are the taste buds, which are located chiefly on the tongue. A few are scattered on the soft palate, the pharynx and the epiglottis. The taste buds lie in papillae on the tongue; there may be a large number of receptors in one papilla. There is an opening called the *taste pore* at the top of each bud through which solutions enter in order to stimulate the receptors. Taste buds are illustrated in Figure 190.

The afferent pathway is the glossopharyngeal or ninth cranial nerve for the posterior third of the tongue, and a branch of the facial (chorda tympani) or seventh cranial nerve for the anterior two thirds of the tongue.

The center for taste is in the area that receives other sensory impulses from the mouth, at the inferior end of the central fissure, near the lateral fissure.

There are 4 primary tastes: sweet, sour, bitter and salt. Some substances stimulate the endings of the trigeminal (touch, temperature and pain) in the tongue and in this way influence taste. Tastes also influence each other; the addition of both salt and sugar to fruit cup brings out a different taste than the addition of either alone. The addition of sugar to lemon juice gives a different taste. These examples indicate that there is fusion or blending of tastes.

Substances must be in solution to be tasted. It is one of the functions of saliva to dissolve substances so that they may stimulate the taste buds. The tongue is not equally sensitive to all 4 tastes in all areas. The back of the tongue is more sensitive to bitter, the tip to sweet, the sides to sour and both the tip and the sides to salt. The regions most sensitive to each of the primary tastes are shown in Figure 191.

The property which we call the taste of certain substances is really the odor; the sense of taste is greatly influenced by the sense of smell. If one has a cold "foods taste differently," since they cannot be smelled.

It has been found, from animal experiments, that taste is important in nutrition, as animals deprived of taste invariably suffer from malnutrition even when all the requirements of an adequate diet are available to them and they choose what they wish. Patients who suffer from diseases of the tongue, injury to the seventh or the ninth cranial nerves or to the sensory area for taste lose this sense.

Vision

The receptors for vision lie in the retina of the eye; **the afferent pathway** is the optic or second cranial nerve, and the **center** for vision is in the occipital lobe of the cerebral cortex.

Structure. It is imperative to study the structures associated with the eye. These are the orbit, the eyeball, the extrinsic eye muscles, the eyelids, the conjunctiva and the lacrimal apparatus.

THE ORBIT is a cone-shaped cavity whose walls are formed by the cranial and the facial bones. The bones which enter into formation of the walls of the orbit are: frontal, maxilla, zygomatic, sphenoid, ethmoid, lacrimal and palatine (Fig. 63). The walls of the orbit are very thin and easily fractured.

THE EYEBALL occupies the anterior one fifth of the orbital cavity. The remainder of the cavity is filled with fat, fascia, nerves, blood vessels, muscles and the lacrimal gland. The eyeball is protected above by the upper margin of the orbit and the eyebrow; the inner margin is protected by the bridge of the nose. The posterior three fourths of the eyeball is covered by fascia called the *capsule of Tenon*. There are some smooth muscle fibers in the fascia; these comprise *Müller's muscle*. This muscle is supplied by fibers from the thoracolumbar division of the autonomic system, and its function is to prevent the eyeball from being dragged back into the orbit (enophthalmos). In Horner's syndrome (p. 281), in which the nerve supply to Müller's muscle is damaged, the eyeball is "sunken" or pulled back into the socket by the unopposed action of the skeletal extrinsic muscles of the eyeball.

THE EXTRINSIC MUSCLES of the eye arise from the apex of the orbit (with the exception of the inferior oblique) and are inserted into the eyeball (scleral coat). These muscles are covered by sheaths of fascia from which extensions pass to the walls of the orbit. Some of the extrinsic muscles are shown in Figure 192. There are 4 recti muscles, which are called *superior, inferior, medial* (internal) and *lateral* (external), and 2 oblique muscles, called *superior* and *inferior*.

The rectus muscles rotate the eyeball in the directions indicated

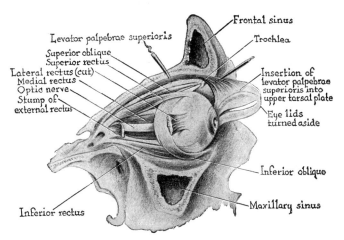

FIG. 192. Lateral view of extrinsic eye muscles after removal of outer wall of orbit; levator of upper eyelid has been pulled upward and inward. Portion of external or lateral rectus is removed. Maxillary and frontal sinuses are shown opened. Optic nerve shown.

by the names. The superior oblique passes through a ring of cartilage at the upper medial angle of the orbit. This determines the
direction of its pull, which is downward and laterally, with a medial
rotation. The inferior oblique muscle turns the eyeball upward
and laterally and rotates it laterally. The superior oblique and
the inferior rectus muscles work together, and the inferior oblique
works with the superior rectus.

The levator palpebrae superioris (meaning "lifter of the upper
lid") arises from the back of the orbit and passes forward to be
inserted into the tarsus (plate of dense connective tissue) as shown
in Figure 192. This muscle draws the upper lid upward and backward.

THE PALPEBRAE or eyelids are movable curtains placed in front
of the eyeball. The space between them is called the *palpebral
fissure.* The upper and the lower lids meet at the medial and the
lateral angles of the eye. The meeting places are called the *inner*
and the *outer canthi.* The tarsus is a plate of dense connective
tissue which gives shape to the lid (Fig. 193). Glands of the sebaceous type, called *meibomian glands,* are associated with the

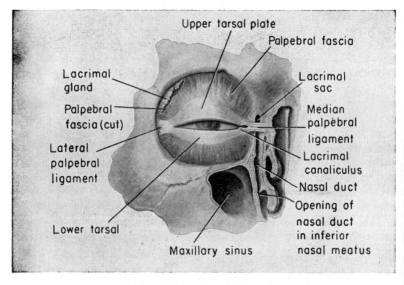

FIG. 193. Eyelids and adjacent structures, showing lacrimal
gland, sac, canal, nasolacrimal duct and tarsal plates.

tarsus. The eyelashes are hairs which are located at the margins of the eyelids. Sebaceous glands are associated with the lashes, and sweat glands are found in the skin between the lashes.

THE CONJUNCTIVA is a sac of mucous membrane which lines the lids (palpebral portion) and is reflected over a part of the eyeball (bulbar portion). The conjunctiva is a thin, transparent membrane, made up of stratified columnar epithelium and delicate fibrous connective tissue. It contains goblet cells which secrete mucus. When the conjunctiva becomes infected, the condition is called *conjunctivitis* or pink-eye. You probably know that drops of silver nitrate are placed in the eyes of newborn babies; this is done to prevent the possibility of infection by gonococcus during delivery through the birth canal of the mother. This treatment is required by law since blindness follows such infection at birth (ophthalmia neonatorum), and it is essential to prevent such a disaster.

THE LACRIMAL APPARATUS consists of the lacrimal gland, its ducts and passages. The lacrimal gland resembles an almond in size and shape. A portion of a lacrimal gland is shown in Figure 193. The lacrimal gland secretes tears, which are carried to the conjunctival sac through about a dozen short ducts. Tears bathe the surface of the eyeball and keep it moist at all times. They protect the cornea (the transparent structure at the front of the eyeball) which would become cornified like the epidermis of the skin, if exposed to air. The tears also wash away any particles that enter the conjunctival sac.

Tears normally drain off through the lacrimal passages which begin at the small opening called the *lacrimal puncta*, at the margin of the lower lid near the medial angle. The tears enter the lacrimal sac (Fig. 193), which is the upper dilated portion of the naso-lacrimal duct. This duct passes through a bony canal formed by bones of the face and opens into the lower portion of the nasal cavity (Fig. 193). Sometimes it is possible to remove a foreign particle from the conjunctival sac by blowing the nose. During emotional crises and during irritation of the conjunctiva, tears are produced in such abundance that they overflow and run down over the cheeks.

COATS OF THE EYEBALL: The eyeball consists of 3 layers: sclera, choroid and retina.

The sclera, also called the *white of the eye,* is composed of dense fibrous tissue. It is the outer, protective and supporting layer of the eyeball. The location of the sclera is shown in Figure 194. In front, the sclera is modified from a white, opaque membrane to the

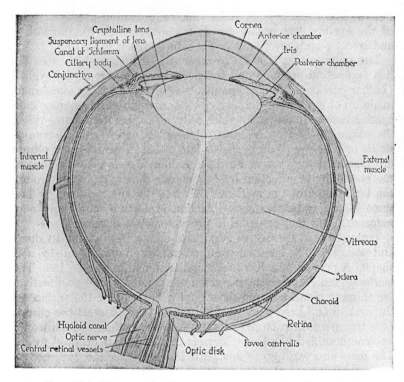

Crystalline lens
Suspensory ligament of lens
Canal of Schlemm
Ciliary body
Conjunctiva
Cornea
Anterior chamber
Iris
Posterior chamber
Internal muscle
External muscle
Vitreous
Sclera
Choroid
Hyaloid canal
Optic nerve
Central retinal vessels
Retina
Fovea centralis
Optic disk

Fig. 194. Diagrammatic transverse section of right eyeball.

transparent cornea. The cornea is composed of a special kind of dense fibrous connective tissue. The cells and the intercellular substance are covered with stratified squamous nonkeratinizing epithelium (p. 27), and no blood vessels are present. It is essential for the cornea to be transparent to let light through to the receptors within the eyeball.

Choroid. The middle coat is the choroid layer. This layer is very vascular, and it fulfills a nutritive function. The choroid is heavily pigmented. The anterior portion is modified to form the ciliary body, which is really a thickening of the choroid layer. The main mass of the ciliary body is made up of the ciliary muscle, a part of which has as its function the adjustment of the eye for vision at different distances.

Part of the ciliary muscle lies between the sclera and the choroid layers; it arises from the sclera at its junction with the cornea and is inserted into the choroid layer.

The iris is the colored portion of the eye and part of the choroid layer. The hole in the center of the iris is called the *pupil*. The iris is made up of 2 sheets of smooth muscle, a circular one, called the *sphincter,* and a radial one, called the *dilator* muscle. The function of the iris is to regulate the amount of light entering the eye. The ciliary muscle, the sphincter, and the dilator muscles of the iris are called the *intrinsic muscles* of the eye. The ciliary and the sphincter muscles are supplied by the visceral efferent fibers of the oculomotor or third cranial nerve, and the dilator is supplied by the thoracolumbar division.

The pupil becomes smaller (contraction of sphincter muscle) as the light becomes brighter (light reflex) and as one looks at a near object (accommodation reflex). The latter response is associated with a contraction of the ciliary muscle, which increases the ability of the eye to refract or bend rays of light. The pupil becomes larger (contraction of dilator muscle) in dim light and when looking at a distant object. The latter response is associated with a relaxation of the ciliary muscle.

Around the circumference of the cornea, where it meets the anterior surface of the iris, there is a sort of groove or recess in which the canal of Schlemm lies (Fig. 194). This is a drainage canal through which the aqueous humor leaves the eyeball and enters the blood.

The crystalline lens is suspended from the inner surface of the ciliary body by circular ligaments called the *suspensory ligaments* (or zonule of Zinn). The function of the lens is to bend rays of light in order to focus an image on the retina. As one ages the crystalline lens loses water, becomes denser and less elastic and is less able to bend rays of light.

The space anterior to the lens (bounded by the lens and the iris, behind, and the cornea, in front) is called the *anterior chamber.* The space back of the iris is called the *posterior chamber* and is bounded in front by the iris, on the sides by the ciliary body and toward the center and the back by the lens and the suspensory ligaments. Both the anterior and the posterior chambers are filled with a fluid called *aqueous humor.* The aqueous humor is formed constantly by filtration from the capillaries in part of the ciliary body and is drained off into the blood through the canal of Schlemm. The amount must be constant to maintain a constant pressure inside the eyeball intra-ocular pressure). So long as the amount of aqueous humor and the intraocular pressure remain normal, the proper shape of the eyeball is maintained. Intraocular pressure is between 20 and 25 mm. Hg. If there is interference with the drainage of aqueous humor, excess fluid accumulates within the eyeball and increases intraocular pressure, causing pain and interference with vision. This condition is called *glaucoma*.

The space posterior to the lens is filled with the vitreous body, which has the consistency of a jelly and helps to maintain the shape of the eyeball.

The retina is the third and inner layer of the eyeball. It is composed of 2 parts, the outer being pigmented and attached to the choroid layer, and the inner, consisting of nervous tissue. In some individuals the retinal layer becomes detached from the choroid in patches and greatly impairs vision in a condition called "detached retina." The optic nerve expands to form the nervous portion of the retina, which ends a short distance behind the ciliary body in a wavy border called the *ora serrata*.

Near the center of the retina, as one looks into the eyeball, there is a small, oval, yellowish spot called the *macula lutea*. The center of the macula lutea is depressed, due to thinning of the retina. This region is called the *fovea centralis* (Fig. 194) and is the area of most acute vision or of highest visual acuity in which cones, only, are present.

A short distance to the nasal side of the fovea centralis a white disk is seen. This is called the *optic disk* or blind spot. The optic disk is the point of exit of the optic nerve from the eyeball; it is a weak spot, since it is not covered by sclera. If intraocular pressure rises, the disk is pushed backward, a condition called *cupped disk*. Conversely, if intracranial pressure rises (as with brain tumor) the optic disk is pushed forward into the eyeball, a condition called *choked disk*. Therefore, the condition of the optic disk gives the examiner valuable information about both intraocular and intracranial pressure.

The blood supply for the retina enters the eyeball as the central artery of the retina, a branch of the ophthalmic, which in turn is a branch of the internal carotid artery (p. 436). The central artery enters the eyeball in the center of the optic disk and divides into

Fig. 195. Cone and rod cells of human retina; the receptors for vision.

FIG. 196. Comparable parts of camera and eye. The shutter and the eyelids are comparable, and the adjustable diaphragm and the iris are comparable.

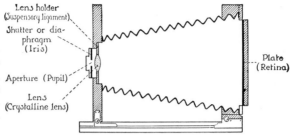

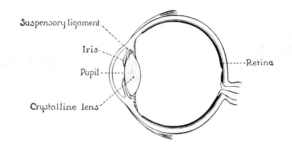

many branches. The appearance of the central artery and its branches also contributes valuable information to the examiner of the retina. Such pathologic conditions as high blood pressure and diabetes mellitus are accompanied by typical changes in the retinal vessels.

The nervous part of the retina is made up of 3 layers of neurons: (1) ganglion cells, (2) bipolar cells and (3) cones and rods. The most sensitive to light are the cones and the rods, and these are the receptors for the sense of sight (Fig. 195). There are about 7 million cones and 100 million rods in each human retina. There are no receptors in the optic disk; this is the reason it is called the *blind spot*. Since there are only 1,250,000 fibers in the optic nerve, it is evident that several receptors are connected with one afferent fiber in the nerve.

The receptors of the eye are adapted for stimulation by light rays. Another way of stating this is to say that light rays are the adequate stimuli for the receptors of the eye.

Comparison of the Eye with a Camera. The human eye and a camera have many features in common (Fig. 196). Each has a *lens* which brings rays of light to a focus and produces an image of external objects. Each has a surface which is sensitive to light;

this is the *retina* in the human eye and the *film* or plate in the camera. The *eyelids* and the *shutter* are comparable. The *iris* and the adjustable *diaphragm* are comparable; by these devices the amount of light that reaches the sensitive surface may be regulated. In the camera there is a mechanism for changing the distance between the lens and the film for taking pictures of objects at different distances from the camera. There is no such mechanism in the human eye, in which the strength of the lens must be changed for clear vision of objects at different distances from the eye. The process by which the strength of the lens is changed is called *accommodation.*

Accommodation is brought about by contraction of the ciliary muscle, by which the choroid coat is pulled forward and the tension on the suspensory ligaments of the lens is lessened. As a result of this, the tension on the capsule of the crystalline lens is lessened, and, since the lens is elastic, it bulges or becomes more convex, thus giving it more bending power. Accommodation takes place whenever we look at near objects.

Two other events accompany near vision: (1) The sphincter muscle of the iris contracts, decreasing the size of the pupil and cutting down the amount of light that enters the eye. (2) The 2

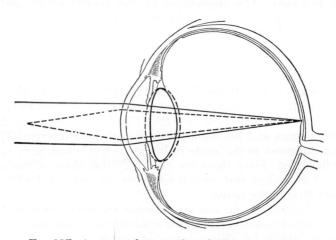

Fig. 197. Accommodation. The solid lines represent rays of light from a distant object, and the dotted lines represent rays from a near object. The lens is flatter for the former and more convex for the latter. In each case the rays of light are brought to a focus on the retina.

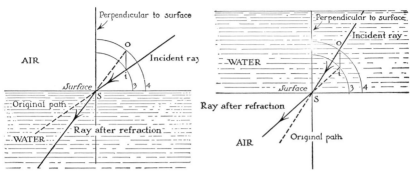

FIG. 198 (*Left*). Path of a ray of light passing from air into water. To construct the path, S is taken as the center, and two arcs with radii of 4 and 3 are drawn. A line is drawn from the point at which the ray crosses the inner arc, to the outer arc, parallel to the perpendicular, i to o. The line which connects o and S is projected into the water; this is the path of the ray after refraction. It is bent toward the perpendicular as it enters the denser medium.

FIG. 199 (*Right*). Path of a ray of light passing from water into air. Arcs are drawn as in Fig. 198. A line is drawn from the point at which the ray crosses the outer arc to the inner, parallel to the perpendicular, o to i. The line which is projected through i and S indicates the path of the ray after refraction. It is bent away from the perpendicular as it enters the less dense medium.

eyes turn slightly toward each other or converge. For distant vision the ciliary muscle is relaxed, the suspensory ligaments are taut, the capsule flattens the lens (thereby decreasing its bending power), and the eyes are not converged. The change in the lens for distant and near vision is indicated in Figure 197.

Path of a Ray of Light. When a ray of light passes from a medium of one density into a medium of a different density, such as from air to glass, the ray is bent or refracted. If the ray passes into a denser medium it is bent toward the perpendicular, as shown in Figure 198. If it passes into a less dense medium it is bent away from the perpendicular, as shown in Figure 199.

The power of a substance to bend light rays is called its *refractive index*. The refractive index for air is taken as 1.0. The index for water is 1.33; for glass, 1.5; for the cornea, aqueous humor and vitreous body 1.33; crystalline lens, 1.44. The refractive surfaces of the eye, therefore, are the cornea, the anterior and the posterior

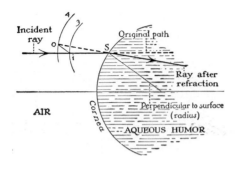

FIG. 200. Path of a ray of light passing from air into cornea. Arcs are drawn as in Fig. 198. A line is drawn from the point at which the ray crosses the inner arc to the outer arc, parallel to the perpendicular, i to o; the perpendicular in this case is the radius of the cornea. The line projected through o and S indicates the path of the ray through the cornea and aqueous humor.

surfaces of the crystalline lens. The path of a ray of light as it enters the cornea is shown in Figure 200.

Physiology of the Retina. The 2 types of receptors in the retina have different functions to perform. The cones are used for daylight vision, during which we see detail and color of objects. The rods, plus the pigment visual purple or rhodopsin associated with them, are used in night vision when we see outlines of objects, but no color or detail. The rods are very sensitive to movements of objects in the field of vision. In the fovea centralis only cones are present; this is the most sensitive area of the retina in daylight.

THE LOCAL SIGN in the sense of sight is about 3,000 times more highly developed than in the sense of touch.

AFTER-IMAGES are long in vision. There are 2 types: (1) After-images which appear in the same color as the original stimulus are called *positive* after-images. A positive after-image can be brought to the attention by fixing the gaze on an electric light bulb for a few seconds and then closing the eyes, the after-image of the bulb appears in the same color as the stimulus. (2) *Negative* after-images are those which appear in a color complementary to the original stimulus. To produce a negative after-image, fix the gaze on a colored object for about 20 seconds and then look at a white surface. The after-image appears in the complementary color.

In the eye the term "adaptation" refers to the changes which occur in the retina when going from a lighted into a darkened room, or vice versa. You have all noted the difficulty in vision when you first step out into the sunlight when the ground is covered with snow, or when you first enter a dark movie theater after passing through a brightly lighted lobby. The sensitivity of the retina can be adjusted to correspond to the intensity of illumination, but it requires a little time. Adaptation is a very remarkable property of the retina; the range of adaptation, with the corresponding change in sensitivity of the retina, is far beyond that of any physical instrument. A dark-adapted retina is 10 billion times as sensitive as a light-adapted retina.

As yet, there is no satisfactory theory of color vision. The Young-Helmholtz theory is the most widely accepted by physiologists. According to this theory, there are 3 fundamental color sensations: red, green and violet. It is assumed that there are 3 kinds of cones, each containing a different photochemical substance. Each type of cone gives rise to impulses which travel over specific fibers to definite areas of the visual center in the occipital lobe. When the 3 types of cones are stimulated equally, a sensation of white results. When there is no stimulation a sensation of black is experienced. Other color sensations are due to the combined stimulation of the 3 types of cones to different degrees.

We know that if we pass white light (sunlight) through a prism, it is divided into a band of colors which is called the *spectrum* (red, orange, yellow, green, blue, blue-green and violet). The red rays are the longest, violet the shortest. Spectral colors may be arranged in pairs called *complementary* colors which produce white light when they are blended. Red and blue-green are complementary colors; also yellow and violet.

Some individuals are color-blind—they may be blind to one, two or all colors. Color blindness is more common in men than in women. Men who are employed in occupations requiring recognition of signal lights must be tested for color blindness before receiving their appointments.

Binocular Vision. This refers to vision with 2 eyes. The 2 advantages of binocular vision are (1) a larger visual field and (2) a perception of depth or "stereoscopic" vision. There is a slight difference in the images on the 2 retinae; there is a right-eyed picture on the right retina and a left-eyed picture on the left retina. It is as if the same landscape were photographed twice, with the camera in 2 positions a slight distance apart. The 2 images blend in consciousness and give us an impression of depth or solidity. In order to experience stereoscopic vision the images must fall on "corresponding or identical" points in the 2 retinae. Only under this condition is there blending in consciousness. Otherwise, one sees 2 views or dissimilar pictures, a condition which is called *diplopia* or double vision.

The optic nerve fibers from the central halves of the retinae

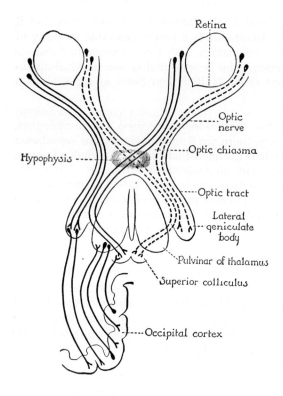

Retina

Optic nerve

Hypophysis — ---Optic chiasma

----Optic tract

Lateral geniculate body

Pulvinar of thalamus

Superior colliculus

----Occipital cortex

cross to the opposite side of the brain in the optic chiasma. As a result of this the fibers from the right half of each eye carry impulses to the right occipital lobe, and fibers from the left half of each eye carry impulses to the left occipital lobe. The optic chiasma is shown by diagram in Figure 201.

In order to bring the images to identical points in the 2 retinae, the movements of the 2 eyes must be perfectly co-ordinated. The pathways for such co-ordinated movements are laid down before birth; consequently, newborn babies show co-ordinated movements of the eyes. People who have been blind from birth nevertheless show co-ordinated movements of the 2 eyes.

Optical Judgments. Judgments of size and distance depend mainly on the size of the retinal images, the amount of detail seen, the color, the clearness of the outlines and the relative positions of the 2 eyes.

Optical illusions are common experiences. An illusion is a false interpretation of a sensation. Examples of optical illusions are: (1) objects appear larger on a foggy night, since the outlines are hazy, and the objects appear to be farther away than they really are; (2) lines with obtuse angles at the ends appear longer than equally long lines with acute angles at the ends. Some optical illusions are illustrated in Figure 202.

HEARING AND POSITION SENSE

Hearing is the sense by which sounds are appreciated; position sense refers to the orientation of the head in space and the movement of the body through space, its balance and equilibrium.

Hearing is called the watchdog of the senses; it is the last to disappear when one falls asleep and the first to return when one awakens. Physicians and nurses should remember this fact and guard their remarks when the patient is going to sleep or "going under" or "coming out" of anesthesia.

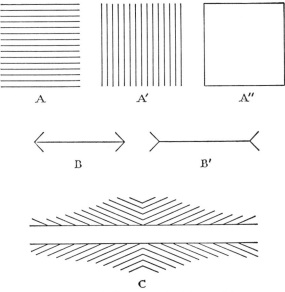

FIG. 202. Optical illusions. A, A′ and A″ are equal squares; A appears taller than A′, and A″ appears smaller than A or A′. Lines B and B′ are of equal length; B′ seems longer than B, because of the obtuse angle. (Muller-Lyer) In C, the horizontal lines are parallel, but they do not appear so. (Hering)

Anatomy. The receptors in the ear serve 2 functions: one set is concerned with hearing and the other set with position sense. The ear consists of 3 parts: external, middle and inner. Each part is illogically called an "ear."

THE EXTERNAL EAR, which receives sound waves, consists of the *pinna* and the *external auditory meatus*. The pinna or auricle consists of yellow elastic cartilage, covered with skin. This part of the ear performs a very small, if any, function in man; in some animals it collects sound waves and directs them into the external auditory meatus. The external auditory meatus is directed inward, forward and downward. It is a passageway for sound waves. The meatus is lined with stratified squamous epithelium and with cartilage and bone to hold it open. The dark brown wax or cerumen which collects there is composed of secretions from sebaceous and the

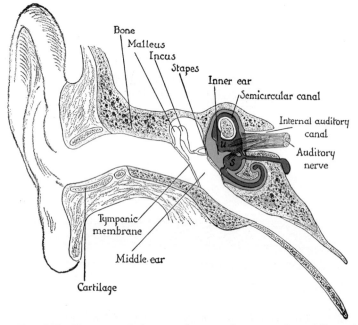

FIG. 203. Diagram of the ear, showing the external, middle and internal subdivisions: u, indicates the utricle; s, indicates the saccule. The perilymph is shown in blue, and the endolymph in red. Auditory tube leading to middle ear is shown. The auditory nerve is now called the *acoustic nerve*.

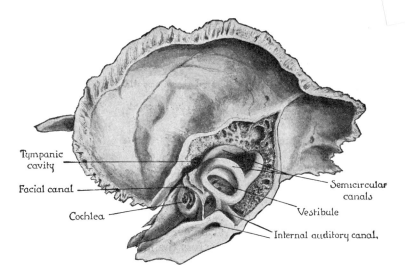

Tympanic cavity

Facial canal

Cochlea

Semicircular canals

Vestibule

Internal auditory canal,

FIG. 204. Right temporal bone. Upper part of petrous portion has been removed to show bony labyrinth lying in position.

ceruminous glands. The tympanic membrane or ear drum lies at the end of the external auditory meatus. The ear drum is composed of fibrous tissue, covered with skin on the outside and mucous membrane on the inside. It is so attached that it can vibrate freely with all audible sound waves that enter the meatus. Parts of the ear are shown in Figure 203.

THE MIDDLE EAR, which transmits sound waves from the external to the inner ear, is an air cavity in the temporal bone. It is connected with the nasopharynx by means of the auditory (eustachian) tube, and with the mastoid air cells. The mucous membrane which lines the middle ear is continuous with that of the pharynx and the mastoid air cells; thus it is very easy for infection to travel along the mucous membrane from the nose or the throat to the middle ear and the mastoid air cells.

The auditory tube serves to equalize the pressure in the middle ear with atmospheric pressure. It opens during swallowing and yawning. It tends to remain closed when the pressure is greater outside, as during rapid descent in a plane. In some individuals, after frequent infection, the tube is closed permanently by adhesions, and the hearing is impaired greatly. Whenever the pres-

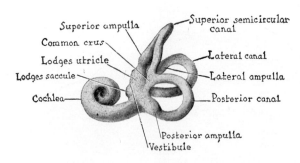

Superior ampulla

Common crus

Lodges utricle

Lodges saccule

Cochlea

Superior semicircular canal

Lateral canal

Lateral ampulla

Posterior canal

Posterior ampulla

Vestibule

Fig. 205. Cast of right bony labyrinth, medial aspect. × 2.

sure is unequal on the 2 sides of the ear drum it is not free to vibrate with sound waves. Sometimes air is forced into the middle ear, by means of a bulb, to break down adhesions.

A chain of 3 small bones (hammer or malleus, anvil or incus, and stirrup or stapes) extends across the middle ear. The malleus is attached to the ear drum, and the stapes fits into a window between the middle and the inner ears. The function of these bones is to transmit sound waves from the ear drum to the fluid in the inner ear. There are 2 small muscles in the middle ear which are called the *stapedius* and the *tensor tympani,* whose function is to protect the membranes and the bones from damage by very loud sounds. In the transfer across the middle ear sound waves are decreased in amplitude but increased in force by the lever system of the bones.

THE INNER EAR, in which sound waves arouse nerve impulses, is called the *labyrinth.* It consists of a series of canals and cavities, called the *bony labyrinth,* which is hollowed out of the petrous portion of the temporal bone. In the bony labyrinth there is a series of sacs and tubes, filled with endolymph, which comprise the membranous labyrinth. In some places the membranous labyrinth is attached to the periosteum of the bony larbyrinth, and elsewhere it is suspended in a fluid called *perilymph.* The bony labyrinth in position in the temporal bone is illustrated in Figure 204.

There are 2 windows in the wall between the middle and the inner ears which are called the *oval* or *vestibular* and the *round* or *cochlear windows.* The base of the stapes fits into the oval window like a piston and moves in and out with sound waves. This makes possible the transmission of sound energy from air to fluid. As the stapes moves in, the membrane of the round window moves out toward the middle ear.

There are 2 kinds of receptors in the inner ear. The first comprises the receptors for hearing, in the cochlea. The second comprises those in the semicircular canals and the utricle, which give rise to 3 types of information: (1) the orientation of the head in space, in relation to gravity; (2) the movement of the head; and (3) changes in rate and direction of movement of the body in space. Impulses from the receptors in the semicircular canals and the utricle set up reflexes that help us to maintain equilibrium.

The cochlea is shaped like a snail shell, as shown in Figure 205.

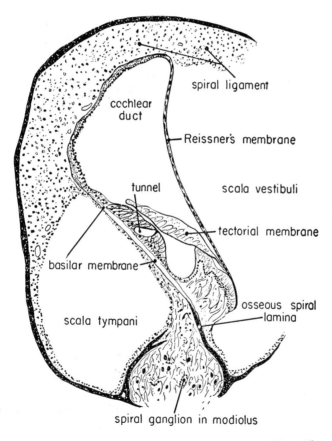

FIG. 206. Drawing of a portion of the bony cochlea. The relation of the cochlear duct to scalae vestibuli and tympani is shown. The basilar, tectorial and Reissner's membranes are shown. (Modified from Ham, A. W.: Histology, ed. 2, Philadelphia, Lippincott)

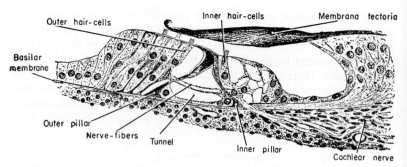

FIG. 207. Section of organ of Corti from human cochlea. × 375.

It is a bony tube which winds spirally around a central pillar of bone called the *modiolus*. The portion of the membranous laby- rinth (called the *cochlear duct*) that extends into the bony cochlea is like a lopsided triangle. It extends like a shelf across the bony canal to the sides of which it is attached. The portion of the bony canal above the cochlear duct is called the *scala* (meaning "stair- way") *vestibuli,* and the portion below is called the *scala tympani* (Fig. 206).

The cochlear duct is thinner on one side than the other. It con- nects with the inner wall of the bony canal by the osseous spiral lamina, and with the outer wall by the spiral ligament. The roof of the cochlear duct is thin and is called *Reissner's membrane.* The floor is composed of the basilar membrane (between the osseous spiral lamina and the spiral ligament) which consists of a large number of transversely placed fibers increasing progressively in length from the base to the apex of the cochlear duct. The spiral organ of Corti rests on the basilar membrane (Fig. 207). It con- sists of a central tunnel, between inner and outer pillars. Beyond the pillars are the inner and the outer hair cells. Dendrites, whose cell bodies are in the spiral ganglion in the modiolus (Fig. 206), are in contact with the bases of the hair cells. The tectorial mem- brane extends from the osseous spiral lamina over the organ of Corti and may be in contact with the hairs of the hair cells (Fig. 207).

Sound waves which reach the ear enter the external auditory meatus and set the tympanic membrane into vibration. These vi- brations are transmitted across the middle ear by the malleus, the incus and the stapes to the perilymph of the labyrinth. This sets into motion the basilar membrane and the organ of Corti. The movement affects the hair cells, which then arouse impulses in the dendrites of the cochlear division of the acoustic nerve, and the impulses are transmitted to the center for hearing in the temporal lobe of the cerebral cortex (Fig. 169). It is thought that analysis of sound takes place in the cochlea. This means that a certain portion of the basilar membrane and certain hair cells are affected by sound waves of one frequency. Waves of a different frequency set up vibrations in another portion of the basilar membrane.

Sounds differ in pitch (number of vibrations per second), in loudness (amplitude) and in timbre (quality, which is dependent on overtones). Figure 208 illustrates 3 sound waves; 2 pitches and 3 degrees of loudness are represented.

There are 3 semicircular canals in each ear; their arrangement is shown in Figures 204 and 205. The canals are filled with endolymph. The receptors are hair cells in the dilated ends of the canals (ampullae); they are called *cristae acustica*. Movement of the endolymph bends the hairs and sets up impulses in the vestibular branch of the acoustic nerve. The cristae are stimulated by sudden movements, or by a change in rate or direction of movement. In other words, whenever movement begins or ends, accelerates or decelerates, or changes in direction, impulses are set up in dendrites of the vestibular nerve.

Utricle. There are hair cells in the utricle (a sac in the vestibular portion of the internal ear) which contain small crystals of calcium carbonate called *otoliths*. The receptors are called *maculae acustica*. Impulses are set up when the otoliths pull on the hairs or push on them and bend them. The impulses which are set up in the receptors in the utricle are ultimately responsible for a recognition of the position of the head in relation to gravity. Impulses from the semicircular canals and the utricle are considered

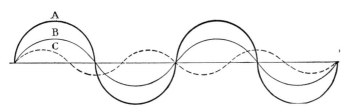

FIG. 208. Three sound waves. Waves A and B have the same pitch, but A has a greater intensity than B. Wave C has a different pitch and is least intense of the three.

to be less important in man than in lower animals, since man uses his eyes to help him maintain equilibrium. However, if he is blind, or even blindfolded, impulses from the vestibular portion of the inner ear assume great importance in orientation in space and in maintaining equilibrium.

Rotation. If an individual is rotated in a chair, the endolymph in the semicircular canals is set into motion and stimulates the hair cells. A sensation of vertigo or dizziness occurs, together with a peculiar movement of the eyes called *nystagmus*. Nystagmus consists of a rapid movement of the eyes in one direction and a slow movement in the opposite direction; they appear to oscillate. Nausea may occur. We speak of these sensations which are set up by rotation as motion sickness. Many somatic reflexes accompany rotation; these involve the muscles of the neck, the trunk and the extremities. Visceral reflexes occur, also. There is a fall in blood pressure and a change in heart rate, and the skin becomes pale, all of which involve visceral efferent nerves.

In summary, it may be stated that the semicircular canals are dynamic sense organs; they arouse sensations of starting and stopping movement, changing its speed (either acceleration or deceleration) and direction. They also originate many reflexes which involve skeletal, smooth and cardiac muscles. The utricle is a static sense organ; it gives information regarding the orientation of the head in space, in relation to gravity and sets into action postural and righting reflexes. The functions of the saccule are unknown.

PRACTICAL CONSIDERATIONS

ANESTHESIA

General anesthetics are administered to produce loss of consciousness and muscular relaxation during surgical operations. They inhibit the production of sensations. Spinal anesthetics produce paralysis of motion and loss of feeling below the level at which they are introduced into the subarachnoid space; they temporarily block afferent pathways. Local anesthetics block impulses in afferent nerves, so no pain is felt in the operative field. If any part of a sensory unit is blocked, no sensation from the area concerned is possible.

DISSOCIATION OF SENSATION

There may be a loss of pain (analgesia) and temperature senses in one area of the skin and retention of touch; in another area there is loss of touch, with retention of pain and temperature senses.

FIG. 209. Formation of an image by a biconvex lens.

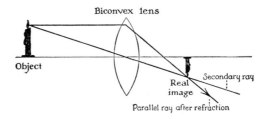

Biconvex lens

Object

Real image

Secondary ray

Parallel ray after refraction

This condition is called *dissociation of sensation*. It occurs when there is destruction of the gray matter of the spinal cord, around the central canal (syringomyelia). The impulses that give rise to touch travel over a different pathway from those that give rise to pain or temperature. The axons of the second neurons in the sensory mechanisms have been destroyed as they cross to the opposite side of the spinal cord in the commissures around the spinal canal.

THE EYE

Injury to the ophthalmic division of the trigeminal nerve leads to a loss of sensitivity in the cornea. The cornea is not protected; therefore, if foreign particles come in contact with it they cause ulceration with impairment of vision.

Hordeolum or sty is an infection of a sebaceous gland associated with follicles of the eyelashes. A *chalazion* is an infection of one of the sebaceous glands associated with the tarsus (tarsal or meibomian glands lie between the tarsus and the conjunctiva). *Blepharitis* is inflammation of the eyelids.

A *cataract* is an opacity of the lens or its capsule; light rays cannot pass through the lens to reach the retina, consequently the lens must be removed. After the lens is removed, corrective lenses must be used in order to see objects clearly. Opacity of the cornea likewise prevents light rays from reaching the retina, but this cannot be aided by use of lenses.

Since so many of us need glass lenses to correct defects in our eyes and to enable us to see objects near at hand when we grow older, we should understand a few fundamental facts about glass lenses. The principal types are: (1) convex or positive lenses, which converge or bring together rays of light and add to the refractive power of the human eye; (2) concave or negative lenses, which diverge or spread apart rays of light and decrease the refractive power of the human eye; and (3) cylindrical lenses, which

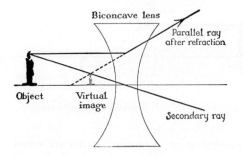

FIG. 210. Formation of an image by a bicon-cave lens.

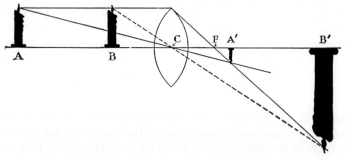

FIG. 211. Change in position and size of the image with change in position of the object. When the object is at A, the image is at A′; when the object is moved to B, the position of the image shifts to B′. $1/A + 1A′ = 1/F$, or 1/distance of object from the lens plus 1/distance of image from the lens equals 1/focal distance of the lens.

equalize refractive power in both the vertical and the horizontal planes, if we happen to have a spoon-shaped cornea instead of a spherical one, as is the case in astigmatism. A convex lens is shown in Figure 209 and a concave lens in Figure 210. The change that occurs in the size and the position of an image when the distance of the object from the lens is changed is illustrated in Figure 211. You will note that the image is inverted; images on the retina are inverted likewise, and it is by experience that we see them right side up. A lens whose focal distance is 1 meter has a strength of 1 diopter. The eye has a strength of 65 diopters.

If the refractive power of the eye is too great or the eyeball too long, the images fall in front of the retina; this condition is called

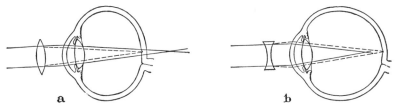

FIG. 212. a. Hyperopia and correction. b. myopia and correction.

myopia or near-sightedness. The refractive power must be decreased by a concave or negative lens, as illustrated in Figure 212.

If the refractive power of the eye is too weak or the eyeball too short, the images fall back of the retina; this condition is called *hyperopia* (far-sightedness). The refractive power must be increased by a convex or positive lens, as illustrated also in Figure 212.

As one grows older the lens loses its elasticity or hardens, just

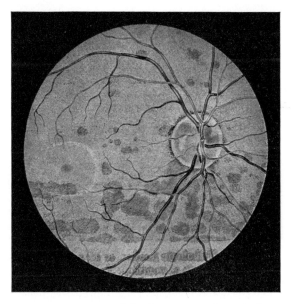

FIG. 213. Normal fundus, as seen in retinal
examination.

as one's arteries harden with age. This condition is called *presby-opia* or old-sight. The refractive power of the eye needs to be increased by convex lenses for near vision. Elderly people wear bifocals, which means that part of the lens is for distant vision and the remainder for near vision.

Retinal Examination. In order to see the retina, reflected light is essential. The reason we do not see retinae when we look at people's eyes is that we are in our own light. We need a device that will enable us to throw more light into the eye and yet not cut it off as it is reflected to the source. The ophthalmoscope is such an instrument, being a mirror with a hole in it. The mirror enables the observer to throw more light into the eye, and the hole permits rays reflected from the patient's retina to enter the observer's eye. The condition of the blood vessels can be seen, as well as the optic disk and the general condition of the retina (called

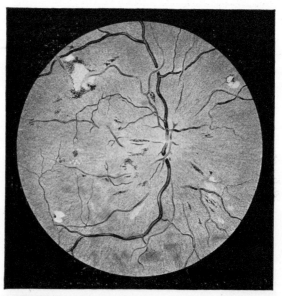

Fig. 214. Pathologic fundus, as seen in retinal examination. Chronic glomerulonephritis. Choked disk, macula not evident, edema, "cotton wool" patches, petechial and flame-shaped hemorrhages and interrupted arteriovenous crossings. (Minneapolis General Hospital)

FIG. 215. Reflection of light by a plane mirror.

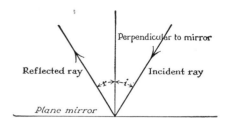

FIG. 216. Formation of an image by reflected light from a concave mirror.

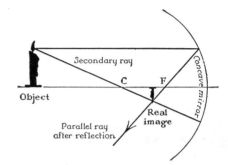

FIG. 217. Formation of an image by reflected light from a convex mirror.

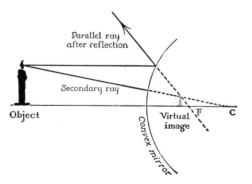

the *eye grounds*). The appearance of a normal retina is shown in Figure 213 and of a pathologic retina in Figure 214.

Reflection. Light that strikes a smooth surface is partly re-reflected. The light that strikes a plane mirror (ordinary looking glass) is reflected as illustrated in Figure 215. The formation of an image reflected from a concave mirror is shown in Figure 216. The formation of an image by rays reflected from a convex mirror is shown in Figure 217. The surfaces in the eye that reflect light as a convex mirror are the cornea and the anterior surface of the lens; that which reflects light as from a concave mirror is the posterior surface of the crystalline lens. This reflected light has nothing to do with one's vision but is responsible for the "lights" that we see in another's eyes. It can be used in determining refractive errors of the eye, by means of an instrument called a

FIG. 218. Light and accommodation reflexes. The pupil on the left is constricted, as when exposed to light or in looking at a near object; the one on the right is dilated, as when light is withdrawn or in looking at a distant object.

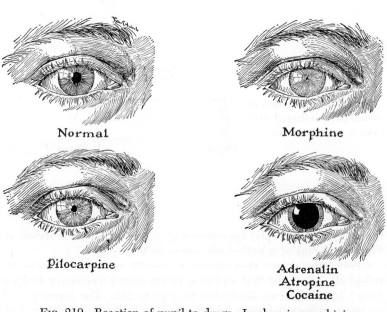

Normal

Morphine

Pilocarpine

Adrenalin
Atropine
Cocaine

FIG. 219. Reaction of pupil to drugs. In chronic morphinism, the pupil approaches a pinpoint; it is moderately constricted after pilocarpine; epinephrine (adrenalin), atropine and cocaine lead to a dilatation.

retinoscope (which is an unsatisfactory name for the instrument, since it is not used to see the retina).

Reflexes of the Eye. Two pupillary reflexes are noted in an ordinary physical examination. One is the *light reflex*, which is tested by flashing a light into the eye and determining if the pupil becomes smaller. The second is the *accommodation reflex*, which is tested by having the patient shift the gaze from a distant to a near object, during which the pupil should become smaller. Figure 218 illustrates these reflexes. In syphilis of the central nervous system the light reflex may be lost, and the accommodation reflex retained; such a condition is called an *Argyll Robertson pupil*. The corneal and conjunctival reflexes are tested by touching these surfaces; the response is a blinking of the eye.

Effects of Drugs on the Size of the Pupil. *Atropine,* which is used in eye examinations, makes the pupil larger by inhibiting the passage of impulses over the visceral efferent fibers of the oculomotor nerve. This means that the sphincter muscle of the iris and the ciliary muscle are paralyzed temporarily. *Epinephrine* and *cocaine* both lead to a dilatation of the pupil also, but through stimulation of the dilator or radial muscle of the iris. *Pilocarpine* leads to a constriction of the pupil by stimulation of the sphincter muscle of the iris. *Morphine* causes the pupil to become exceedingly small; it is called a "pin-point" pupil. The effects of various drugs on the pupils are illustrated in Figure 219. Drugs that dilate the pupils are called "mydriatics," and those that constrict the pupils are called "miotics."

The visual field may be mapped out by the use of a perimeter. If there is injury to one occipital cortex, blindness in the corresponding half of each eye results and is called *hemiopia*. If the pituitary gland becomes enlarged, it may exert pressure on the optic chiasma and produce blindness in the medial half of each retina, as can be understood if Figure 201 is studied carefully.

Strabismus, which sometimes is called *squint,* is a deviation of one of the eyes from its proper direction due to a muscle defect or a lack of co-ordination in the movements of the 2 eyes. Sometimes it is corrected by prismatic lenses; otherwise operative procedures are performed to correct the muscle at fault.

The Ear

Hardening of Wax. The wax that is produced by the ceruminous and the sebaceous glands in the skin of the external auditory meatus may harden and cause pressure on the ear drum; this is a very common cause of earache. The wax may be removed by gently syringing the passage with warm water.

Middle-Ear Infections (Otitis Media). It is very easy for infections to spread from the nose or the throat to the middle ear by way of the auditory tube. When pus forms in the middle ear, the drum should be lanced to allow drainage and prevent the backing up of pus into the mastoid air cells. Early treatment is advisable for any middle-ear infection. If the drum is not lanced it will rupture spontaneously, and when it heals the scar will be large and irregular instead of small and regular as occurs after lancing. The danger of permitting the infection to spread to the mastoid air cells is the nearness of these cells to the venous sinuses and the meninges of the brain.

Deafness. An impairment of the sense of hearing is called *deafness*. There are 2 types of deafness: conduction and nerve deafness.

Conduction deafness is due to difficulty in the middle ear. There may be injury to the tympanic membrane, ankylosis (stiffness of joints) of the bones of the middle ear or closure of the auditory tube by adhesions and the inability to equalize pressure on the 2 sides of the ear drum. If the small bones of the middle ear are not free to move, sound waves can be transmitted through the cranial bones to the fluid in the inner ear. The hearing aids for deaf individuals are made so as to take advantage of this fact.

Nerve deafness occurs in the inner ear (cochlea), in the cochlear branch of the acoustic nerve or in the auditory center in the cerebral cortex. There is no ability to hear, even with hearing aids.

The instrument designed to measure one's ability to hear is called the *audiometer*. It is useful in testing hearing in relation to occupational fitness or disability, in school children, in workmen who are subjected to excessive noise in their jobs and in fitting hearing aids for patients. Schools for the deaf and training in lip reading are important in preparing deaf individuals for occupations in which their handicap does not prevent them from being able to support themselves.

Menière's syndrome is a condition in which the patients hear buzzing noises in the ears and also have severe attacks of dizziness or vertigo. During an attack they cannot stand up and may even show rolling movements when lying down. It is due to hardening of the blood vessels in the ear. The only treatment is to cut the vestibular branch of the acoustic nerve, which relieves the distress. The hearing of subjective buzzing, high-pitched noises is called *tinnitus*.

Speech. The sense of hearing is important in learning to speak. Children who are born deaf will be dumb (unable to speak) unless speech is taught by some channel other than the ear. The sense of sight may be used, by watching the position of the lips and the tongue. It is quite unnecessary and cruel indeed for a child to be compelled to remain dumb if the intelligence is sufficient to enable him to speak. The sense of hearing is important in modulating the voice; deaf individuals cannot modulate their voices, since they cannot hear them.

Balance Sense. Injury to the semicircular canals or utricle leads to disturbances in maintaining one's orientation and balance. Vertigo is the most common symptom. Nystagmus is also a common sign of vestibular pathology.

SUMMARY

1. Sensory mechanisms
    A. Sense organs
    B. Afferent pathway to brain
    C. Sensory areas in cerebral cortex
2. Characteristics of sensations
    A. Projection
    B. After-images
    C. Adaptation
    D. Local sign
    E. Contrast
    F. Intensity
3. Classification of senses
    A. Cutaneous senses: distribution of receptors; sensitivity; receptors
        a. Touch: types of receptors; afferent pathway; sensory area; adequate stimulus; after-images; local sign; importance
        b. Temperature sense: receptors; afferent pathway; sensory area; successive contrast; local sign; adaptation; after-images
        c. Pain: receptors; types of pain; afferent pathway; sensory area; adaptation; discussion of visceral afferent division; theory of referred pain
    B. Muscle sense: receptors; afferent pathway; sensory area; importance
    C. Hunger
    D. Thirst
    E. Smell: receptors; afferent pathway; center. Importance; adaptation; rivalry; memory

F. Taste: receptors; afferent pathway; center; primary tastes; importance

G. Vision: receptors, afferent pathway, center

    a. Orbit

    b. Eyeball

    c. Extrinsic muscles of the eye

    d. Eyelids

    e. Conjunctiva

    f. Lacrimal apparatus

    g. Layers of eyeball: sclera and cornea; choroid, ciliary body and iris; crystalline lens; anterior and posterior chambers; aqueous humor; vitreous body; retina; macula lutea; fovea centralis; optic disk or blind spot; cones and rods

    h. Comparison of eye with camera

    i. Accommodation

    j. Path of a ray of light

    k. Physiology of the retina: functions of cones; functions of rods. Local sign; after-images; dark and light adaptation; color vision; binocular vision; optical judgments; illusions

H. Hearing and position sense

    a. Parts of the ear

        (1) External: pinna, external meatus, ear drum

        (2) Middle: connections; bones

        (3) Inner: membranous and osseous labyrinths; oval and round windows; receptors for hearing in cochlea; receptors concerned with dynamic equilibrium-cristae acustica; receptors concerned with static equilibrium-maculae acustica

SITUATION AND QUESTIONS

Mae Meir had an ophthalmologist examine her eyes as a part of her regular yearly physical checkup. This year the doctor told her that she would need to wear glasses because of presbyopia.

1. The doctor explained to Miss Meir that older folks should wear glasses because they have some failure of vision. This occurs because: _____(a) as one grows older the power of accommodation decreases because of a loss of elasticity of lens; _____ (b) because of extended use the optic nerve can no longer conduct impulses rapidly; _____(c) with old age there is a lack of co-ordination of the extrinsic eye muscles, therefore they cannot converge accurately; _____(d) the lens becomes opaque and, therefore, light cannot pass through to reach the retina.

2. Miss Meir did not object too strenuously to the wearing of glasses. She was thankful to have had good vision thus far. Many of our American youth have impaired vision. Some of these common defects are:

Strabismus, which is a defect of the: _____(a) lens; _____ (b) cornea; _____(c) extrinsic eye muscles; _____(d) ciliary muscles.

Astigmatism, which is a defect of the _____(a) optic nerve; _____(b) occipital lobe of cerebral cortex; _____(c) cornea; _____(d) choroid layer.

When light rays are focused behind the retina because an eyeball may be too short, the condition is referred to as: _____(a) myopia; _____(b) hyperopia; _____(c) presbyopia; _____(d) diplopia.

3. Dr. Jones commented on the pretty blue-green color of Miss Meir's eyes. He explained that this colored portion of the eye is called the iris and that it has as its function: _____(a) bending of light rays; _____(b) regulating the amount of light entering the eyeball; _____(c) perceiving color; _____ (d) containing the rods and cones which in turn contain the visual purple of the eye.

4. Miss Meir also had a small amount of cerumen removed from her external ear during her physical checkup. The doctor very gently irrigated the ear as he did not want to injure the tympanic membrane. _____(a) The tympanic membrane separates the middle and the internal ears. _____(b) The tympanic membrane is set into vibration when sound waves enter the external ear. _____(c) The tympanic membrane is composed mostly of cartilage. _____(d) The tympanic membrane amplifies sound as it is transmitted through the auditory pathways.

5. Deafness which cannot be relieved by the use of a hearing aid would result from: _____(a) damage to the organ of Corti; _____(b) perforation of the tympanic membrane; _____ (c) immobility of the ossicles of the middle ear; _____(d) absence of fluid from the semi-circular canals of the inner ear.

UNIT 4

MAINTAINING THE METABOLISM OF THE BODY

9. Blood, Tissue Fluid and Lymph

INTRODUCTION

Hemopoietic tissue is the kind of connective tissue that is highly specialized for both the production of new blood corpuscles and the removal of old ones. The intercellular substance of blood is liquid, and the cells are the blood corpuscles which are not fixed as in other tissues. The corpuscles are carried around the body continuously in the circulating blood. Old corpuscles wear out and must be removed, and new ones must be added to the blood each day, in order to keep the number fairly constant.

The lymph, which contains white blood corpuscles, moves slowly along in the lymphatic vessels since there is no pump or "lymph heart" to drive it along rapidly as the heart drives the blood. Lymph is derived from blood plasma and is returned, eventually, to the vascular system.

Tissue fluid, or interstitial fluid, cannot be classed as a tissue, since it contains no cells. It is derived from blood plasma and fills all the spaces between other tissues; it is not confined to vessels. Some of it enters the lymphatic system, some enters tissue cells, and some re-enters the blood from which it came.

BLOOD

FUNCTIONS OF THE BLOOD

The chief function of the blood is to keep the "internal environment" of the tissues of the body constant or, in other words,

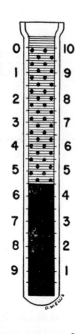

FIG. 220. Wintrobe tube. When blood is prevented from coagulating and allowed to stand undisturbed in this tube for 1 hour, the corpuscles begin to settle out, and a clear layer of plasma may be seen above the corpuscles. The depth of the plasma is read on the scale at the left, in millimeters (1 cm.=10 mm.); this is called the *sedimentation index*. Then the tube is centrifuged; this packs the corpuscles. The height of the corpuscle layer is read on the scale at the right; this is called the *cell volume*. As drawn, the cell volume (hematocrit) is 45 per cent. The Wintrobe tube thus serves a double function as a sedimentation tube and as a hematocrit tube.

to preserve homeostasis. There are numerous processes going on all the time in the body which tend to change the chemical composition of internal environment, such as the chemical changes that accompany contraction of muscles, conduction of nerve impulses and secretion of glands. All of these forms of metabolism use food and oxygen and produce waste products. The circulating blood makes it possible for the various organs to "take these changes in their stride" and yet remain normal.

The blood transports oxygen, from the lungs to the tissues, and carbon dioxide, from the tissues to the lungs to be eliminated. It carries food materials from the intestine to all parts of the body and returns waste to the kidneys to be excreted. The blood distributes the heat produced in active muscles and thus aids in the regulation of body temperature. It transports internal secretions from the glands in which they are produced to the tissues on which each exerts its effects. By means of the buffers (p. 564) in the blood, acid-base balance is maintained. The blood is concerned with immunity to disease and in protecting the body against invading bacteria.

QUANTITY OF BLOOD

The total volume of blood is about 7 per cent or one fourteenth of the body weight. If you weigh about 100 pounds you have about 7 pounds of blood or 2.6 quarts. If you weigh about 140 pounds, you have about 10 pounds of blood or about 3.7 quarts. In round figures, 1 pound of blood is equal to about 0.37 quart. If an individual has more than the normal amount of blood for his weight he is said to have *plethora* (meaning "fullness"); less than the normal amount of blood is called *oligemia* (meaning "little blood").

CHARACTERISTICS OF BLOOD

The color of whole blood (plasma and corpuscles) is bright scarlet if it is oxygenated arterial blood. Blood from veins is dark red, since it is not saturated with oxygen. Whole blood is opaque, which means that we are unable to see through it.

Structure. So far as structure is concerned, the blood consists of a little more than half plasma (53 to 58 per cent) and a little less than half corpuscles (42 to 47 per cent). The relative volumes of plasma and corpuscles in a tube of blood are shown in Figure 220. Plasma is pale yellow and transparent in healthy, fasting individuals. It is milky after meals which contain fat. The red color of whole blood is due to the corpuscles. The color of plasma may vary in disease; for example, it may be greenish yellow in jaundice.

The viscosity of blood refers to its resistance to flow. It is thick and sticky, and it normally flows with difficulty. It has been found that the viscosity of whole blood is about 5 times as great as that of water. Part of the viscosity is due to the corpuscles and part to the proteins of the plasma. When either of these factors is altered, the viscosity changes.

Specific gravity refers to the weight of blood compared with that of water. The specific gravity of water is taken as 1.00 (1 milliliter of water weighing 1 Gm. at 4° C). The specific gravity of whole blood is between 1.055 and 1.065, with an average of 1.060 which means that 1 milliliter of whole blood weighs 1.060 Gm.

The specific gravity of plasma is between 1.028 and 1.032. The corpuscles are much heavier than the plasma. If clotting of blood is prevented, the corpuscles tend to settle out, or sink to the bottom of a tube, as blood stands. They have no opportunity to settle out in the body, as the blood is kept moving in the vessels due to the pumping action of the heart.

CORPUSCLES

There are 3 kinds of corpuscles in the blood: red corpuscles,

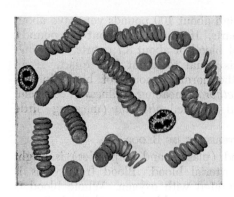

FIG. 221. Human blood corpuscles. Two leukocytes are noted among the red corpuscles; most of the latter are grouped in rouleaux. ×625.

or erythrocytes; white corpuscles, or leukocytes; and platelets, or thrombocytes.

Erythrocytes. DESCRIPTION. Erythrocytes are thin in the center and thick around the edge, which means that they are shaped like a biconcave disk. Erythrocytes in circulating blood have no nuclei; that is the reason we call them corpuscles instead of cells. They are flexible and elastic. They can bend and twist in order to get through narrow blood vessels and then spring back into shape. You can note this if you look at the web of a foot of an anesthetized frog under the microscope. If you never have seen the blood circulating in a living animal before, this should give you a real thrill. You will note that every now and then a red corpuscle seems to get stuck in a capillary, or at a *bifurcation* (meaning "branching") of an artery, and then it suddenly bends or squeezes through somehow and is carried along on its way back to the heart.

When a drop of blood is drawn from the body and put on a glass slide, it will be noted on microscopic examination that the red corpuscles tend to stick together and to stack up like rows of coins. This is called *rouleaux formation,* and it is illustrated in Figure 221.

As stated previously, if blood is withdrawn from a vein (called *venipuncture*) of an individual, kept from clotting by adding an anticoagulant and allowed to stand in a tube, the corpuscles then settle or *sediment.* The speed of settling or sedimentation depends on the condition of the blood and the state of health of the individual. The rate can be determined easily by measuring the depth of the plasma layer above the settling corpuscles 1 hour after the blood is drawn. This depth, in milli-

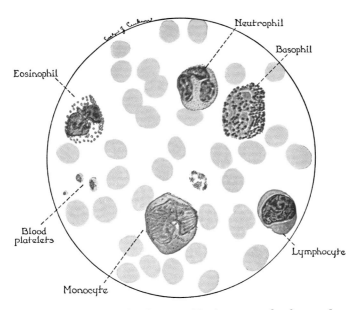

Eosinophil

Center of Cushions

Neutrophil

Basophil

Blood
platelets

Lymphocyte

Monocyte

FIG. 222. Normal blood smear. Erythrocytes, platelets, and
various types of leukocytes are noted.

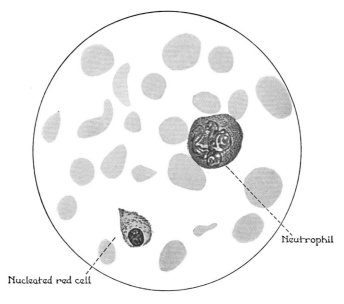

Neutrophil

Nucleated red cell

FIG. 223. Blood smear in pernicious anemia. Changes are
evident in the erythrocytes and in the neutrophil.

meters, is called the *sedimentation index*. The tube shown in Figure 220 is used for sedimentation tests.

Erythrocytes consist of a framework or stroma (bedding), in which hemoglobin is held, and a membrane. The membrane possesses important properties like other cell membranes. One property is that of selective permeability. For example, potassium salts enter erythrocytes readily, but sodium salts are rejected. Watⱼr, glucose and urea pass freely in and out of erythrocytes. Normally, the plasma and the erythrocytes have the same osmotic pressure; hence, they are isotonic. When erythrocytes are placed in hypotonic solutions, water enters, and the corpuscles swell (p. 67).

There is a clinical test, called the *fragility test*, which is based on the behavior of erythrocytes in varying strengths of hypotonic sodium chloride solutions. Blood is drawn by venipuncture, and one drop is placed in each of a series of tubes containing sodium chloride solutions ranging from 0.7 to 0.3 per cent. The corpuscles swell in each solution, and some burst and allow hemoglobin to escape from the corpuscles into the solution and color it. Rupture of the membrane and escape of hemoglobin is called *laking* or *hemolysis*. The aim of the fragility test is to see at which concentration hemolysis begins and at which it is complete, and to compare the results with those of normal individuals.

Hemolysis is brought about not only by hypotonic salt solution but also by lipid solvents (such as ether) which alter the membrane, by snake venoms, by incompatible plasma (p. 409) and other agents.

SIZE. The diameter of normal erythrocytes varies from 6 to 9 microns, with an average of 7.5 (one micron is one one-thousandth of a mm. or 1/25,000 inch). In normal blood, the erythrocytes in a blood "smear" are all about the same size, as illustrated in Figure 222.

ORIGIN. There are 2 types of hemopoietic tissue: myeloid or bone marrow and lymphatic tissue. Hemopoietic tissue originates from the mesenchyme of the embryo; it contains undifferentiated cells which are called *primitive reticular* cells or *fixed stem* cells. Some of the cells undergo differentiation to form blood corpuscles, and others differentiate to form reticuloendothelial cells which remove worn-out erythrocytes. The origin of blood corpuscles in the embryo and the fetus is discussed on page 793. After birth, erythrocytes are formed only in red

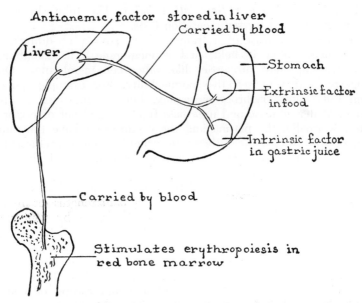

FIG. 224. Factors important in normal erythropoiesis. The extrinsic factor probably is vitamin B$_{12}$; the intrinsic factor has not been isolated or identified. The mechanism of its action is still obscure, but it may be involved in facilitating the absorption of vitamin B$_{12}$ from the small intestine.

bone marrow, from cells called *myeloblasts*. In the newborn infant, the cavities of all the bones contain red marrow; later it is replaced by yellow bone marrow in most bones. In adults, red bone marrow is found only in the bodies of the vertebrae, the ribs, the sternum, the cranial bones and the proximal epiphyses of femur and humerus. A sample of bone marrow for microscopic examination can be obtained by sternal puncture. In section, red bone marrow shows a delicate connective tissue stroma which supports blood vessels and contains numerous cells, as shown in Figure 36, 3.

There are both immature and mature types of red corpuscles in red bone marrow. The mature types are *erythrocytes*, such as are seen in circulating blood. The immature forms of red corpuscles are called *erythroblasts* and *normoblasts*; various stages of development are noted in red bone marrow. As the nucleus undergoes fragmentation it is seen as granules in the cytoplasm of the almost mature red corpuscles which now are called *reticulocytes*. These also can be found in small numbers in circulating blood.

In order for red corpuscles to mature normally, one needs not only normal red bone marrow but also a special factor called the *erythrocyte-maturing* factor. There is some component of food called the *extrinsic factor* and a second component in gastric juice called the *intrinsic factor* that must interact to form the erythrocyte-maturing or antianemic factor. This factor is then absorbed from the intestine by the blood and stored in the liver until needed, then transported to the bone marrow by means of the blood. These events are shown by diagram in Figure 224. Vitamin B_{12} is thought to be identical with the erythrocyte-maturing factor. Liver extract contains this factor, and when it is given, first the reticulocytes in the circulating blood increase, and then the erythrocytes increase. In order to form normal erythrocytes, one needs a well-balanced diet, plenty of protein, iron, cobalt, copper, vitamin B (riboflavin and nicotinic acid) and vitamin C. The internal secretions also exert an influence on the activity of red bone marrow in a manner unknown at present.

NUMBER. Erythrocytes are about 700 times as numerous as leukocytes. The average number is 5½ million per cu. mm. in men and 5 million in women.

FUNCTION. The chief function of erythrocytes is to carry oxygen from the lungs to the tissues, and carbon dioxide back from the tissues to the lungs. The amount of oxygen that is dissolved in the plasma is small, and it would be impossible to supply the demands of the tissues if this were the only means of transport. The hemoglobin in the erythrocytes, by means of its iron, makes it possible to carry an abundance of oxygen to tissues for ordinary requirements.

In the lungs, oxygen diffuses from the alveolar air into the blood, then it is taken up rapidly by the hemoglobin to form oxyhemoglobin, which gives the bright scarlet color to arterial or oxygenated blood.

In the systemic capillaries, oxygen leaves the hemoglobin and diffuses out through the tissue fluid to the tissue cells. As hemoglobin loses its oxygen, or is reduced, the blood turns dark red in color.

In a way, hemoglobin may be thought of as being fickle, since as it gives up its oxygen it combines immediately with carbon dioxide, which has been formed in the tissue cells, and diffuses into the tissue fluid, and then on into the blood. In the lung capillaries, hemoglobin gives up carbon dioxide, which diffuses into the alveolar air, and again takes on oxygen as it diffuses into the blood from the alveolar air. The transport of gases is considered in greater detail on page 562.

It is essential to have hemoglobin confined in erythroycytes, since whenever it does escape (during laking or hemolysis) and enters the plasma, it passes through glomerular capillary walls in the kidneys and escapes into the urine. So it would not be possible to have it remain in the body if it were not confined in the erythrocytes as it is. Hemoglobin is an ideal substance for transport of oxygen. Not only does it combine with oxygen for transport, but it takes oxygen up very easily and releases it just as rapidly, according to differences in concentration in the immediate environment of pulmonary and systemic capillaries.

Hemoglobin can unite also with carbon monoxide, which is unfortunate. The union of hemoglobin with carbon monoxide is a firm one, and when this occurs hemoglobin is not available to carry oxygen. It is really lack of oxygen that causes death in poisoning with carbon monoxide. The color of carbon monoxide-hemoglobin is bright cherry red.

In connection with a complete physical examination, the amount of hemoglobin is determined. The average amount is 15 Gm. per 100 cc. of blood. Normally, the hemoglobin in arterial blood is about 98 per cent saturated with oxygen. If the degree of saturation is low, there is interference with the functions of the central nervous system and the heart, and there is a bluish discoloration of the skin called "cyanosis."

LIFE CYCLE. After the erythrocytes leave the red bone marrow they circulate in the blood stream for about 4 months, according to studies with radioactive tracers. Each erythrocyte takes up oxygen and unloads it about twice every minute, which is more than 300,000 times in 4 months. Worn-out erythrocytes are destroyed by phagocytes in the spleen, the liver and the red bone marrow (reticuloendothelial system). The iron is retained and used over again in making hemoglobin. The remainder of the hemoglobin molecule is transformed into bile pigments, excreted by the liver into bile and eliminated in the feces from the large intestine.

Leukocytes. DESCRIPTION. Leukocytes are nucleated corpuscles found in the blood. There are 2 main classes of leukocytes: the nongranular, which have no granules in their cytoplasm; and the granular, which have granules in their cytoplasm. The nongranular leukocytes may be divided into 2 subgroups: lymphocytes and monocytes. There are 3 subgroups of granular leukocytes: neutrophils, basophils and eosinophils.

Nongranular Leukocytes. Lymphocytes are slightly larger than erythrocytes and are distinguished by having very large nuclei surrounded by a thin layer of cytoplasm. They comprise from 20 to 35 per cent of the total number of leukocytes.

Monocytes may be a little more than twice the size of erythrocytes. They have large nuclei which may be round, oval or indented. The cytoplasm forms more than one half of the cell, so is more abundant than in lymphocytes. Monocytes form only 2 to 8 per cent of the total number of leukocytes.

Granular Leukocytes. The nuclei in granular leukocytes consist of several lobes, which may be of different shapes. Sometimes this class is called *polymorphonuclear leukocytes* because of the variations seen in the shape of the nuclei. The subgroups are named according to the staining characteristics of the granules in the cytoplasm.

Neutrophils have nuclei that exhibit from 3 to 5 lobes. The granules are stained by neutral dyes. They may be twice as large as erythrocytes. Neutrophils are the most numerous of all leukocytes; they make up from 60 to 70 per cent of the total number.

Eosinophils have nuclei made up of 2 oval lobes. The cytoplasm is stuffed with granules which stain with eosin. Eosinophils may be twice as large as erythrocytes. They form only 1 to 3 per cent of the total number of leukocytes but are increased in allergic individuals.

Basophils have nuclei which are bent into an S-shape. The granules in the cytoplasm are very large and they practically obscure the nucleus; they stain with basic dyes. Basophils are about the size of erythrocytes and form only about 0.5 per cent of the total number of leukocytes. The various subgroups of leukocytes are illustrated in Figure 222.

ORIGIN. Leukocytes are formed in both types of hemopoietic tissue: lymphatic tissue and red bone marrow or myeloid tissue. Nongranular leukocytes are formed in lymphatic tissue (p. 472), which is found in lymph nodes, tonsils, Peyer's patches (p. 601), spleen and thymus. There are germinal centers in these masses of lymphatic tissue in which intense formation of leukocytes of the nongranular type goes on continuously. The granular leukocytes are formed in myeloid tissue or red bone marrow. They originate from myeloblasts. Immature forms of leukocytes are called promyelocytes and myelocytes.

NUMBER. The total number of leukocytes is between 5,000 and 9,000 per cu. mm. There is daily variation in the count as a result of meals and exercise. The hormones of the adrenal cortex (p. 735) influence the number of lymphocytes in circulating blood, as does ACTH (p. 722).

FUNCTIONS. *Response to Injury.* Let us assume that an individual receives a cut in the skin of his finger. This is like opening the door to admit the bacteria that are always present on the surface of the skin. The neutrophils and the monocytes, due to their property of ameboid movement, pass through the capillary walls by diapedesis and rush to the site of injury. They wall off the area and then ingest and digest the bacteria, which are multiplying rapidly. The term applied to ingestion and digestion of bacteria is *phagocytosis* (meaning "condition of eating cells"). The area around the cut is inflamed due to dilatation of blood vessels and to swelling. The swelling results from accumulation of fluid from the plasma, since the capillary walls are damaged, allowing plasma to leak out readily. The skin feels hot because dilatation of the blood vessels brings more blood to the area. There is pain, due to pressure of swollen tissues. This response is one of the mechanisms of the body for defense.

If the leukocytes win the battle, pus forms (consisting of fragments of damaged tissue cells and leukocytes), and healing then begins. If the leukocytes lose the battle, the bacteria continue to multiply and are not walled off successfully. They enter the lymphatic channels and eventually reach the blood stream and infect it, causing a condition called *septicemia* (meaning "a condition of putrefaction of the blood") or blood poisoning.

The functions of leukocytes are to wall off infection and to engulf and digest bacteria. In addition, the lymphocytes release gamma globulin when they disintegrate. Gamma globulin, which is concerned with immunity to infection, is sometimes called *antibody protein.* It has been suggested that leukotaxine is formed whenever there is tissue injury; it possesses a chemical attraction for migrating leukocytes.

LIFE CYCLE. It is thought that leukocytes live only a few days in the blood stream; in fact, some investigators think that the lymphocytes in the blood stream may be replaced 2 to 3 times daily. Leukocytes are destroyed, as well as produced, in hemopoietic tissue. Many leukocytes probably migrate into the lumen of the intestinal tract and are lost in the feces.

Blood Platelets. DESCRIPTION. Blood platelets are small granular bodies which are fragments of cells. They stick to each other and to all wettable surfaces with which they come in contact when blood is shed. They are shown in Figure 222.

ORIGIN. Blood platelets are fragments of giant cells called *megakaryocytes* in red bone marrow. Megakaryocytes are about 6 times as large as erythrocytes.

NUMBER. There are 250,000 to 350,000 platelets per cu. mm. of blood.

FUNCTIONS. Platelets perform 3 functions.

(1) They agglutinate or stick to the inner surfaces of blood vessels wherever there is damage, plug up leaks and cement over injured tissues. They attract other platelets and finally form a mass large enough to close off the lumen of small vessels. A mass of platelets sticking together within a vessel through which blood is flowing is called a *white thrombus* or white clot. This is a protective function performed by platelets.

(2) Platelets, by disintegration when blood is shed or flowing free from the vessels, release a substance called *thromboplastin* (cephalin) which sets up the coagulation process.

(3) Once a blood clot has formed, platelets make it shrink or retract, during which process it is changed from a soft mass to a firm one. This helps to stop bleeding from damaged vessels.

LIFE CYCLE. Platelets probably live only a few days in the blood stream.

PLASMA

Plasma is the liquid portion of circulating blood.

Composition. Plasma contains more than 100 constituents. The normal amount of each of the commonly determined constituents is shown in Figure 225. A few of the constituents of plasma and their functions will now be considered.

WATER comprises from 91 to 92 per cent of plasma. The numerous functions of water are discussed on page 60.

PROTEINS comprise from 6 to 8 per cent of plasma. Most of the plasma proteins are formed in the liver; the remainder are formed or released by the disintegration of lymphocytes (or perhaps plasma cells). It is now known that all of the proteins of the body (in plasma, lymph, liver and various tissues) form a large dynamic

Glucose	70-90	High in emotional stress, after meals, during anesthesia, in hyperthyroidism and in untreated diabetes mellitus; it may reach 1000 or more in diabetic coma. Low in starvation, severe and prolonged muscular exertion, Addison's disease, myxedema, cretinism, and hyperinsulinism.
Non-protein nitrogen	25-35	High in nephritis, in which it may reach 300; high in acute intestinal obstruction, in hemolytic anemia, on high protein diet. Low on low protein diet.
Urea nitrogen	10-15	High in nephritis, malignancy, intestinal obstruction, and lead poisoning. Low in nephrosis, and in liver disease.
Uric acid	2-3	High in nephritis, arthritis, pneumonia, carcinoma, leukemia, and severe febrile conditions. It may be 10 or more in gout.
Creatinine	1-2	It may reach 5 in nephritis; it is low in diseases associated with muscular atrophy.
Calcium	9-11	It may reach 20 in hyperparathyroidism; it is low in tetany, advanced nephritis, pellagra, jaundice, osteomalacia, and colitis.
Inorganic Phosphate	2-5 in adults 4-7 in infants	High in nephritis; low in active rickets. Ca x PO_4 important; calcification will occur only if this product is 40 or more.
Sodium chloride (plasma)	560-630	High in nephritis, eclampsia, anemia, malignancy, cardiac disease. Low in fevers, diabetes, pneumonia, and intestinal obstruction.
Total protein	6.5-8.2%	Albumin averages 4.5 and globulin 2.4. The total protein is decreased in nephritis with edema, primary anemia, chronic malnutrition.
Fibrinogen	0.35%	High in most infections; low in liver disease.
Total fatty acids	290-450	High in diabetes and nephritis.
Cholesterol	150-200	High in nephritis, nephrosis, diabetes, pregnancy, myxedema, and biliary obstruction. Low in malignancy, Addison's disease, exophthalmic goiter, pneumonia, and starvation.
Acetone bodies	1.3-2.6	High in diabetes, starvation, vomiting. May reach 300 in diabetic coma.
Lactic acid	5-20	High in exercise, after insulin, during ether anesthesia, and in pregnancy.
Carbon dioxide Whole blood Plasma	45-65 volumes per cent. 55-75	High in alkalosis associated with persistent vomiting or diarrhea; may reach 100 in severe alkalosis. Low in acidosis; may reach 30 in severe acidosis.
Bilirubin	0.2-1.0	High in obstructive jaundice and in hemolytic anemia.

Fig. 225. The values given are in milligrams per hundred cc., unless otherwise stated.

pool, which may be drawn upon by any tissue which needs protein. Proteins are dynamic in the sense that a particular molecule may be synthesized in the liver, travel in the blood as part of the plasma pool, make up part of an enzyme in some cell, and eventually be incorporated into hemoglobin in an erythrocyte.

The functions and the clinical uses of some of the plasma proteins will be mentioned.

Albumin, the most abundant protein in plasma, is formed by the liver. It is especially important because of its osmotic relationships, since it is the protein mostly responsible for the "colloid osmotic pressure" of the plasma. It helps to regulate the volume of plasma within the blood vessels by pulling in water from tissue fluid. Frequently, it is given with sodium chloride by vein to patients when whole blood or plasma is not available. It is particularly valuable in the treatment of extensive burns and when an individual has been deprived of protein until his body is "starved" for it.

Gamma globulin is released from lymphocytes (or perhaps plasma cells) and is important in developing immunity to certain infections or contagious diseases. It is used clinically in epidemics of measles, infectious hepatitis (liver disease) and poliomyelitis.

Prothrombin, which plays a part in coagulation of blood, is made in the liver. An abundant supply of vitamin "K" is essential; if this is lacking the liver is unable to make sufficient prothrombin, and clotting disturbances will occur.

Fibrinogen also is made in the liver; it is in a liquid or "sol" form in circulating blood. When blood clots, fibrinogen changes from a liquid state to a solid state, or from a sol to a "gel" called *fibrin.* Fibrin films and fibrin foams are useful clinically to stop bleeding during general surgery, in making skin grafts, in surgical operations on blood vessels and in neurosurgery (surgery of the central nervous system).

Plasma proteins have been fractionated or separated into individual proteins, and there are many clinical uses for several fractions in addition to those listed above.

CARBOHYDRATES. Carbohydrate is present in the blood chiefly as glucose. This is carried to all tissues where it is used to supply energy or stored as reserve food.

LIPIDS are present in plasma as neutral fats, cholesterol and phospholipid. Lipids are carried to tissues and are used to supply energy or are stored as fat. Many vitamins are combined with fats.

INORGANIC SALTS. These form about 0.9 per cent of the plasma and consist of chlorides of sodium, potassium, calcium and magnesium; sodium iodide; sodium bicarbonate; phosphates; sulfates; and traces of many others.

GASES. The gases present in solution in the plasma are oxygen, carbon dioxide and nitrogen; the amounts in solution are small.

WASTE PRODUCTS, such as urea, uric acid, lactic acid and creatinine, are present.

MISCELLANEOUS SUBSTANCES. Antitoxins, lysins and agglutinins are present in the plasma. Hormones, produced by the glands of internal secretion, are present in the plasma in small amounts.

Reaction of the Blood. The reaction of the plasma is slightly alkaline, with a pH of about 7.4. "Alkaline reserve" refers to the amount of base in combination with weak acids that can be replaced by stronger acids. More specifically, it refers to the sodium in combination with carbonic acid as sodium bicarbonate. The bicarbonate molecule (HCO_3) can be replaced by anions of acids such as hydrochloric, sulfuric or phosphoric, to form $NaCl, Na_2SO_4$ and NaH_2PO_4 or Na_2HPO_4. Such a substance as sodium bicarbonate is called a *buffer;* it can take up large amounts of acid without a change in pH.

Plasma proteins and hemoglobin are buffers, also; they can neutralize either acids or bases as fast as such substances enter the blood stream and thus help to maintain the pH constant at the normal value. Thus, plasma proteins, hemoglobin of erythrocytes and sodium bicarbonate of plasma help to maintain the acid-base balance of the body (p. 563). Since all cellular functions are sensitive to changes in reaction, it is imperative to keep the pH at a fairly constant level and avoid both acidosis and alkalosis in which conditions the pH shifts away from the normal range.

COAGULATION

Many details of the coagulation process are unknown, and many components have several names. A brief outline will be given. The first stage involves the formation of a mildly active thromboplastin by the interaction of some substance from the platelets, and several plasma components, namely, antihemophiliac globulin, *plasma thromboplastin component,* plasma *thromboplastic antecedent* and calcium ions. The second stage involves the conversion of the above thromboplastin to a powerful form, under the influence of so-called *factors V and VII* of the plasma. The next stage consists of the interaction between powerful thromboplastin and prothrombin to form thrombin. The final stage is the change of fibrinogen to fibrin under the influence of thrombin.

Fibrin first appears as a meshwork of threads; this becomes denser and catches the red corpuscles among the threads. Although erythrocytes are found among the threads of a clot, it has been shown that they have nothing to do with actual coagulation, since clotting will occur in plasma even after the erythrocytes are removed.

The time required for blood to coagulate varies from 3 to 10 minutes in normal individuals. As a clot stands, it shrinks, due to the action of platelets, and a liquid called *serum* is squeezed out. Shrinking of the clot is called *syneresis* (meaning "a taking together"). Serum is plasma from which fibrinogen has been removed by the coagulation process.

If, when an artery of an animal is opened, the blood collected in a vessel is stirred as it is being shed, fibrin will form and stick to the stirring rod. The fibrin can be removed easily in this manner. Serum and corpuscles remain, and this combination is called *defibrinated blood.*

Blood remains fluid within the vessels of the body under normal conditions because of (1) the stability of the platelets and (2) the presence of a small amount of anticoagulant called *heparin.*

TISSUE FLUID

Definition. Tissue fluid is that fluid which is found in all parts of the body, filling tissue spaces, lying between cells and fibers of connective tissue and between the cells of organs. It fills serous cavities (pleural, pericardial and peritoneal) and synovial sacs and occupies such special spaces as the subarachnoid space, the space between the bony and the membranous labyrinths, the space within the membranous labyrinths and within the chambers of the eyes. The cells of the body live in tissue fluid and are surrounded by it.

Importance. The cells of the body are not in contact with blood, so nutrient materials and oxygen must pass through the walls of the capillaries and through tissue fluid to reach the cells. Wastes must pass from cells through tissue fluid and through the walls of capillaries to be carried by the blood to the organs of excretion. Tissue fluid may be considered as a "middleman" through which exchanges between blood and cells take place continuously.

Formation. Tissue fluid is formed by outward filtration and diffusion of all constituents of plasma except large protein molecules. Blood pressure, which is due to the pumping action of the heart, furnishes the filtering force, and the molecular movement makes diffusion possible.

The walls of capillaries resemble collodion membranes in permitting everything except large molecules to pass through. There are pores in the capillary walls through which water and crystalloids pass easily, but large protein molecules pass through only with difficulty, so that at least 90 per cent of the protein molecules remain inside the capillary wall and exert osmotic force which opposes filtration. Since crystalloids pass through the capillary walls easily, they exert the same osmotic pressure on both sides of the capillary wall and, therefore, are not responsible for the movement of water. Water leaves the capillary by filtration at the arterial end and is pulled back into the capillary at the venous end by osmosis, as shown in Figure 226.

Composition. The composition of tissue fluid is practically identical with plasma except for less protein.

Fate. The fluid that filters out at the arterial end of the capillary has several courses available to it. (1) It may be pulled back into the capillary by osmosis at the venous end. (2) It may move on into the cells and become part of the intracellular fluid (Fig. 376, p. 687). (3) It may remain in the tissue spaces as part of the tissue fluid reservoir. (4) It may enter the lymphatic capillaries and form lymph, in which case it eventually enters the blood again. Any protein molecules which escape from the vascular capillaries have no choice but the last course.

LYMPH

Definition. Lymph is the fluid that is present in lymphatic vessels.

FORMATION OF TISSUE FLUID

1. ARTERIAL END OF CAPILLARY

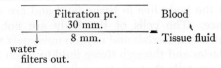

2. VENOUS END OF CAPILLARY

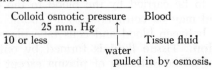

FIG. 226. Diagram illustrating the formation of tissue fluid from plasma. Filtration is represented at the arterial end and osmosis at the venous end of the capillary.

Origin. Lymph is derived from plasma, by way of tissue fluid, and it finally enters the blood again at the end of its journey.

Composition. Lymph resembles plasma in composition. It has almost the same concentration of salts and other constituents, but the protein concentration is below that of plasma. The protein concentration varies in the lymph from different parts of the body; liver lymph contains 6 per cent, that from the legs contains from 0.5 to 2.0 per cent, and thoracic duct lymph contains 3.5 to 4.0 per cent of protein.

Lymph from the thoracic duct (p. 469) is opalescent, watery and alkaline in reaction. After a fatty meal it looks like cream. It contains between 500 and 72,000 lymphocytes per cu. mm. Lymphocytes are added to lymph as it passes through lymph nodes (p. 472). The circulation of lymph is described on page 465.

Lymphatic capillaries are more permeable than vascular capillaries, and protein molecules can pass through the walls readily. Any protein that escapes from vascular capillaries into tissue fluid enters lymphatic capillaries. In addition, the liver constantly forms new plasma proteins which eventually reach the blood stream by way of the lymph.

Functions. The main functions of the lymphatic system are (1) to return escaped protein to the blood stream, (2) to carry newly formed plasma proteins from the liver to the blood, (3) to manufacture new lymphocytes and monocytes and add them to the lymph, which eventually delivers them to the blood, and (4) to filter out foreign matter as lymph passes through lymph nodes in its course from lymphatic capillaries to the thoracic duct.

PRACTICAL CONSIDERATIONS

Sludged Blood. In certain diseases, such as malaria, red corpuscles tend to stick together in the body and to form clumps in the vessels. These clumps make it much more difficult for the blood to circulate; therefore, its speed of circulation is slow. This thick, highly viscous blood with its clumped corpuscles is called *sludged blood.* Human beings are examined for the presence of sludge by looking at the capillaries of the conjunctiva with a special microscope.

Sedimentation Test. The rate of settling of erythrocytes is rapid in anemia, pregnancy, rheumatic fever and infectious diseases in general. It is not a specific test for any condition or disease, but it does aid in making diagnoses, when used with other tests.

Fragility Test. In congenital hemolytic jaundice, erythrocytes are especially fragile and hemolyze at higher concentrations than do normal corpuscles. This test is specific in hemolytic jaundice.

Variation in Size of Erythrocytes. If there is great variation in size of the erythrocytes in a blood smear, the condition is called *anisocytosis* (meaning "a condition of not equal cells"). If there is great variation in shape, it is called *poikilocytosis* (meaning "condition of varied cells"). The shape and the size of erythrocytes is important in diagnosis. Figure 223 is a smear from a patient with pernicious anemia; both anisocytosis and poikilocytosis are evident. Pernicious anemia is a condition in which there are too few erythrocytes. There are various types of anemia; in all cases there are either too few erythrocytes or too little hemoglobin. The erythrocytes may be normal in size in certain types of anemia; this condition is called *normocytic anemia.* They are small in microcytic anemia and large in macrocytic anemia.

Effect of Liver Extract. If liver extract is given to a patient, it stimulates the red bone marrow, and an increased number of reticulocytes is noted in the circulating blood. This increase is a test of the efficiency of liver therapy.

Number of Blood Corpuscles. The apparatus used in making "blood counts" is called a *hemocytometer* and is illustrated in Figure 227. The details of the methods used in counting erythrocytes and leukocytes will not be given here, since they may be found in any textbook of laboratory methods.

The number of leukocytes is increased in most infections and is called *leukocytosis.* The number of leukocytes is decreased in such infectious diseases as typhoid fever, tuberculosis, influenza and virus pneumonia and is called *leukopenia.* In leukemia the number of leukocytes may be almost as great as that of erythrocytes; this condition is somewhat like a cancer of lymphatic tissue or myeloid tissue concerned with the production of leukocytes.

A *differential count* is an estimation of the number or percentage of each variety of leukocyte in the blood. It is made on a film of blood stained with Wright's stain. Each leukocyte seen is tabulated, until 100, or even 200, are counted, and then the percentage of each type is noted. For example, if a total of 200 have been counted and 140 of them are neutrophils, this means that 70 per cent of the leukocytes are neutrophils, and if 6 eosinophils are found, it means that 3 per cent of the total leukocytes are eosinophils. Variations in the percentage of certain types of leukocytes are characteristic of some diseases.

Estimation of Hemoglobin Content. There are numerous

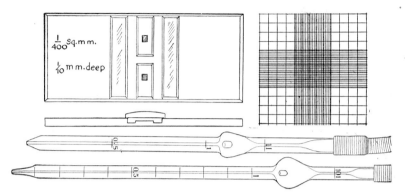

Fig. 227. Diagram of hemocytometer. The lowest pipet is used for counting red blood corpuscles. The blood is drawn up to the 0.5 mark, and the diluting fluid is drawn up until the mixture reaches the 101 mark. The bead in the bulb facilitates mixing.

The pipet used for counting white blood corpuscles is shown just above. The blood is drawn up to the 0.5 mark, and the diluting fluid is drawn up until the mixture reaches the 11 mark.

Just above the white pipet is shown the counting slide as it appears in side view. The space between the central portion of the slide and the cover slip is 1/10 mm. deep. The cover slip in the diagram is thicker than it is in reality. The top view of the slide is shown above the side view. The shaded areas in the center indicate the ruled portions. The figure at the top right indicates a ruled area as seen under the microscope. Each small square in the center is 1/20 mm. long and 1/20 mm. wide, with an area of 1/400 sq. mm.; with the cover slip in place, the volume of each small space becomes 1/4,000 cu. mm. Each of the larger squares in the corners is equal to 25 of the smaller central ones.

methods of determining hemoglobin content; each involves a comparison of the hemoglobin in the patient's blood with the color of a glass or paper standard. Hemoglobin should be reported in terms of grams per 100 cc. of blood, instead of percentage.

Color Index. This refers to the relationship between hemoglobin content and number of erythrocytes. Fifteen grams of hemoglobin is taken as 100 per cent, and 5 million erythrocytes as 100 per cent. If an individual had 15 Gm. of hemoglobin per 100 cc. of blood and 5 million erythrocytes per cu. mm., the color index would be 100/100, or 1.0. If an individual had 7.5 Gm. of hemoglobin and 3 million erythrocytes, his color index would be (50/60)

0.83. When the color index is less than 1.0 it means that each corpuscle has less than the normal amount of hemoglobin. If the color index is above 1.0, it means that the corpuscles are very large and well supplied with hemoglobin. The color index is of importance in making a differential diagnosis for the type of anemia.

Oxygen Saturation. There is now an instrument available (oximeter) by which the saturation of hemoglobin with oxygen can be followed minute by minute in such situations as delivery of an infant or surgical operations. Normally, the hemoglobin in arterial blood is about 98 per cent saturated with oxygen. If the degree of saturation is low, there is interference with the functions of the central nervous system and the heart.

Infectious Mononucleosis. This is a fairly common communicable disease of unknown cause. It is characterized by fever, sore throat, swollen cervical lymph nodes and an increase in mononuclear leukocytes.

Agranulocytosis refers to a condition in which there is a deficiency of granulocytes (granular leukocytes). It is characterized by fever, prostration, ulcerative lesions in the mucous membranes of the mouth and the pharynx and by a very low granulocyte count. It may occur in patients who have been taking thiouracil (for overactive thyroid gland) or sulfonamide drugs or in individuals who are particularly sensitive to drugs.

Composition of Plasma in Disease. The amount of certain constituents of the plasma is of great diagnostic importance. In diabetes mellitus the blood sugar is above the normal level of 80 to 120 mg. per 100 cc. of blood, but in hyperinsulinism or after an overdose of insulin in a diabetic, the blood sugar is decreased. In nephritis the nitrogenous waste products accumulate in excessive amounts in the blood.

The average amount of calcium is 10 mg. per 100 cc. of blood. Usually, it is low in hypoparathyroidism (p. 733) and high in hyperparathyroidism (p. 733). The calcium-inorganic phosphate ratio is disturbed in rickets.

These few examples illustrate the importance of determining the composition of the plasma as an aid in the diagnosis of disease. Figure 225 illustrates the changes in composition of the plasma in certain diseases. The course of many diseases may be followed by repeated determinations of certain plasma constituents.

Intravascular Coagulation. Under abnormal conditions the blood clots within the vessels of a living person; this is called *intravascular coagulation*. There are two types of intravascular coagulation: phlebothrombosis and thrombophlebitis. The former means the formation of a clot within a vein, and the latter means inflammation of a vein associated with formation of a clot. There is more danger of pulmonary embolism in phlebothrombosis than in thrombophlebitis. A great danger of thrombosis is the occlusion of a vital vessel, such as a coronary artery.

Intravascular coagulation is less frequent since the policy of early ambulation is practiced. It may be prevented in patients who are unable to move about by the use of intravenous heparin or the oral administration of Dicumarol. Great care is needed in the use of these anticoagulants, else the patient may bleed to death. Tests are made each day to guard against such a disaster.

Abnormal Bleeding. COAGULATION TIME. When blood is drawn by pricking the finger or the ear coagulation takes place in from 2 to 6 minutes. There are many simple methods of determining coagulation time. Since it is important in the diagnosis of hemorrhagic diseases, it should be done before operations on all patients and as a daily routine on patients who are being given intravenous heparin for the prevention of intravascular coagulation.

BLEEDING TIME. This test is performed to determine the time required for a small sharp incision to cease bleeding. The normal bleeding time is from 1 to 3 minutes. It is greatly prolonged in conditions in which platelets are reduced in number. It should be determined before operation on all patients.

PROTHROMBIN TIME. This test is important in patients who are receiving Dicumarol for the prevention of intravascular coagulation. The response of the liver to the administration of vitamin K (as determined by prothrombin time) is the basis of one of the liver function tests. Vitamin K is essential in the formation of prothrombin by the liver.

In certain liver diseases or in sulfonamide therapy for intestinal tract infections, there may be bleeding tendencies due to hypoprothrombinemia. In the latter condition and in other situations in which bacterial action is inhibited in the intestine, the synthesis of vitamin K by bacteria is prevented. Conditions in the intestine must be favorable, also, for the absorption of vitamin K.

HYPERHEPARINEMIA. In atom-bomb victims and in patients suffering from radiation sickness, there is a tendency to hemorrhage, due to low platelet counts and hyperheparinemia. The latter can be prevented or controlled by the injection of protamine (salmine sulfate) or toluidin blue.

HEMOPHILIA. Congenital bleeding tendencies occur when there is failure to form powerful thromboplastin. At present five types of this abnormality are recognized, but only the most common will be discussed. It is hemophilia A. It is due to lack of antihemophiliac globulin in plasma.

The inheritance of hemophilia A is known. The abnormality is transmitted by a recessive gene located in the X-chromosome. If a woman is a carrier, the chances are that half of her daughters will be carriers and half of her sons will be hemophiliacs. If both of her X-chromosomes carry the abnormal gene, a woman will have the disease. All of her daughters will be carriers and all of her sons will be hemophiliacs.

THROMBOCYTOPENIC PURPURA. This is a condition characterized by the formation of purple patches on the skin and in the mucous membranes due to subcutaneous extravasation (escape of blood from the vessels into the tissues) of blood. The platelets are reduced in number, and the bleeding time is prolonged greatly.

HEMORRHAGE is a condition in which there is excessive bleeding; it may be stopped by applying tourniquets (meaning "to turn"), hemostats, ligatures, pressure or cold compresses. Sometimes gauze applied over the bleeding surface will help to stop the flow by favoring the breakdown of platelets and hastening coagulation. The signs and symptoms of hemorrhage are discussed on page 521. The plasma volume is regained within a few hours by pulling in tissue fluid by osmosis from tissue spaces. The erythrocytes and the plasma proteins are restored rather slowly. It takes about 50 days for a healthy donor to regenerate corpuscles and hemoglobin. An individual in good health can recover from a loss of blood amounting to as much as 3 per cent of the body weight (almost one half of his blood volume), but several months are required for complete recovery.

Transfusion. Whole blood is the ideal substance to use for transfusions. The best preservative is acid-citrate-dextrose, in which the erythrocytes survive longest after removal from the body. Plasma is the next best substance to use for transfusions.

The person from whom blood is taken is called a *donor;* the person who receives blood is called a *recipient.* Before a person is permitted to serve as a donor, the blood should be tested for the absence of a syphilitic infection by a Wassermann or similar test.

Blood from any donor should be tested for compatibility before being given to any recipient. The sera of many species and individuals possess the property of agglutinating or clumping erythrocytes of other species and other individuals. This is followed by hemolysis or rupture of the membrane of erythrocytes allowing hemoglobin to escape into the plasma. Human erythrocytes differ in their antigenic (ability to produce antibodies) properties and human sera differ in their agglutinin content.

There are 4 groups into which human blood may be classified. These groups are called *O, A, B* and *AB* (international classification). There are 2 antigens or agglutinable substances, called *A* and *B*, that may be present in erythrocytes, making it possible for them to be agglutinated. Neither antigen is present in the erythrocytes of group O individuals; A is present in group A, B in group B, and both A and B in group AB.

There are 2 antibodies or agglutinins, called *alpha* and *beta*, that may be present in plasma, making it possible for plasma to agglutinate certain erythrocytes. Both antibodies are present in the plasma of group O, beta in group A, alpha in group B, and neither alpha nor beta in group AB.

If the antigen A in the erythrocytes of a donor comes in contact with the antibody or agglutinin alpha in the plasma of a recipient, or if antigen B in erythrocytes of a donor comes in contact with beta agglutinin in the plasma of a recipient, agglutination followed by hemolysis of the donor's erythrocytes occurs. Such bloods are incompatible and lead to a "transfusion reaction." Agglutination is illustrated in Figure 228.

The hemoglobin that escapes into the plasma, in the course of a transfusion reaction, is excreted in the urine. Masses of it may block the kidney tubules and make it impossible for the kidneys to function normally. Urticaria (hives), chills, fever and hematuria

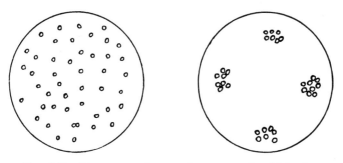

Fig. 228. Diagram to show agglutination of red blood corpuscles. The normal distribution is shown on the left and agglutination on the right. Agglutination is followed by hemolysis.

(blood in the urine) are the indications of incompatible bloods. Thus, the event to be avoided in transfusions is the destruction of erythrocytes of the donor by the plasma of the recipient. We need not worry about the possibility of destruction of the recipient's erythrocytes by the donor's plasma, since the latter is immediately so greatly diluted by the plasma of the recipient that the agglutinins have little opportunity to destroy the recipient's erythrocytes.

The following table indicates the results in compact form; alpha agglutinin is indicated by *a*, beta by *b*; *plus* indicates agglutination and hemolysis; *minus* indicates absence of such a reaction (compatible bloods).

GROUP	PLASMA CONTAINS	ERYTHROCYTES GROUP O	GROUP A	GROUP B	GROUP AB
O	a and b	—	+	+	+
A	b	—	—	+	+
B	a	—	+	—	+
AB	neither	—	—	—	—

Individuals in group O are called *universal donors;* their erythrocytes are not agglutinated by any plasma, since they contain no antigen. Individuals in group AB are called *universal recipients;* since there is no antibody (agglutinin alpha or beta) in their plasma, erythrocytes from any group will not be agglutinated. However, there are subgroups, and it is safest to cross-agglutinate the blood of the particular donor and recipient before any transfusion is given.

The inheritance of one's blood group is definitely established and follows mendelian laws—A and B antigens are mendelian dominants; the agglutinins alpha and beta are recessives. The determination of the characteristics of the blood is valuable in establishing whether or not a certain man could possibly have been the father of a certain child and is a deciding factor in cases of disputed parentage.

Other antigens called *M* and *N* have been found in human erythrocytes. There are no antibodies present in the plasma for these antigens. The possible groups are M, N and MN; this characteristic likewise is valuable in establishing nonpaternity.

The most recent antigen found in human erythrocytes is called the *Rh antigen,* since it was discovered first in the blood of Rhesus monkeys. Human plasma contains no corresponding antibody, so one's Rh classification must be detected by use of prepared animal sera or by sera from immunized human beings who are Rh negative. There are at least 27 Rh subgroups.

The Rh classification of any individual who is likely to require repeated transfusion for some pathologic condition should be determined. It is becoming common to have one's Rh classification determined before marriage. Eighty-five per cent of the population is Rh positive, and only 15 per cent is Rh negative. It is possible for about one Rh-negative woman in 50, who is married to an Rh-positive man, to have difficulty during pregnancy. Difficulty may arise when an Rh-negative woman has an Rh-positive fetus, if the Rh antigen from the fetus crosses the placenta and enters the mother's blood. She may become sensitized and develop antibodies, which, in turn, cross the placenta, enter the fetal circulation and destroy fetal erythrocytes. Such a condition in the fetus is called *erythroblastosis fetalis.*

Disturbances Between the Formation and the Drainage of Tissue Fluid.

(1) There may be too much filtration due to high hydrostatic pressure in the capillaries. This happens when the pressure in the veins is high and blood backs up into the capillaries. Excessive filtration due to back pressure from distended veins occurs in heart failure.

Edema (meaning "swelling"), anasarca (meaning "through the flesh") and ascites (meaning "a bag" or "bladder") occur. In *edematous* tissue the cells are spread apart by the accumulation of tissue fluid between them. As filtration continues, and tissue fluid accumulates outside of the capillary, it raises the pressure in the tissue spaces and thus opposes filtration pressure, so edema does reach a limit. *Anasarca* refers to widespread or generalized edema; the term is not in common use at the present time. *Ascites* refers to an excessive accumulation of fluid within the abdominal cavity.

(2) There may be too little osmosis at the venous end of the capillary. This is due to low plasma protein content as a result of protein starvation or kidney disease. Whenever filtration is not balanced by osmosis, edema occurs.

(3) There may be blockage of lymphatic vessels due to the presence of a parasite (filaria) that lives in lymph channels. The lower extremities are involved, and the swelling is enormous; the condition is called *elephantiasis.* The tissue fluid contains more protein in such patients, which makes the edema worse. A similar condition sometimes develops in the upper extremity after a radical breast operation, followed by deep x-ray therapy. Repeated x-ray treatments of the axillary nodes sometimes damages lymphatic channels, and elephantiasis follows.

(4) Damage to the capillary wall, as after burns or frostbite,

DISTURBANCES IN THE FORMATION OF TISSUE FLUID

1. CAPILLARY PRESSURE HIGH (with increased venous pressure, in cardiac failure)

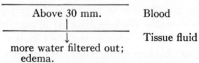

2. CAPILLARY PRESSURE LOW (after hemorrhage)

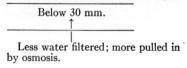

3. LOW PROTEIN CONTENT IN PLASMA (loss of albumin through kidneys)

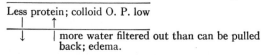

FIG. 229. Diagram to illustrate disturbances in the formation of tissue fluid. The causes of disturbance are too high pressure in the capillary, too low pressure and a decrease in the protein content of plasma.

is another cause of difficulty. So much fluid leaks out of the capillaries in these conditions that the blood becomes concentrated, as fluid accumulates in the tissue. Such cases are treated by giving plasma transfusions.

(5) After hemorrhage or marked loss of blood, the blood pressure is low, and the driving force for filtration is decreased. The colloid osmotic pressure is increased with the result that fluid is pulled into the blood stream, and the tissues become dehydrated. Unless a transfusion is given there will be collapse of the circulation, and death.

(6) In the air sacs of the lungs there is no fluid. This is due to the very low blood pressure in the pulmonary capillaries. No filtration occurs in these capillaries because there is no driving force. If the pressure is raised, as in failure of the heart, then fluid is formed and it accumulates in the air sacs, giving rise to the condition known as *pulmonary edema*. Another situation which leads to pulmonary edema is damage to the walls of the lung capillaries by inhalation of poisonous gas. As you would expect, pulmonary

edema leads to death, since oxygen cannot get into the lungs to replenish the supply in the blood. In Figure 229 the edema described in (1), (5) and (2), respectively, is illustrated.

Treatment of Open Flesh Wounds. One of the most beneficial therapeutic measures that came out of World War II is the treatment of open flesh wounds, crush injuries of the extremities and extensive burns by placing plaster casts on them, which prevent swelling. Immobilization reduces lymph flow from the damaged area and thereby tends to keep infections localized. Toxic products are absorbed more slowly into the general circulation. Through the prevention of local edema, the normal circulation is assured, and through immobilization, the spread of infection is limited, and wounds heal more readily. Plasma transfusions are used liberally to prevent dehydration and to assure a good supply of protein.

SUMMARY

1. Introduction
2. Blood
   A. Functions
   B. Quantity of blood
   C. Characteristics of blood
      a. Color
      b. Structure
      c. Viscosity
      d. Specific gravity
   D. Corpuscles
      a. Erythrocytes: description, size, origin, number, functions, and life cycle
      b. Leukocytes: description, classes, origin, number, response to injury, functions and life cycle
      c. Blood platelets: description, origin, number, functions and life cycle
   E. Plasma
      a. Definition
      b. Composition: water, proteins (albumin, gamma globulin, prothrombin and fibrinogen), carbohydrates, lipids, inorganic salts, gases, waste products and miscellaneous substances
      c. Reaction
   F. Coagulation of the blood

a. First stage: calcium, thromboplastic substance and prothrombin interact to form thrombin

b. Second stage: thrombin and fibrinogen interact to form fibrin

c. Time required

d. Suggestions as to why blood remains fluid within the vessels of the living body

3. Tissue Fluid
    A. Definition
    B. Importance
    C. Formation
    D. Composition
    E. Fate
4. Lymph
    A. Definition
    B. Origin
    C. Composition
    D. Functions

SITUATION AND QUESTIONS

Of paramount importance in any first aid course is the control of hemorrhage.

1. Nature provides a coagulation mechanism in order to prevent excessive loss of blood.

A. The substance which initiates the blood coagulation mechanism is: _____(a) Vitamin K; _____(b) thromboplastic substance; _____(c) prothrombin; _____(d) fibrinogen.

B. What ions are essential for blood coagulation? _____ (a) Calcium; _____(b) Potassium; _____(c) Chloride; _____(d) Iron.

C. What insoluble gel forms when blood coagulates? _____(a) thrombin; _____(b) prothrombin; _____ (c) fibrinogen; _____(d) fibrin.

2. A loss of approximately one third of the blood volume would prove to be fatal. With excessive blood loss many of the processes would be disturbed.

A. Transportation of oxygen would be disturbed. Oxygen is carried by: _____(a) erythrocytes; _____(b) lymphocytes; _____(c) platelets; _____(d) neutrophils.

B. With the loss of white blood cells, there may be disturbance in: _____(a) blood coagulation; _____(b) transportation of oxygen; _____(c) defence against invasion of micro-organisms; _____(d) transportation of waste products.

C. Loss of the plasma proteins could result in a disturbance of formation of tissue fluids and water balance. The plasma protein most concerned is: _____(a) albumin; _____(b) globulin; _____(c) hemoglobin; _____(d) prothrombin.

10. Anatomy of the Circulatory System

INTRODUCTION

The circulatory system is composed of the heart and the blood vessels; consequently, it is known also as the *cardiovascular system.* The heart is a pump, composed of muscle, which drives the blood through the blood vessels, contracting about 72 times each minute of one's life. The heart pumps blood into the arteries, which are elastic tubes carrying the blood along to the capillaries. Food and

416

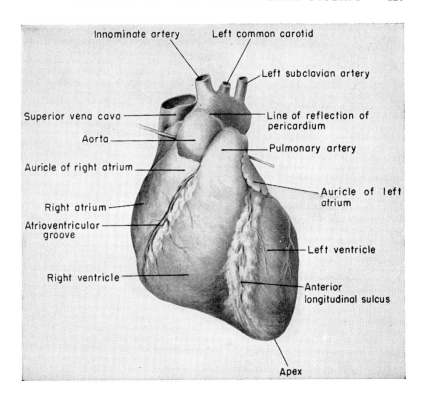

Innominate artery   Left common carotid

Left subclavian artery

Superior vena cava

Line of reflection of pericardium

Aorta

Pulmonary artery

Auricle of right atrium

Auricle of left atrium

Right atrium

Atrioventricular groove

Left ventricle

Right ventricle

Anterior longitudinal sulcus

Apex

FIG. 230. Anterior aspect of heart, showing grooves, beginning of aorta and pulmonary artery, position of right atrium and right and left ventricles. The probe is in the transverse sinus of the pericardium.

oxygen leave the blood to supply the tissues, and carbon dioxide and other waste products enter the blood from the tissues. The blood then is collected into veins which carry it back to the heart. As the blood continues to circulate, each organ of the body withdraws materials that it needs for repair, maintenance, growth and its own particular functions. For example, the brain is absolutely dependent on oxygen and glucose; if these are not supplied continuously by the circulating blood, consciousness is lost. Muscles need oxygen, glucose and amino acids, as well as the proper ratio of sodium, calcium and potassium salts in order to contract normally. The glands need sufficient supplies of raw materials from which to manufacture their specific secretions. All such functions are made possible because the heart pumps blood continuously to all parts of the body, and the capillaries permit the essential exchanges of water, gases, salts, nutritive and waste materials between the blood and the tissues.

THE HEART

SIZE AND LOCATION

The heart is a hollow muscular organ a little larger than the fist. It lies in the pericardial cavity in the mediastinum, between the lungs. About two thirds of the heart lies to the left of the midline of the body. Its relation to other organs is shown in Figure 7. The heart is cone-shaped, with the base directed upward and to the right and the apex downward and to the left. You can feel the apex come in contact with the chest wall with each heart beat if you place your fingers below the left nipple at the lower edge of the breast. You can count the heart rate easily by listening with a stethoscope over the apex.

COVERING OF THE HEART

The heart is covered by a sac called the *pericardium,* which is attached to the diaphragm, below, and to the great vessels, above. The pericardium consists of 2 layers, an outer fibrous portion and an inner serous portion.

The fibrous pericardium is a tough fibrous membrane; this layer is attached (1) to the large vessels that enter or leave the heart, (2) to the diaphragm and (3) to the sternum.

The inner serous portion consists of an inner or visceral layer which covers the heart (epicardium) and an outer or parietal layer which lines the fibrous pericardium. There is a potential space between the visceral and the parietal layers of the serous portion of the pericardium which contains a very small amount of pericardial fluid and reduces friction due to movements of the heart.

WALLS OF THE HEART

The walls of the heart are composed of 3 layers. The outer layer is the *epicardium* (visceral pericardium), the middle layer is mus-

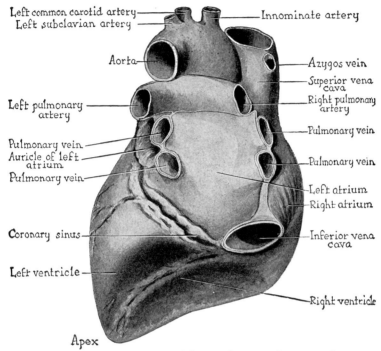

Left common carotid artery —
Left subclavian artery —
Aorta —
Left pulmonary artery —
Pulmonary vein —
Auricle of left atrium —
Pulmonary vein —
Coronary sinus —
Left ventricle —
Apex

— Innominate artery
— Azygos vein
— Superior vena cava
— Right pulmonary artery
— Pulmonary vein
— Pulmonary vein
— Left atrium
— Right atrium
— Inferior vena cava
— Right ventricle

Fig. 231. Posterior aspect of heart, showing the apex, the coronary sinus, pulmonary veins and venae cavae. The posterior longitudinal sulcus is shown (but not labeled) between the right and left ventricles. The azygos vein is shown as it empties into the superior vena cava.

cular, called the *myocardium,* and the inner layer is the *endocardium.* The myocardium consists of interlacing bundles of cardiac muscle fibers. The endocardium lines the inner surface of the myocardium; it is composed of thin endothelium continuous with that of the blood vessels. It assists in forming the valves of the heart.

CHAMBERS OF THE HEART

The cavity of the heart is divided into 4 parts by partitions or septa. The 2 upper chambers are called the *right* and the *left atria,* and the 2 lower are called the *right* and the *left ventricles.* You can see 2 grooves on the anterior surface of the heart—the atrioventricular groove and the anterior longitudinal sulcus (Fig. 230).

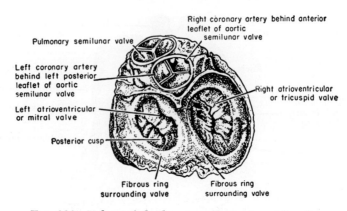

Right coronary artery behind anterior leaflet of aortic semilunar valve

Pulmonary semilunar valve

Left coronary artery behind left posterior leaflet of aortic semilunar valve

Right atrioventricular or tricuspid valve

Left atrioventricular or mitral valve

Posterior cusp

Fibrous ring surrounding valve

Fibrous ring surrounding valve

FIG. 232. Valves of the heart, superior view, after the removal of the atria and the greater part of the aorta and the pulmonary artery.

The former indicates the division into right atrium and right ventricle, and the latter into right and left ventricles. The coronary vessels lie in these grooves.

Right Atrium. The right atrium is larger than the left; its walls are very thin. It receives blood from the upper portion of the body via the superior vena cava and from the lower portion of the body by way of the inferior vena cava. The venae cavae are called the *great veins.* The terminations of the great veins are shown in Figure 231. The right atrium also receives blood from the heart muscle itself by way of the coronary sinus (Fig. 231). In the septum between the 2 atria there is a thin place called the *fossa ovalis* which indicates the location of the opening between the 2 atria (foramen ovale) during fetal life.

The right atrium opens into the right ventricle; this opening is surrounded by a fibrous ring which is large enough to admit 3 or 4 finger tips. Three leaflets or cusps of the tricuspid or right atrioventricular valve are attached to the fibrous ring. These leaflets completely close off the atrium from the ventricle during contraction of the latter. The valve as it appears when looking down at it from the atrium is shown in Figure 232. The leaflets are composed of folds of endocardium, reinforced with a flat sheet of dense connective tissue. The purpose of the valves of the heart is to keep the blood flowing in the proper direction. They permit it to flow from atria into ventricles, and then from ventricles into the

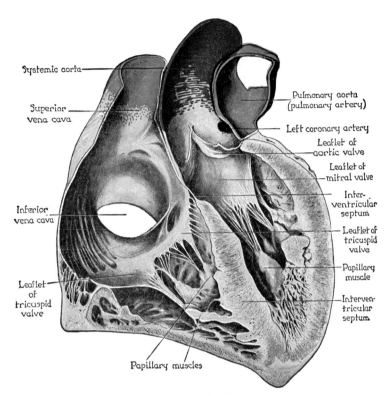

Systemic aorta

Superior
vena cava

Inferior
vena cava

Leaflet
of
tricuspid
valve

Papillary muscles

Pulmonary aorta
(pulmonary artery)

Left coronary artery

Leaflet of
aortic valve

Leaflet of
mitral valve

Inter-
ventricular
septum

Leaflet of
tricuspid
valve

Papillary
muscle

Interven-
tricular
septum

Fig. 233. Posterior portion of heart, superior view, showing
interior of right atrium, right and left ventricles, atrioventricular
valves, aortic semilunar valve, columnae carneae, chordae tendineae, papillary muscles, interventricular septum, the entrance of
the great veins and the origin of the aorta and pulmonary artery.

pulmonary artery or aorta but prevent it from flowing in the reverse
direction.

Left Atrium. The left atrium has thicker walls than the right.
It receives blood from the lungs by way of 4 pulmonary veins (Fig.
231). The opening between the left atrium and the left ventricle
admits only 2 fingertips, and the 2 leaflets of the bicuspid, mitral
or left atrioventricular valve are attached to the fibrous ring around
this opening. The valve is shown from above in Figure 232.

Right Ventricle. The right ventricle is separated from the left
by the interventricular septum (Fig. 233). The pulmonary artery

arises from the right ventricle. Its origin is guarded by the pulmonary semilunar valve, which consists of 3 crescent-shaped cups or pockets which face toward the artery. The wall of the right ventricle is much thicker than the walls of the atria, but only about one third as thick as that of the left ventricle, since it has to pump blood to the lungs only, whereas the left ventricle has to pump it to all other parts of the body.

The inner surface of the ventricle shows a latticework of muscular columns called the *columnae carnae,* which are evident in Figure 233. Some of the muscle projects like papillae; they are called *papillary muscles.* From the summits of the papillae you will see very delicate fibrous strands which extend upward to be attached to the edges of the leaflets of the atrioventricular valve. These strands are called *chordae tendineae* and are composed of dense fibrous connective tissue covered with endocardium. The function of the chordae tendineae is to keep the valve leaflets from turning inside out as they would do otherwise when the pressure is high in the ventricle. Papillary muscles and chordae tendineae are shown in Figure 233.

Left Ventricle. The lowermost left portion of the left ventricle is called the *apex of the heart* (Fig. 230). The walls of the left ventricle are very thick, and the inner surface is like that of the right ventricle. The aorta, which is the largest artery in the body, takes origin from the left ventricle. The orifice is guarded by the aortic semilunar valve, which is constructed like the pulmonary semilunar valve (Fig. 232).

Modified Cardiac Muscular Tissue

The muscle mass of the 2 ventricles is separate and distinct from the muscle mass of the 2 atria except for one small bundle of modified muscular tissue found in the septum. This one connecting link between the atria and ventricles is called the *atrioventricular bundle* or the *bundle of His,* after its discoverer. By means of this bundle the "beat" is transmitted from the atria to the ventricles, so that the contraction of the ventricles normally follows that of the atria.

In certain regions modified cardiac muscular tissue forms nodes. One node, called the *sinu-atrial node,* is located in the groove between the superior vena cava and the right atrium. A second node is the *atrioventricular node,* which is located in the lower part of the interatrial septum and is continuous with the atrioventricular bundle. The bundle divides into 2 branches which run halfway

ANATOMY OF THE CIRCULATORY SYSTEM   423

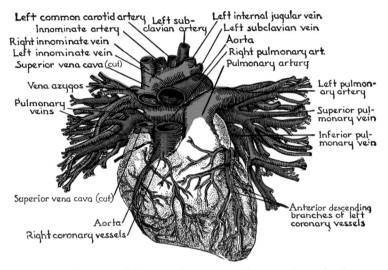

FIG. 234. Injected heart and great vessels, seen from the front.
Part of the superior vena cava and aorta have been removed to
show right pulmonary artery. The coronary vessels and the pulmonary veins are shown.

down the 2 sides of the interventricular septum before they become continuous with the Purkinje fibers. The Purkinje fibers form
a widespread network just under the endocardium. They are characterized by a large amount of sarcoplasm around the nuclei and
a large amount of glycogen in the sarcoplasm. They have fewer
myofibrils and less distinct cross-striations than other cardiac muscle fibers. They merge with cardiac muscular fibers at their terminations.

BLOOD SUPPLY

You might think that since blood is flowing through the heart
almost constantly no other blood supply is needed, but the blood
in the cardiac chambers comes in contact only with the endocardium and does not reach the myocardium. Consequently, the
thick myocardium needs its own blood supply, like any other
mass of muscular tissue.

The arteries that supply the myocardium are called the *coronary arteries*. They are shown in Figure 234. After the blood
passes through the capillaries of the heart muscle it drains even-

tually into the coronary sinus and then back into the right atrium. The heart muscle is very dependent on a sufficient blood supply if it is to perform its pumping function efficiently.

NERVE SUPPLY

The heart is abundantly supplied with nerve fibers. The afferent fibers belong to the visceral afferent division; they carry impulses that give rise to a sensation of pain whenever the heart is deprived of oxygen. The efferent fibers are derived from both divisions of the autonomic system; the vagus nerves, which represent the cranial division, slow and weaken the beat of the heart. The augmentor nerves, which represent the thoracic division, speed up and strengthen the beat of the heart. The efferent nerves which supply the heart change the rate and the force of the beat to meet the constantly changing conditions of the body from minute to minute. Note the change in your heart beat the next time you walk up the stairs or after your next meal or the next time the teacher asks you a question in class.

THE BLOOD VESSELS

STRUCTURE

Arteries. The arteries are the vessels that carry blood away from the heart. They need strong walls to withstand the pressure of the blood within them. The large arteries are widened or stretched and lengthened by the blood delivered to them from the heart with each beat. The largest artery, the aorta, gives off branches that divide and subdivide, on and on, until they become very small. The smallest arteries are called *arterioles.*

There are 3 layers of tissue in the walls of arteries.

THE INNER LAYER, called the *tunica intima,* consists of endothelium with some delicate elastic tissue beneath it. This lies on coarser elastic tissue which is condensed into a thick plate called the *internal elastic lamina.*

THE MIDDLE LAYER of the wall of arteries is called the *tunica media.* It constitutes the bulk of the wall and is composed of elastic connective tissue. The outermost portion of the middle layer is the *external elastic lamina.*

THE OUTER LAYER of arteries, called the *tunica adventitia,* is composed of irregularly arranged connective tissue, which contains both collagenic and elastic fibers. A cross-section of a medium-sized artery is shown in Figure 235.

The walls of small arteries become thinner. The elastic tissue

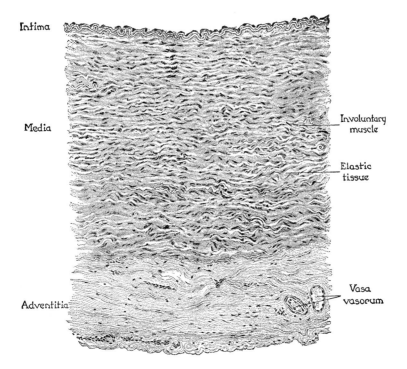

Intima

Media

Adventitia

Involuntary muscle

Elastic tissue

Vasa vasorum

FIG. 235. Cross-section of radial artery, showing the tunica intima, tunica media and tunica externa (adventitia), in which vasa vasorum are seen. Both smooth muscle and elastic tissue are present in the tunica media.

disappears from the tunica media and is replaced by smooth muscle.

Nutrient blood vessels are present within the walls of the larger vessels; they are called *vasa vasorum*. Lymphatic vessels also are present within the walls of the larger blood vessels.

Arteries are well supplied with nerve fibers. Afferent nerves are found which carry impulses to the central nervous system and lead to reflex changes in heart rate and size of blood vessels; sometimes this arrangement is called the *intrinsic control* of the cardiovascular system. In other words, when there is a change in pressure in the blood vessels in one part of the body, messages are sent to the central nervous system which immediately set into operation reflexes to compensate for the original change. These reflexes tend

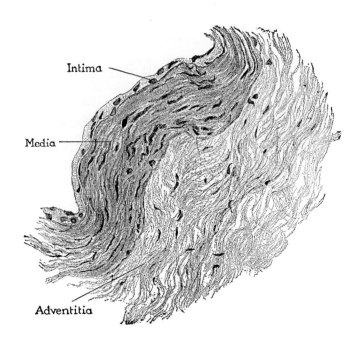

Intima

Media

Adventitia

FIG. 236. Cross-section of medium-sized vein, showing the tunica intima, tunica media and tunica externa (adventitia). ×250.

FIG. 237. Portion of femoral vein opened, to show valves.

to maintain normal conditions or a steady state (homeostasis) throughout the vascular system.

Efferent nerves from the visceral efferent division supply the smooth muscle in the walls of small arteries; when the muscle contracts, the vessels become smaller (lumen reduced), and when it relaxes, the vessels become larger (lumen increased). Efferent nerves are called *vasomotor* nerves. They are exceedingly important in the control of the size of small arterioles.

In many regions of the body there are anastomoses between adjacent arteries, so that if the blood supply from one source is cut off, another source is available. In some regions such anastomoses are not present. The arteries in these areas are called *end* arteries. It is in the latter areas that gangrene (death of tissue) occurs when the only source of blood supply is cut off.

Veins carry blood from the capillaries to the heart. They have thinner walls than the corresponding arteries; they contain less elastic tissue and less smooth muscle than arteries. The tunica intima consists of endothelium and an internal elastic membrane. The tunica media consists of a thin layer of smooth muscle and a few collagenic and elastic fibers. The tunica adventitia is composed of collagenic connective tissue. A section of a medium-sized vein is shown in Figure 236. Great variation exists in the structure of veins.

The walls of veins are supplied by numerous small arteries called *vasa vasorum* which are distributed to the outer and the middle layers. Lymphatic vessels are limited to the outer layer of vein walls.

Veins are well supplied with nerves which form a coarse network in the outer layer of the wall. Branches from this network enter the tunica media and form a second network, which gives off twigs to the muscle fibers and sends fine filaments into the inner layer of the wall.

The veins of the extremities are abundantly supplied with valves, as shown in Figure 237. These valves are like pockets which are distended with blood when the valve is closed. The valves keep the blood from flowing back into the capillaries and are especially important in the long veins that carry blood back from the lower extremities. Anastomoses between veins are common.

Capillaries carry blood from arterioles to veins. Their walls are only one cell thick and consist of endothelial cells that are held together by cement substance. They usually form networks in tis-

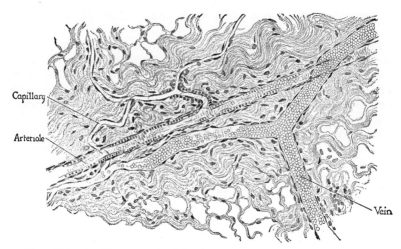

Fig. 238. Capillary arising from branch of arteriole, passing under arteriole to enter tributary of small vein; from the omentum. ×150.

sues. A capillary is shown in Figure 238. Exchanges take place between the plasma in the capillaries and the tissue fluid that bathes the tissue cells. You should think of the capillaries as the focal point of the entire cardiovascular system, since it is for these exchanges between plasma and tissue fluid that all the rest of the system was fashioned.

Sinusoids are capillarylike vessels found in such organs as liver and spleen. They connect afferent or efferent vessels of the same kind; consequently, they may be either arterial or venous.

Arteriovenous anastomoses are found in the distal parts of the extremities. When they are open a large amount of blood flows through the skin directly from small arteries to small veins, without going through capillaries. This arrangement is important in connection with the regulation of body temperature.

GENERAL PLAN OF THE CIRCULATION

Pulmonary Circulation

The blood from all parts of the body and from the wall of the heart itself enters the right atrium, passes through the right atrioventricular valve into the right ventricle, then through the pulmonary semilunar valve into the pulmonary artery, through the branches of the pulmonary artery into the pulmonary capillaries where it picks up a fresh load of oxygen and gives off some carbon dioxide. The oxygenated blood then enters the pulmonary veins and passes to the left atrium. This short path through the lungs is called the pulmonary circulation and is illustrated in Figure 239.

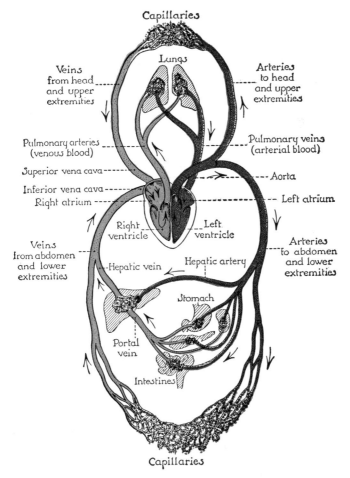

FIG. 239. Diagram of the pulmonary and systemic circulations. The pulmonary circulation includes the pulmonary artery, capillaries of the lungs and pulmonary veins. The systemic circulation includes all the other arteries, capillaries and veins of the body. The portal circuit is indicated.

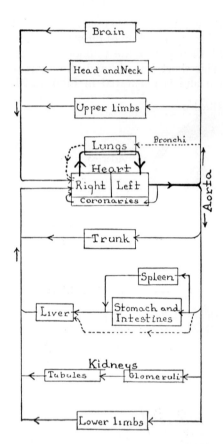

Fig. 240. Scheme of the human circulation. (Modified from Winton and Bayliss)

The pulmonary artery arises from the right ventricle and passes upward, backward and to the left, then divides into the right and the left pulmonary arteries. It is shown in Figure 234.

The right pulmonary artery passes transversely toward the base of the right lung; it divides into 3 branches at the root of the lung, and one branch goes to each lobe of the right lung. The left pulmonary artery is shorter than the right; it passes to the root of the left lung, divides into 2 branches and sends one branch to each of the 2 lobes of the left lung. A short cord called the *ligamentum arteriosum* passes from the upper border of the pulmonary artery to the under surface of the transverse portion of the aortic arch, a little beyond the origin of the subclavian artery. This is the remains of the ductus arteriosus, a fetal structure which

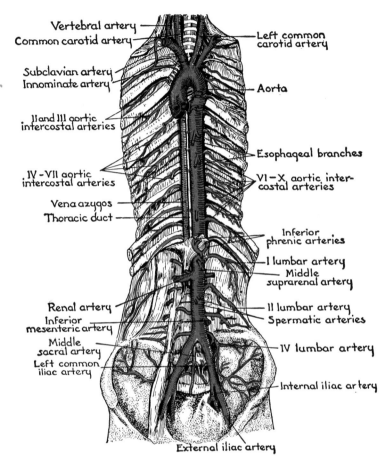

Vertebral artery
Common carotid artery
Left common carotid artery
Subclavian artery
Innominate artery
Aorta
II and III aortic intercostal arteries
Esophageal branches
IV - VII aortic intercostal arteries
VI - X aortic intercostal arteries
Vena azygos
Thoracic duct
Inferior phrenic arteries
I lumbar artery
Middle suprarenal artery
Renal artery
II lumbar artery
Inferior mesenteric artery
Spermatic arteries
Middle sacral artery
IV lumbar artery
Left common iliac artery
Internal iliac artery
External iliac artery

FIG. 241. Aorta and its branches. The aortic arch, thoracic aorta, abdominal aorta and terminal branches are shown. The former terminology for hypogastric artery was *internal iliac*.

permitted blood to pass between the right and the left sides of the heart without going through the lungs.

From the arteries the blood enters the pulmonary capillaries, where it takes on oxygen and gives up carbon dioxide and then is collected into the 4 pulmonary veins (Figs. 231 and 234). Two pulmonary veins arise from the hilum of each lung. They pass to the posterior surface of the left atrium, into which they open.

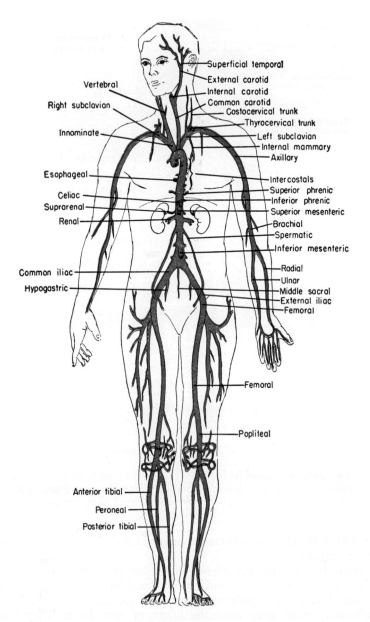

FIG. 242. Schematic drawing of the arterial system.

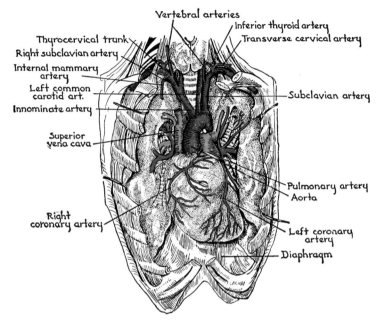

FIG. 243. Dissection showing aortic arch and its branches. The lungs have been pulled aside. The coronary arteries are shown.

Each is formed by the union of a number of small veins which originate in the pulmonary capillaries.

SYSTEMIC CIRCULATION

From the left atrium the blood passes through the left atrioventricular valve into the left ventricle; then it is pumped through the aortic semilunar valve into the aorta. It is distributed to all the systemic arteries of the body, then to the systemic capillaries where oxygen and nutritive materials are given to the tissues and carbon dioxide and waste materials are picked up. From the capillaries the blood passes to the veins and eventually returns to the right atrium to begin its circuit all over again. This longer path through all parts of the body except the lungs is called the *systemic circulation;* it is illustrated in Figures 239 and 240.

The systemic circulation comprises the blood flow through the aorta and all its branches, capillaries and all the tributaries of the veins that enter the right atrium.

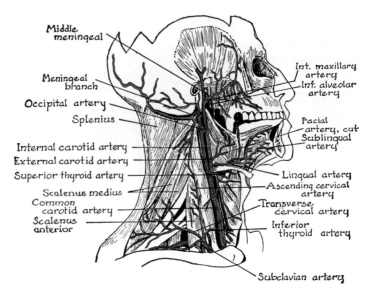

FIG. 244. Deep dissection, showing the common carotid artery and its branches.

Arteries of the Systemic Circuit. The aorta arises from the base of the left ventricle, arches over to the left side of the vertebral column and passes downward along the vertebral column to the level of the fourth lumbar vertebra. At this level it terminates by dividing into the common iliac arteries. The aorta is shown in Figures 241, 242 and 243.

For convenience the aorta may be divided into the ascending aorta; the aortic arch, which extends to the left side of the fourth thoracic vertebra; the thoracic aorta, which extends from the arch to the diaphragm; and the abdominal aorta, which extends from the diaphragm to the fourth lumbar vertebra.

ASCENDING AORTA. The branches of the ascending aorta are the coronary arteries. The right and the left coronary arteries arise just above the origin of the aorta, immediately above the leaflets of the aortic semilunar valve. The coronary arteries supply the myocardium with blood. Figures 234 and 243 illustrate the coronary arteries and their branches.

AORTIC ARCH. The arch of the aorta (Fig. 243) curves to the left and backward and then bends downward and passes along the left side of the body to the fourth thoracic vertebra to become continuous with the thoracic aorta. The branches of the arch of the aorta are the innominate, the left common carotid and the left subclavian arteries.

The innominate artery is the largest branch that arises from the arch of the aorta. It is shown in Figures 241, 242 and 243. It passes upward to the level of the right sternoclavicular joint and there divides into the right common carotid and the right subclavian arteries.

The left common carotid artery arises from the arch of the aorta, and the right common carotid artery arises from the innominate artery (Fig. 244). Each common carotid artery passes upward along the side of the trachea and the larynx and ends at the upper border of the thyroid cartilage, by dividing into the external and the internal carotid arteries. You can feel the common carotid arteries pulsating if you press in along the trachea gently with your finger tips. These are the arteries from which blood spurts when the neck is slashed or "throat cut." Near the origin of the internal carotid artery on either side is a dilatation that is called the carotid sinus.

(a) The external carotid artery ascends to the level of the neck of the mandible where it divides into the superficial temporal and the internal maxillary arteries. It gives off the following branches in its course: ascending pharyngeal, superior thyroid, lingual, external maxillary, sternocleidomastoid, occipital and posterior auricular. The structures of the head and the neck that are supplied by the external carotid artery and its branches are the pharynx, thyroid gland, tongue, teeth, gums, sternocleidomastoid muscle, muscles of mastication, buccinator muscle, mucous membrane of the maxillary sinus, part of the ear and most of the dura mater. The superficial temporal artery is one of the arteries in which you can feel the pulse easily. Place your finger tips immediately in front of the ear, at the level of the eye and you can feel the pulse in the superficial temporal artery.

The Internal Maxillary Artery (Fig. 244). This vessel arises from the external carotid artery opposite the neck of the mandible. It gives off the alveolar arteries to the teeth and branches to the muscles of mastication.

(i) The inferior alveolar artery (Fig. 244) arises from the internal maxillary artery, enters the mandibular foramen, passes along the canal and gives off branches to the molar, the premolar and the canine teeth.

(ii) The posterior superior alveolar artery arises from the internal maxillary and gives off branches to the maxillary sinus, the molar and the premolar teeth, the gums and the buccinator muscle.

(iii) The anterior superior alveolar branch arises from the infratemporal branch of the internal maxillary artery and supplies the incisor and the canine teeth and the mucous membrane of the maxillary sinus.

(iv) The middle meningeal artery (Fig. 244) is the largest of the branches of the internal maxillary artery. It enters the cranium, divides into anterior and posterior terminal branches and supplies most of the dura mater.

(b) *The internal carotid artery* is shown in Figure 245. It arises from the common carotid artery and supplies the anterior part of

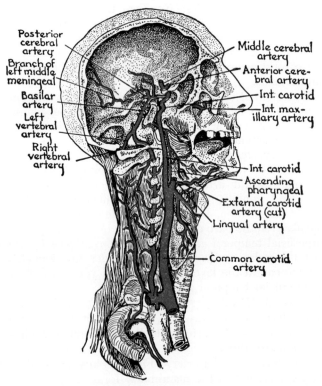

Posterior
cerebral
artery
Branch of
left middle
meningeal
Basilar
artery
Left
vertebral
artery
Right
vertebral
artery

Middle cerebral
artery
Anterior cere-
bral artery
Int. carotid
Int. max-
illary artery

Int. carotid
Ascending
pharyngeal
External carotid
artery (cut)
Lingual artery

Common carotid
artery

FIG. 245. Deep dissection, showing the internal carotid artery and the vertebral arteries.

the brain, the eye and its appendages and sends branches to the forehead and the nose. The main branches are the anterior meningeal, the ophthalmic, the posterior communicating and the anterior choroid arteries. It ends by dividing into the middle and the anterior cerebral arteries.

The subclavian artery is shown in Figure 243. It arises at the division of the innominate artery on the right side and from the arch of the aorta on the left side. You can feel the pulsations in

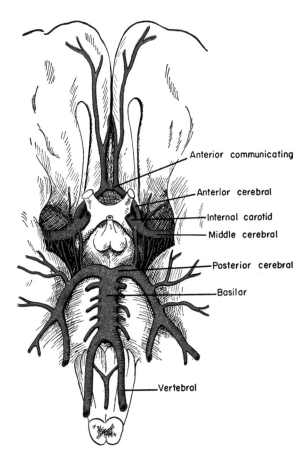

FIG. 246. Circle of Willis, showing communicating branches from the basilar and internal carotid arteries.

the subclavian artery if you press inward on the tissues just above the clavicle. The branches of the subclavian arteries supply some of the neck muscles, parts of the spinal cord, the meninges, the brain, the mediastinal structures, the intercostal structures, the mammary glands, parts of the neck, the back, the thyroid gland and the whole of the upper extremity. The chief branches are: (1) vertebral, (2) internal mammary, (3) costocervical trunk and (4) thyrocervical trunk. The subclavian artery becomes the axillary at the outer border of the first rib.

(a) The vertebral artery is shown in Figure 245. It gives off branches which supply some of the muscles of the neck, parts of the spinal cord, the meninges and the cerebellum. The 2 vertebral arteries unite to form the basilar artery (Fig. 246), which in turn divides into the posterior cerebral arteries, to supply part of the brain.

Circle of Willis. The blood supply of the brain is derived mainly from vessels which may be considered as branches of the circle of Willis (Fig. 246). The circle is formed by the proximal portions of the posterior cerebral arteries, the posterior communicating, the internal carotid, the proximal portions of the anterior cerebrals and the anterior communicating artery. By means of this arrangement, communication is established at the base of the brain between the 2 internal carotids and between these and the vertebrals.

(b) The internal mammary artery arises from the subclavian (Fig. 242) and gives off the mediastinal, the anterior intercostal and the anterior perforating arteries, which supply the mammary glands, the mediastinal structures and the superficial structures of the anterior part of the thorax. It terminates at the level of the sixth intercostal space by dividing into the musculophrenic and the superior epigastric arteries.

(c) The costocervical trunk, which arises from the subclavian artery, gives off the deep cervical artery, and then becomes the highest intercostal artery. It supplies the upper part of the back, the neck, the spinal cord and the meninges.

(d) The thyrocervical trunk (Figs. 242 and 243) ends by dividing into the inferior thyroid, the transverse cervical and the transverse scapular branches. It supplies the thyroid gland and the structures of the neck.

Axillary Artery. This is the continuation of the subclavian artery through the axillary space (Fig. 242). It passes downward to the lower border of the teres major where it becomes the brachial artery. Its branches are the highest thoracic, the thoraco-acromial, the lateral thoracic, the subscapular, the anterior humeral circumflex and the posterior humeral circumflex. These supply the tissues in the upper part of the thorax in the region of the shoulder and the axilla. The brachial artery is the continuation of the axillary artery down the arm. It ends about 1 cm. below the bend of the elbow by dividing into the radial and the ulnar arteries. At the bend in the elbow the brachial lies in front of the humerus, midway between its two epicondyles. It supplies the muscles of the arm and the humerus. It is shown in Figures 242 and 247.

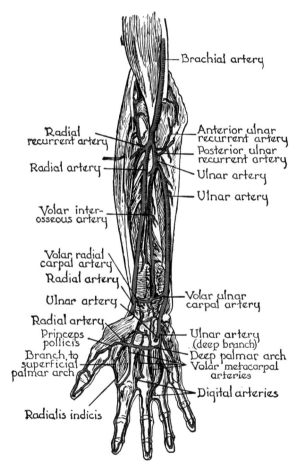

FIG. 247. Deep arteries of right forearm and hand, anterior view.

(i) The ulnar artery is the larger terminal branch of the brachial artery (Fig. 247). It passes down the medial side of the forearm; when it reaches the wrist it crosses to the radial side of the pisiform bone, then passes across the palmar surface of the hand, forming the main component of the superficial volar arch. It terminates opposite the second intermetacarpal space by anastomosing with the superficial volar branch of the radial artery. It gives off many branches which supply the tissues of the forearm and the hand.

(ii) The radial artery is the smaller terminal branch of the brachial artery (Fig. 247). It continues the course of the brachial down the lateral border of the forearm. At the styloid process of the radius it bends laterally, passes down to the interval between the first and the second metacarpal bones, then forward into the palmar surface of the hand, continues across the second, the third and the fourth metacarpals and forms the main component of the deep volar arch. It terminates by anastomosing with the deep volar branch of the ulnar artery. It supplies tissues of the forearm and the hand. The pulse is counted in the radial artery in about 99 per cent of patients; other arteries are used only when the radial arteries are inaccessible.

THORACIC AORTA. This vessel gives off visceral and parietal branches.

The visceral branches supply the pericardium, the lungs, the bronchi, the lymph nodes and the esophagus. These arteries are the pericardial, bronchial, esophageal and mediastinal. The bronchial arteries are the nutrient arteries of the lungs and are distributed mainly to the walls of the bronchi.

The parietal branches supply the intercostal muscles, the muscles of the thoracic wall, the pleurae, the spinal cord, the vertebral column and the posterior part of the upper surface of the diaphragm. These arteries are called intercostal, subcostal and superior phrenic. The intercostal arteries traverse the intercostal spaces and anastomose with the branches of the internal mammary artery.

ABDOMINAL AORTA. The abdominal aorta gives off both visceral and parietal branches.

The visceral branches are the celiac, the superior mesenteric and the inferior mesenteric, which are unpaired, and the middle suprarenal, the renal and the internal spermatic or ovarian, which are paired.

(a) The celiac artery (celiac axis) is shown in Figure 248. It

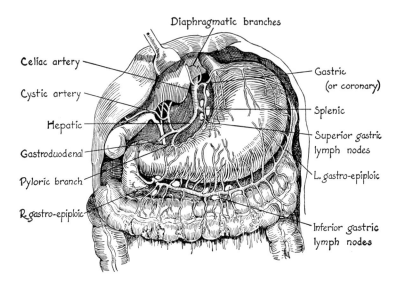

Diaphragmatic branches

Celiac artery

Cystic artery

Hepatic

Gastroduodenal

Pyloric branch

R. gastro-epiploic

Gastric
(or coronary)

Splenic

Superior gastric
lymph nodes

L. gastro-epiploic

Inferior gastric
lymph nodes

FIG. 248. Blood supply and lymphatics of the stomach. The celiac
artery and its branches are shown.

arises from the anterior surface of the abdominal aorta a short
distance below the diaphragm. It is very short and ends by dividing into the left gastric, the hepatic and the splenic (lienal) arteries.

(i) The left gastric supplies a part of the stomach and the
esophagus. It anastomoses with esophageal branches from the
thoracic aorta.

(ii) The hepatic artery is the nutrient artery of the liver. It
supplies, in addition, a part of the stomach, the duodenum and
the gallbladder.

(iii) The splenic artery supplies a part of the stomach, the pancreas and the spleen.

(b) The superior mesenteric artery is shown in Figure 249. It
arises from the anterior surface of the abdominal aorta just below
the celiac. It ends near the junction of the large and the small
intestines by anastomosing with one of its own branches (ileocolic).
It supplies the whole small intestine (except the duodenum) and
a part of the large intestine (cecum, appendix, ascending colon
and part of the transverse colon).

(c) The inferior mesenteric artery (Fig. 249) arises from the

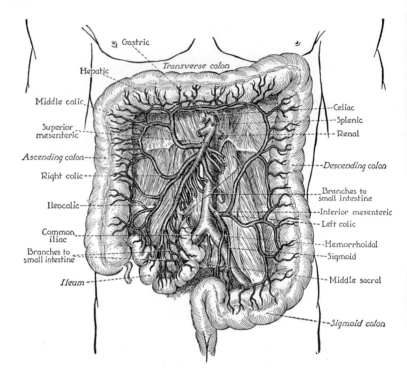

FIG. 249. Course and distribution of the superior and the inferior mesenteric arteries, semidiagrammatic. Ascending and descending colons are drawn laterally, the transverse colon superiorly, out of the abdominal cavity. All other viscera, peritoneum and mesenteries removed.

anterior surface of the abdominal aorta. It supplies the lower portion of the large intestine (part of transverse colon, descending colon, sigmoid colon and rectum) and terminates in the superior hemorrhoidal artery.

The blood from the organs supplied by the branches of the celiac, the superior mesenteric and the inferior mesenteric arteries is collected into the portal vein and carried to the liver (p. 606).

(d) The middle suprarenal arteries (Figs. 241 and 242) pass to the suprarenal glands and anastomose with other branches.

(e) The renal arteries (Figs. 241 and 242) pass to the kidneys.

(f) The spermatic (or ovarian) arteries arise from the abdom-

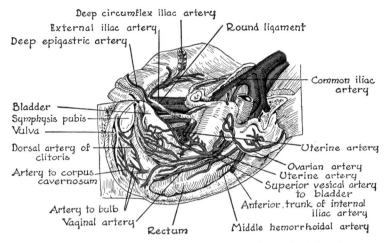

Deep circumflex iliac artery
External iliac artery
Deep epigastric artery
Round ligament
Common iliac artery
Bladder
Symphysis pubis
Vulva
Dorsal artery of clitoris
Artery to corpus cavernosum
Artery to bulb
Vaginal artery
Rectum
Uterine artery
Ovarian artery
Uterine artery
Superior vesical artery to bladder
Anterior trunk of internal iliac artery
Middle hemorrhoidal artery

FIG. 250. Arteries of female pelvis, seen from the left side.

inal aorta just below the origin of the renal arteries. The spermatic is shown in Figure 242. It passes to the testes and divides into several branches. The ovarian arteries supply the ovaries and terminate by joining the uterine arteries.

The parietal branches of the abdominal aorta are the inferior phrenic, the lumbar and the middle sacral arteries.

(a) The inferior phrenic arteries (Fig. 241) arise from the abdominal aorta, supply the suprarenal glands and under surface of the diaphragm and end by anastomosing with branches of other arteries.

(b) The lumbar arteries (Fig. 241) are arranged in 4 pairs; they supply muscles of the abdominal wall, the skin, the lumbar vertebrae, the spinal cord and the meninges.

(c) The middle sacral artery is unpaired (Fig. 241). It supplies the sacrum and the coccyx and terminates opposite the tip of the coccyx by dividing into several small branches.

TERMINAL BRANCHES OF THE AORTA. The terminal branches of the abdominal aorta are the common iliac arteries. These arise opposite the fourth lumbar vertebra (Figs. 241 and 250) and pass to the level of the sacro-iliac joint, where they terminate by dividing into the hypogastric and the external iliac arteries. They give off small branches to the psoas muscles, the peritoneum, the lymph nodes and the ureters.

The hypogastric arteries (Figs. 241 and 242) pass into the pelvis and, opposite the upper border of the greater sciatic notch, each divides into anterior and posterior divisions. These divisions give off branches which supply the pelvic walls, the pelvic viscera, the external genitalia, the buttocks, the medial side of the thigh and, in addition, the uterus in women.

The external iliac arteries are shown in Figure 241. Each extends

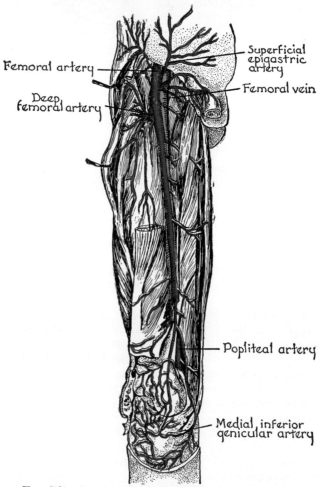

Femoral artery

Deep femoral artery

Superficial epigastric artery

Femoral vein

Popliteal artery

Medial, inferior genicular artery

Fig. 251. Arteries of anterior thigh, deep dissection.

from the division of the common iliac to a point beneath the inguinal ligament halfway between the anterior superior spine of the ilium and the symphysis pubis, where it becomes the femoral artery. It gives off some branches to the psoas major muscle and the lymph nodes, and then it gives rise to the inferior epigastric and the deep

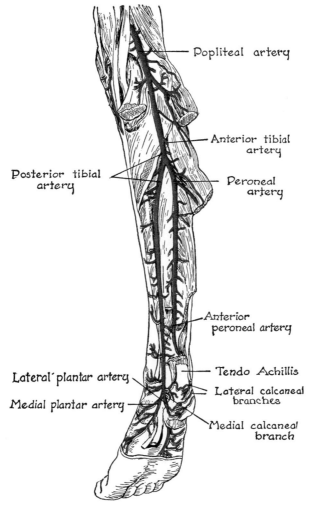

Fig. 252. Arteries of posterior and medial aspect of right leg.

circumflex iliac arteries. It supplies some structures of the abdomen and the lower extremity.

Femoral Artery (Fig. 251). This is the continuation of the external iliac artery below the inguinal ligament. It gives off the superficial epigastric, the superficial circumflex iliac, the superficial

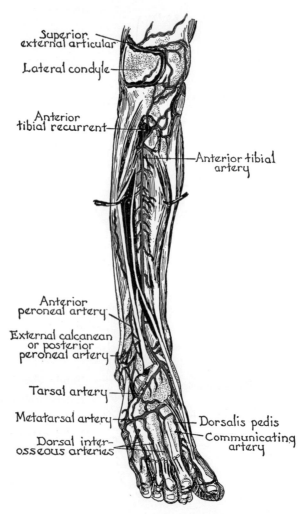

Superior external articular

Lateral condyle

Anterior tibial recurrent

Anterior tibial artery

Anterior peroneal artery

External calcanean or posterior peroneal artery

Tarsal artery

Metatarsal artery

Dorsal interosseous arteries

Dorsalis pedis

Communicating artery

FIG. 253. Arteries of anterior leg and dorsum of foot.

external pudendal, the profunda femoris, the muscular branches and the highest geniculate arteries. It supplies some structures of the abdomen and the lower extremity. The popliteal artery (Figs. 251 and 252) is the continuation of the femoral artery. It extends to the lower border of the popliteus muscle where it divides into the anterior and the posterior tibial arteries. It gives off muscular, articular and cutaneous branches, which supply structures in the lower thigh and the upper leg.

(a) The posterior tibial artery (Fig. 252) is the direct continuation of the popliteal artery down the posterior surface of the leg. It passes distally to the groove between the medial malleolus and the calcaneus, where, opposite the tip of the malleolus, it terminates by dividing into the medial and the lateral plantar arteries. Its branches are made up of the muscular vessels, the nutrient artery to the tibia, the peroneal artery, the communicating artery, the posterior medial malleolar artery, the medial calcaneal artery and the terminal branches. It supplies structures of the posterior portion of the leg and the foot.

(i) The lateral plantar artery (Fig. 252) is the larger of the terminal branches of the posterior tibial artery. It passes forward and laterally across the sole of the foot and, opposite the base of the fifth metatarsal bone, it turns medially and again crosses the sole of the foot, forming the plantar arch, which terminates at the proximal end of the first intermetatarsal space by uniting with the communicating branch from the dorsalis pedis.

(ii) The peroneal artery (Fig. 252) arises from the posterior tibial a short distance below the lower border of the popliteus muscle. It passes down the medial side of the tibia and terminates in the foot as the lateral calcaneal artery. It gives off branches which nourish the muscles, a nutrient branch to the fibula and communicating and perforating branches.

(b) The anterior tibial artery (Fig. 253) is one of the terminal branches of the popliteal artery. It passes downward to the ankle joint where it becomes the dorsalis pedis artery. It gives off the muscular vessels, the fibular artery, the posterior current tibial artery, the anterior recurrent tibial artery, the medial anterior malleolar artery and the lateral anterior malleolar branches.

The dorsalis pedis (Fig. 253) is the continuation of the anterior tibial artery beyond the ankle joint. It extends to the proximal portion of the first intermetatarsal space and then passes forward along the intermetatarsal space as the dorsalis hallucis artery. It gives off branches to the skin and the muscles, and the medial tarsal,

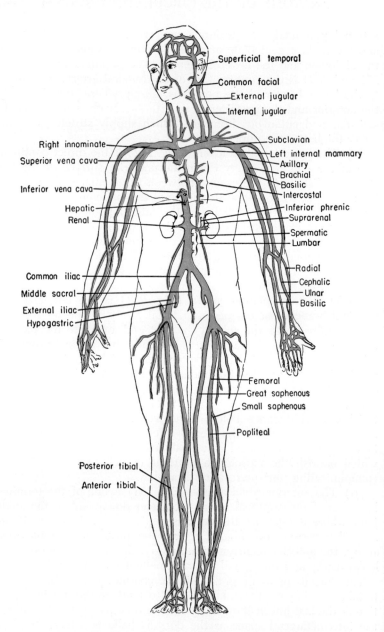

Superficial temporal

Common facial

External jugular

Internal jugular

Subclavian

Left internal mammary

Axillary

Brachial

Basilic

Intercostal

Inferior phrenic

Suprarenal

Spermatic

Lumbar

Radial

Cephalic

Ulnar

Basilic

Right innominate

Superior vena cava

Inferior vena cava

Hepatic

Renal

Common iliac

Middle sacral

External iliac

Hypogastric

Femoral

Great saphenous

Small saphenous

Popliteal

Posterior tibial

Anterior tibial

FIG. 254. Schematic drawing of the venous system.

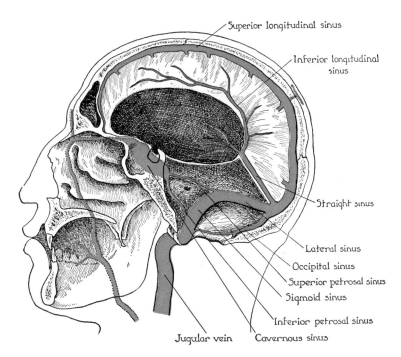

FIG. 255. The cranial venous sinuses, showing the superior sagittal or longitudinal, the inferior sagittal or longitudinal and the transverse or lateral. The sigmoid portion of the transverse or lateral sinus continues on as the internal jugular (labeled jugular) vein.

lateral tarsal, arcuate and deep plantar arteries. Physicians often palpate the dorsalis pedis artery to gain an idea of the condition of the arteries of the body and to obtain information about the circulation in the foot.

Veins of the Systemic Circuit. The small veins (venules) receive blood from the capillaries and the sinusoids. Small veins then unite to form larger ones; these unite to form still larger ones, and so on until the great veins, or venae cavae, are formed.

The veins in the extremities are arranged in 2 groups: superficial and deep.

The *superficial* veins lie just under the skin and drain the skin and the superficial fascia. They can be seen easily in most of us.

The *deep* veins accompany the principal arteries of the extremi-

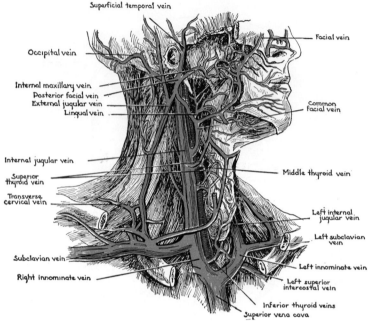

FIG. 256. Dissection showing the deep veins of the head and neck.

ties and take the name of the artery with which they travel. They are arranged in pairs and are called the *venae comitantes* (meaning "accompanying" or "companion veins"). The superficial and the deep sets of veins anastomose freely. The general scheme of the venous circulation is illustrated in Figure 254.

Blood enters the right atrium from 3 sources: (1) the heart muscle by way of the coronary sinus, (2) the upper portion of the body by way of the superior vena cava and (3) the lower portion of the body by way of the inferior vena cava.

CORONARY SINUS AND ITS TRIBUTARIES. The coronary sinus occupies the right half of the groove which lies between the left atrium and the left ventricle (Fig. 231). It opens into the right atrium on the posterior surface, below the opening of the inferior vena cava. It receives blood from the great cardiac vein (left coronary), the posterior vein of the left ventricle, the middle cardiac vein and the oblique veins of the left atrium. It is evident that the coronary sinus, through its tributaries, drains most of the heart muscle.

FIG. 257. Superficial veins of the anterior aspect of right forearm and axillary vein and its tributaries.

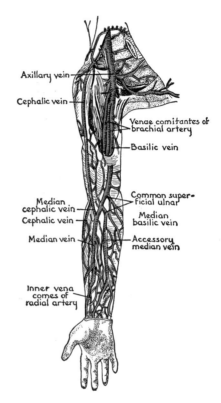

Axillary vein

Cephalic vein

Venae comitantes of brachial artery

Basilic vein

Common super-ficial ulnar

Median cephalic vein

Cephalic vein

Median basilic vein

Median vein

Accessory median vein

Inner vena comes of radial artery

SUPERIOR VENA CAVA AND ITS TRIBUTARIES. The superior vena cava receives, from its tributaries, blood from the head and the neck, the upper extremities and a part of the thorax.

Veins of the Head and the Neck. (a) Cranial Venous Sinuses. The cranial venous sinuses lie between the 2 layers of the dura mater and possess no valves. They form a series of channels and receive blood from the cerebral, the meningeal and the diploic veins and communicate with veins outside of the cranium by numerous veins, called *emissary veins,* and eventually drain into the internal jugular veins.

There are 16 cranial venous sinuses; 6 are median and unpaired, and the remaining 10 consist of 5 lateral pairs. The median venous sinuses are: (1) superior sagittal or longitudinal, (2) inferior sagittal or longitudinal, (3) straight, (4) occipital, (5) circular and (6) basilar plexus. The lateral paired venous sinuses are: (1) transverse or lateral, (2) superior petrosal, (3) inferior petrosal, (4) cavernous and (5) sphenoparietal sinuses. Many of the cranial venous sinuses are illustrated in Figure 255.

(b) The internal jugular vein (Fig. 256) is the principal vein of the neck and is the continuation of the transverse sinus (sigmoid portion) at the jugular foramen. The internal jugular veins descend to the level of the sternoclavicular joints where each unites with the subclavian of that side to form the innominate veins. The internal jugular veins receive blood from parts of the head, the neck and the brain.

(c) The external jugular vein (Fig. 256) is formed near the angle of the mandible by the union of its tributaries (the posterior facial and the posterior auricular veins). It drains some of the structures of the head and the neck and pours its contents into the subclavian vein of the same side. When the head is turned to the side, or when one wears a tight collar, this vein will stand out, along the edge of the sternocleidomastoid muscle. Sometimes you will see pulsations, just above the clavicle, in the external jugular vein; these pulsations are called the *central venous pulse* and are reflected changes in pressure from the right atrium, since there are no valves at the entrance of the superior vena cava into the right atrium.

Veins of the Upper Extremity. (a) Superficial Veins. All of the veins of the upper extremity are tributaries of the subclavian vein of that side.

(i) The cephalic vein (Fig. 257) begins in the radial portion of the dorsal network of the hand, ascends along the radial side of the forearm and the lateral border of the biceps brachii in the arm, passes between the deltoid and the pectoralis major muscles and ends in the axillary vein just below the clavicle. It receives blood from small veins of the hand and the forearm.

(ii)) The basilic vein (Fig. 257) begins in the ulnar portion of the dorsal network of the hand, ascends along the ulnar side of the forearm and the medial side of the biceps brachii in the arm and then joins the brachial vein to form the axillary vein of that side. The basilic is the largest of the superficial veins of the upper extremity, receiving blood from small veins of the hand, the forearm and the arm.

(b) Deep Veins. (i) The radial veins (Fig. 257) are the upward continuation of the veins of the deep volar arch.

(ii) The ulnar veins (Fig. 257) are formed by the union of the ulnar ends of the venae comitantes of both the superficial and

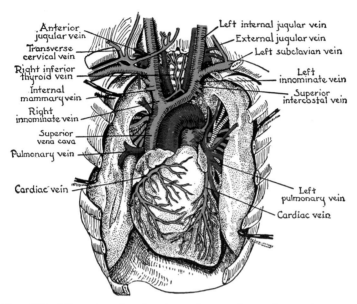

Anterior jugular vein
Transverse cervical vein
Right inferior thyroid vein
Internal mammary vein
Right innominate vein
Superior vena cava
Pulmonary vein
Cardiac vein

Left internal jugular vein
External jugular vein
Left subclavian vein
Left innominate vein
Superior intercostal vein
Left pulmonary vein
Cardiac vein

FIG. 258. Dissection showing innominate veins and superior vena cava in position. The lungs have been pulled aside.

the deep volar venous arches. Both the ulnar and the radial veins accompany the arteries of the same names.

(iii) The brachial veins (Fig. 257) are the companion veins of the brachial artery and are formed at the elbow joint by the union of the radial and the ulnar veins. At the level of the lower border of the pectoralis major muscle the brachial and the basilic veins unite to form the axillary vein.

(iv) The axillary vein (Fig. 257), formed by the union of the brachial venae comitantes and the basilic vein, becomes the subclavian vein at the outer border of the first rib.

(v) The subclavian vein (Fig. 256) is the end of the venous system of the upper extremity. It extends to the sternal end of the clavicle, where it unites with the internal jugular to form the innominate vein of that side.

Veins of the Thorax That are Tributaries to the Superior Vena Cava. The innominate vein (Figs. 256 and 258) is formed by the union of the internal jugular and the subclavian veins, on each side. The innominate ends opposite the first costal cartilage, by uniting with its fellow to form the superior vena cava. In addition to the subclavian and the internal jugular veins, which return blood from the upper extremity, the head and the neck region, the innominate vein receives blood from the deep cervical, the vertebral, the internal mammary and the inferior thyroid veins. The left innominate receives, in addition, the superior phrenic, the thymic, the pericardial, the anterior mediastinal and the left superior intercostal veins. The inferior thyroid receives blood from the trachea and the esophagus. In summary, the innominate vein receives blood from the upper extremity, the head, the neck and the upper thorax.

The superior vena cava (Figs. 256 and 258) is the main venous trunk which delivers blood returning from the head, the neck, the upper extremity and the thorax to the right atrium. It is formed immediately below the lower border of the first costal cartilage on the right side by the union of the right and the left innominate veins. It opens into the upper posterior portion of the right atrium, on a level with the third costal cartilage on the right side. In addition to the innominate veins, the superior vena cava receives the azygos vein and small veins from the mediastinum and the pericardium.

The Azygos Group. The azygos group comprises the hemiazygos, the accessory hemiazygos and the azygos veins. The azygos group is the connecting link between the superior and the inferior vena caval systems. In cases of obstruction of the inferior vena caval system, these azygos veins carry the blood back from the lower portion of the body through collateral communication with the common iliac, the renal and the lumbar veins.

(a) The azygos vein (Fig. 259) begins just below the diaphragm as the continuation of the right ascending lumbar vein. The right ascending lumbar vein is formed by the union of tributaries of the lumbar veins and one from the common iliac. The principal tributaries are the right intercostal veins which drain the muscles of the intercostal spaces. It also receives tributaries from the esophagus, the lymph nodes of the posterior mediastinum, the posterior surface of the pericardium and the substance of the right lung through the posterior bronchial veins. At the level of the fourth thoracic vertebra the azygos empties into the superior vena cava.

(b) The hemiazygos vein (Fig. 259) arises just below the diaphragm as the continuation of the left ascending lumbar vein. It receives a tributary from the left renal vein and the lower 4 or 5 intercostal veins and tributaries from the esophageal veins and the posterior mediastinum. At the level of the eighth or the ninth thoracic vertebra, the hemiazygos empties into the azygos vein.

FIG. 259. Portion of the posterior body wall, showing the azygos vein entering superior vena cava. The inferior vena cava and tributaries are shown. Internal iliac now called *hypogastric*.

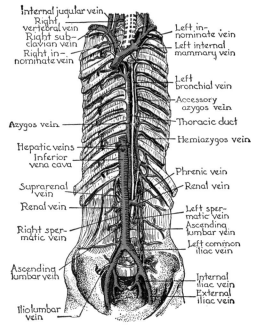

Internal jugular vein
Right vertebral vein
Right subclavian vein
Right innominate vein
Left innominate vein
Left internal mammary vein
Left bronchial vein
Accessory azygos vein
Thoracic duct
Azygos vein
Hemiazygos vein
Hepatic veins
Inferior vena cava
Phrenic vein
Suprarenal vein
Renal vein
Renal vein
Left spermatic vein
Right spermatic vein
Ascending lumbar vein
Left common iliac vein
Ascending lumbar vein
Internal iliac vein
External iliac vein
Iliolumbar vein

(c) The accessory hemiazygos vein (Fig. 259) is similar to the hemiazygos except that it begins at about the second intercostal space and receives the upper 7 or 8 left intercostal veins and the left posterior bronchial vein. It crosses the mid-line to the right side, and at the level of the seventh or the eighth thoracic vertebra it empties into the azygos vein.

INFERIOR VENA CAVA AND ITS TRIBUTARIES. Through its tributaries the inferior vena cava receives blood from the body wall below the level of the diaphragm and from the abdomen, the pelvis and the lower extremities.

Veins of the Body Wall Below the Diaphragm. (a) The inferior phrenic (Fig. 254) is formed by the union of many small veins on the under surface of the diaphragm, and it receives blood, also, from the upper portion of the suprarenal gland. It empties into the inferior vena cava.

(b) Lumbar Veins. There are 4 pairs of lumbar veins (Fig. 254). Each arises in the muscles of the abdominal wall and receives tributaries which return blood from the skin and muscles of the dorsal part of the trunk, the spinal cord and the meninges. The lumbar veins empty into the inferior vena cava. Each lumbar vein is con-

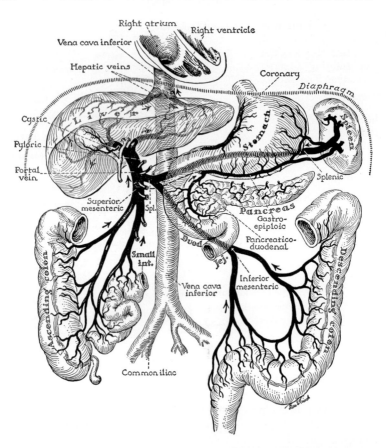

FIG. 260. The portal system, semidiagrammatic. The various organs have been moved somewhat out of position to expose the portal vein and its tributaries. The transverse colon and most of the small intestine have been removed. The veins which belong to this system are shown in heavy black. The pancreatic veins, which are shown cut, drain into the splenic vein. The direction of the flow is indicated by arrows. The branching of the portal vein within the liver is indicated. The collection of blood from the liver by the hepatic veins is shown; these enter the inferior vena cava, which passes through the diaphragm to the right atrium.

nected with the one above by an ascending tributary; the lowest is also connected with the iliolumbar (Fig. 259) or with the common iliac vein. The ascending tributary from the uppermost lumbar vein continues as the ascending lumbar vein to join the azygos on the right and the hemiazygos on the left.

Veins of the Abdomen and the Pelvis. The portal system comprises the veins that drain all of the digestive tract below the diaphragm (except the lower part of the rectum) and those that drain the pancreas, the spleen and the gallbladder, in addition. A diagram of the portal system is shown in Figure 260.

The tributaries to the portal vein are the superior mesenteric and the splenic veins, by whose union it is formed.

(a) The superior mesenteric vein (Fig. 261) begins near the terminal portion of the ileum, receives the blood from veins that drain the stomach, the small intestine, part of the large intestine and the pancreas.

(b) The splenic vein (Figs. 260 and 262) is formed by the union of several small veins which drain the spleen, and it receives blood from the stomach and the pancreas, in addition.

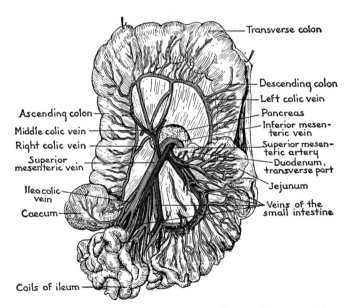

FIG. 261. Superior mesenteric vein and its tributaries. The transverse colon has been turned upward.

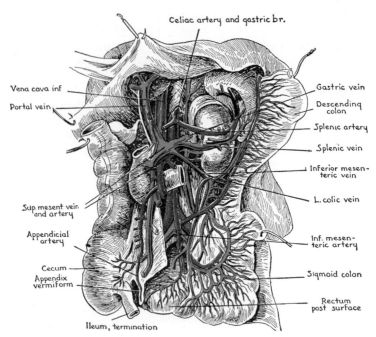

FIG. 262. Blood vessels of large intestine, showing tributaries of the portal vein. The stomach and transverse colon have been removed and the liver turned upward. The portal vein is seen to break up into branches as it enters the liver.

(i) The inferior mesenteric vein (Figs. 260 to 262) is formed by the union of the superior hemorrhoidal and the sigmoid veins opposite the sigmoid colon. It receives blood from the lower portion of the large intestine and empties into the splenic vein.

(ii) The coronary vein of the stomach (Fig. 260) arises at the pyloric end of the stomach, receives blood from the stomach, and the esophagus and then empties into the portal (or splenic) vein.

(iii) The pyloric and the cystic veins may empty into the portal vein.

The portal vein carries the blood it receives from the above sources on to the sinusoids of the liver. You will recall that the liver receives blood by way of the hepatic artery also. The arterial blood from the hepatic artery and the venous blood from the portal vein mix in the sinusoids of the liver, and eventually all the

FIG. 263. Superficial veins of the right lower extremity, medial aspect.

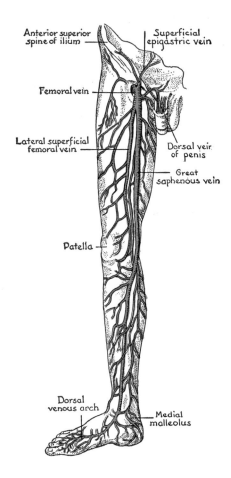

Anterior superior spine of ilium

Superficial epigastric vein

Femoral vein

Lateral superficial femoral vein

Dorsal vein of penis

Great saphenous vein

Patella

Dorsal venous arch

Medial malleolus

mixed blood leaves the liver by way of the hepatic veins, which empty into the inferior vena cava.

The unusual arrangement of the portal circuit gives the liver an opportunity to remove whatever it so desires of food materials that have been absorbed from the intestinal tract. Some of this may be stored temporarily in the liver; some is modified by the liver for easier oxidation in various tissues; some is detoxified. In other words, the liver stands guard, as it were; it censors or prepares food material before it goes on to other tissues.

(c) The hepatic veins (Figs. 259 and 260) are formed by the

union of the central veins of the liver. They drain the liver sinusoids and empty into the inferior vena cava.

Other Veins of the Abdomen and the Pelvis. (a) Each renal vein (Figs. 254 and 259) is formed by the union of from 3 to 5 tributaries that drain the kidney. Each renal vein receives blood, also, from the lower part of the suprarenal gland and from the ureter and empties into the inferior vena cava.

(b) The suprarenal veins (Figs. 254 and 259) arise in the suprarenal glands. They drain the middle portion of the glands, and the right one empties into the inferior vena cava; the left, into left renal vein.

(c) The spermatic vein (Figs. 254 and 259) begins at the abdominal inguinal ring as the continuation of the venous plexuses that surround the spermatic cord. It receives blood from the testis, the epididymis, the ureter, the peritoneum and the capsule of the kidney. The right spermatic vein empties into the inferior vena cava; the left, into the left renal vein.

(d) The ovarian veins arise from the ovaries. They receive blood from the uterus also. The right empties into the inferior vena cava, and the left into the left renal vein.

Veins of the Lower Extremity and the Pelvis. The veins of the lower extremity are tributaries of the common iliac veins.

(a) Superficial Veins. (i) The small saphenous vein (Fig. 254) begins behind the lateral malleolus and ascends the posterior surface of the leg. It drains the lateral border of the foot and the whole of the posterior, superficial portion of the leg. It terminates by dividing into 2 veins, one of which empties into the popliteal and the other into the deep femoral vein.

(ii) The great saphenous vein (Figs. 263 and 264) arises at the junction of the medial end of the dorsal arch of the foot with the medial marginal vein. It receives blood from the foot and the superficial parts of the leg and the thigh and then empties into the femoral vein on the same side, below the inguinal ligament. It is the longest vein in the body.

(b) Deep Veins. (i) The posterior tibial vein (Fig. 254) is formed behind the medial malleolus by the union of the medial and the lateral plantar veins. It ends at the lower border of the popliteus muscle by uniting with the anterior tibial veins to form the popliteal vein.

(ii) The anterior tibial veins (Fig. 254) are the upward continuation of the venae comitantes of the dorsalis pedis artery. They unite with the posterior tibial veins to form the popliteal vein.

(iii) The popliteal vein (Fig. 254) is formed by the union of the anterior and the posterior tibial veins at the lower border of the popliteus muscle. It receives blood from the articular and the muscular tributaries and receives the small saphenous vein. At the junction of the middle and the distal thirds of the thigh, the popliteal vein passes through the tendinous opening in the adductor magnus muscle and becomes the femoral vein at this point.

(iv) The femoral vein (Fig. 264) is the direct continuation of the popliteal vein. It receives the great saphenous, the deep

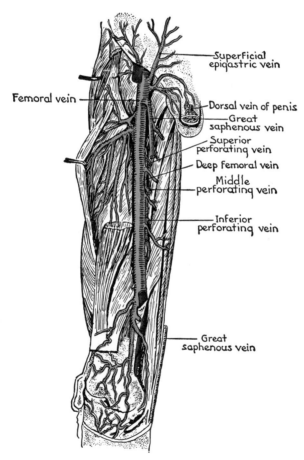

Femoral vein

Superficial epigastric vein

Dorsal vein of penis

Great saphenous vein

Superior perforating vein

Deep femoral vein

Middle perforating vein

Inferior perforating vein

Great saphenous vein

FIG. 264. Right femoral vein and its tributaries.

femoral, the venae comitantes of the femoral artery and the highest genicular veins, and it becomes the external iliac vein at the level of the inguinal ligament.

(v) The external iliac vein (Figs. 254 and 259) begins at the level of the inguinal ligament, receives the inferior epigastric and the deep circumflex iliac veins and unites with the hypogastric vein to form the common iliac.

(vi) The hypogastric vein (Figs. 254 and 259) arises near the greater sciatic notch. It receives blood from the pelvic walls, the pelvic viscera, the external genitalia, the buttocks and the medial side of the thigh by way of the superior gluteal, the lateral sacral, the iliolumbar, the inferior gluteal, the internal pudendal, the obturator, the middle hemorrhoidal, the vesical and, in the female, the uterine veins. It unites with the external iliac of its side to form the common iliac vein.

(vii) The common iliac vein (Figs. 254 and 259) is formed opposite the sacroiliac joint by the union of the hypogastric and the external iliac veins. At the level of the intervertebral disk, between the fourth and the fifth lumbar vertebrae, the 2 common iliac veins unite to form the inferior vena cava.

The inferior vena cava (Figs. 254 and 259) is formed by the union of the 2 common iliac veins. It is the largest vein in the body. It receives blood from the common iliac veins, the inferior phrenic, the lumbar, the hepatic, the renal, the suprarenal and the spermatic (or ovarian) veins, and then it empties into the right atrium.

A summary of the anatomy of the circulatory system is presented in chart form between pages 460 and 461.

The Coronary Circuit

The coronary arteries carry blood from the aorta to the heart wall. The blood passes through branches of the coronary arteries, into the capillaries of the muscle of the heart and then is collected into cardiac veins. The chief veins that receive blood from the myocardium are the great cardiac and the small cardiac veins, which are tributaries of the coronary sinus. In addition to the principal veins of the heart, several open directly into the right atrium. These are called the *anterior cardiac* veins. Some very small cardiac veins open directly into various heart chambers through small openings called *thebesian foramina.*

Digestive Circuit

The blood passes from the aorta into the celiac, the superior mesenteric and the inferior mesenteric arteries and through their

Fig. 265. Diagram of the fetal circulation shortly before birth; course of blood is indicated by arrows. Oxygenated, poorly oxygenated and mixed blood indicated by red, blue and purple, respectively. P, placenta; UA and UV, umbilical arteries and vein; U, umbilicus; DV, ductus venosus; IVC, inferior vena cava; PV, portal vein; HV, hepatic vein; RV and LV, right and left ventricles; PA, pulmonary artery; DA, ductus arteriosus; SVC, superior vena cava; AA, abdominal aorta; HA, hypogastric arteries (internal iliacs); EIA, external iliac arteries; I, intestine; L, lungs; K, kidneys.

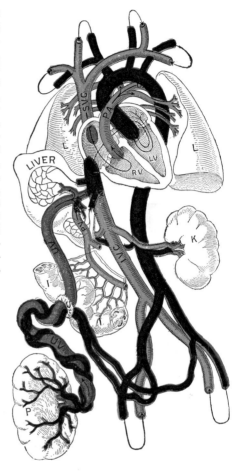

branches into the capillaries of the abdominal portion of the digestive system, where nutritive material is added to it. From these capillaries, the blood enters the corresponding veins in each organ and eventually reaches the portal vein, from which it passes into the sinusoids of the liver, then into the hepatic veins that carry it on to the inferior vena cava and the right atrium. It passes through two sets of capillaries in the systemic circuit.

RENAL CIRCUIT

The blood passes from the aorta into the renal arteries, through their branches into the capillaries of the glomeruli, then into the efferent arterioles to the tubules, where it passes through a second set of capillaries. Then it is collected into the renal veins and is carried to the inferior vena cava and on to the right atrium.

FETAL CIRCULATION

In the fetus the lungs, the gastro-intestinal tract and the kidneys do not carry out the functions that they perform after birth. Since the fetus derives all of its oxygen and nutritive material from the mother's circulation and depends on her for the elimination of carbon dioxide and other waste products, we must look for certain differences between the prenatal and the postnatal circulatory systems.

Since the fetal lungs are collapsed, there must be some means of getting the blood from the right side to the left side of the heart other than by way of the pulmonary circuit. There are two such channels—the foramen ovale and the ductus arteriosus. The *foramen ovale* is an opening between the right and the left atria, in the interatrial septum. The *ductus arteriosus* is a vessel that connects the pulmonary artery and the aorta.

The vessels that connect the fetal circulation with the maternal circulation are the umbilical arteries (Fig. 265) and the umbilical vein. The blood leaves the fetus through the 2 umbilical arteries, which branch off the hypogastric arteries. After circulating through the capillaries of the placenta, where it receives food and oxygen and eliminates waste, it returns to the body of the fetus by way of the umbilical vein. The umbilical vessels lie in the umbilical cord. The ductus venosus is a fetal vessel which makes it possible for the blood to get to the inferior vena cava without going through the fetal liver.

Circulation through the lower portion of the body is like that in the postnatal individual. As the blood returns from the lower portion of the body of the fetus, it is mingled with the blood that is returning from the placenta laden with oxygen and nutritive materials. The mixing takes place in the inferior vena cava, and the blood then enters the right atrium.

Circulation through the upper portion of the body is like that in the postnatal individual. After circulating through the upper portion of the body the blood is returned to the right atrium by the superior vena cava. The blood from the inferior vena cava mixes with that from the superior vena cava in the right atrium. A large part passes through the foramen ovale into the left atrium and then into the left ventricle. The remainder passes into the right ventricle, on into the pulmonary artery, through the ductus arteriosus and into the aorta.

The mixed blood is carried to all parts of the body through branches of the aorta. On reaching the bifurcation of the common iliac artery, part of the blood goes into the hypogastric arteries, into the umbilical arteries and on to the placenta, from which it is returned to the fetus by the umbilical vein. The umbilical vein is the only vessel in the fetus that carries fully oxygenated blood. Figure 265 is a diagram of the fetal circulation.

After the birth the ductus arteriosus and the ductus venosus soon undergo atrophy and become fibrous cords. The foramen ovale closes in about one week after birth.

LYMPHATIC SYSTEM

GENERAL PLAN

The lymphatic system consists of a set of closed vessels. The system begins in complex capillary networks that collect lymph from tissue fluids in various organs. Lymphatic capillaries unite to form an elaborate system of collecting vessels that conduct lymph from the capillaries to the veins in the neck, where it is emptied into the blood stream. On their way to the veins, the lymphatic vessels pass through lymph nodes where they break up into capillaries and sinuses; they combine again into closed vessels before leaving the nodes. In the nodes a large part of the lymph is absorbed by venous networks, and only a small residue is passed along.

CIRCULATION OF LYMPH

There is no pumping mechanism in the lymphatic system; the vessels merely collect and convey lymph from tissue spaces to veins. The lymph is kept moving along slowly by contractions of voluntary muscles squeezing on the lymph vessels in them, by the pulsations in nearby arteries which exert a massaging effect on the lymphatic vessels, by peristaltic contractions of intestinal muscles and by the suction due to negative pressure in the thoracic cavity. Lymphatic vessels are abundantly supplied with valves that direct the flow of lymph onward; the valves occur at such close intervals that they give the vessel a beaded appearance.

STRUCTURE OF VESSELS

The walls of lymphatic capillaries consist of a single layer of thin, flat, endothelial cells. They are wider and more irregular in

form than the vascular capillaries. Lymphatic capillaries lie in
connective tissue spaces in various regions of the body and are
bathed by tissue fluid. The beginning of lymphatic capillaries is
shown in Figure 266. There are both superficial and deep capillary plexuses, with anastomoses between them. Lymphatic capillaries of the intestine are called *lacteals.*

Lymphatic capillaries join to form collecting vessels. These are
small and delicate, and their walls are transparent, enabling the
lymph to be seen through the walls. The collecting vessels contain
many valves. Lymphatics tend to occur in streams of individual
vessels instead of combining to form larger and larger trunks.
Lymphatic vessels are distributed in most of the vascular regions
of the body; they are absent from the central nervous system, the
meninges, the eyeball, the orbit, the internal ear, the nails and the
cartilage. The walls of larger lymph vessels resemble those of veins
and consist of 3 coats; a cross section of a small lymphatic vessel
is illustrated in Figure 267.

Lymphatic vessels are essentially subepithelial in position. They
are abundant in skin, mucous membranes, all glands, serous and
synovial membranes. The course of the vessels is in the loose subcutaneous tissues and in the connective tissue between muscles and

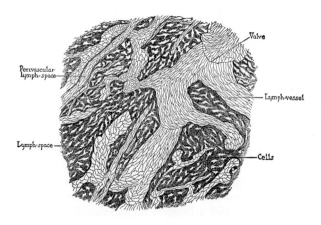

Fig. 266. Lymph spaces and vessels shown as light
areas in dark ground substance. From central tendon of
rabbit's diaphragm, treated with silver nitrate. ×120.

organs; they often accompany arteries and veins and form networks around them.

Superficial lymphatic vessels lie in the skin and the subcutaneous tissue and accompany superficial veins. On each side of the body the cutaneous lymphatic vessels converge from 3 large areas to 3 groups of nodes, as shown in Figure 268. These are: (1) from the skin of the lower extremity, the perineum, the external genitalia, the buttocks and the trunk below the level of the umbilicus, into the inguinal nodes in the groin; (2) from the skin of the upper extremity and the trunk above the umbilicus to the level of the clavicle, in front, and halfway up the back of the neck, behind, into the axillary nodes in the axilla; and (3) from the scalp, the face and the rest of the neck, into the cervical nodes in the neck.

The deep lymphatic vessels lie beneath the deep fascia and accompany deep blood vessels.

Afferent lymphatic vessels penetrate the capsule of a lymph node, break up into capillaries and sinuses within the node (Fig.

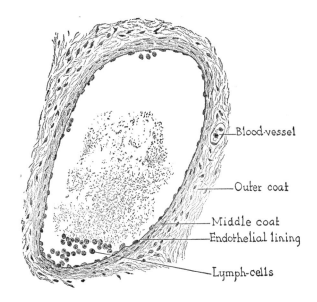

Blood-vessel

Outer coat

Middle coat

Endothelial lining

Lymph-cells

FIG. 267. Cross section of small lymphatic vessel. Lymphocytes (lymph cells) are present in the lumen. ×210.

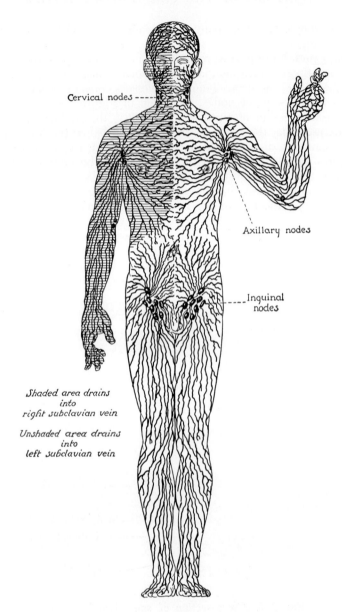

Cervical nodes

Axillary nodes

Inquinal nodes

Shaded area drains
into
right subclavian vein

Unshaded area drains
into
left subclavian vein

FIG. 268. Diagram of superficial lymphatic vessels and
cervical, axillary and inguinal nodes.

269) and then unite as they leave the node, into one or two efferent vessels. The efferent vessels may pass to another node of the
same group or to a node in a different group. From the most
central group of each chain of nodes, the efferent vessels unite to
form trunks. The collecting trunks tend to be grouped in the
vicinity of blood vessels. The principal large lymphatic trunks in
the body are the lumbar, the intestinal, the intercostal, the bronchomediastinal, the subclavian and the jugular (Fig. 270). Each trunk
drains a definite area of the body. All the trunks empty eventually
into the great terminal vessels, which are the thoracic duct and the
right lymphatic duct, or into veins directly.

The thoracic duct is the terminal duct for all the unshaded
areas in Figure 268. It extends from the level of the second lumbar
vertebra to the root of the neck. It begins in the cisterna chyli,
passes with the aorta through the diaphragm and ends by opening
into the angle of junction of the left subclavian and the left internal
jugular veins. There are valves at the end to keep the venous blood
from entering the duct. The thoracic duct is shown in Figures 270
and 271.

The cisterna chyli receives the lumbar and the intestinal trunks.
The thoracic duct receives intercostal tributaries and is joined in
the neck by the left subclavian, the jugular and the bronchomedi-

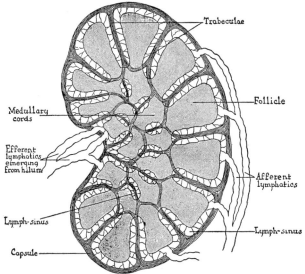

FIG. 269. Diagram illustrating structure of lymph node.

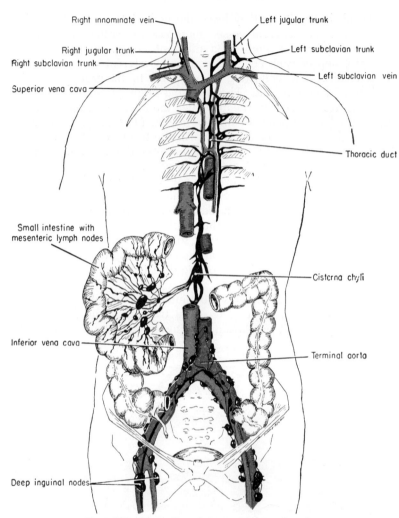

FIG. 270. Deep lymphatic vessels and nodes.

astinal trunks. In some individuals, some of these trunks empty
separately into veins, instead of joining the thoracic duct.

THE LUMBAR TRUNKS receive lymph from the lower extremities,
the perineum, the external genitalia, the walls and viscera of the
pelvis, the kidneys, the suprarenal glands, the part of the digestive
tract supplied by the inferior mesenteric artery and the deep

Fig. 271. Dissection of posterior body wall, showing thoracic duct and right lymphatic duct. The veins have been displaced laterally to expose the terminations of the thoracic duct.

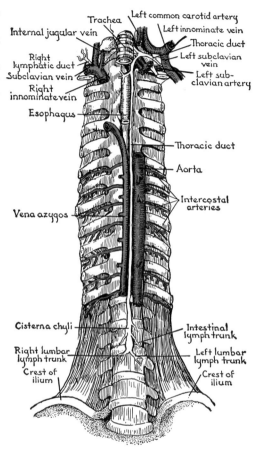

lymphatics of the greater part of the abdominal wall below the umbilicus.

THE INTESTINAL TRUNK receives lymph from the stomach, the intestines, the pancreas, the spleen and the lower part of the liver.

THE JUGULAR TRUNK receives lymph from the head and the neck; the subclavian from the upper extremity and part of the thorax and the bronchomediastinal from the side of the thorax, the lungs, the heart and part of the liver. These empty either into the thoracic duct or the right lymphatic duct. The right lymphatic duct (Fig. 271) is not always present; when it is, it empties into the right innominate vein near its origin.

LYMPHATIC TISSUE

Lymphatic tissue is the second variety of hemopoietic tissue (myeloid is the other). It consists of a meshwork of reticular fibers among which there are fixed and free cells. The former are called *primitive reticular* or fixed stem cells, and they differentiate to form reticuloendothelium and free rounded stem cells of great potentiality or lymphoblasts. The production of lymphocytes is restricted to localized areas in lymphatic tissue called *germinal centers.*

Lymphatic tissue that is designed to filter tissue fluid is found under wet epithelial surfaces that are exposed to contamination, such as the alimentary tract and the respiratory and the urinary passages. Examples of this type are found in the palatine, the pharyngeal and the lingual tonsils and in Peyer's patches in the ileum.

Lymphatic tissue that is designed to filter lymph is found in lymph nodes. Such nodes vary in size from a pinhead to an almond and are found along lymphatic vessels that empty into the thoracic duct and the right lymphatic duct. They may occur singly or in groups of 2 to 15. Each consists of an outer cortex and an inner medulla. Lymph nodes are enclosed in fibrous capsules, in which there are elastic fibers and smooth muscular tissue. Trabeculae extend in from the capsule and divide the node into compart-

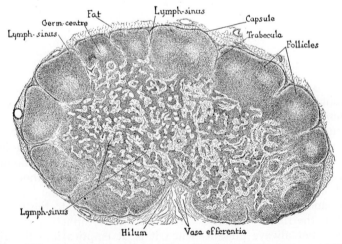

FIG. 272. Section of small lymph node, through the hilum. ×25.

ments filled with masses of lymphatic tissue. Between the tissue and the trabeculae, there are spaces that form a system of channels called *lymph sinuses.* Germinal centers are present in the cortex. Blood vessels and nerves are present. A section of a lymph node is shown in Figure 272.

Spleen. Lymphatic tissue which is designed to filter blood is found in the spleen. The shape of the spleen is variable, since it is accommodated to the surfaces of the adjacent viscera. It is an elongated, ovoid body, located in the left hypochondrium behind the stomach (Figs. 7 and 8).

The spleen exhibits colic, phrenic, renal and gastric surfaces. The *colic* surface is triangular. The *phrenic* surface is the largest and lies against the diaphragm in the left hypochondrium. The *renal* surface faces medially; the upper third rests against the suprarenal gland, and the lower two thirds rests against the left kidney. The *gastric* surface fits over the stomach; it contains the hilum through which vessels enter and leave the spleen. The lower end of this surface rests against the splenic flexure of the colon.

The peritoneum is attached to the spleen only near the hilum, so the spleen is free to follow the movements of the diaphragm during respiration.

The spleen is covered by a capsule composed of fibrous and elastic connective tissue, together with a few smooth muscle fibers. At the hilum, the tissue of the capsule enters the organ and forms

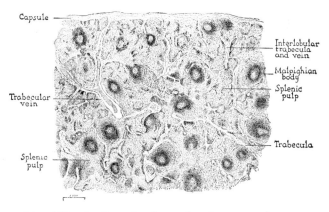

FIG. 273. Section of spleen, showing general arrangement of splenic tissue. Malpighian bodies are dense collections of lymphocytes. ×10.

a framework for vessels and nerves. Trabeculae extend into the spleen from the capsule and divide the spleen into lobules, as illustrated in Figure 273. The spaces within the framework are filled with vascular lymphatic tissue, which is called the *splenic pulp*. The white pulp consists of ordinary lymphatic tissue; the malpighian bodies of the spleen contain germinal centers. Red pulp fills the spaces between the venous sinuses. Nongranular leukocytes are the most numerous cells in the red pulp.

The arteries are closely connected with the white pulp, and the veins with the red pulp. Lymphatic vessels are found only in the capsule and the larger trabeculae. Nerve networks are present. The blood supply is derived from the splenic artery, which is a branch of the celiac artery. The splenic vein, which is a tributary of the portal vein, drains the spleen. The smooth muscle in the capsule, the framework and the blood vessels receives a nerve supply from each division of the autonomic system.

Although the spleen may be removed without causing death, it performs many important functions. It removes most of the worn-out red corpuscles from the blood, makes bile pigment (bilirubin) from their hemoglobin and releases it into the blood stream to be removed by the liver. It removes iron from hemoglobin and releases it into the blood stream so that it may be used again by the red bone marrow in the manufacture of erythrocytes. It produces antibodies which confer on us immunity to various diseases. It produces lymphocytes and monocytes which are released into the blood. In animals the spleen can release stored blood into the circulatory system during times of stress.

Thymus. The thymus "gland" consists of two pyramidal-shaped lobes. It lies beneath the sternum in the mediastinum. It is relatively large in children, reaches its maximum development at the age of puberty and then undergoes involution, during which thymic tissue is replaced by adipose tissue.

The thymus is surrounded by a capsule, from which trabeculae extend into its substance. It is divided into lobes, which, in turn, are divided into lobules. The substance of the organ is composed of lymphatic tissue, with an outer cortex and an inner medulla. There are no germinal centers, but cell nests called *concentric corpuscles of Hassall* are present. The blood supply is derived from branches of the subclavian or internal mammary arteries. Lymphatic vessels pass from the thymus to the anterior mediastinal lymph nodes. The nerves that supply the thymus are derived from the autonomic system.

The functions of the thymus are still a mystery. It has been found to be enlarged in many individuals suffering from myasthenia gravis. It manufactures lymphocytes and perhaps this is its only function. There is no evidence of any endocrine function. It is enlarged in about one half the patients with thyrotoxicosis (overactive thyroid gland). Its congenital absence is limited to anencephalic monsters and stillbirths. It is essential to fetal development, but its contribution to this period of life is not understood.

PRACTICAL CONSIDERATIONS
DISEASES OF THE HEART

Pulse Deficit. In the normal individual the rate of the heart counted at the apex is the same as the rate counted in an artery such as the radial. In some cardiac conditions (atrial fibrillation) you will hear more beats at the apex than you can feel at the wrist. This condition is referred to as *pulse deficit.*

Pericarditis. An infection of the pericardium is called *pericarditis.* In some cases of pericarditis the amount of fluid in the pericardial sac may be greatly increased (called *pericarditis with effusion*), or there may be an accumulation of pus in the pericardial sac, and the normal activity of the heart is disturbed. The fluid must be drained off (pericardial paracentesis) to permit the heart to perform its normal pumping function.

Valvular Disease. Two types of difficulty may arise in connection with heart valves. One type arises when there is narrowing of the fibrous ring to which the leaflets are attached or when the leaflets themselves become thick and stiff and fail to open widely. This condition is called *stenosis,* and when it exists there is difficulty in pumping the blood through the narrowed opening as rapidly as it should be going through. In the second type of difficulty, the edges of the valve leaflets are eroded, or the fibrous ring is stretched. This condition is called *insufficiency* or *regurgitation,* and when it exists the valve cannot be closed completely, and blood leaks back through the valve when it is supposed to be flowing in the forward direction. These valvular difficulties are of frequent occurrence in bacterial endocarditis. Patients will be encountered who have mitral stenosis, mitral regurgitation, aortic stenosis or aortic regurgitation or tricuspid or pulmonary valve impairments. In some patients one valve may exhibit both types of difficulty; the leaflets may be thickened and stiff, and their edges may be eroded by the same disease process.

Heart Block. The bundle of His (atrioventricular) may be involved in disease. If the ventricles are functionally separated from the atria, they will beat at their own rhythm instead of following the atrial beat. This condition is called *heart block,* and it can be recognized by the very slow pulse rate. The "isolated" ventricles beat much slower than the normal ones which are following the rate of the atria.

Coronary Disease. In some patients the muscle in the walls of the coronary arteries now and then goes into a spasmodic contraction, and severe pain results as the heart muscle is temporarily deprived of its blood supply. Such an attack is called a *heart attack,* but the correct term for this is *angina pectoris.* The pain may be referred to the left shoulder and may radiate down the left arm. The spasm is relieved by inhalation of amyl nitrite. In other patients, the walls of the coronary arteries undergo hardening or sclerotic changes, and this condition, likewise, interferes with the proper supply of oxygen and nourishment to the massive heart muscle. You frequently hear of sudden deaths due to heart attacks and, in most cases, it is the result of sudden deprivation of oxygen to the heart muscle as a result of interference with the coronary blood flow.

DISEASES OF THE ARTERIES

As you might expect, there can be abnormal changes in the walls of the arteries. Sometimes there is such a change in structure that the wall becomes weak and undergoes a marked dilatation in some portion. The dilated sac which results is called an *aneurysm.*

Aneurysms are pulsating masses; they may exert pressure on nerves, with resulting pain and paralysis. The most frequent site of aneurysm formation is the ascending portion of the aorta. The next most frequent site is the popliteal artery. This is due to frequent minor strains occurring during flexion and extension of the knee, to lack of muscular support around the artery and to the irregular distribution of pressure in this artery due to its curved course. One danger of aneurysm is the possibility of rupture, with fatal hemorrhage; another danger is that of choking to death from pressure on the trachea in aortic aneurysm.

In most of us as we grow older, the arteries undergo changes which we call *hardening of the arteries* (arteriosclerosis). A part of the difficulty is due to an excessive deposit of calcium in the arterial wall, and a decrease in elastic tissue. The changes in function which follow such changes in structure are disturbing.

In some patients the smooth muscle in the walls of small arteries of the fingers goes into spasmodic contraction whenever they are exposed to cold. This condition is called *Raynaud's disease*. In some patients, small blood vessels close, and this is called *Buerger's disease* or thromboangiitis obliterans. Whenever there is deprivation of blood supply to tissues, with no opportunity for collateral circulation, the tissues die. Death of tissues of a part of the body is called *gangrene*.

DISEASES OF THE VEINS

In individuals who stand a great deal of the time, such as teachers and salesladies, the valves of the leg veins seem to wear out and, eventually, are unable to resist the pressure of the long column of blood which they are called upon to support. In these instances, the superficial veins become tortuous and dilated, and we speak of them as *varicose veins*. Varicose veins may appear during pregnancy, due to the pressure in the pelvis which offers some interference with the return of blood from the lower extremities.

CATHETERIZATION OF THE HEART

When the heart of a human being is to be catheterized for purposes of diagnosis, the catheter is passed into the venous system through one of the superficial veins of the forearm (cephalic or basilic), and pushed along, under fluoroscopic guidance, until it enters the right ventricle or pulmonary artery. Then samples of blood may be withdrawn from the heart for analysis, and pressure relationships in the various parts of the right heart and the pulmonary artery can be determined. One of these superficial veins is selected for venipuncture, also, when blood is needed for ordinary chemical analysis. The one in the bend of the elbow is usually the easiest one to locate; you may not be able to see an accessible superficial vein in a patient who is well padded with fat.

Congenital Heart Disease. If the foramen ovale or the ductus arteriosus fail to close after birth, the child is said to have a *congenital heart*. If either opening fails to close after birth, some blood goes from the right side to the left side of the heart without going through the lungs, and the result is that the blood that is distributed to various organs by branches of the aorta is not fully oxygenated, as some of it has not gone though the lungs to pick up a new load of oxygen. When the blood is not saturated with oxygen, it assumes a different color due to the presence of so much unsaturated (or reduced) hemoglobin, and the skin assumes a bluish color called *cyanosis*. Often these little patients are called *blue babies*.

In some congenital heart patients there is a severe degree of

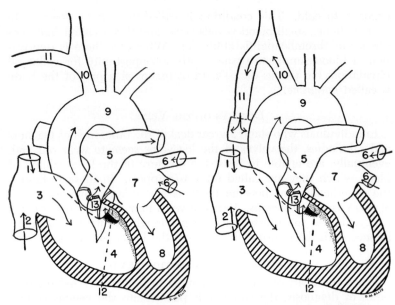

FIG. 274. Diagram of the cardiac and pulmonary circulation before, *left,* and after, *right,* the Blalock-Taussig operation. 1, superior
vena cava; 2, inferior vena cava; 3, right atrium; 4, right ventricle;
5, pulmonary artery, dividing into right and left branches; 6, left
pulmonary veins; 7, left atrium; 8, left ventricle; 9, aorta; 10, innominate artery; 11, right subclavian artery; 12, defect in interventricular
septum; 13, pulmonary stenosis. (*Right*) the anastomosis between
the right subclavian artery and the right branch of the pulmonary
artery is shown. (Redrawn and greatly simplified from Blalock, A.,
Hanlon, C. R., and Scott, H. W., Jr.: Surg., Gynec. & Obst. 87:386-
387)

pulmonary stenosis with inadequate circulation to the lungs. In
this type of malformation, in which the primary difficulty is lack
of circulation to the lungs, the Blalock-Taussig operation is of value.
This operation consists of joining the end of a systemic artery
(subclavian or innominate) with the side of the pulmonary artery.
This greatly increases the volume of blood which reaches the lungs
to be oxygenated. The arterial blood shows a great increase in
oxygen saturation after the operation. One patient whose arterial
oxygen saturation before operation was 36 per cent showed a
saturation of 81 per cent after the operation, but this is still below
the normal of about 98 per cent. The situation before and after
the Blalock-Taussig operation is shown in Figure 274.

The importance of cardiac catheterization in the diagnosis of various types of congenital heart disorders has been well established. It is a routine procedure in many hospitals. In addition to its importance in clinical medicine, cardiac catheterization has become equally important in the study of cardiovascular physiology in experimental laboratories. Another means of diagnosis in congenital heart disease is the injection of radiopaque material (Diodrast) and making x-ray pictures of the heart and the thoracic vessels. This is called *angiocardiography.*

CEREBRAL HEMORRHAGE

Of all the affections of the brain, hemorrhage is the most frequent. Hemorrhage from the meningeal vessels is usually due to injury; it may be under the dura (subdural) or outside the dura (extradural). Hemorrhage within the brain substance is usually due to arteriosclerosis. A sudden strain with a rise in blood pressure may rupture a weakened vessel. The vessels in the region of the basal ganglia are end arteries (no anastomoses), so that when one of them is ruptured the part of the brain supplied is deprived thereafter of blood and undergoes necrosis or death. The most common site of cerebral hemorrhage is the region of the internal capsule, and the artery that is ruptured most frequently is the lenticulostriate, which is called the *artery of cerebral hemorrhage.* Cerebral hemorrhage also is called *stroke* and *apoplexy.* Paralysis of one side of the body follows in its wake, if the patient survives.

Portal Obstruction. Obstruction of the portal system occurs fairly frequently. It may be due to tumors of the liver, enlargement of the gallbladder or back pressure in the inferior vena cava and the hepatic veins in valvular disease of the heart. As the obstruction increases, a collateral circulation is established between the hemorrhoidal and the inferior mesenteric veins and the gastric and the esophageal veins. The superficial abdominal veins around the umbilicus become prominent and form a radiating pattern that is called the *caput medusae.*

DISTURBANCES IN THE LYMPHATIC SYSTEM

Lymphadenitis is an inflammation of lymph nodes. The presence of an infection in almost any part of the body is accompanied by enlargement and tenderness of the lymph nodes which drain that region.

Lymphangitis is an inflammation of lymphatic vessels. When an infection is traveling along superficial lymphatic vessels the course may be evident by red streaks in the skin. This is dangerous, since it indicates that unless the infection is stopped, eventually the invading organism will reach the blood stream, and septicemia (blood poisoning) will ensue.

Elephantiasis is a condition that results when the lymph vessels become chronically inflamed and obstructed, leading to an enormous swelling of the blocked portion.

Leukemia. The lymphatic tissue may undergo malignant changes like carcinoma (cancer) elsewhere. When this occurs the number of lymphocytes in the blood is increased greatly, and the lymphatic tissue is hypertrophied.

SUMMARY

1. Heart
    A. Size and location
    B. Covering; pericardium: external serous and internal serous and outer fibrous
    C. Walls: myocardium, endocardium, epicardium or visceral pericardium
    D. Chambers of the heart: right atrium, left atrium, right ventricle and left ventricle
    E. Modified cardiac muscular tissue: sinu-atrial node, atrioventricular node, atrioventricular bundle, branches and Purkinje fibers; conducting tissue
    F. Blood supply: coronaries
    G. Nerve supply: afferent and efferent
2. Blood vessels
    A. Structure: arteries, veins, capillaries, sinusoids and arteriovenous anastomoses
3. General plan of the circulation
    A. Pulmonary circulation: to take up oxygen and give off carbon dioxide
    B. Systemic circulation: to give up oxygen and take up carbon dioxide
4. Pulmonary circulation
    A. Pulmonary artery: right and left branches; branches to each lobe of the lung
    B. Pulmonary capillaries
    C. Pulmonary veins: to left atrium
5. Systemic circulation
    A. Arteries of the systemic circuit: aorta and its branches
        a. Ascending aorta: coronary arteries

b. Arch of the aorta: innominate, left common carotid and left subclavian

(1) Innominate: right common carotid and right subclavian

(2) Each common carotid: external and internal carotid arteries. External carotid: superficial temporal and internal maxillary arteries; many small branches. Internal carotid arteries: many branches, end by dividing into middle and anterior cerebral arteries

(3) Subclavian: vertebral, internal mammary, costocervical trunk and thyrocervical trunk; becomes the axillary, brachial, ulnar and radial

c. Thoracic aorta: visceral and parietal branches

d. Abdominal aorta

(1) Visceral branches: celiac, superior mesenteric and inferior mesenteric; middle suprarenal, renal and internal spermatic or ovarian

(2) Parietal branches: inferior phrenic, lumbar and middle sacral arteries

e. Terminal branches: common iliac arteries

(1) Common iliac: hypogastric and external iliac

(A) Hypogastric to pelvis

(B) External iliac: femoral, popliteal, anterior and posterior tibial; dorsalis pedis

B. Veins of the systemic circuit

a. Coronary sinus and its tributaries

b. Superior vena cava and its tributaries

(1) Veins of the head and neck: cranial venous sinuses, internal jugular and external jugular

(2) Veins of the upper extremity. Superficial: cephalic and basilic. Deep: radial, ulnar and brachial. Axillary; subclavian; union of subclavian and internal jugular to form innominate

(3) Veins of the thorax which drain into superior vena cava

(4) Superior vena cava formed by union of right and left innominate veins. Opens into right atrium. Also receives the azygos vein. Azygos group: azygos, hemiazygos and accessory hemiazygos

c. Inferior vena cava and its tributaries

(1) Veins of the body wall below the diaphragm: inferior phrenic; lumbar veins

(2) Veins of the abdomen and pelvis

(A) Portal system: superior mesenteric and splenic; other tributaries

(B) Other veins of abdomen and pelvis: renal, suprarenal, spermatic or ovarian

(C) Veins of the lower extremity and pelvis: Superficial small saphenous and great saphenous. Deep: posterior tibial, anterior tibial, popliteal, femoral and external iliac to common iliac. Hypogastric receives blood from pelvis and adjacent structures

(D) Common iliac formed by union of hypogastric and external iliac

(E) Inferior vena cava formed by union of the two common iliac veins

C. Review of three circuits: coronary, that of the digestive system with portal vein, renal

6. Fetal circulation

A. Foramen ovale

B. Ductus arteriosus

C. Umbilical arteries

D. Umbilical vein

7. Lymphatic system

A. General plan; no pump; walls of lymphatic capillaries and lymph vessels

B. Arrangement of vessels: superficial and deep

C. Thoracic duct and its tributaries; right lymphatic duct

D. Lymphatic tissue: to filter tissue fluid, to filter lymph, and to filter blood

E. Spleen: location, structure, functions

F. Thymus gland: location, structure, functions unknown

SITUATION AND QUESTIONS

A. Heart disease is still one of the leading causes of death. Some abnormal conditions of the heart are:

(1) Mitral Stenosis. Stricture of the mitral valve prevents the easy flow of blood: _____ (a) from right atrium to right ventricle; _____ (b) from left atrium to left ventricle; _____ (c) from right ventricle through the pulmonary artery; _____ (d) from the left ventricle through the aorta.

(2) Bacterial endocarditis. This refers to an inflammation of: _____ (a) heart muscle; _____ (b) covering of the heart; _____ (c) lining of the heart; _____ (d) nodes and bundle.

(3) Ventricular hypertrophy. This means that: _____ (a) the

lower chambers of the heart are overdeveloped; _____(b) the lower chambers are wasted away; _____(c) the upper chambers of the heart are overdeveloped; _____(d) the upper chambers are underdeveloped.

(4) Angina pectoris. This occurs as a result of decreased blood supply to heart muscle. The blood vessels which supply heart muscle with blood are: _____(a) the vena cava; _____ (b) myocardial; _____(c) coronaries; _____(d) pulmonary veins.

B. Most patients being treated in hospitals for a "heart attack" receive nutrients intravenously. Trace a molecule of glucose after injection into the brachial veins until it is stored in the liver.

~~~~~~~~~~~~~~~~~~~~~~~~~~~~~~~~~~~~

11. Physiology of the Circulatory System

~~~~~~~~~~~~~~~~~~~~~~~~~~~~~~~~~~~~

INTRODUCTION

The pulmonary and the systemic circuits of the circulatory system are joined in series, and each has a pump. Each ventricle of the heart is comparable to a cylinder pump having a piston and intake and exhaust valves. The right ventricle pumps blood through the pulmonary circuit, which is short, and the blood is delivered in spurts under a small head of pressure to the lungs. The left ventricle pumps blood through the systemic circuit. Blood is delivered into the systemic arteries in spurts, under such great pressure that these arteries need strong, thick, distensible walls.

In spite of the intermittent delivery of blood into the large arteries, the flow must be even and steady through the capillaries to enable them to perform their functions. In order to convert the spurts of blood from the heart to a steady flow in the capillaries, the elastic tissue in the walls of large arteries is stretched with each ventricular contraction and undergoes recoil between beats.

At the end of ventricular contraction, the aortic semilunar valves close, and the elasticity of the large arteries comes into play and forces blood on into capillaries. The very high pressure in the large arteries, generated during contraction or systole of the left ventricle, is called the *systolic pressure*. The relatively high pressure in the arteries, maintained by stretched elastic tissue of arterial walls between contractions of the left ventricle (during relaxation or diastole of the ventricle), is called *diastolic pressure*. Diastolic pressure is maintained by the stretched elastic tissue of the arterial walls, which continues to exert its influence during relaxation of the ventricle.

There is great variation in the amount of blood required in different parts of the vascular system during activity and rest, so there must be a means of regulating the blood flow to suit the needs of each organ. The smooth muscle in the walls of the smallest arteries (arterioles) makes this possible. The degree of contraction of the smooth muscle, which determines the size of the lumens of the arterioles, is under the control of the nervous system. It is evident that this smooth muscle makes possible a graded contraction. The blood is under lower pressure than in the large arteries because of the resistance to flow in the small vessels, which have narrow lumens and thick walls. Therefore, there is great reduction in pressure in the arteriolar area, and the blood reaches the capillaries under very low pressure.

THE HEART

The sole function of the heart is to pump blood. The right ventricle pumps blood to the lungs where oxygen is taken up and carbon dioxide given off. The left ventricle pumps blood under great pressure into the already stretched systemic arteries. Much of the force of the left ventricular contraction is stored as potential energy in the stretched arterial walls. Then, during relaxation of the ventricle the stored energy is converted to kinetic energy by the decrease in size of the stretched walls, and this moves the blood along to the capillaries in a steady flow. The steady flow of blood under low pressure through the capillaries gives ample opportunity for the exchanges between blood and tissue fluid to take place. In this way the tissue fluid is kept fresh, with an abundant supply of oxygen and food, and accumulation of waste in it is prevented.

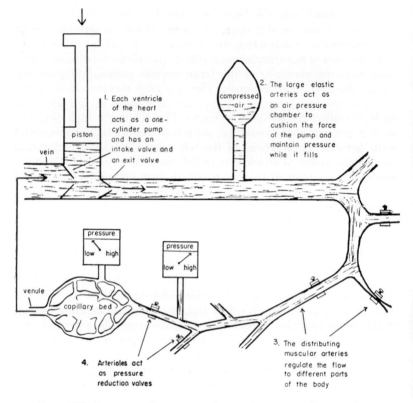

FIG. 275. Diagram illustrating the mechanics of the circulatory system. The ventricle is the pump. The large elastic arteries are distended further with each beat of the heart or stroke of the pump, and their elastic recoil between beats, while the pump refills, keeps arterial pressure high and forces blood onward. Arterioles, which can be regulated by vasomotor nerves, regulate the amount of blood flow to each organ, like reduction valves. The capillary bed receives blood all the time, for the flow of blood is steady in this part of the vascular system. Exchanges between the blood plasma and tissue fluid takes place through the capillary walls. The veins return blood to the pump. (From Ham, A. W.: Histology, ed. 2, Philadelphia, Lippincott)

In other words, homeostasis is maintained by means of the circulating blood, and flow of blood to various organs is regulated in accordance with the need. The general plan of the circulatory system is illustrated by diagram in Figure 275.

PROPERTIES OF THE HEART MUSCLE

Extensibility. This property of heart muscle makes it possible for the heart to dilate enough to receive the blood as it enters from the veins. As the heart fills with blood its fibers are stretched, and, as was found in both skeletal and smooth muscle, when muscle fibers are stretched the contraction is more forceful. The better the heart fills, which means the greater the diastolic volume of the ventricle, the more forceful is the beat. This occurs so consistently that it is called *Starling's law of the heart* (so called because it was first described by Dr. Starling).

Rhythmic Contractility. This property is highly developed in cardiac muscle. It is inherent in the muscle, which means that the heart beats rhythmically independently of nerves. If a heart is removed from the body and kept under proper conditions, it will beat for a long time. In an embryo, the heart begins to beat long before any nerves have grown out to it, which is additional proof that the beat is independent of nerves. A third proof of the "myogenic" origin of the heart beat is the fact that fragments of heart muscle that are growing in tissue cultures beat rhythmically.

In order to keep a heart beating rhythmically, it must be bathed by a "balanced" solution of sodium, potassium and calcium chlorides. If the solution is not balanced properly a frog's heart will soon stop beating; likewise, if the salts in one's plasma are not in proper balance, the activity of the heart is altered. As a routine practice, the action current of the heart is recorded and examined when it is necessary to give potassium chloride by vein in order to decide if the amount given is correct. If too little or too much potassium is given, the change in activity of the heart serves to indicate a lack of balance of these 3 essential chlorides in the plasma.

Refractory Periods. The *absolute* refractory period is the time during which an excitable tissue will not respond to any stimulus,

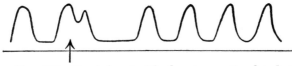

FIG. 276. Frog's heart. The heart was stimulated at the time indicated by the arrow. A premature systole (contraction) followed; the next diastole (relaxation) was of longer duration than usual. This long rest period is called the compensatory pause.

no matter how strong the latter is. The absolute refractory period is very long for heart muscle, since it lasts throughout systole. Because of the long absolute refractory period, no summation or tetanic contractions are possible in heart muscle. This is an excellent protection, since the heart would be worthless as a pump if it went into a tetanic or sustained contraction.

When the absolute refractory period is over, the *relative* refractory period begins, and the heart gradually recovers its excitability. The relative refractory period coincides with the early diastolic period of the ventricle. A strong stimulus given at this time can cause a contraction before the next rhythmic contraction is due. The early beat is smaller in amplitude than a regular beat and is called a *premature systole*. Thus, it is possible to make a beat appear ahead of time, by applying a strong stimulus early in diastole.

A premature systole is followed by a longer diastole, to compensate for its lack of rest after the previous beat. The long diastole is called a *compensatory pause*. Such a pause, following a premature beat is illustrated in Figure 276.

An occasional premature beat is of frequent occurrence in the human heart. The cause is not known, but it is some stimulus within the heart muscle itself. The premature beat is small and passes unnoticed, but the individual is conscious of the compensatory pause and says, "My heart has just skipped a beat." The heart does not skip a beat, but the premature contraction is not recognized, and only the compensatory pause comes to the attention. This is the most frequent irregularity that you will encounter when you count patients' pulses.

The All-or-None Law. This refers to the fact that if a heart beats, it gives the strongest contraction that is possible under the conditions existing at that moment. There is no such thing as "gradation" in heart beats, as is possible in skeletal muscle contractions. In skeletal muscle it is possible to have different numbers of motor units active, but in the heart the muscle mass of the atria is one unit and that of the ventricles is a second unit, due to the branching and the interlacing of the muscle fibers.

In order to illustrate the above fundamental fact about heart muscle in the laboratory, it is necessary to have a quiescent ventricle. This means that only the lower portion of the ventricle of a frog's heart is retained and arranged for stimulation and recording. The strength of the stimulus is increased, and the resulting contractions are recorded. No matter how greatly the stimulus is increased, the height of contraction always is the same (Fig. 124).

This is in striking contrast to skeletal muscle, in which an increase in the strength of the stimulus brings more motor units into activity and a greater contraction follows.

Electrical Change. Every contraction of the heart is accompanied by an electrical change which we call an *action current.* Action currents due to heart beats are sufficiently strong to be led off from the surface of the skin to a galvanometer in an instrument called an electrocardiograph. The action current causes a movement of the string of the galvanometer. This movement is photographed, and the record is called an *electrocardiogram.* This is a valuable method of studying the human heart in a living subject.

CONDUCTING SYSTEM

In order to work efficiently, certain events of the heart must follow each other in orderly sequence. The atrioventricular bundle is of great importance (Fig. 277) since it is the only muscular connection or functional bridge between the atrial and the ventricular muscle masses.

The heart beat begins in the sinu-atrial node, which is called the *pacemaker* of the heart. The beat spreads from the sinu-atrial node directly through atrial muscle over the branching fibers, causing the entire mass of both atria to contract simultaneously.

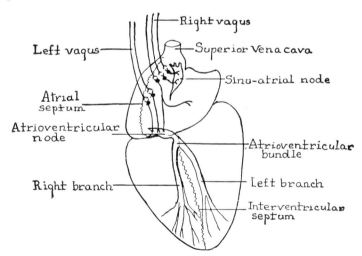

FIG. 277. Conducting system. Diagram showing relations of the sinu-atrial node and the atrioventricular node, bundle and its branches.

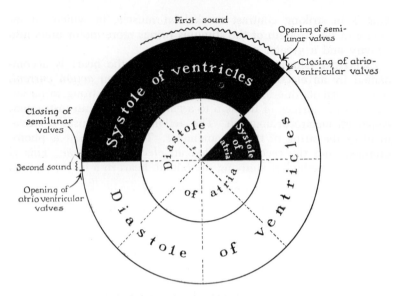

Motion Counterclockwise

Fig. 278. Cardiac cycle. The heart rate represented in the diagram is 75 beats per minute; each cycle lasts 8/10 of a second; each sector represents 1/10 second. The inner circle represents the atria; atrial systole lasts 1/10 second, and atrial diastole, 7/10 second. The outer circle represents the ventricles; ventricular systole lasts 3/10 second, and diastole, 5/10 second. The atrioventricular valves close at the beginning of ventricular systole; the semilunar valves open shortly thereafter. The latter valves close at the beginning of ventricular diastole, and the atrioventricular valves open shortly thereafter. The first sound is due to the closing of the atrioventricular valves and systole of the ventricle; the second sound is due to the closing of the semilunar valves; it is of shorter duration than the first.

The beat reaches the atrioventricular node, is conducted very slowly over the node and the atrioventricular bundle and its branches, through the Purkinje network and then to ventricular muscle. In the muscle it spreads rapidly from fiber to fiber, throughout the mass of both ventricles, causing them to contract simultaneously. The slight delay in conduction over the bundle and its branches permits enough time for the atria to complete their contraction before the ventricles begin to contract.

CARDIAC CYCLE

Figure 278 illustrates the events that occur during one heart beat or cardiac cycle. The rate indicated in the diagram is 75 beats per minute, which means that each beat lasts eight tenths of a second. Each sector in the diagram is equal to one tenth of a second. The inner circle represents the events that occur in the atria, and the outer circle represents the ventricular events. Systole is shown in black. Atrial systole lasts one tenth of a second, and diastole seven tenths of a second. In other words, the atria work one tenth and rest seven tenths of each cycle. Ventricular systole lasts three tenths of a second, and diastole five tenths, which means that the ventricles work three tenths and rest five tenths of each cycle. The entire heart rests four tenths of a second, and the period during which both atria and ventricles are relaxed is called *diastasis*.

PRESSURE CHANGES IN THE HEART

The amount of blood along with the pressure exerted by it varies in the cardiac chambers at different times in the cardiac cycle. The valves of the heart are inert structures which are opened and closed only because of differences in pressure exerted by the blood on their two surfaces.

Let us begin with the moment at the end of ventricular systole, when the atria are relatively full of blood and the atrioventricular valves are still closed, and trace the events step by step. As the blood continues to enter the atria from the veins, the pressure in the atria soon exceeds that in the relaxed ventricles, and the atrioventricular valves open due to the greater pressure on the atrial surface of the leaflets.

When the atrioventricular valves open, blood flows into the ventricles rapidly, and the atrioventricular valve leaflets float in midstream, getting into a proper position for closing. The 2 atria contract simultaneously and pump the blood remaining in them into the ventricles, and ventricular systole begins.

As soon as the ventricles begin to contract, the atrioventricular valves close, due to the increasing pressure on the ventricular surface of their leaflets. The leaflets are kept from being pushed up into the atria, like an umbrella being prevented from turning inside out, by the contraction of the papillary muscles, which hold the chordae tendineae taut.

Ventricular systole continues with a very sharp rise in intraventricular pressure, until it becomes great enough to force the semilunar valves open. The extent to which the pressure rises to accomplish this varies in the two ventricles. The pressure in the right ventricle rises to only about one sixth that of the left ventricle, since the pressure in the pulmonary artery is only about one sixth that in the aorta, and the intraventricular pressure forces the valves to open simultaneously as soon as the pressure in the corresponding artery is exceeded.

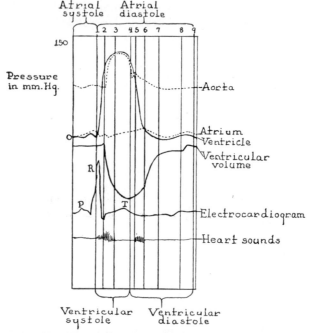

Fig. 279. Diagram showing pressure changes in atrium, ventricle and aorta. The opening and closing of the valves is indicated. A single cycle is shown. The atrioventricular valves close at the moment the ventricular pressure exceeds that of the atrium, just beyond line 1, and open at 6, when the ventricular pressure falls below atrial pressure. The semilunar valves open just before line 2, when the ventricular pressure rises above aortic pressure, and close at 5, when the ventricular pressure drops below aortic pressure. Below the pressure diagram, the changes in the ventricular volume, the main waves of the electrocardiogram and the time of the cardiac sounds are indicated.

As soon as the semilunar valves are open, the ventricles begin to empty, the right into the pulmonary artery and the left into the aorta. Ventricular systole continues for about three tenths of a second, during which most of the blood is pumped out. With the onset of ventricular diastole, the intraventricular pressure falls rapidly.

As soon as the pressure in the right ventricle falls below that in the pulmonary artery and that in the left ventricle falls below the pressure in the aorta, the blood tends to come back into the ventricles as well as to go forward. The backward flow closes the semilunar valves. The elasticity of the large arteries then comes into play and forces the blood onward.

Meanwhile, the atria have been filling with blood coming in from the veins. As the ventricular diastole continues, the pressure within the ventricles falls below that of the atria, and the atrioventricular valves open, and the cardiac cycle begins over again. The above events are repeated over and over with each beat, as long as you live.

Figure 279 illustrates the events that occur in a single cycle in the left heart; those for the right heart are exactly the same, so far as time relation goes, but the pressure in the pulmonary artery and the right ventricle are lower than in the aorta and the left ventricle, respectively. By studying the diagram, it is easy to follow the changes in atrial pressure, ventricular pressure and the relation between the pressure in the ventricle and the aorta.

The opening and the closing of the valves are indicated in Figures 278 and 279. You should study valvular action in connection with pressure changes in order to understand it clearly. The sole function of the valves is to keep blood flowing in an onward direction. When the atrioventricular valves close at the beginning of ventricular systole, they prevent the passage of blood from the ventricles, back into the atria. When the semilunar valves are forced open early in ventricular systole, they allow blood to flow from left ventricle into the aorta (or from right ventricle into the pulmonary artery). When ventricular systole is completed, the semilunar valves are closed because the elasticity of the large arteries tends to force blood in both directions, and that which flows back toward the heart closes the semilunar valves. Blood enters the right atrium from the great veins and the coronary sinus throughout ventricular systole and diastasis. When ventricular diastole occurs, the pressure in the ventricle falls, and the weight of blood in the atrium forces the atrioventricular valves to open, and blood enters the ventricle. Similar changes occur in the left atrium and the left ventricle.

HEART SOUNDS

If you listen (auscultate) with a stethoscope over the heart you will hear two sounds with each heart beat. The first is longer and louder than the second and sounds like "lubb"; it is due to the closure of the atrioventricular valves and contraction of the mass of ventricular muscle. The second sound is shorter and softer and is due to the closure of the semilunar valves; it sounds like "dup." The time in the cycle in which each sound is heard is indicated in Figures 278 and 279.

CARDIAC OUTPUT

Each ventricle pumps out about 70 cc. of blood at each beat. This is called the *stroke volume.* In a trained athlete, the amount can be increased to as much as 140 cc. during exercise.

If the stroke volume is multiplied by the number of beats per minute, one arrives at the "minute volume" or cardiac output. For example, if the stroke volume is 70 and the rate 70, the cardiac output is 4,900 cc. or 4.9 L. This is an average value during rest. During exercise, with a stroke volume of 140 and a rate of 120, the cardiac output increases to 16,800 cc. or 16.8 L. Healthy, trained individuals, such as young athletes, have enormous reserve power in their hearts. A physician can get a fair idea of the condition of one's heart by the way it responds to exercise, that is, by the increase in heart rate during a standard exercise, and the length of time it takes for the rate to return to normal after the exercise is over.

The cardiac output varies during many physiologic activities and in disease. Its determination in clinical laboratories is becoming more and more frequent. Many methods are now available by which this information can be obtained in a living, unanesthetized person.

VARIATIONS IN HEART RATE

Size. The heart rate is influenced by many factors, of which exercise is only one. The size of the individual influences the rate; the larger the size, the slower the heart rate. This is true also of animals and is shown by the following examples: elephants, below 20; rabbits, 150; and mice, 700 beats per minute.

Sex has an influence on heart rate. Women have rates between 70 and 80, men between 65 and 70.

Age is another factor in determining heart rate. In the fetus the rate is between 120-160; in the infant, 110-130; in the child, 72-92; and in adults, 65-80.

Other Factors. Many other factors affect the heart rate. It is faster after meals. It is faster in the standing position than when lying down. Emotional crises and excitement are accompanied by fast heart rates. Epinenephrine causes the heart to beat faster and also strengthens its beat. An increase in the amount of thyroid hormone in the blood speeds up the heart rate. When the body temperature rises, as during fever, the heart rate is faster.

NERVE SUPPLY OF THE HEART

Efferent Supply. The nerves that supply the heart are important in adjusting the rate to meet changing body needs. There is

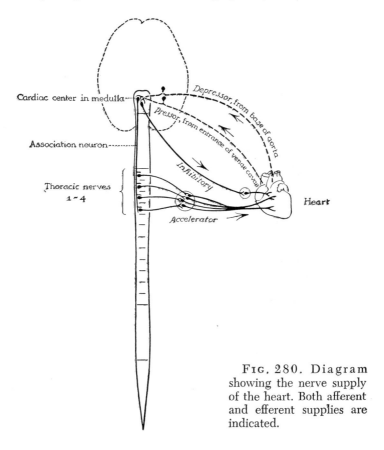

FIG. 280. Diagram showing the nerve supply of the heart. Both afferent and efferent supplies are indicated.

a double efferent nerve supply from the autonomic division of the nervous system. One efferent supply is derived from the cranial autonomic or parasympathetic division, by way of the vagus nerves. The synapses are in terminal ganglia, upon or within the heart muscle. Postganglionic vagal fibers supply the sinu-atrial and the atrioventricular nodes and the atrial muscle; no vagal fibers supply ventricular muscle. Stimulation of the vagus nerves slows the heart and weakens the atrial contractions or may even stop the heart completely in experimental animals. The cessation of the heart following stimulation of the right vagus nerve was the first example noted of an "inhibitory" nerve; that is, one which stopped activity. The vagus nerves to the heart are in tonic activity, which means that impulses are passing continuously to the heart from the center in the medulla. If the vagus nerves, which maintain a slow rate, are cut, the heart beats much faster than when the nerves are intact.

The other efferent supply to the heart is from the thoracic division of the autonomic or sympathetic nervous system. The preganglionic fibers arise from the upper thoracic region of the spinal cord and extend to the lateral chain of autonomic ganglia, where the synapses are located. The postganglionic fibers supply all parts of the heart; that is, nodes, bundle and muscle of atria and ventricles. Stimulation of the thoracic fibers causes the heart to beat faster and also strengthens its beat. Consequently, these are called the *augmentor* nerves of the heart. Figure 280 is a diagram of the nerve supply of the heart.

Afferent Supply. There is also an afferent nerve supply to the heart. The receptors are located in the heart muscle and in the pericardium. Afferent fibers carry impulses from these receptors to the central nervous system. The only sensation that may be aroused by impulses from the heart is that of pain. Whenever there is interference with the blood flow in the coronary arteries, a sensation of pain is experienced. This signifies that the muscle is not receiving the necessary amount of oxygen. Inflammation of the pericardium gives rise to pain.

Of less importance clinically, but of great importance throughout the activities of one's life, are afferent impulses from receptors at the base of the aorta, in the carotid sinuses and in the great veins and atria. These receptors are sensitive to sudden changes in pressure of the blood bathing them and are called *pressorecep-tors* or *baroceptors*.

When there is a sudden increase in blood pressure, the pressoreceptors are stimulated, and impulses are sent to the central nervous system. These arouse reflexes that adjust the heart rate and the size of the blood vessels in such a manner that the blood pressure is restored to the previous level.

Cardiac Center. There is a cardiac center in the medulla, and it consists of cardio-inhibitory and cardio-augmentor portions. The former establishes connections with the vagus (inhibitory) nerves, and the latter with the neurons in the upper thoracic region of the spinal cord that give rise to the augmentor nerves.

The afferent impulses that are aroused by sudden changes in blood pressure in the aorta, the carotid sinuses, the great veins and the atria reach the cardiac center, and reflex regulation of both the rate and the strength of the beat are mediated or handled here. This arrangement makes possible an automatic regulation for keeping the activity of the heart and the blood pressure within normal ranges (another example of homeostasis).

If the cardiac center is affected by impulses that come to it by way of other afferent nerves, reflexes which can be called *incidental* are aroused. For example, you can see or hear something that produces a marked change in your heart rate and blood pressure. These changes are temporary, and the usual heart rate and blood pressure are restored by the reflexes originating in the sensitive receptors near the heart.

BLOOD PRESSURE

Blood pressure refers to the force exerted by the blood against the walls of the blood vessels. It varies in different parts of the system. Blood pressure is expressed in terms of millimeters of mercury (above atmospheric pressure, which is 760 mm. Hg). For example, if one's blood pressure is said to be 100 mm. Hg, it really means 860. If the pressure in the blood vessels were not above atmospheric pressure, air would enter, instead of blood leaving, whenever vessels are severed.

Since there are 3 types of blood vessels in the vascular system, there are 3 "blood pressures" to be considered. These are arterial, capillary and venous pressures.

Arterial blood pressure is the pressure against the walls of the arteries and, as you would anticipate, it varies with the cardiac cycle. It averages 110 mm. Hg, during *systole*, in the brachial artery in young adults. During *diastole* the pressure falls to between 65 and 75 mm. Hg. Therefore, we speak of systolic and diastolic arterial pressures, and we write the systolic above the diastolic, in this manner: 110/75.

The difference between systolic and diastolic arterial blood pres-

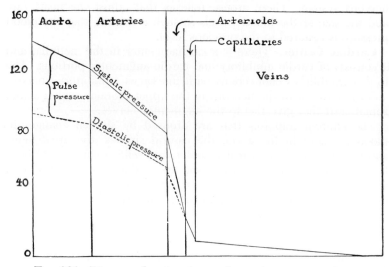

Fig. 281. Diagram showing the gradient of pressure in the various parts of the vascular system, between the aorta and the great veins. The gradient is steepest in the arterioles. The pulse pressure disappears as the capillaries are reached.

sure is called the *pulse pressure,* and it is usually between 25 and 40 mm. Hg. In the recumbent position, arterial blood pressure is highest in the large arteries near the heart. However, in the standing position the pressure in the dorsalis pedis arteries may be 100 mm. Hg higher than it is in the brachial arteries, due to the weight of the column of blood above; while in the recumbent position the pressures are equal in the brachial and the dorsalis pedis arteries.

Capillary blood pressure is the force exerted by the blood against the walls of the capillaries. It is about 32 mm. Hg at the arterial end of the capillaries and 12 at the venous end. The importance of the capillary blood pressure (hydrostatic) is discussed in relation to the production of tissue fluid on page 401. It is the driving force in filtration through capillary walls.

Venous blood pressure, or the force exerted by the blood against the walls of veins, decreases from 12 mm. Hg at the beginning of the smallest veins to zero (atmospheric pressure) in the great veins near the heart. Venous pressure increases in patients who are suffering from "heart failure" and is of great clinical interest in this condition.

The gradient of pressure in different parts of the vascular system is illustrated by diagram in Figure 281. It is evident that the most marked fall of pressure occurs in the smallest arteries or arterioles.

Factors Involved in the Maintenance of Arterial Blood Pressure

Several factors are involved in the maintenance of arterial blood pressure at its usual high level. These are the rate and the force of the heart beat, the elasticity of large arteries, the peripheral resistance, the quantity of blood in the vascular system in relation to the capacity and the viscosity of the blood.

Rate and Force. The faster the rate of the heart's beats and the greater its force of contraction, the higher the arterial pressure will be. The heart is the pump, and if it changes, the pressure in the system is bound to change. A decrease in the rate or force of the beat of the heart leads to a lowering of the arterial blood pressure.

Elasticity of the large arteries is responsible for the maintenance of arterial blood pressure between beats of the heart or diastolic pressure. Elasticity keeps the flow steady from the arteries into the capillaries. If the large arteries lose their elasticity the pressure is unusually high during systole and falls to a low level during diastole, which means that the pulse pressure is greater than usual. With rigid arteries, the flow into the capillaries is intermittent,

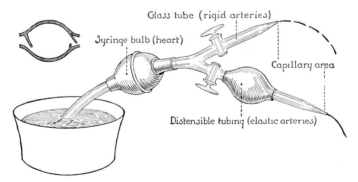

Fig. 282. Diagram to show the effects of elastic vessels. If the vessels were rigid, as in the glass tube, the blood flow would be intermittent. Since the vessels are elastic, as in the bulb, the flow is continuous. The recoil of the vessels keeps the blood flowing between beats of the heart. (Adapted from Howell)

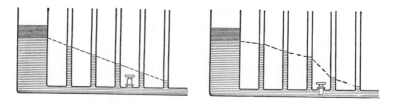

FIG. 283. Diagram of pressure conditions in the vascular system. (*Left*) A direct fall in pressure is noted with increase in distance from the reservoir. (*Right*) The effect of increasing the peripheral resistance (vasoconstriction) is shown. The screw represents the arteriolar area. On constriction, the pressure rises on the arterial side and falls on the venous side. (Redrawn from Howell)

coming in spurts with each ventricular systole and ceasing during diastole.

Normally, the force or energy of ventricular systole is expended in two ways: (1) it moves blood along into capillaries during systole, which requires kinetic energy, and (2) it is stored as potential energy by stretching the walls of the large elastic arteries. The latter energy (potential) is converted to kinetic energy to keep the blood flowing from arteries into capillaries during diastole, as the elasticity of the large arteries comes into play. Figure 282 illustrates the steady flow in an elastic system in contrast with the intermittent flow in rigid tubes.

Peripheral resistance refers to the resistance offered by arterioles to the flow of blood. By offering resistance to flow, arterioles maintain a high pressure behind them in the larger arteries and a lower pressure in front of them in the veins. It has been stated by one author that they "act as nozzles that gently spray blood into the capillary beds."

The amount of resistance to flow varies with the size of the lumens of the arterioles. If the lumens are wide there is little resistance to flow. In this case the pressure on the arterial side becomes lower and that on the venous side higher than usual. If the lumens are narrow, the arterioles offer more resistance to the flow of blood, and in this case the pressure on the arterial side becomes higher and that on the venous side lower than before.

The arteriolar region of the vascular system may be thought of as a reducing valve or screw in the outflow tube, as indicated in Figure 283. The size of the lumens of the arterioles, which really means the peripheral resistance, is controlled reflexly by nerves which supply the smooth muscle in the walls of the arterioles (vasomotor nerves). Peripheral resistance is very high in individuals who have high blood pressure or hypertension.

By the time the blood enters the venules from the capillaries, it exerts very little pressure on the walls of the veins. This means that the force imparted to it by the heart and the elasticity of the walls of the large arteries is almost spent.

Quantity of blood in the vascular system in relation to the capacity of the system is exceedingly important. If a considerable amount of blood is lost suddenly by hemorrhage, the blood pressure falls. Any condition in which the amount of blood is small compared with the capacity of the system is called *oligemia*. The walls of the arteries are not put on stretch, and the supply to the vital organs, such as the heart and the brain, is not sufficient to maintain homeostasis.

An increase in the amount of blood in the vascular system is called *plethora*. The pressure is high as long as plethora persists.

Whenever the quantity of blood is altered, protective mechanisms are brought into action as a result of the attempt to maintain the arterial blood pressure at the usual level. The heart rate is faster, and the arterioles are markedly constricted after blood is lost.

Viscosity of blood is due to the presence of erythrocytes and plasma proteins. If the number of erythrocytes is increased, in proportion to the plasma, the viscosity in increased, and the blood pressure is higher. This is noted in polycythemia vera, in which there is a very high erythrocyte count. If the number of erythrocytes is decreased, as in anemia, the viscosity is low, and the arterial blood pressure is below the average.

If the concentration of plasma proteins is low the blood pressure is low. If albumin solutions are injected, viscosity increases, and blood pressure rises.

METHOD OF MEASURING ARTERIAL BLOOD PRESSURE

Frequently, nurses are called upon to measure arterial blood pressure. The instrument used is called a *sphygmomanometer*. In order to measure blood pressure, a wide elastic cuff, enclosed in nonextensible material, is placed around the arm above the elbow. The nonextensible material is fastened snugly in place to hold the elastic cuff. By means of a bulb air is pumped into the elastic cuff, putting pressure on the arm. Sufficient pressure is applied to compress the brachial artery. This shuts off the blood flow to the portion of the upper extremity distal to the cuff.

The elastic cuff has a second outlet; this leads to a glass tube which contains mercury. The mercury rises in the tube as air is pumped into the cuff. Along the side of the tube in which the mercury rises is a scale ruled in millimeters. The distance to which the mercury rises indicates the amount of pressure necessary to stop the flow of blood in the forearm.

When the brachial artery has been compressed completely, the air is slowly released from the cuff by means of a valve on the bulb. As the air is released, a point is reached (indicated by a sound) at which the pressure of the blood in the artery is just equal to that of the air in the cuff. Below this point the blood pressure exceeds the air pressure in the cuff, and blood begins to flow into the forearm again. The principle is shown by diagram in Figure 284.

One listens for sounds over the course of the brachial artery with a stethoscope. The bell is placed just below the bend in the elbow.

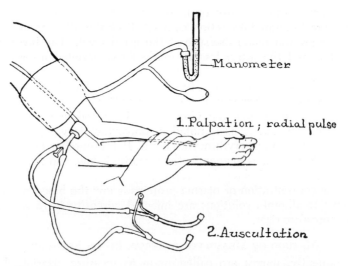

FIG. 284. Various methods of estimating the blood pressure. 1. By palpation; the cuff is inflated until the pulse can no longer be felt at the wrist. Air is released from the cuff until the pulse returns. The pressure at which the pulse can first be felt is taken as the systolic pressure. The auscultation method, 2, is described in the text and shown in Fig. 285. The palpation method is less satisfactory than the auscultatory method. (After Harris)

As the pressure is being released in the cuff, a sound is audible with each heart beat; blood is flowing through the partially compressed artery. The first sound heard indicates the systolic or highest pressure; the height of the column of mercury is noted as the sound is heard. As the air is released gradually, changes in the sounds are heard. No sound is heard when the pressure is released sufficiently to relieve the compression of the artery; therefore, the pressure at the disappearance of the sound equals diastolic pressure. The method of taking the blood pressure is illustrated in Figure 285.

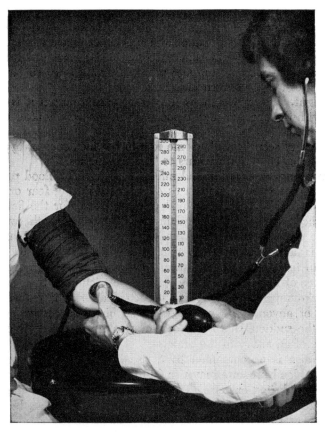

FIG. 285. Method of taking blood pressure by auscultation.

Systolic blood pressure is influenced by many factors, such as age, weight, heredity, emotions and exercise.

Age. So far as age is concerned, newborn babies have blood pressures which average 55/40. By the end of the first month the pressures have reached 80/50, and then the pressures rise slowly during childhood and reach the adult level at the age of puberty. Blood pressure may remain at the same level until an individual reaches 50 or 60 years of age, or may rise at any time if changes occur in the walls of large arteries (hardening or arteriosclerosis).

Walls of arteries deteriorate earlier than walls of veins. The arterial walls are under constant tension and are not really well supplied with blood. The capillaries which supply arterial walls collapse when the walls are stretched (which is practically all of the time), and the lymphatic drainage is not efficient. It is often said that a man is "as old as his arteries." This means that if arterial walls are damaged by the age of 30, the man is 70 so far as his blood pressure is concerned.

Weight. Excess weight is important because often it is associated with the onset of high blood pressure, especially after the age of 40 years.

Heredity seems to play some role in the incidence of hypertension, as this condition appears to "run in families."

Emotions have a profound influence on systolic blood pressure, which may increase as much as 40 mm. Hg during fear or anger. If a patient is having his blood pressure taken for the first time, the procedure should be explained to him briefly, otherwise the systolic pressure may be elevated due to fear. In emotional crises there is an outpouring of epinephrine, and two of its effects serve to increase blood pressure: (1) an increase in the rate and the force of the heart beat and (2) a constriction of the arterioles. A quick-tempered person with hardened arteries is really at the mercy of anyone who wishes to make him lose his temper, because the sudden, sharp increase in systolic pressure may cause a rupture of an artery in the brain.

Exercise is accompanied by a rise in arterial blood pressure. Systolic blood pressure may rise 60 to 70 mm. Hg (above the resting level) during exercise. There is great danger in running for a bus or carrying out a short bout of exercise if one has hardened arteries, as there may be rupture of one of the diseased arteries when the pressure within them increases.

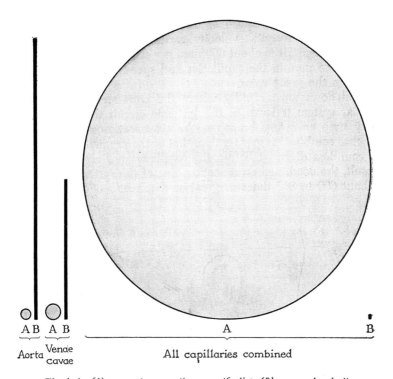

AB A B   A   B

Aorta Venae   All capillaries combined
       cavae

The circles (A) represent cross section area; the lines (B) represent velocity

FIG. 286. Comparative velocities and cross-section areas in different parts of the vascular system. In the aorta, where the cross-section area is small, the velocity is most rapid. In the venae cavae, the cross-section area is about twice as great as it is in the aorta, and the velocity is about half as rapid. In the capillaries, the combined cross-section area is from 600 to 800 times as great as it is in the aorta, and the velocity is correspondingly slowed.

VELOCITY OF BLOOD FLOW

The distance that a particle of blood travels in a given time is called the *velocity* or speed of the blood flow. It is expressed in millimeters per second. Velocity varies in different parts of the vascular system. It is about 300 mm. per second in the aorta, slows down to 0.5 mm. in the capillaries and speeds up to 150 mm. per second in the great veins.

Blood flows most rapidly where the cross-section area of the vascular system is least; in the systemic circuit this is the aorta. Every time an artery branches, the cross-section area of its two branches combined is greater than that of the original vessel. There are countless divisions before the capillaries are reached, and, as a result, the combined cross-section area of the systemic capillaries is about 600 to 800 times as great as the cross-section area of the

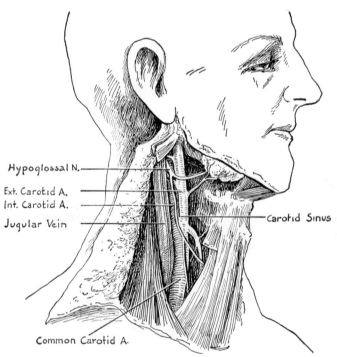

Hypoglossal N.

Ext. Carotid A.
Int. Carotid A.

Jugular Vein

Carotid Sinus

Common Carotid A.

Fig. 287. Carotid sinus; the glossopharyngeal nerve is not shown.

aorta. Therefore, the blood flows only 1/600 to 1/800 as fast as in the aorta (1/600 × 300 = ½ mm.). The combined cross-section area of the superior and the inferior venae cavae is about twice that of the aorta, and the speed of blood flow is half as fast. The relationship between cross-section area and velocity in different parts of the vascular system is illustrated in Figure 286.

Circulation time depends on velocity of blood flow. It is the time required for a particle of blood to start in the right atrium, go through the pulmonary circuit to the left heart, then through the systemic circuit and back to the right atrium. It takes about 23 seconds for the round trip. This means that it takes about 27 heart beats to drive a given unit of blood around the two circuits.

Arterial Pulse

The arterial pulse is a wave of distention or expansion and recoil which sweeps over the arterial system with each systole of the left ventricle. The pulse wave grows weaker as it passes over the arterial system and disappears completely in the capillaries. The pulse wave travels rapidly, at a rate of 6 to 9 m. per second. It reaches the periphery before the blood which was pumped from the left ventricle at the same time. In other words, we feel the wave of distention in the wall of the radial artery due to ejection of blood before that blood gets out of the aorta.

Since the arterial pulse is indicative of the action of the heart, its rate and characteristics are noted several times a day on hospitalized patients. In counting the pulse, place the fingertips over the artery, press lightly and note the waves of distention. Never use your thumb in taking a patient's pulse, as you have a pulse in your own thumb and you may be counting that instead of the patient's pulse. Instead of taking the arterial pulse, you may count the rate of the heart by stethoscope over the cardiac area. Two sounds are heard for each beat.

Venous Pulse

The pulse dies out in the capillaries and is absent in the peripheral veins. However, in the large veins near the heart, a venous pulse is noted. This is called the *central venous pulse,* and it is due to the pressure changes which are reflected from the right atrium. By using suitable apparatus, the central venous pulse may be recorded, and it gives the same type of information as the electrocardiogram in some cardiac disorders. You can see the pulse in the external jugular vein of some individuals.

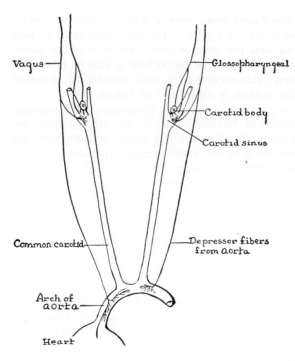

Vagus

Glossopharyngeal

Carotid body

Carotid sinus

Common carotid

Depressor fibers from aorta

Arch of aorta

Heart

Fig. 288. Innervation of the base of the aorta, the carotid sinus and the carotid body. Glossopharyngeal and vagus nerves are shown. Depressor fibers are those whose stimulation leads to a reflex fall in blood pressure. (After Heymans)

NERVE SUPPLY TO BLOOD VESSELS

All 3 types of blood vessels are supplied with both afferent and efferent nerves.

Afferent Supply. The most important afferent fibers are those whose endings (receptors) are in the walls of the aortic arch and the carotid sinuses. The carotid sinus is an expansion of the internal carotid artery near its origin and contains pressoreceptors or baroceptors which are affected by sudden changes in arterial blood pressure within the vessel. The location of the carotid sinus is shown in Figure 287, and a diagram of its nerve supply in Figure 288. The afferent fibers from the carotid sinuses travel to the central nervous system with the glossopharyngeal nerves, and those from the aortic arch travel with the vagus nerves. Impulses from these regions are very important in the regulation of the circulation.

Efferent Supply. The efferent nerves which supply the smooth muscle of blood vessel walls are called *vasomotor nerves*. There are 2 classes of vasomotor nerves: (1) vasoconstrictor and (2) vasodilator nerves.

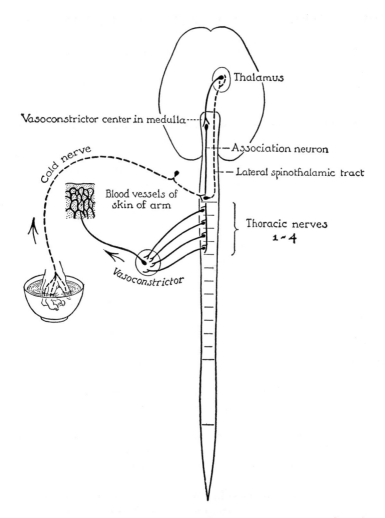

FIG. 289. Diagram of pathway of a vasoconstrictor impulse. As the hand is immersed in cold water, the cold nerve endings are stimulated. An impulse travels to the spinal cord, and is relayed on to the thalamus. An internuncial neuron transmits the impulse to the vasoconstrictor center in the medulla; a second internuncial neuron transmits the impulse from the center to the cells in the upper thoracic region of the spinal cord. The impulse is relayed to a cell in a lateral ganglion, and, then it passes to the smooth muscular tissue in the wall of the blood vessels. The vessels become smaller, and, thereby, decrease the loss of heat from the skin. Thus, reflex vasoconstriction follows exposure to cold.

VASOCONSTRICTOR NERVES make the lumens of blood vessels smaller. They are especially abundant in the arterioles of the skin and the abdominal viscera. The main control of peripheral resistance is mediated by variations in the degree of contraction of the muscular coats of arterioles. Vasoconstrictor fibers are derived from the thoracolumbar division of the autonomic system and are under the control of a vasoconstrictor center in the medulla. The pathway of an impulse from the center in the medulla to a blood vessel in the skin of the arm is indicated in Figure 289. The constriction of the blood vessel in the illustration is a reflex response to stimulation of cold receptors in the skin of the hand.

The vasoconstrictor center is in tonic activity, which means that it is constantly sending impulses to the smooth muscles in the walls of the arterioles to keep them relatively constricted and the arterial blood pressure high. If the vasoconstrictor nerves are inhibited, the arterioles relax, and the blood pressure falls due to the reduction in peripheral resistance. When vasoconstrictor activity is increased, there is a rise in blood pressure due to increase in peripheral resistance.

VASODILATOR NERVES are those which make lumens of arterioles wider or cause active vasodilatation. There is probably a center in the medulla which controls vasodilator nerves, which are of 2 types.

The first type of vasodilator nerves is found in the craniosacral division of the autonomic system. The cranial vasodilator fibers travel in the facial, the glossopharyngeal and the vagus nerves. They supply the arterioles of the salivary glands, the tongue, the larynx and the mucous membrane of the mouth and the nose. The sacral vasodilator fibers supply the arterioles of the external genitalia.

The second type of vasodilator nerves is found in the thoracolumbar division of the autonomic system. These are distributed to the blood vessels of skeletal muscles and to the coronary arteries. This happy combination is a great advantage to us since, in a bout of exercise, there is a more abundant blood supply to both skeletal muscles and heart muscle.

Blood vessels in the skin dilate when the skin is irritated; this response is due, not to vasodilator nerves, but to "axon reflexes."

The vasomotor center in the medulla is affected by nerve impulses from the baroceptors in the aortic arch and the carotid sinuses and also from those in the great veins and the atrial muscle. The center may be affected also by impulses from any afferent nerve. For example, you can hear something that makes you blush or see something that makes you turn pale; the former is inhibition of vasoconstriction, and the latter is active vasoconstriction.

Not only does the vasomotor center receive impulses from all parts of the body but it can be affected also by changes in the composition of the blood flowing through it. A high concentration of carbon dioxide in the blood stimulates the vasomotor center. This happens in exercise and, as a result, the vessels in the skin and the abdominal viscera are constricted. Meanwhile those in the skeletal muscles are dilated, bringing about a shift of blood from inactive to active areas. As exercise continues, the vessels in the skin dilate in accordance with demands for regulation of body temperature.

Peripheral blood vessels, especially arterioles and capillaries, are affected not only by nerve impulses but also by temperature and chemical factors in local areas. For example, in active muscle there is elevation of temperature, and this serves to dilate further the vessels in that muscle. In the same active muscle there is a greater production of carbon dioxide, and this also dilates the vessels locally. It will be noted that carbon dioxide has two effects, a local and a general. The local effect is the dilatation of blood vessels

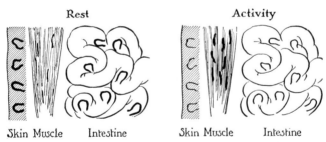

Rest   Activity

Skin Muscle   Intestine   Skin Muscle   Intestine

FIG. 290. Shifting of blood from one area to another. During rest, the blood supply to the skin and intestine is abundant; the blood supply to the skeletal muscles is limited, as shown by the few capillaries which are open. During muscular activity, less blood flows to the skin and intestine, but the supply to the skeletal muscles is abundant. More vessels are open, and all in the muscles are dilated. The carbon dioxide which is produced during activity has two effects on circulation: (1) local dilatation of the vessels in the muscles and (2) central vasoconstriction. Both effects favor the desired shift of blood from areas where it is not needed in large amounts at the moment to areas where an abundant supply is needed.

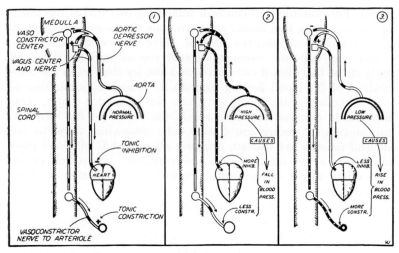

FIG. 291. Diagram showing the effect of changing pressure in the aorta. The afferent pathway is the nerve from the base of the aorta or depressor nerve. The impulses are shown as shaded segments. The arrows indicate the direction in which the impulses are passing. The spacing of the impulses indicates the frequency of the impulses in the nerves. The efferent fibers to the heart and blood vessels are indicated. The changes in the heart and blood vessels on changing from normal to high and low arterial pressures are indicated. With high pressures, the heart is slower and the vasoconstrictor center less active than usual; with low pressures, the opposite is found. (Carlson, A. J., and Johnson, Victor: The Machinery of the Body, Chicago, Univ. Chicago Press)

in the active area, and the general effect, through the vasomotor center, is constriction of vessels in skin and viscera. Both of these effects are such as to increase the blood flow through the active muscle (Fig. 290).

REGULATION OF THE CIRCULATION

The 2 main types of control in the circulatory system are chemical and nervous.

Chemical. Two classes of agents that play a role in the chemical control are metabolites and hormones. The chief metabolite is carbon dioxide, whose action is discussed above. The hormones that play a role in the control of circulation are epinephrine, pituitrin and renin. Epinephrine increases the rate and the force

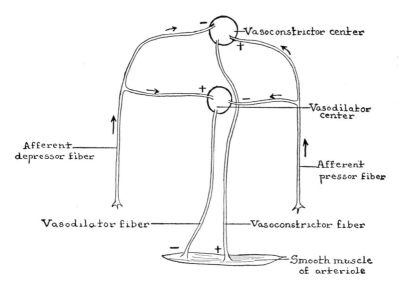

FIG. 292. Diagram showing probable arrangements of the vasomotor nerves, showing the muscle of arteriole, the vasodilator fiber
(—), terminating on muscle; the vasoconstrictor fiber (+), terminating on muscle. These fibers arise from their respective centers.
An afferent depressor fiber divides into two branches, one inhibits
the constrictor center and the other excites the dilator center. An
afferent pressor fiber is shown; one branch inhibits the dilator center
and the other stimulates the constrictor center. (After Bayliss)

of the heart beat and causes constriction of arterioles in skin and
viscera, together with dilatation of those in skeletal muscle and
heart. Pituitrin causes constriction of all arterioles. Renin, which
reacts with one of the proteins in the plasma to form hypertensin,
constricts all arterioles.

Nervous. Changes in pressure within the vascular system itself
play a role in the nervous control of the circulation. Stimulation
of the baroceptors in the aorta and the carotid sinuses brings about
a reflex slowing of the heart rate and inhibition of vasoconstrictor
activity. Both reflexes lead to a fall in arterial blood pressure. The
variation in the number of impulses conducted to the central nervous system, with changes in arterial blood pressure, is illustrated
in Figure 291. The nerve pathways involved in reflexes which
regulate circulation are illustrated in Figures 292 and 293.

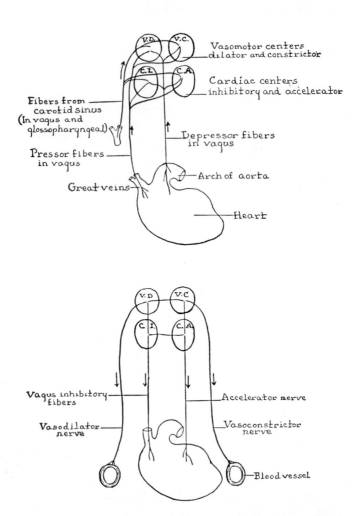

FIG. 293. Diagram of cardiovascular reflex mechanisms. Afferent fibers from the aorta, the carotid sinus and the great veins are shown in the upper diagram. The connections of these with the vasomotor and cardiac centers are shown. In the lower diagram the efferent fibers from the centers to the blood vessels and heart are indicated. It can be seen that the afferent fibers exert reciprocal effects on the medullary centers.

The baroceptors in the great veins and the atria are stimulated by high venous pressure. The impulses that are conducted to the central nervous system bring about an increase in heart rate (called the *Bainbridge reflex*) and a constriction of the arterioles in the skin and the viscera (called the *MacDowall reflex*). These reflexes are partly responsible for the rapid heart and the high blood pressure during exercise.

The purpose of all the cardiac and vascular reflexes is to keep the heart rate and the arterial blood pressure as near the normal level as possible and thereby maintain homeostasis. Sufficient examples have been presented to impress upon the reader the beauty of the self-regulation in the cardiovascular system. There can be no changes in the heart rate or in blood pressure in any part of the system which do not set into action reflexes to restore conditions to normal so long as one remains "in circulatory health."

EFFECTS OF GRAVITY

The pull of gravity makes the return of blood from the lower extremities difficult when one assumes the upright position. The factors that help to get the blood back to the heart are the force of the heart beat, the contraction of the abdominal muscles, the contraction of the muscles of the lower extremities and the respiratory movements.

The contraction of the muscles of the abdominal wall prevents the accumulation or stagnation of blood in the vessels of the viscera. The muscles of the lower extremities exert a pumping action on the veins each time they contract and relax. The respiratory movements exert a sort of sucking action (due to negative intrapleural pressure, p. 549) which helps to pull blood up into the thorax. The venous return is good so long as we can move about and make use of the muscular pump mechanism.

A great strain is put on the circulatory system when we are required to stand quietly at attention. The muscular pump cannot be used; in fact, one cannot even shift the weight from one leg to the other, nor can a deep breath be taken. Under such circumstances, blood tends to accumulate (stagnate) in the lower portions of the body, and venous return becomes inadequate. If the heart does not receive venous blood it cannot pump enough to supply the brain, and the individual faints. Many people cannot stand quietly for as long as 15 minutes without fainting. Salesladies and people who stand a great deal and cannot walk about much while on duty wear girdles to prevent stagnation of blood in the abdominal vessels. Some wear elastic stockings to help prevent accumulation of blood in the superficial veins of the legs.

The essential cause of fainting is a decrease in the blood supply to the brain. The first effect of a decrease in the blood supply to the brain is a loss of consciousness, and the individual falls. This is nature's remedy. Consciousness is soon regained in the horizontal position, since the blood supply to the brain improves, and venous return is no longer a problem.

When a person begins to feel faint, he should lie down if this is possible; if not, then he should sit down, bend over and get his head between his knees. The most unphysiologic and ridiculous thing one can do is to try to walk out of a room when feeling faint. Nurses frequently faint on the first day in the operating room; those who remember what they have been taught in physiology should not disrupt the operating room routine by falling.

PRACTICAL CONSIDERATIONS

Electrocardiogram of a normal heart is illustrated in Figure 294. In this record the contraction of the atria is indicated by the letter *P*, and the contraction of the ventricles by the letter *R*. The interval between P and R waves is the time required for the beat to be propagated or conducted from atria to ventricles and represents the delay at the atrioventricular node and bundle.

Irregularities in conduction can be detected by electrocardiograms. Disease of the atrioventricular bundle prevents conduction of the beat from atria to ventricles. This condition is called *heart block* and is characterized by R waves which have no relation to P waves. The R waves appear about 20 times per minute, and the P waves about 72.

In some patients the atria do not beat normally but show the pathologic type of contraction called *fibrillation*. In atrial fibrilla-

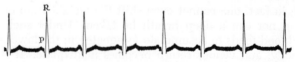

FIG. 294. Normal electrocardiogram, showing action current of heart muscle. The small waves, P, indicate the activity of the atria; the large waves, R, indicate the activity of the ventricles. (From Minneapolis General Hospital)

tion the electrocardiogram shows no P waves at all, and the R waves appear at a rapid and irregular rate.

The electrocardiogram is a record of the action currents or electrical changes that accompany each beat of the heart.

Murmurs. Since heart sounds are due to valvular action, if the valves fail to perform properly, due to disease, one would expect to hear abnormal sounds called *murmurs*. If valves fail to close tightly and blood leaks back, it gives rise to an abnormal sound. If a valve orifice is stenosed or narrowed, an abnormal sound is heard when blood is pumped through.

In mitral regurgitation or insufficiency the first heart sound is

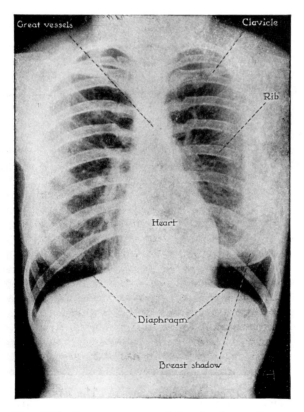

FIG. 295. Roentgenogram of female thorax; breast shadows are visible. (From Univ. Minnesota Hospital)

altered; blood leaks back into the left atrium during left-ventricular systole and is responsible for a systolic murmur. In aortic regurgitation blood leaks back into the left ventricle from the aorta during diastole and is responsible for a diastolic murmur. In mitral stenosis a murmur is heard late in ventricular diastole, at the time of atrial systole, and is called a *presystolic murmur*. In aortic stenosis a systolic murmur is heard.

The valves of the left side of the heart are the ones commonly involved by pathologic changes in adult life. As the condition progresses the valves of the right are secondarily involved due to

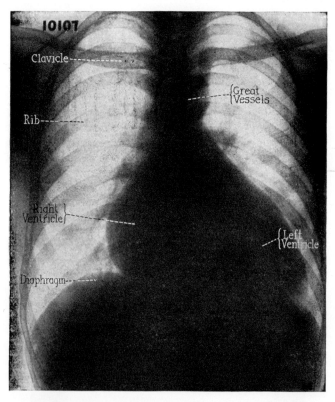

Fig. 296. Roentgenogram of chest. The left ventricle is markedly enlarged; the right ventricle is moderately enlarged. The great vessels are moderately dilated. (From Dr. Vastine, Woman's Medical College Hospital)

the backing up of blood in the lungs and the pulmonary artery. Ultimately, the right ventricle dilates, and both pulmonary and tricuspid regurgitation appear.

Congenital defects usually involve the right side of the heart. Any type of murmur may be heard, but there is no correlation between the severity of the condition and the murmur heard.

In order to diagnose a pathologic heart condition, the physician makes use of electrocardiograms, roentgenograms of the chest, heart sounds and other findings of physical examinations. Figure 295 is an x-ray picture of a normal heart, and Figure 296 illustrates left ventricular enlargement or hypertrophy. Hypertrophy of the left ventricle occurs in such conditions as aortic regurgitation and hypertension.

If the heart is able to supply an adequate amount of blood to the various organs according to their needs in spite of valvular lesions, it is said to be "compensated." If the heart is unable to maintain an adequate circulation it is said to be "decompensated." In decompensation there may be pulmonary edema due to increased pressure in the capillaries of the lungs, with filtration of tissue fluid into the air sacs of the lungs. Venous pressure is high, the liver is congested and enlarged, and generalized edema occurs. This represents backward failure of the heart and is called *congestive heart failure.* Digitalis is used in many types of cardiac pathology to improve the condition of the myocardium.

Disorders of Blood Pressure. A systolic blood pressure which is above 140 mm. Hg at rest is above the normal range, and the individual is said to have *high blood pressure* or *hypertension.* This may accompany disease of the kidneys (nephritis). In many cases the cause of hypertension is unknown, and these patients are said to have "essential hypertension." Overweight and nervous strain are predisposing factors. Patients with hypertension are advised to live quiet lives, as free from strain as possible. The greatest danger is cerebral hemorrhage.

A systolic pressure consistently below 100 mm. Hg is below the normal range, and the individual is said to have *hypotension.* The only difficulty in such a condition is the frequent fatigue and lack of physical endurance.

Effects of Drugs on Blood Pressure. Epinephrine leads to a marked, but temporary, increase in blood pressure. Inhalation of amyl nitrite leads to a marked fall in blood pressure by relaxing the smooth muscle of the arterioles, which reduces peripheral resistance.

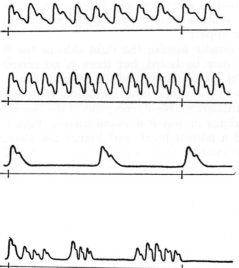

Fig. 297. Radial pulse tracings. (*Top*) Pulse in normal individual; the notch on the descending limb indicates the time of closing of the semilunar valves. (*Center*) Pulse in hyperthyroidism; the rate is rapid (tachycardia). (*Bottom*) Pulse in heart block; the rate is extremely slow.

Fig. 298. Radial pulse tracing in atrial fibrillation. The pulse is totally irregular; it lacks rhythm, and the beats vary in size.

Pulse. A patient is said to have *tachycardia* if the rate is above 120. A rate below 50 is said to be *bradycardia*. A very rapid and weak pulse is described as a *thready* or *running pulse*. Pulse tracings representing tachycardia and heart block are illustrated in Figure 297.

So far as rhythm of pulse is concerned, many cases of premature systoles will be encountered. It is the compensatory pause that follows a premature systole which gives the impression that the heart has skipped a beat. In atrial fibrillation the pulse is totally irregular, which means that it is irregular in both rhythm and force. Strong and weak beats are intermingled (Fig. 298).

The pulse may be full, bounding, dicrotic (notched), waterhammer (rapid rise and rapid fall) or weak in character.

Results of Inadequate Blood Supply. Tissues and organs cannot be kept in good condition without an adequate blood supply. A tight bandage or cast interferes with circulation of blood in the part involved. If a part of the body is not receiving sufficient blood, the temperature of that part falls, swelling occurs and cyanosis is evident. These danger signals should be watched for whenever a part is bandaged or in a cast.

In patients who are confined to bed for long periods of time,

No compress   Hot compress   Cold compress

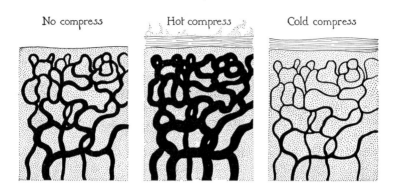

FIG. 299. Changes in the cutaneous blood flow. (*Left*) The size
of the vessels under the usual conditions is shown. (*Center*) The increase in size (vasodilatation) which accompanies the application
of hot compresses is indicated. (*Right*) The decrease in size (vasoconstriction) which accompanies the application of cold compresses
is indicated. This effect is a temporary one.

bedsores may develop. These appear where there is pressure over
bony prominences. To prevent such sores (decubitus ulcers) there
must be frequent change in position, alcohol rubs and massage to
improve the circulation in the skin over such prominences, for
only excellent care of the skin can prevent bedsores. The efficiency
of the nursing service of a hospital may be judged by the presence
or the absence of bedsores in patients who have been confined to
bed for long periods of time.

Hot and Cold Compresses. HOT COMPRESSES sometimes are
used to relieve pain. They increase the blood flow to the part involved by dilating the blood vessels. Figure 299 illustrates the
change in blood flow due to application of heat. The temperature
of the skin of the extremities may be increased from about 24° to
44° C. by hot compresses.

COLD COMPRESSES cause a constriction of blood vessels in the
skin. This reduces the swelling of an infected area and may relieve
pain in this way. The change in blood vessels is illustrated in Figure 299.

Hemorrhage. EXTERNAL hemorrhage refers to a hemorrhage
in which blood escapes from the body. Any person at hand may
aid in hemostasis or checking the flow of blood in an external
hemorrhage. Aid can be given by applying pressure at specific

spots. If the hemorrhage is on the inner side of the thigh, pressure is made against the femoral artery over the femur. If it is in the upper temporal region, the temporal artery is compressed against the maxilla in front of the external ear. If the palm is bleeding, the radial artery should be compressed against the radius in the wrist, and the ulnar artery should be compressed against the ulna, on the opposite side of the wrist. Bleeding from the nose is called *epistaxis;* sometimes it is necessary to pack the nasal cavity to stop epistaxis.

INTERNAL hemorrhage follows an operation if a bleeding vessel is overlooked. It may follow childbirth, if the uterus fails to remain contracted after it is emptied. Nurses should be familiar with signs of hemorrhage; failure to recognize such a condition promptiy may cost the life of a patient.

During hemorrhage there is a discrepancy between the volume of blood and the capacity of the vascular system, and the supply to vital organs becomes inadequate. The primary difficulty is failure of the heart to maintain a normal output, since the venous return is poor, and the volume of blood is low. There is air hunger, which is characterized by a gasping type of respiration. The skin is pale, cold and clammy. The pulse is rapid and thready. The blood pressure falls after all means of compensation fail. The patient is very restless; this is nature's method of making use of the muscular pump mechanism to increase venous return, but the effort is wasted because of the lack of sufficient blood. A transfusion can save the life of the patient if administered before it is too late, and the bleeding is checked.

Shock. If bleeding continues and no transfusion is given, the patient goes into a state called *shock,* and the blood pressure continues to fall. The condition is now irreversible, and transfusion can do no good. Many explanations have been suggested as to the impossibility of saving life by transfusion in this irreversible stage. Only one explanation will be presented; this states that since the liver, as well as other organs, fails to receive its usual blood supply and oxygen, its metabolism changes. Owing to the metabolic disturbance, the liver permits a vasodepressor material (called *VDM*) to escape into the blood. VDM leads to a dilatation of capillaries, with stagnation of blood within them. This blood is technically "out of circulation," and thereby the blood volume is reduced still further. Once the capillaries are dilated, transfusions are of no avail.

ANAPHYLACTIC SHOCK. Under certain conditions, the injection of a toxin, a serum or a foreign protein solution produces a sensitization of an individual which makes a second dose far more harmful than the first. The patient goes into a state of collapse after the second dose; the condition is called *anaphylactic shock*. In some people, such sensitization is the basis for the susceptibility to particular foods, such as strawberries and shell fish.

Skin Reactions. The color of the skin depends on the size of the veins in the plexuses beneath the skin. If these venous plexuses are dilated and blood is flowing through rapidly, the skin is red. If the venous plexuses are relaxed, the blood stagnates in them, and the skin is blue or cyanosed. If the plexuses are constricted the skin is pale.

If the skin is stroked lightly, a white line appears over the area stroked, in about 15 seconds, and lasts about 3 minutes. This is due to local capillary constriction in the line of the stroke.

In very sensitive skins, a triple response follows stroking. First, a red line is noted, due to capillary dilatation. The second response is a flare or widespread flush, which appears after 15 to 30 seconds and is due to dilatation of the arterioles in the surrounding area. The skin appears mottled in color. The third response is the formation of a wheal, which reaches its maximum in 5 minutes and may project a little above the skin surface. This wheal is due to increased permeability of the capillaries and the escape of an excessive amount of tissue fluid from the capillaries into the tissue spaces.

Exposure to Ultraviolet Light. If a white skin is exposed to sunlight, the exposed area becomes red in about 20 minutes and remains red for 2 hours. This condition is called *heat erythema*. About 1 hour later an erythema due to ultraviolet light appears; this is *sunburn*. Sunburn reaches its maximum in about 12 hours and remains for 2 to 3 days. It is associated with capillary dilatation and edema, with occasional blistering.

SUMMARY

1. The heart
    A. Properties of heart muscle
        (a) Extensibility
        (b) Rhythmic contractility
        (c) Refractory periods; premature systoles and compensatory pauses
        (d) All or none law
        (e) Electrical changes

B. Conducting system: sinu-atrial node, atrioventricular node, atrioventricular bundle and its branches and Purkinje fibers

C. Cardiac cycle: systole, diastole and diastasis

D. Pressure changes in the heart; valvular action

E. Heart sounds: cause of two heart sounds

F. Cardiac output: at rest and during exercise

G. Variations in heart rate: size, sex, age and miscellaneous factors

H. Nerve supply of the heart

(a) Efferent: inhibitory and augmentor

(b) Afferent

(c) Cardiac center in medulla: affected by many impulses

2. Blood pressure

A. Definition and means of expressing it

B. Pressure in different parts of the vascular system

(a) Arterial blood pressure: systolic, diastolic and pulse

(b) Capillary blood pressure

(c) Venous blood pressure

C. Factors involved in the maintenance of arterial blood pressure

(a) Rate and force of heart beat

(b) Elasticity of large arteries

(c) Peripheral resistance: size of arterioles

(d) Quantity of blood in the vascular system

(e) Viscosity of the blood

D. Method of measuring arterial blood pressure

E. Physiologic variations in arterial blood pressure: age, weight, heredity, emotions and exercise

3. Velocity of blood flow

A. Dependence on cross-section area

B. Circulation time

4. The pulse

A. Arterial pulse

B. Venous pulse in central veins

5. Nerve supply to blood vessels

A. Afferent: aortic arch and carotid sinuses; baroceptors

B. Efferent

(a) Vasoconstrictor: to arterioles of skin and viscera

(b) Vasodilator

(1) Craniosacral fibers

(2) Thoracolumbar fibers

C. Vasomotor center in medulla; affected by impulses from

aorta and carotid sinus; from the great veins and atria; from any part of the body. Also affected by change in chemical composition of the blood, particularly the carbon dioxide content

    D. Chemical control of peripheral blood vessels

  6. Regulation of the circulation

    A. Chemical: metabolites and hormones

    B. Nervous: changes in pressure within the vascular system itself

    C. Effects of gravity: fainting

SITUATION AND QUESTIONS

Applicants receive a complete physical examination before acceptance into a School of Nursing. Miss Belle checked and recorded the vital signs, which included the pulse rate and blood pressure.

1. She most likely counted the pulse rate at the site of the: _____(a) jugular vein; _____(b) ulnar artery; _____ (c) radial artery; _____(d) aorta.

2. She found that in normal hearts the pulse rate increased after a short period of exercise. One of the reasons for this temporary increase in heart action is: _____(a) increased carbon dioxide content in the blood; _____(b) with exercise the craniosacral division of the autonomic system is stimulated, and this augments the heart's activity; _____(c) due to the increased pressure in the aorta and the carotid sinus; _____(d) due to the increase in the quantity of blood within the system as one exercises.

3. One of the applicants was found to have a rather severe anemia. Her blood pressure was found to be low, probably because of: _____(a) a decrease in the amount of circulating blood; _____(b) decrease in peripheral resistance; _____ (c) decrease in the viscosity of the blood; _____(d) decrease in the velocity of blood flow.

4. Several students were found to have abnormal heart sounds. Heart sounds give information concerning: _____(a) cardiac output; _____(b) action current of the heart; _____(c) blood pressure; _____(d) the efficiency of heart valves.

5. The function of the efferent nerve supply of the heart is to: _____(a) change the heart rate to meet body needs; _____ (b) initiate the heart beat; _____(c) prevent constant changing of the rate and rhythm of the heart beat; _____(d) inform the central nervous system of cardiac activity.

12. Anatomy of the Respiratory System

INTRODUCTION

Respiration means to *breathe again*. It may be defined in several ways, such as: (1) respiration is the act of breathing; (2) respiration is taking fresh air into, and expelling stale air from, the lungs; (3) respiration is the interchange of gases (taking up oxygen and giving up carbon dioxide) between a living organism and its environment; or (4) respiration is taking up oxygen and giving off carbon dioxide.

For an organism as complex as man, a large, moist surface where air and blood can come in close contact is needed. Such an area for diffusion is provided by the lungs. In addition, a passageway through which air can be moved to and from the lungs is needed. A bellows arrangement, such as the thoracic cage, with muscles to operate it and nerves to control it in renewing the air in the lungs, completes the requirements for external respiration.

However, internal respiration really takes place at the cellular level, so a transport system, such as the heart and the blood vessels, together with a pigment which can combine easily with oxygen where the pressure is high and as easily give it up where the pressure is low, is required for this phase of respiration. The cells of the tissues may be likened to tiny chemical factories in which oxygen makes possible reactions by which energy is released from the foodstuffs. Despite all the phases listed, respiration is an integrated activity with the single aim of permitting an adequate gas exchange between the cells of the tissues and the surrounding air.

ORGANS OF THE RESPIRATORY SYSTEM

The organs which are concerned with external respiration are (1) the conducting portion, consisting of the nose, the pharynx, the larynx, the trachea and the bronchi and (2) the respiratory portion, consisting of the lungs.

Conducting Portion

The nose consists of the 2 nasal cavities, separated by the nasal septum.

The nasal cavities lie in the skull between the base of the cranium and the roof of the mouth, in front of the nasopharynx. The right and the left nasal cavities communicate with the outside by means of the anterior nares or nostrils, and with the nasopharynx

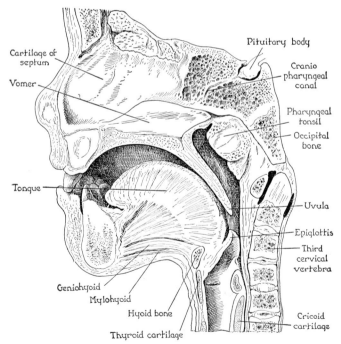

Fig. 300. Sagittal section of the head of a child, to left of nasal septum. Pharyngeal region with pharyngeal tonsil as seen from left side.

by means of the choanae or posterior nares. The paranasal sinuses and the nasolacrimal duct communicate with the nasal cavities on either side.

Each nasal cavity is bounded by a roof, a floor, and medial and lateral walls. The middle of the roof of the nasal cavity is made up chiefly by the cribriform plate of the ethmoid bone; the nasal bone and the spine of the frontal bone form the roof, in front, and the body of the sphenoid, the sphenoidal concha, the ala of the vomer and the sphenoidal process of the palatine bone, behind. The floor of the nasal cavity is formed by the palatal process of the maxilla in front, and the horizontal process of the palate bone, behind.

THE MEDIAL WALL is formed in front by the crest of the nasal bones and the frontal spine, in the middle by the perpendicular plate of the ethmoid and behind by the vomer and part of the

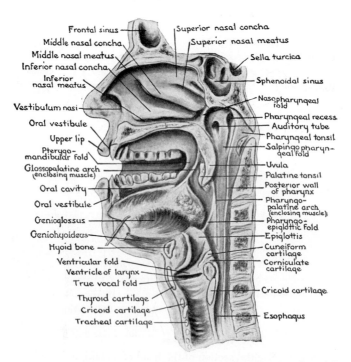

FIG. 301. Sagittal section of head. Lateral walls of oral, nasal, pharyngeal and laryngeal cavities are shown.

sphenoid. The nasal septal cartilage completes the septum (Figs. 63 and 300). The medial wall or septum often deviates from the mid-line and may almost occlude one nasal cavity. The lateral wall of the nasal cavity is formed, in front, by the frontal process of the maxilla and by the lacrimal bone; in the middle, by the ethmoid, the maxilla and the inferior nasal concha; behind, by the vertical plate of the palatine bone and a part of the sphenoid (Fig. 301).

Three plates of bone, arranged one above the other like sagging shelves, are present in the lateral wall of each nasal cavity. The bones look like shells; hence, they are called the *superior, middle* and *inferior conchae.* The name *turbinate* (meaning "scroll-like") is also used for these bones. The nasal conchae are shown in Figures 77 and 301.

The 3 nasal conchae divide each nasal cavity into 4 regions, called from above downward, the *sphenoethmoidal recess* and the *superior, middle* and *inferior meatuses.*

VESTIBULE AND RESPIRATORY PORTION. *The vestibule* is the widened portion just behind the naris in each cavity. The front part of the vestibule is lined with epidermis of the skin and contains hair follicles with coarse hairs and sebaceous and sweat glands. The adjoining part of the vestibule is lined with stratified squamous epithelium which is not keratinized. Beyond this the lining is made up of pseudostratified ciliated epithelium, with goblet cells.

Respiratory Portion. The mucous membrane which lines the respiratory portion of the nasal cavities rests on a supporting tissue (the lamina propria) that contains both mucous and serous glands. This mucous membrane is adherent to the periosteum of bone or perichondrium of cartilage beneath it and consequently is called *mucoperiosteum* or *mucoperichondrium.*

The surface of nasal cavity epithelium is covered with mucus, which is secreted continuously. The mucus collects dust from the air that passes over it, and the cilia move the particles of dust along to the oropharynx.

The lamina propria, which contains both collagenic and elastic fibers, together with many types of cells, is very vascular. As air passes over the mucous membrane it is "air-conditioned," which means that it is warmed or cooled, strained, and moistened. The importance of breathing through the nose is obvious.

The upper parts of the sides and the roof of the posterior part of each nasal cavity are covered with olfactory mucous membrane (p. 350).

There are structures, like large veins, in the lamina propria that covers the middle and the inferior nasal conchae; normally, these are collapsed but they can become turgid with blood very rapidly. When this occurs, the mucosa is so thick that it encroaches on the airway, and breathing through the nose becomes difficult.

THE PARANASAL SINUSES are air spaces in the bones of the skull. There are 4 sinuses which communicate with each nasal cavity. Since they take the names of the bones in which they lie, they are called the maxillary, the frontal, the ethmoidal and the sphenoidal sinuses.

The maxillary sinuses, which lie in the bodies of the maxillae, are the largest of the paranasal sinuses. Each maxillary sinus has a capacity of about 15 cc. The maxillary sinus is shown in Figures 192 and 193; its opening into the middle meatus is shown in Figures 302 and 303.

Frontal Sinuses. There are 2 frontal sinuses (Figs. 77 and 302) which communicate with the middle meatus of each nasal cavity. The capacity of each frontal sinus varies between 3 and 8 cc.

The ethmoidal air cells make the lateral masses of the ethmoidal bone look like a honeycomb. The anterior group of air cells, which open into the middle meatus (Fig. 302), ranges from 2 to 8 in number. They are shown in Figure 303. The posterior group of air cells, which open into the superior meatus (Fig. 302), ranges from 1 to 7 in number. They are shown in Figure 303.

The sphenoidal sinuses are paired and are shown in Figures 77, 301, 302 and 303. The opening into the spheno-ethmoidal recess is shown in Figure 302. The capacity of each is about 7.5 cc.

The nasolacrimal duct (p. 355) opens into the inferior meatus, as shown in Figures 193 and 302.

The paranasal sinuses and the nasolacrimal duct are lined with mucous membrane which is continuous with that lining the nasal cavities. The openings of the sinuses into the nasal cavities may be blocked if the mucosa swells or is inflamed.

BLOOD AND NERVE SUPPLY. The blood supply of the nose is derived from branches of the external and the internal carotid arteries. The trigeminal is the sensory nerve for the mucosal lining of the nose. The glands of the lamina propria are supplied by fibers of the autonomic system.

The pharynx or throat is a vertical, tubular passageway which extends from the base of the skull to the esophagus. The walls are composed of skeletal muscle, and the lining consists of mucous membrane. The pharynx is divided into 3 parts: the nasopharynx,

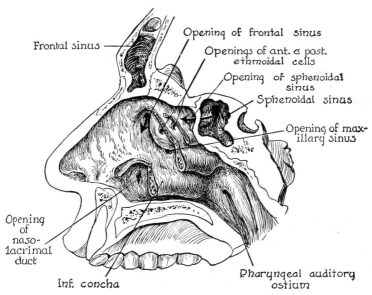

FIG. 302. Lateral wall of the nasal cavity. The nasal conchae, the meatuses, the openings of the paranasal sinuses and the nasolacrimal duct are shown.

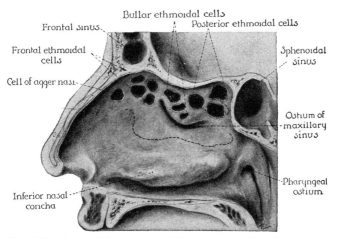

FIG. 303. Some of the paranasal sinuses opened, and the opening or ostium of the maxillary sinus. (Modified from Pratt)

the oropharynx and the laryngopharynx. The oropharynx and the laryngopharynx are common to the digestive and the respiratory systems, since both food and air pass through them. The blood and the nerve supplies are abundant.

THE NASOPHARYNX has 4 openings in its walls. It communicates with the nasal cavities by way of the 2 posterior nares or choanae, which are separated from each other by the nasal septum. The upper surface of the soft palate forms the floor of the nasopharynx. The openings of the auditory tubes are in the lateral walls of the nasopharynx, as shown in Figure 301. The mucous membrane lining the auditory tubes is continuous with that of the nasopharynx. The auditory tube in children is short, wide and straight, so infection of the throat is very likely to spread along the auditory tube to the middle ear, from which it can spread readily on to the mastoid air cells.

The pharyngeal tonsil is a mass of lymphatic tissue in the lamina propria of the mucous membrane lining the dorsal wall of the nasopharynx. When this mass is enlarged it is called *adenoids* (meaning "glandlike"), and it may obstruct the air passage to such an extent that the child breathes through the mouth. The pharyngeal tonsil is shown in Figure 300.

THE OROPHARYNX communicates with the mouth through the fauces or archway into the mouth. This is the only opening in the oropharynx. The fauces is bounded above by the uvula, which is a structure composed of muscle, connective tissue and mucous membrane, hanging from the soft palate above the root of the tongue (Figs. 300 and 301). The fauces is bounded, laterally, by the glossopalatine arch (Fig. 301) and, below, by the dorsum or back of the tongue.

The palatine tonsils are oval, flat bodies, located on each side of the oropharynx, in the lateral walls (Fig. 301). They are masses of lymphatic tissue covered with epithelium. The lateral surface is covered with a fibrous capsule which is continuous with the pharyngeal wall. The medial surface is covered with mucous membrane. There are pits on the free surface which open into slitlike spaces.

The mucosa over the root of the tongue contains masses of lymphatic tissue which compose the lingual tonsil. The 2 palatine tonsils, together with the lingual tonsil, below and the pharyngeal tonsil above, form an almost complete ring of tonsillar tissue surrounding the pharynx (Waldeyer's tonsillar ring).

The only known function of the tonsillar tissue is the formation of lymphocytes. The palatine tonsils often become infected, and tonsillitis results. It is customary to remove them in an operation called *tonsillectomy.*

LARYNGOPHARYNX. There are 2 openings in the laryngopharynx: (1) an anterior opening, into the larynx, and (2) a posterior opening, into the esophagus.

The larynx is the voice box, and it serves as a passageway from the pharynx to the trachea. It lies in the mid-line of the neck, below the hyoid bone, in front of the fourth, the fifth and the sixth cervical vertebrae, and between the sheaths containing the common carotid arteries, the internal jugular veins and the vagus nerves. It is referred to as the watchdog for the lungs, since it usually prevents anything but air from entering the lower air passages. When foreign matter enters the larynx, a cough reflex is set up in an attempt to expel the intruder.

The larynx is pulled upward and forward during the act of swallowing, and in this way the air passages are closed to the entrance of food. Exhalation of air through the larynx is controlled by voluntary muscles and so enables the larynx to become the organ of voice.

The larynx is a triangular box composed of 9 cartilages that are joined together by ligaments and controlled by skeletal muscles. The larynx is lined with ciliated mucous membrane, and the cilia move particles upward to the pharynx.

CARTILAGES. There are 3 single cartilages in the larynx (cricoid, thyroid and epiglottis), and 3 paired cartilages (arytenoid, corniculate and cuneiform). Some of these are shown in section in Figure 301.

The cricoid cartilage is shaped like a signet ring, with the band in front and the signet at the back of the larynx. It lies at the lower end of the larynx and is connected with the first ring of the trachea.

The thyroid, a shield-shaped cartilage, which is the largest in the larynx, is composed of 2 broad plates, a right and a left, which meet and fuse in the mid-line in front. The plates form a more acute angle with each other in the male than in the female, and the ventral edges form the subcutaneous laryngeal prominence known as the *Adam's apple.*

The epiglottis (Fig. 300) is thin and leaf-shaped and extends above the thyroid cartilage in front of the entrance to the larynx. The aryepiglottic folds of mucous membrane are attached to its sides.

The arytenoid cartilages, which are above the cricoid cartilage, furnish attachment for the vocal ligaments. The position and the

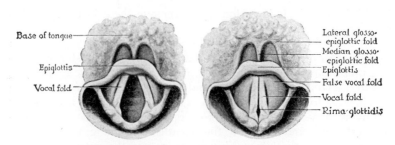

FIG. 304. Interior of larynx, as seen with laryngoscope. (*Left*) Rima glottidis, wide open; (*right*) rima closed.

tension of these ligaments are altered by changes in position of the arytenoid cartilages. The apex of each arytenoid is covered by one of the *corniculate* cartilages.

The cuneiform cartilages are small, rodlike bodies found in the aryepiglottic folds, just anterior to the *corniculate* cartilages.

LIGAMENTS. There are extrinsic and intrinsic ligaments in the larynx. The extrinsic ligaments connect the thyroid cartilage and the epiglottis with the hyoid bone and the cricoid with the trachea. The intrinsic ligaments connect the cartilages of the larynx with each other.

CAVITY OF THE LARYNX. The entrance to the larynx is bounded by the epiglottis, in front, the apices of the arytenoids and the corniculates, in the back, and the aryepiglottic folds, on the sides. The cavity of the larynx extends from the entrance to the lower border of the cricoid cartilage where it is continuous with that of the trachea. It is narrowed to an anteroposterior slit in two places by folds of mucous membrane which project like shelves from each side. The upper pair of folds are called *false vocal cords*. The second pair lie below the first pair, and their free margins are the true vocal cords (Fig. 301). The opening between the 2 vocal cords is called the *rima glottidis* (Fig. 304) (meaning "slit of the glottis").

The parts of the vocal cords nearest their free edges are composed of connective tissue with an abundance of elastic fibers. The slit between the cords and the tension of the cords is controlled by muscles which act on the cords directly and by muscles that affect them indirectly by shifting the cartilages to which they are anchored.

The epithelium of the mucous membrane covering the vocal cords is stratified squamous nonkeratinizing. The epithelium which lines the larynx both above and below the vocal cords is of the pseudo-stratified columnar ciliated type with goblet cells. Except over the vocal cords, the lamina propria of the mucous membrane contains mucous glands, and lymph nodules are present.

The interior of the larynx as seen with laryngoscope is illustrated in Figure 304.

MUSCLES OF THE LARYNX. *The extrinsic* muscles which arise from neighboring structures are inserted into the larynx and depress it after the act of swallowing is completed.

The intrinsic muscles which are confined entirely to the larynx modify the size of the slit between the vocal cords and the tension.

The muscles of the larynx perform the following functions: (1) ensure a free passage for air, (2) control the exhalation of air in speech and singing, (3) alter the position of the larynx with respect

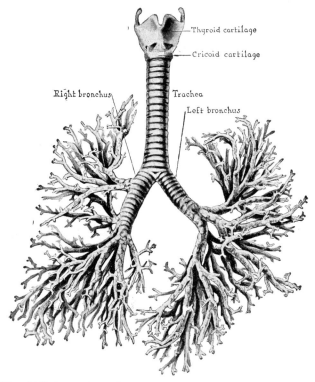

Thyroid cartilage

Cricoid cartilage

Right bronchus

Trachea

Left bronchus

FIG. 305. Larynx, trachea and bronchial tree, ventral aspect.

to that of the hyoid bone and the tongue in movements of the neck and (4) prevent the entrance of food during swallowing. A serious condition occurs if the muscles of the larynx go into a spasmodic contraction. Asphyxia may result from interference with the passage of air unless the spasm is relieved promptly.

THE BLOOD SUPPLY to the walls of the larynx is derived from branches of the external carotid arteries.

THE VAGUS NERVES receive afferent fibers from the mucous membrane of the larynx, which is so sensitive that any irritation produces a cough reflex. The vagus nerves also supply efferent fibers to the striated muscles of the larynx.

SPEECH. As expired air passes through the larynx, it can be made to set the vocal cords into vibration, and this, in turn, sets the whole column of air above the vocal cords into vibration. The pharynx, the mouth and the nasal cavities (and the paranasal sinuses, perhaps) are resonating cavities. The muscles of the neck, the face, the tongue and the lips are used to modify the sounds into words. The speech center in the cerebral cortex integrates the activity of all the muscles concerned so that intelligible sounds or words may be spoken. The loudness of the voice depends on the volume and the force of the expired air and amplitude of vibrations of the vocal cords. The pitch of the voice is determined by the number of vibrations per second and the length and the tension of the vocal cords. The longer the cords, the lower is the pitch of the voice.

The trachea or windpipe is about 11 cm. long. It extends from the larynx at the level of the sixth cervical vertebra to the level of the disk below the fourth thoracic vertebra. It lies in the mid-line of the neck, anterior to the esophagus.

There are 20 U-shaped cartilages placed near together in the trachea (Fig. 305). You can feel them easily in your own neck. The open end of the U is at the back, and the gap is bridged by connective tissue and smooth muscle. This arrangement permits expansion of the esophagus during swallowing of a *bolus* (meaning "a morsel" or "a swallow") of food, since it can encroach on the posterior wall of the trachea. The cartilage rings keep the trachea open at all times for the passage of air to and from the lungs. The trachea is lined with ciliated mucous membrane containing goblet cells. There are glands in the lamina propria, also. The dust particles stick to the mucus, and the cilia move them upward to the pharynx. The branches of the subclavian artery supply the tracheal structures with blood. The nerve supply is from the vagi.

Bronchial Tree. The trachea divides into right and left primary bronchi which extend to the *hilus* (meaning "the notch" or "fissure" through which vessels, nerves, etc., enter an organ). The right primary bronchus is more nearly vertical, shorter and wider than the left (Fig. 305). Consequently, when foreign bodies enter the respiratory passages they are likely to be found in the right primary bronchus. As soon as each primary bronchus enters its respective lung it branches. The right primary bronchus sends a branch to the upper lobe, one to the middle lobe and then continues on to the lower lobe. The left primary bronchus sends one branch to the upper lobe of the left lung and then continues on to the left lower lobe (Fig. 305). At each hilus the primary bronchus and its branches are closely associated with arteries, veins and lymphatic vessels, which together make up the root of the lung.

The bronchi continue to subdivide, as shown in Figure 305. As they become smaller, less and less cartilage is present in their walls, and more and more smooth muscle appears. The smooth muscle completely encircles the lumen; it is arranged in right and left spirals. If you take two narrow ribbons and wind them around an applicator, winding one in a clockwise direction and the other in a counterclockwise direction, you will duplicate the spiral arrangements of smooth muscle in the small bronchi. The contraction of this smooth muscle throws the mucous membrane into longitudinal folds. The mucous membrane is ciliated and contains goblet cells; the mucus and the cilia help to keep the bronchi free of foreign particles.

Cranial autonomic fibers (parasympathetic), which travel in the vagus nerves, cause contraction of the smooth muscle in the walls of the bronchioles. Fibers from the thoracolumbar division (sympathetic) cause relaxation of the smooth muscle and, therefore, dilate the lumens of the bronchioles (smallest bronchi).

RESPIRATORY PORTION

The lungs constitute the respiratory portion of the respiratory system. They lie in the thoracic cavity, on either side of the mediastinum, enclosed in the pleurae.

The thoracic cavity is the space above the diaphragm, within the walls of the thorax, that is occupied by the thoracic viscera. The cavity is closed, below, by the diaphragm; above, by the scalene muscles and the fascia of the neck; and, on the sides, the front and the back, by the ribs, the intercostal muscles, the vertebrae, the sternum and the ligaments. The thoracic cavity is changing constantly in size in the various phases of respiration. The lungs lie in the pleural cavities, and the mediastinum is the space between the lungs.

Mediastinum. The mediastinal cavity is the space between the pleural cavities. The right and the left boundaries of the mediastinal cavity are the mediastinal portions of the parietal pleurae. The contents of the mediastinal cavity are: (1) heart and pericardium, (2) thoracic aorta and its branches, (3) pulmonary artery and pulmonary veins, (4) the venae cavae and the azygos vein, (5) thymus gland, lymph nodes and vessels, (6) trachea, esophagus and thoracic duct and (7) vagus nerves, cardiac and phrenic nerves.

The pleurae are paired, closed, serous sacs, composed of a fibro-elastic membrane, lined with squamous mesothelial cells. Each pleura consists of 2 layers—a visceral and a parietal layer. The thick visceral layer covers the outer surface of the lungs and dips into the fissures and separates the lobes of the lungs. It is continuous with the mediastinal pleura at the root of each lung.

The parietal pleura lines the walls of the cavities in which the lungs lie and consists of costal, diaphragmatic and mediastinal portions. The parietal and the visceral layers join around and below the root of each lung. There is a small amount of fluid between

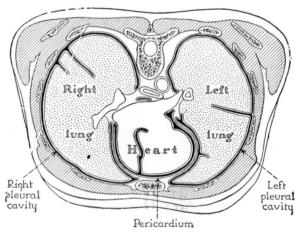

Fig. 306. The parietal and visceral pleurae are shown in transverse section. The pleural cavity is shown in black; this is a potential cavity between the two layers of pleura. (Adapted from Eycleshymer)

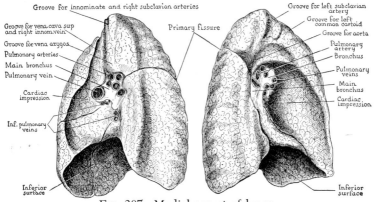

FIG. 307. Medial aspect of lungs.

the 2 layers of pleurae which acts as a lubricant. The arrangement of the parietal and the visceral pleurae is illustrated in Figure 306.

The lungs are the organs in which diffusion of gases between the blood and air takes place. The lungs lie free in the pleural cavities, being attached only by the root and the pulmonary ligaments, which means that they are freely movable except at the hilus.

The lungs are light, porous and spongy, and they float when placed in water. The lung tissue is highly elastic and is constantly on stretch. Within the spongy tissue are the bronchi, which pipe the air in and out of the lungs.

Each lung is cone-shaped, with the base resting on the diaphragm and the apex extending into the root of the neck. The projections of the lungs on the surface of the body are shown in Figures 7 and 8.

STRUCTURE. Each lung exhibits 3 surfaces: the costal, the mediastinal and the diaphragmatic.

The costal surface is in close contact with the wall formed by the ribs and the intercostal muscles. The apex is part of this surface and rises to about 1 cm. above the first rib.

The mediastinal surface is concave and shows the imprint of the heart. The hilus is above and behind the imprint of the heart. It is the slit through which the bronchus, the pulmonary and the bronchial vessels, the lymphatic vessels and the nerves enter or leave the lung. Grooves for the aorta, the azygos vein, the trachea, the subclavian artery, the superior vena cava and the left innominate vein are evident on the mediastinal surface.

The diaphragmatic surface is concave and rests on the diaphragm. A deep interlobular primary fissure divides each lung into a smaller superior and larger inferior lobe. There is a secondary fissure in the right lung which divides it again so that there is a middle lobe, in addition to the superior and the inferior lobes. The lobes are shown in Figure 307; lobes are subdivided into lobules.

Lobules are irregular in shape and size. A bronchiole enters each lobule and branches repeatedly within its substance. Bronchioles divide into terminal bronchioles, each of which leads into respiratory bronchioles. Respiratory bronchioles open into long corridors called *alveolar ducts*. Small cross-corridors, called *atria*, contain open doors which lead into individual rooms called *alveoli*. The partitions between alveoli (walls between adjacent rooms) are capillary networks, supported by elastic and reticular connective tissue. It has been estimated that there are about 700 million alveoli in the human lungs, and the surface that they present for diffusion of gases is about 70 square meters. The alveolar walls are single layers of epithelial cells, and the walls of capillaries are single layers of endothelial cells; therefore, the air in the alveoli and the blood in the pulmonary capillaries are separated by partitions 2 cells in thickness.

In summary, an anatomic unit or lobule of lung is composed of a terminal bronchiole, a respiratory bronchiole, its alveolar ducts, atria and alveoli, blood vessels and nerves. The parts of a lung

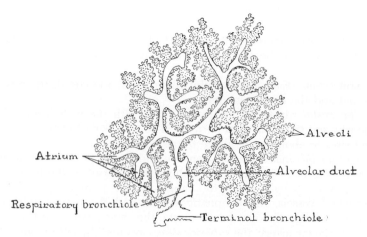

Fig. 308. Parts of a lung unit. (After Willson)

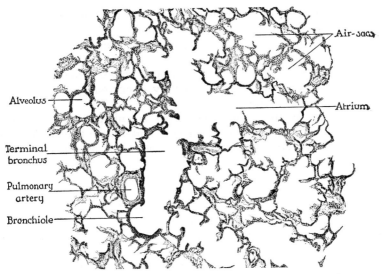

FIG. 309. Section of lung, showing relations of terminal bronchus to alveoli. ×50.

unit are illustrated in Figure 308. A section of lung tissue and the divisions of a terminal bronchiole are shown in Figure 309.

There are 2 separate arterial blood supplies for the lungs. The pulmonary arteries and their branches give rise to pulmonary capillaries in the walls of alveoli, through which exchanges of respiratory gases take place. The bronchial arteries and their branches supply the walls of the bronchi, the walls of blood vessels, the lymph nodes and the pleurae with blood. They are the nutrient arteries for the lung tissue and play no part in oxygenation of the blood.

Lymphatic vessels are present in the visceral pleura and in the dense connective tissue around bronchioles, bronchi, arteries and veins.

PRACTICAL CONSIDERATIONS

Rhinitis. A common cold or rhinitis is an inflammation of the mucous membrane of the nose. It is characterized by an acute congestion of the mucous membrane and increased secretion. It is difficult to breathe through the nose because of the swelling of the mucous membrane and accumulated secretions.

Infection may spread from the nose into the nasolacrimal duct and lead to conjunctivitis, or into the paranasal sinuses and lead to pansinusitis (infection of all the sinuses). Pansinusitis may be acute or chronic. Infection may spread from the nose along the auditory tube into the middle ear; if not stopped there, it may spread to the mastoid air cells. The last is very dangerous because of the nearness of the mastoid air cells to the brain.

Pharynx. If the pharyngeal tonsil is enlarged (adenoids) it necessitates mouth breathing, which is undesirable because the air is not properly strained, warmed and moistened as it is in breathing through the nose. Inspired air is not "air-conditioned" unless it passes through the nose and the nasopharynx, as well as through the lower passages.

Infection of the palatine tonsils is called tonsillitis. When pus is present in the tonsils, it is thought to increase the susceptibility of the individual to arthritis and rheumatism. Removal of tonsils is called *tonsillectomy.*

Larynx. A visual examination of the larynx is called a *laryngoscopic examination.* Cancer of the larynx is a very distressing condition, since it necessitates removal of the larynx (laryngectomy).

In some inflammatory conditions the submucous tissue in the upper part of the larynx becomes infiltrated with fluid and produces edema of the glottis that can easily lead to death by suffocation, if not relieved promptly. The close adhesion of the mucous membrane to the vocal folds prevents the edema from extending below the level of the glottis; therefore, an opening made into the respiratory passage below this level always restores a free passageway for air. Such an opening into the trachea is called a *tracheotomy.* After this operation, a patient requires special nursing care, for the tube which has been inserted into the trachea must be kept free of mucus. Patients with tracheotomy tubes are particularly susceptible to pulmonary infections, since the air is not "conditioned" before it reaches the lungs.

A laryngospasm (laryngismus stridulus) is a sudden, violent, involuntary contraction of the muscles of the larynx. It is seen most commonly in young children as croup and is characterized by a sudden crowing inspiration followed by a stoppage of respiration for several seconds, with cyanosis, then ending with long, loud, whistling inspirations.

Aspirate. The word "aspirate" has at least 2 meanings. One of the meanings is to "suck in," and this refers to the breathing in of blood, mucus or a foreign body. If a patient aspirates blood and pus during a tonsillectomy, he may develop penumonia as a result. This condition is called aspiration pneumonia. Another meaning is the aspiration or withdrawal of fluid from a cavity by means of a negative pressure apparatus which sucks up the fluid. Thus, a patient may take foreign material into his respiratory tract by aspirating it and a nurse may withdraw fluid from the stomach, the pleural cavity or the respiratory tract by aspirating it. These 2 meanings should be kept in mind.

Bronchitis is an infection of the mucous membrane of the bronchi, in which fluid collects in the passages and is expelled by coughing.

Bronchiectasis is the condition in which there is pathologic dilatation of a bronchus. It is characterized by spasms of coughing and the expectoration (coughing up and spitting out) of mucopurulent (mucus and pus) material.

Postural drainage refers to the removal of bronchial secretions or material from a lung abscess by placing the patient head downward for a short time each day. It is recommended as a treatment for bronchiectasis.

Bronchoscopy is the visual examination of the interior of the primary bronchi.

Asthma. The word "asthma" means *panting*. Asthma is characterized by attacks of difficult breathing, coughing, wheezing, raising mucoid sputum and a sense of constriction of the chest. There is spasm of the bronchial muscles, edema of the mucous membrane and secretion of a mucuslike substance. It is usually due to sensitivity to inhaled or ingested substances. The attacks are relieved by the use of drugs which inhibit the action of the smooth muscle of the bronchioles, such as epinephrine (stimulation of dilator fibers or relaxation of smooth muscle) or atropine (inhibition of impulses to constrictor muscles).

Disorders of the Lungs. ATELECTASIS means *incomplete expansion*. It refers to imperfect expansion of the lungs at birth or partial collapse of the lung after birth. The latter is caused by occlusion of a bronchus, perhaps by a plug of heavy mucus, with subsequent absorption of the air, or by external compression, as from a pleural effusion or a tumor. The atelectatic portion of the lung plays no part in the respiratory function.

EMPHYSEMA. The word "emphysema" means *to puff up*. It is the term applied to a pathologic distention of the lung, as if in full inspiration (and also to air in the tissues). The chest is enlarged and barrel-shaped. It may follow repeated attacks of asthma.

PLEURISY is inflammation of the pleura; it may be a dry pleurisy or pleurisy with effusion. The pain of pleurisy is due to friction between the visceral and the parietal pleurae which are not able to glide over each other smoothly.

EMPYEMA is the condition in which pus accumulates in the pleural cavity. It may be drained by aspiration or thoracentesis.

PNEUMONIA is the condition in which there is inflammation of lung tissue or of the walls of the bronchi. The former is called *lobar pneumonia* and the latter *bronchopneumonia*. There is also a "virus" pneumonia, which is similar to influenza. When fluid collects in the alveoli, the condition is called *consolidation*. In any condition in which the blood is not sufficiently oxygenated, such as lobar pneumonia, cyanosis results. This is a purplish color of the skin and is due to the large amount of "reduced" hemoglobin which gives the blood a dark color. Cyanosis is seen first in the finger tips, the lips and the lobes of ears, where capillaries are abundant in the skin.

ABSCESS. A lung abscess is a localized collection of pus in a lung.

SILICOSIS is a diffuse fibrosis of the lungs caused by the inhalation, over a period of many years, of dust having a large amount of silicon dioxide particles in it. It is also called *miner's asthma* and *grinder's asthma*. The lungs lose their elasticity as fibrous tissue replaces the normal elastic tissue.

TUBERCULOSIS is an infectious disease characterized by the formation of tubercles. Pulmonary tuberculosis is treated by giving the infected lung as much rest as possible. The following means of keeping the lung at rest and thus favoring healing are in use: (1) Pneumothorax refers to the presence of air in the pleural cavity. Spontaneous pneumothorax may occur as a result of disease; artificial pneumothorax is produced by forcing air into the pleural cavity. In either case, collapse of the lung occurs. (2) Thoracoplasty, or permanent collapse of the lung by removal of portions of several ribs, is performed in advanced cases. (3) Destruction of the phrenic nerve by phrenicectomy, phrenicotomy or phrenicoexairesis causes paralysis of the diaphragm on that side and prevents expansion of the lung. (4) Lobectomy refers to removal of a lobe of one lung.

CARCINOMA or cancer of the lung is treated by lobectomy or by pneumonectomy, which is excision of an entire lung.

SUMMARY

1. Organs of the respiratory system
   A. Conducting portion

a. Nose: nasal cavities; location, communications, roof, floor, medial wall or septum and lateral wall; nasal conchae. Vestibule and respiratory portions. Mucous membrane; lamina propria

(1) Paranasal sinuses: maxillary, frontal, ethmoidal, sphenoidal; nasolacrimal duct

(2) Blood and nerve supply

b. Pharynx: nasopharynx: openings; pharyngeal tonsil. Oropharynx; fauces; palatine tonsils. Lingual tonsil. Laryngopharynx

c. Larynx: location; movement during swallowing. Cartilages: cricoid, thyroid, epiglottis, arytenoid cartilages, corniculate and cuneiform. Ligaments: extrinsic and intrinsic. Cavity of the larynx: entrance, extent of cavity, false vocal cords and true vocal cords; glottis. Function of vocal cords; regulation of position and tension. Muscles: extrinsic and intrinsic; four functions. Blood and nerve supply. Speech

d. Trachea; extent and location; structure

e. Bronchial tree: primary bronchi; branches to each lobe of the lung. Change in structure with change in size

B. Respiratory portion

a. Thoracic cavity: boundaries; contains lungs, etc.

b. Mediastinum: location and contents

c. Pleurae; visceral and parietal

d. Lungs: location, structure, surfaces and unit

SITUATION AND QUESTIONS

Three-year-old Sally Mayfair was given a shiny new penny. Not long after receiving the penny she put it into her mouth and promptly aspirated it. She was taken to the broncho-esophagology department of a nearby hospital.

1. Upon examination the doctor found that, as he had suspected, the penny was lodged in a branch of the right primary bronchus. Foreign bodies are most frequently found in the right lung because: _____(a) The right lung has 3 lobes and, therefore, is larger; _____(b) The right primary bronchus is more nearly vertical than the left, and it is also shorter and wider; _____(c) The walls of the right primary bronchus are more stiff and rigid than the left; _____(d) There are no cilia in the right primary bronchus.

2. Normally food and other foreign bodies by-pass the air passages and are swallowed, because during swallowing the position of the larynx changes and it is pulled up and against the base of the tongue. The name of the cartilage which stands upright at the

entrance of the larynx is the: _____(a) cricoid; _____(b) thyroid; _____(c) epiglottis; _____(d) arytenoid.

3. Foreign objects must be removed almost immediately so that air may enter the lung to allow for exchange of gases. The place of contact between the blood and inspired air is the: _____ (a) terminal bronchi; _____(b) trachea; _____(c) pleura; _____(d) alveoli.

4. As can be seen with a microscope, when the bronchi subdivide there is in the walls: _____(a) less cartilage and more smooth muscle; _____(b) more cartilage and more smooth muscle; _____(c) more cartilage and less smooth muscle; _____(d) less cartilage and less smooth muscle.

5. The tissue that lines the larynx, the trachea and the bronchial tubes is: _____(a) simple squamous epithelium; _____ (b) nonciliated columnar epithelium; _____(c) ciliated mucous membrane; _____(d) serous membrane.

6. After treatment and the removal of the penny, Sally had some hoarseness. The reason is that the vocal folds are located in the: _____(a) pharynx; _____(b) larynx; _____(c) trachea; _____(d) bronchi.

~~~~~~~~~~~~~~~~~~~~~~~~~~~~~~~~

13. Physiology of the Respiratory System

~~~~~~~~~~~~~~~~~~~~~~~~~~~~~~~~

MOVEMENTS OF RESPIRATION

In the preceding chapter, 3 statements were made which indicate the purpose of respiratory movements:

1. External respiration is taking fresh air into, and expelling stale air from, the lungs.

2. To complete the requirements for external respiration, a bellows arrangement, such as the lungs and the thoracic cage, with muscles to operate it and nerves to control it, is needed.

3. The thoracic cavity is a closed cavity which is changing constantly in size in various phases of respiration.

It is essential to study the movements of respiration in detail.

INSPIRATION

Inspiration is the act of taking air into the lungs. It is made up of a series of 4 events.

547

1. The diaphragm and the external intercostal muscles contract because impulses from the central nervous system come to them by way of the phrenic and the intercostal nerves, respectively.

2. As the diaphragm contracts, its dome moves downward and enlarges the thoracic cavity from top to bottom. The contraction of the external intercostal muscles raises the ribs and, at the same time, rotates them slightly, thereby pushing the sternum forward. This enlarges the thoracic cavity from side to side and from front to back.

3. The enlargement of the thoracic cavity in its 3 dimensions is accompanied by a lowering of pressure in the lower air passages and lungs.

4. Since the lungs are connected with the outside air by passages which are always open, air enters the lungs until the pressure of air within them is equal to atmospheric pressure.

This series of events is necessary to complete inspiration.

Expiration

Expiration is the act of expelling air from the lungs. It also is made up of a series of 4 events.

1. The diaphragm and the external intercostal muscles relax, due to cessation of impulses from the central nervous system. This is entirely passive.

2. As these muscles relax, the thoracic cavity is decreased in its 3 diameters.

3. As the thoracic cavity decreases in size, the pressure of air within the lungs is raised above atmospheric pressure.

4. Since the lungs communicate freely with the outside, air is forced out until the pressure of air within the lungs is again equal to atmospheric pressure.

This series of events is necessary to complete expiration.

By the movements of respiration some of the air in the lungs is renewed with each inspiration, and the same volume of stale air is expelled with each expiration. In this way the air in the alveoli is kept relatively fresh. The bronchial tree elongates with each inspiration and shortens with each expiration, as indicated in Figure 310.

PRESSURE CHANGES WITH RESPIRATORY MOVEMENTS

The pressure of air within the air passages and the lungs is called *intrapulmonic pressure*. Intrapulmonic pressure is below atmospheric pressure during inspiration, equal to atmospheric pressure

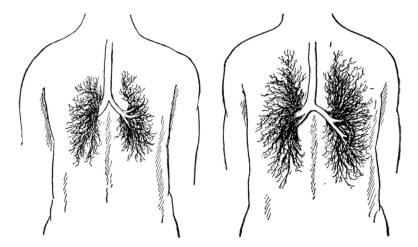

Fig. 310.   Drawn from roentgenograms of the bronchial tree.
(*Left*) In full expiration. (*Right*) In full inspiration.

at the end of inspiration, above atmospheric pressure during expiration and again equal to atmospheric pressure at the end of expiration.

This series of changes in intrapulmonic pressure is repeated with
each respiratory cycle. Whenever the size of the thoracic cavity
remains constant for a few seconds, or in a position of rest, the
intrapulmonic pressure is equal to atmospheric pressure.

There is another series of pressure changes which plays an important part in respiration: the changes in *intrapleural* pressure.
Intrapleural pressure is that pressure which exists between the 2
layers of the pleura or between the walls of the thoracic cage and
the lungs. Normally, the intrapleural pressure is below atmospheric
pressure throughout the respiratory cycle, because the thoracic cage
is larger than the lungs, which are greatly distended and always
tending to collapse due to their elasticity. The elastic recoil of the
lungs exerts a sort of pull on the thoracic walls. Although the intrapleural pressure is always negative or below atmospheric, it undergoes changes with each respiratory cycle, becoming lower or more
negative during inspiration and higher or less negative during
expiration. The negative intrapleural pressure not only plays a
part in respiration but it also has a decided effect on venous return of blood to the heart (p. 515).

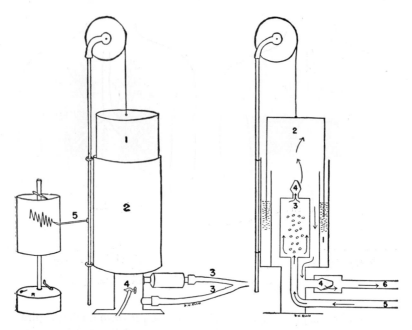

Fig. 311. (*Left*) Spirometer: 1, spirometer bell or inverted cylinder; 2, double-walled tank, for water seal; 3, inspiratory and expiratory tubes, which connect with mouthpiece; 4, stopcock through which spirometer bell may be filled with oxygen or room air; 5, inkwriter, which traces the movements of the spirometer bell on the kymograph. (*Right*) Longitudinal section of spirometer: 1, water seal in double-walled tank; 2, spirometer bell or chamber; 3, sodalime cannister through which expired air passes in order to remove carbon dioxide; 4, flutter valves which permit air to flow in only one direction, as indicated by arrows; 5, expiratory tube; 6, inspiratory tube. The tubes 5 and 6 are connected with a mouthpiece; the patient's nostrils are closed by a clip, and the respiratory tract is connected with the spirometer by means of the mouthpiece and the tubes.

VOLUME CHANGES WITH RESPIRATORY MOVEMENTS

The volume of air that moves in and out of the lungs with inspiration and expiration can be measured by means of a spirometer. The inside parts of a spirometer and the arrangement for recording are shown in Figure 311. The record produced by a patient breathing in and out of a spirometer is called a *spirogram* (Fig. 312) and it resembles in some respects the record made during a basal metabolism test.

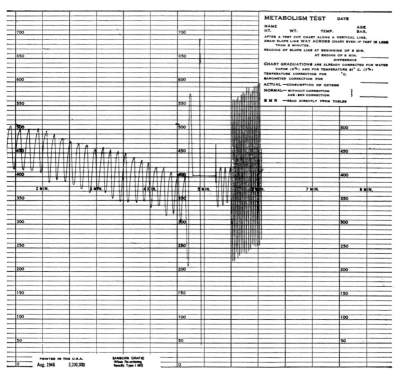

FIG. 312. Spirogram of healthy young woman, in sitting position. Three minutes of normal respiratory movements are shown. From this portion of the record the rate, the tidal volume, the minute volume of respiration and the oxygen use (from slope of record) may be determined. A record of vital capacity is shown next; the deepest possible inspiration is followed by the deepest possible expiration; the vital capacity, the inspiratory reserve and the expiratory reserve air may be measured. Then follows a record of the deepest and fastest respiration possible for half a minute (soda-lime cannister out); from this the maximal breathing capacity is determined.

PULMONARY FUNCTION TESTS

Tests of respiration, called *pulmonary function studies,* are very important in chest surgery. On spirograms made from patients the following information can be obtained:

1. Rate of Respiration. The number of respirations per minute can be counted. There are usually between 14 and 18 respiratory cycles per minute.

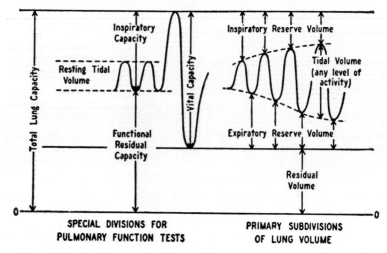

Fig. 313. Subdivisions of lung volume. (Federation Proc. 9:602)

2. Tidal Volume. This is the volume of air (or oxygen) moved in and out of the lungs with each respiratory movement. The average tidal volume is 500 cc. or 0.5 L.

3. Minute Volume of Respiration. This is calculated by multiplying the tidal volume by the number of respirations per minute. If an individual has an average tidal volume of 500 cc. and he breathes 15 times a minute, his minute volume of respiration is 7,500 cc. or 7.5 L.

4. Ratio of Inspiration to Expiration. This ratio is usually 1:1.2. In other words, if inspiration lasts 2 seconds, expiration lasts 2.4 seconds. The ratio is changed in an asthmatic patient in whom expiration is greatly prolonged.

5. Inspiratory Reserve. This is the volume of air, in excess of the tidal, that can be inhaled by the deepest possible inspiration. It averages 3,000 cc. or 3 L. Individuals who play wind instruments can inhale much more than this.

6. Expiratory Reserve. This is the volume of air, in excess of the tidal, which can be exhaled by the deepest possible expiration, after a normal inspiration. It is about 1,000 cc. or 1 L.

7. Vital Capacity. This may be defined in 2 ways. (A) It is the volume of air that can be exhaled by the deepest possible expiration after the deepest possible inspiration. (B) It is the sum of the tidal, the inspiratory reserve and the expiratory reserve air.

The average vital capacity is 4,500 cc. or 4.5 L. Physical education students, athletes and individuals who play wind instruments have much greater vital capacities than average individuals.

8. Oxygen Use. This can be calculated from the slope of the spirogram. The average is 300 cc. or 0.3 L. per minute.

9. Maximal Breathing Capacity. This refers to the greatest volume of air that can be moved in and out of the lungs in 1 minute. It is determined by breathing as rapidly and as deeply as possible

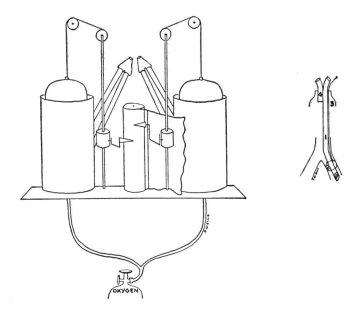

Fig. 314. Bronchospirometer and Norris catheter. The bronchospirometer is a double spirometer; it permits the registration of the exchanges of each lung separately and simultaneously. In the catheter (right), 1 is the tube introduced into the left main stem bronchus; 2 is the balloon which, when distended, permits the passage of air to and from the left lung only through the tube; 3 is the face mask. 4 is the tube which permits the passage of air to and from the right lung. As the tubes leave the face mask they are connected with their respective spirometers, and the exchanges for each lung are recorded. The face mask is used instead of a mouthpiece. Bronchospirometry is done under local anesthesia of pharynx, larynx, trachea and bronchi; the patient is not in a basal state.

for 30 seconds, and then multiplying this volume by 2 to get the results for 1 minute. It is about 100 L. for a young adult.

10. Ventilatory Equivalent. This refers to the volume of air moved in and out of the lungs in order to absorb 100 cc. of oxygen. It averages between 2 and 3 L.

The measurable volumes of air are shown by diagram in Figure 313.

BRONCHOSPIROMETRY

It may be necessary to remove a lobe of one lung, or even an entire lung, from patients who have cancer of the lung. Before such an operation is done, it is essential to know the condition of the healthy lung. Bronchospirometry is the study of the function of the two lungs separately, at the same time. A bronchospirometer is a double spirometer; each lung is connected with one spirometer. The apparatus is shown in Figure 314.

Under local anesthesia a special catheter is introduced into the respiratory passages which establishes connection between each lung and its respective spirometer. An illustration of a record made by bronchospirometry is shown in Figure 315. The record from the right lung is above, and the one from the left lung is below. It is obvious that the right lung is taking a much smaller share of the respiratory work than the left. Normally, the right lung does about 55 per cent of the total work, and the left about 45 per cent.

RESIDUAL VOLUME

The residual air remains in the lungs even after the deepest possible expiration and cannot be removed by voluntary effort. The average volume of residual air is 1.5 L. It is eliminated only by collapse of the lungs. Thus, in the lungs we normally have 1.5 L. of residual air and 1 L. of expiratory reserve air or 2.5 L. at the end of a normal expiration. We breathe in only 0.5 L. with each inspiration and thus renew only one fifth of the air in the lungs with each respiratory cycle. It is evident that a sudden, great change in the composition of alveolar air is prevented.

Minimal Air. If a baby has taken even one breath, the lungs retain some air that is trapped in the alveoli and is not eliminated even by collapse of the lungs. This is called *minimal air,* and it is important in medicolegal practice.

Dead-space Air. The volume of air that remains in the passages during inspiration (larynx, trachea and bronchial tree) plays no

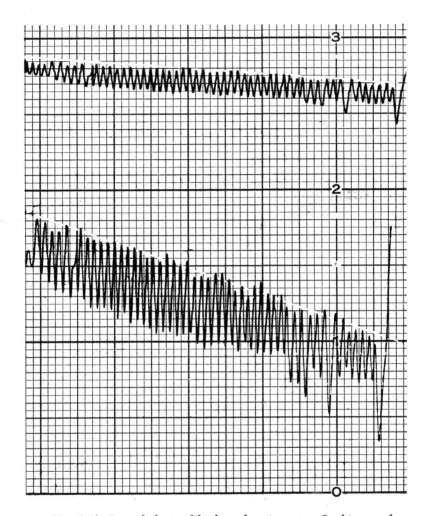

FIG. 315. Record obtained by bronchospirometry. In this record the right lung exchanges are above and the left below. Oxygen use, rate, tidal volume, minute volume and vital capacity for each lung can be determined from such a record. In chest surgery it is imperative to know the functional capacity of one lung before the other is removed.

part in gaseous exchanges of respiration; consequently, it is called *dead-space air.* It is about 150 cc. for men and 110 for women.

CONTROL OF RESPIRATION

A high degree of co-ordination is necessary to bring about contraction of the inspiratory muscles at the proper time and with the proper gradation to meet the changing requirements of the body for oxygen. A respiratory center is needed to correlate the activities of the respiratory muscles, and such a center, consisting of inspiratory and expiratory portions, is located in the medulla.

The respiratory center can be affected by impulses from various parts of the nervous system and by impulses from any part of the body, as well as by the chemical composition and the temperature of the blood flowing through the center. In other words, respiration is controlled by both nervous and chemical factors.

You may think of the nervous control as regulatory, in that it enables respiration to meet the changing needs of the body. You may consider the chemical control as fundamentally basic, in that it keeps you breathing in spite of your attempts to control respiration voluntarily, and it maintains respiration when the nervous control is at a minimum, such as during sleep.

NERVOUS CONTROL

During normal, quiet breathing or *eupnea* (meaning "well breathing") the only muscles that contract to bring about inspiration are the diaphragm and the external intercostal muscles. In normal expiration, the diaphragm and the external intercostal muscles relax; this phase of normal respiration is passive. The phrenic nerves supply the diaphragm, and the intercostal nerves supply the external intercostal muscles. These nerves may be considered as "final common paths."

In order to breathe more deeply, as during mild exercise, there must be forceful contractions of the above muscles. More and more motor units are brought into action, and there are more impulses per unit of time conducted over each axon. This means that the responses of the inspiratory muscles progress through various degrees of incomplete tetanic contractions to complete short tetanic contractions. There is a wide range of gradation possible in the depth of respiration, since any number of motor units may be brought into activity.

Difficult breathing (called *dyspnea*), such as occurs in disease or in severe exercise, makes use of any muscles by whose action the ribs are elevated. The following muscles may be brought into use in inspiration during dyspnea: trapezius, rhomboids, sterno-cleidomastoids, scalene muscles, pectoralis major and minor muscles, levatores costarum, serratus posterior and anterior muscles.

Expiration is normally passive; in dyspnea it may become active, and the muscles that depress the ribs are used. These are the internal intercostals, the triangularis sterni and the muscles of the abdominal wall.

In order to breathe more rapidly, there are shorter intervals of rest between bursts of impulses in the phrenic and the intercostal nerves. In this way the rate of respiration is increased.

The nervous control of respiration may be divided into voluntary and reflex types of control.

Voluntary Control. Impulses pass from the motor cortex to the respiratory center. Therefore, a person may voluntarily hold his breath for a short time or may breathe more rapidly, more slowly, more deeply or more superficially for short periods of time. However, voluntary control is limited, and soon the respiration progresses in a normal fashion despite one's voluntary efforts to control it.

Reflex Control. The reflex control of respiration is exceedingly important. Afferent impulses which set up respiratory reflexes may arise from any region of the body.

AFFERENT IMPULSES FROM THE LUNGS. Afferent impulses which arise from the lungs are of the greatest significance in the reflex control of respiration. Each time the lungs are distended, during inspiration, receptors, which are sensitive to stretch or distention, are stimulated. Such receptors are located in the alveolar ducts. Impulses are conducted to the central nervous system by way of the vagus nerves. These impulses inhibit the inspiratory center, and impulses to the diaphragm and the external intercostal muscles cease, thereby bringing about relaxation of these muscles, which means that expiration occurs. It is evident that each inspiration is cut short by impulses from the lungs themselves. This reflex control, called the *Hering-Breuer reflex,* is a self-steering mechanism.

The Hering-Breuer reflex is important in the minute-to-minute regulation of respiration. If the afferent fibers from the lungs are cut, inspiration is greatly prolonged, and the respirations become slower and deeper.

Chemoreceptors in Aortic and Carotid Bodies. (Combination of nervous and chemical control.) The carotid and the aortic bodies are cords and clumps of epithelial-like cells, with sinusoidal capillaries between them. The cells are richly supplied with nerve endings and constitute the chemoreceptors which are so called because they are sensitive to changes in the chemical composition of the blood. Whenever the amount of oxygen dissolved in the plasma (called the *oxygen tension*) falls, the chemoreceptors are stimulated, and impulses are sent in to the central nervous system over the vagus nerves (from the aortic body) and the glossopharyngeal nerves (from the carotid bodies, Fig. 288). Such impulses stimulate the inspiratory center and thereby increase the depth and the rate of respiration. These reflexes are of great importance in emergencies in which the oxygen supply to the body is below normal (as in flying at high altitudes, in lung diseases and in heart disease) and are protective in nature.

Baroceptors or Pressoreceptors in Aortic and Carotid Sinuses. These receptors are affected by sudden, marked changes in blood pressure. When arterial blood pressure rises suddenly, impulses are sent in from the baroceptors by way of the vagus and the glossopharyngeal nerves to the central nervous system. Such impulses depress the activity of the respiratory center, and respiration becomes slower and more shallow, temporarily.

When the arterial blood pressure falls suddenly, as after a severe hemorrhage, the number of impulses reaching the central nervous system from the baroceptors decreases, and the respiratory center increases its activity, thereby increasing the rate and probably the depth of respiration.

However, it must be kept in mind that the baroceptors are not nearly as important in the control of respiration as they are in the control of circulation, while the chemoreceptors are of greater importance in the control of respiration than in the control of circulation.

Afferent Impulses from the Respiratory Passages. There are receptors in the mucous membrane lining the respiratory passages that are sensitive to irritating substances. An irritating substance in the nose, such as pepper, induces a sneeze. The presence of a crumb in the larynx or the trachea induces a spell of coughing. Reflexes which are aroused by stimulation of receptors in the mu-

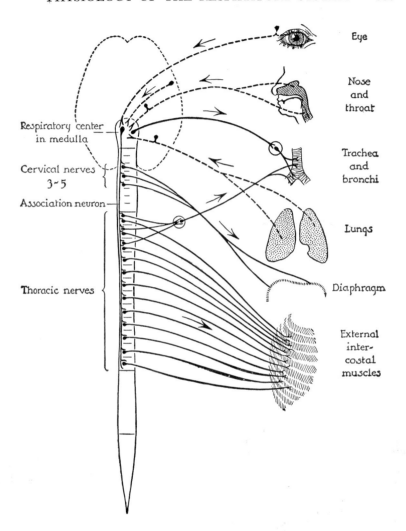

Eye

Nose
and
throat

Trachea
and
bronchi

Lungs

Diaphragm

External
inter-
costal
muscles

Respiratory center
in medulla

Cervical nerves
3-5

Association neuron

Thoracic nerves

FIG. 316. Connections of the respiratory center in the medulla. Any afferent fiber, fibers from higher centers, from the respiratory passages and from the lungs may influence the activity of the respiratory center. Internuncial (associational) neurons establish connections between the center and the cells in the spinal cord; axons from these cells go to the muscles of respiration. Hence, the respiratory movements may be altered by a variety of stimuli.

cosa of the respiratory passages are protective and tend to remove the irritating substance from the body.

Afferent Impulses from Other Areas of the Body. Receptors of various kinds in other parts of the body may give rise to "incidental" reflexes of respiration. You may see something that makes you gasp or hold your breath momentarily. You may hear a shriek that either speeds up your respiratory rate or stops all respiratory movements for a few seconds. When you touch something cold and slimy, you gasp. Thus, respiratory reflexes can be aroused by a variety of stimuli which affect many types of receptors.

Figure 316 illustrates the respiratory center and some of the afferent pathways by which impulses reach the central nervous system and alter activity in the respiratory system. The efferent pathways for all respiratory reflexes are the phrenic and the intercostal nerves, which are the final common paths for such reflexes.

CHEMICAL CONTROL

The chemical control is responsible for the fundamental rhythm of the respiratory center and is active throughout the day and the night. It keeps us breathing when the nervous control is at a minimum, such as in sleep. It is the chemical control of respiration which comes to the rescue of the distraught mother whose child, in a fit of temper, is holding his breath until he becomes "blue in the face." If only she can remain calm a few seconds longer, he will breathe whether he wishes or not, as the chemical control overcomes the voluntary effort, and the air in his little rebellious lungs will be freshened.

The cells in the respiratory center are exceedingly sensitive to carbon dioxide dissolved in arterial plasma (called *carbon dioxide tension*). When this increases to the slightest extent above normal, the respiratory center is stimulated, and one breathes faster and deeper until the excess carbon dioxide is blown off. An increase in carbon dioxide tension is called *hypercapnia*.

If there is a decrease in carbon dioxide tension (called *acapnia*) in arterial blood, cessation of breathing or apnea ensues. This situation follows any period of hyperventilation, such as in hysteria from fear. Acapnia does not persist long, since carbon dioxide is produced constantly by metabolic processes in all cells, and it soon accumulates to the required level to stimulate the respiratory center again.

In summary, the fundamental rhythm of respiration, which is due to the carbon dioxide tension of arterial blood, is modified by

afferent impulses from the lungs, the respiratory passages, the baroceptors in the aortic and the carotid sinuses, the chemoreceptors
in the aortic and the carotid bodies and other regions of the body,
in accordance with changes in internal or external environment.
The center that controls respiration is affected not only by carbon
dioxide and afferent impulses but also by the temperature of the
blood that flows through it. When the temperature of the blood is
above the normal range, as during fever or severe muscular exercise, the respiratory center is stimulated, and respiration is increased markedly in rate and perhaps also in depth.

CHEMISTRY OF RESPIRATION

COMPOSITION OF INSPIRED, EXPIRED AND ALVEOLAR AIR

The amounts of respiratory gases vary in inspired, expired and
alveolar air, as indicated in the table. In each case, the remainder
of the air is mostly nitrogen, which brings the total to 100 per cent.

	PERCENTAGE OF OXYGEN	PERCENTAGE OF CARBON DIOXIDE
Inspired air	21.00	0.04
Expired air	16.00	4.40
Alveolar air	14.00	5.50

You will note that expired air contains less oxygen and more
carbon dioxide than inspired air, and that alveolar air contains less
oxygen and more carbon dioxide than expired air. Expired air is
really a mixture of alveolar and inspired air from the dead space.
The composition of alveolar air is fairly constant, and only one
fifth of the air in the lungs is renewed by each inspiration. In this
way, sudden and marked changes in the composition of alveolar
air are prevented.

In addition to the differences in content of oxygen and carbon
dioxide, there are physical differences between inspired air and expired and alveolar air. Expired and alveolar airs are saturated with
water vapor and warmed to body temperature. The amount of
water vapor and the temperature of inspired air vary markedly in
different localities and in different seasons. One loses heat by warm-
ing the inspired air whenever its temperature is below body temperature; one also loses heat by saturating inspired air whenever
it is not saturated as it enters his respiratory passages.

DIFFUSION OF GASES

Gases diffuse rapidly from higher to lower concentrations, due
to molecular movement. Diffusion continues until concentrations

are equal throughout the space in which the gases are contained.

In the body the concentration of oxygen is higher in alveolar air than it is in venous blood coming to the lungs from the right ventricle; therefore, oxygen diffuses into the blood from the alveolar air. The concentration of oxygen is low in the cells of the body tissues and in tissue fluid; therefore, oxygen diffuses from the blood in the capillaries into the tissue fluid and on into tissue cells.

The concentration of carbon dioxide in the tissue cells and the tissue fluid is higher than it is in the blood in the capillaries. Therefore, carbon dioxide diffuses from tissue cells and tissue fluid into blood. The concentration of carbon dioxide is higher in venous blood coming to the lungs from the right ventricle than it is in alveolar air; therefore, it diffuses from blood in pulmonary capillaries into the alveolar air.

TRANSPORT OF GASES IN THE BLOOD

Oxygen is carried in 2 ways in the blood.

1. A small amount is carried in solution in the plasma. It is this portion that exerts "tension" and is available for diffusion whenever the blood reaches a region of low oxygen tension, such as in the systemic capillaries where the oxygen tension of the surrounding tissue fluid and the tissue cells is low.

2. The remainder of oxygen in the blood is combined with hemoglobin in erythrocytes to form oxyhemoglobin. This oxygen is given up readily by the hemoglobin whenever the oxygen tension of the plasma decreases, so that as fast as oxygen diffuses from the plasma in tissue capillaries it is replenished by more from the oxyhemoglobin. Hemoglobin that has given up its load of oxygen is called *reduced hemoglobin.*

When blood returns to the lungs from the right ventricle, its reduced hemoglobin is ready to take up a new load of oxygen and become oxyhemoglobin again. The total amount of oxygen in 100 cc. of arterial blood is about 20 cc.; of this, 0.5 cc. is dissolved in the plasma and 19.5 cc. are combined with hemoglobin in erythrocytes.

Carbon dioxide is carried in 4 ways in the blood.

1. A small amount is carried in solution in the plasma; it is this portion that exerts "tension," which means that it is available for diffusion whenever it encounters a region of lower tension, such as in the pulmonary capillaries in the presence of alveolar air.

2. A large amount of carbon dioxide is carried as sodium acid

carbonate (commonly called *sodium bicarbonate*) in the plasma.

3. A small amount is carried in the erythrocytes as potassium acid carbonate.

4. A moderate amount is carried in the erythrocytes in combination with hemoglobin, in the form of a carbamino compound.

The total amount of carbon dioxide in 100 cc. of venous blood is about 60 cc. Of this, about 2.5 cc. are carried in solution in the plasma, 43 cc. as sodium acid carbonate, about 2.5 cc. as potassium acid carbonate in erythrocytes, and the remainder, which is about 12 cc., is carried as the carbamino compound of hemoglobin in erythrocytes.

The events which follow the diffusion of carbon dioxide into the blood from the tissue fluid and the tissue cells are as follows: As carbon dioxide enters the blood it passes at once into erythrocytes and unites with water to form carbonic acid. This union is accelerated by an enzyme, *carbonic anhydrase*, that is present in the erythrocytes. Carbonic acid dissociates immediately into hydrogen ions and bicarbonate ions (HCO_3). Some of the bicarbonate ions then unite with potassium (from hemoglobin) to form potassium acid carbonate. More bicarbonate ions diffuse out into the plasma, take the place of Cl in NaCl and form sodium acid carbonate. The displaced Cl ions diffuse into erythrocytes. Some bicarbonate ions combine with hemoglobin (by means of its NH_2 groups) to form the carbamino compound of hemoglobin. The reverse process occurs in the lungs. The passage of Cl ions into erythrocytes in the systemic capillaries and back out into the plasma in the pulmonary capillaries is called the chloride shift.

Nitrogen is carried only in solution in the plasma; it is not a respiratory gas, and it takes no part in gaseous exchanges concerned with metabolism.

MAINTENANCE OF ACID-BASE BALANCE

Since respiration is of such great importance in the regulation of acid-base balance, the latter merits consideration at this time.

REACTION OF THE BLOOD

In order for the cells of the body to perform their functions normally, under optimal conditions, a liquid environment with a slightly alkaline reaction (pH 7.4) is essential. The reaction of the internal environment must be maintained at a fairly constant level, in spite of great fluctuations in the amounts of acid and base ingested in food and the equally great fluctuations in the amounts of acids produced by the metabolism of the cells. The only source of fixed base is the food; the sources of acid are the food and the metabolic processes.

Two groups of factors are involved in the maintenance of a normal acid-base balance or constant pH; these factors are (1) physicochemical and (2) physiologic.

Physicochemical Factors. These deal with the buffers of the blood. Buffers are substances which make it possible for the blood to take up large amounts of acid or base without a marked change in reaction or pH. To give you an idea of the importance of buffers of the blood, you can add 300 times as much acid to blood as you can to distilled water before the pH changes by an equal amount.

The buffers of the blood are arranged in the following pairs: $NaHCO_3$ and $HHCO_3$; Na_2HPO_4 and NaH_2PO_4; alkali protein and acid protein; oxyhemoglobin (alkali hemoglobin) and reduced hemoglobin (acid hemoglobin).

All of the ability of the body to neutralize acid or base resides in these buffers. "Alkaline reserve" refers to the sodium that is combined with bicarbonate and is available to neutralize acid at once. Suppose, for example, that hydrochloric acid (HCl) is added to the blood. Immediately there is a reaction between sodium acid carbonate and hydrochloric acid, as follows: $NaHCO_3 + HCl = NaCl + HHCO_3$. Sodium chloride is a neutral salt; the carbonic acid immediately dissociates into water and carbon dioxide (H_2O and CO_2). Of these, water is neutral in reaction, but carbon dioxide stimulates the respiratory center, so that the excess is blown off immediately, and the normal level of carbon dioxide is attained again. Despite the addition of such a strong acid as hydrochloric acid, the reaction or pH of the blood is not changed, as shown above.

Under ordinary conditions, acids are neutralized by buffers as rapidly as they are produced by metabolic processes. Under the following conditions, the production of acid may exceed the capacity of the buffers for neutralization, and the reaction of the fluids of the body be changed: (1) during violent muscular exercise, when lactic acid may accumulate in large amounts; (2) in severe asphyxia, when lactic acid may accumulate in large amounts; (3) in severe untreated diabetes mellitus (p. 741), when the acetone bodies may accumulate; (4) in advanced kidney disease, when phosphoric and sulfuric acids may accumulate in the blood; (5) in prolonged starvation, when acetone bodies may accumulate. Excess acids are eliminated in the form of salts by the kidneys. This means that acids combine with base and in this way carry base out with them in the urine, thereby depleting the alkaline reserve of the body and leading to acidosis.

During prolonged vomiting one loses large amounts of hydrochloric acid in the gastric juice which is present in the vomitus. In such a case, the blood is depleted of chloride (an acid radical), and too much base is left in the blood (alkalosis). A similar condition may follow the intake of large amounts of sodium acid carbonate in the treatment of peptic ulcer.

In the examples given above, it is evident that under certain circumstances the capacity of the buffers to neutralize acids or bases may be exceeded. When this happens the reaction (or pH) of the body fluids does change. If the pH changes toward the acid side, the condition is called *acidosis;* if the pH rises above 7.4 the condition is called *alkalosis.*

Physiologic Factors. Two important physiologic factors are involved in the maintenance of acid-base balance: (1) pulmonary ventilation or respiration and (2) production of urine by the kidneys or output of acid and base in the urine.

PULMONARY VENTILATION. Respiration is adjusted by the level of carbon dioxide in the blood. The respiratory center is stimulated by an increase in carbon dioxide (hypercapnia) and inhibited by a decrease in carbon dioxide (acapnia). This means that excess carbon dioxide is blown off in hypercapnia, and respiration is decreased in acapnia, permitting carbon dioxide to accumulate until the usual level is reached.

RENAL EXCRETION OF ACID AND BASE. There are 3 ways in which the kidneys can regulate the amount of acid or base which they eliminate in the urine.

1. The kidneys produce ammonia, which replaces some of the sodium united with acid radicals. In this way fixed base or sodium is conserved for the body, and ammonium salts are excreted. The amount of ammonia produced varies, with tendencies toward acidosis or alkalosis.

2. Both Na_2HPO_4 (which is alkaline) and NaH_2PO_4 (which is acid) can be eliminated in the urine. Normally, as the urine flows through the distal convoluted tubules (p. 663) the amount of Na_2HPO_4 decreases and the amount of NaH_2PO_4 increases, due to activity of the tubular cells, which tend to conserve sodium. If there is a tendency toward acidosis, more of the acid salt is excreted than usual, and if there is a tendency toward alkalosis, more of the alkaline salt is excreted than usual.

3. Normally, no sodium bicarbonate appears in the urine. If

there is a tendency toward alkalosis, this salt does appear in the urine, and in this way the body gets rid of some of the excess base.

The renal adjustments are slower than those made by changes in respiration, but they are exceedingly important in helping to prevent marked changes in pH of the body fluids.

If normal amounts of buffers are present in the blood, and if the lungs and the kidneys are normal, one can recover promptly from the effects of severe muscular exercise, intake of acid or base, unbalanced diets (so far as acids and bases are concerned), short periods of starvation, short bouts of vomiting and other adverse conditions. But there are limits to the adjustments that the body can make; if the capacity is exceeded, the pH changes, and this prevents the body cells from performing their functions normally.

MUSCULAR EXERCISE

During exercise more oxygen is needed for the active muscles, and many changes are essential to meet this demand.

Changes in Respiration. Breathing is deeper and faster during muscular exercise. There is an increase in minute volume of respiration, so that more air is moved into and out of the lungs each minute. If the exercise is severe, not enough oxygen can be taken in to supply the demand, and the individual runs into debt for oxygen.

Changes in Circulation. The contractions of skeletal muscles pump venous blood back to the heart more rapidly than normal. This increases venous pressure in the great veins, and there is better filling of the heart during diastole. A more forceful beat and a faster rate mean a greater cardiac output, which raises arterial blood pressure.

The vessels in skeletal muscles and the coronaries are dilated, and this means a better blood supply both to the active skeletal muscles and to the heart muscle. More capillaries are open in active muscles, and they are widely open, due to a higher concentration of metabolic products.

Changes in the Blood. The venous blood that returns from active muscles contains less oxygen than usual; more lactic acid is present than during rest. The temperature of the active tissues is elevated. The dissociation of oxyhemoglobin is increased, so a greater amount of oxygen is given up to the active muscles than under resting conditions.

Changes in Body Temperature. More heat is produced by active muscles, and the body temperature rises because the loss of heat cannot keep pace with the increased production. The higher temperature means that the speed of chemical reactions in the active muscles is faster, the dissociation of oxyhemoglobin is more nearly complete, and the respiratory center is stimulated.

Changes in Kidney Function. The blood flow through the kidneys is decreased during severe exercise, which means a decreased output of urine.

Changes in Metabolism. The muscles cannot get enough oxygen to "pay as they go" during severe muscular exercise. As glycogen breaks down to pyruvic acid, there is not enough oxygen to oxidize pyruvic acid to carbon dioxide and water. Consequently, it changes to lactic acid and accumulates as such. As soon as exercise is over, the oxygen debt must be paid; this is accomplished by increased respiration which continues for a long time after severe exercise is over. Most of the lactic acid is reconverted to glycogen (by way of pyruvic acid) to pay off the debt; some of it is excreted in the urine as lactic acid. The concentration of lactic acid in the blood and the urine may be 10 times as great as normal in severe exercise.

The possibility of running up an oxygen debt means that we can work for a short time far in excess of our available oxygen, but the debt must be paid off immediately at the close of the bout of exercise.

PRACTICAL CONSIDERATIONS

Respiratory failure leads to lack of oxygen in the cells of the body, a condition called *anoxia*. A more appropriate term is *hypoxia*, since some oxygen is present, but not enough. The term *anoxemia* means "lack of oxygen in the blood"; it should be replaced by *anoxia*. Nervous tissue is very sensitive to lack of oxygen; the cells of the cerebral cortex are damaged beyond repair if deprived of oxygen for as short a time as 8 minutes.

There are 4 common causes for lack of sufficient oxygen for the cells of the body.

Anoxic Anoxia. This refers to decreased oxygen saturation of hemoglobin in the blood because there is insufficient oxygen in the alveolar air. This condition occurs most often when one ascends rapidly to high altitudes in airplanes, without inhaling oxygen or being in a pressurized cabin. It occurs also when there is a sudden obstruction in the air passages.

2. Anemic Anoxia. This occurs in patients who are suffering from anemia, in whom there is not enough hemoglobin to carry

the required amount of oxygen. This is a chronic type of anoxia, and damage to the cells of the nervous system is evident as the condition continues.

3. STAGNANT ANOXIA. This is due to a slow rate of circulation of blood in heart disease. More oxygen than usual diffuses from the capillaries to the tissue fluid, as the blood flow slows, but new supplies are brought too slowly to meet the requirements of the tissue cells.

4. HISTOTOXIC ANOXIA. This occurs when poisons such as cyanide enter the body. Such poisons destroy the enzyme systems present in cells, and the oxygen that is present cannot be used, owing to the destruction of enzymes.

Cyanosis. This refers to a bluish coloration of the skin; it is due to the greater amount of reduced hemoglobin (hemoglobin that has given up its oxygen) in the blood. Cyanosis is evident in the anoxic and stagnant types of anoxia. A patient may be suffering from anoxia and yet not be cyanosed in the anemic and the histotoxic types of anoxia.

Similarity of Acute Alcoholism and Acute Anoxia. Acute fulminating anoxic anoxia and acute alcoholism are similar in some respects. In both, there is a feeling of euphoria or well-being, at first, and then the judgment is lost, and there is inability to concentrate, to co-ordinate muscular movements, and eventually paralysis and unconsciousness occur.

Chronic Anoxia. Individuals who live at high altitudes may suffer from chronic anoxic anoxia. There are some compensatory mechanisms which tend to make up for the lack of oxygen, such as an increased number of erythrocytes, increased pulmonary ventilation and output of alkaline urine which contains no ammonia. These changes serve to "acclimatize" individuals who dwell at high altitudes.

Pneumothorax. If an opening is made into the pleural cavity through the intercostal muscles, a sucking noise is heard, as air is drawn in from outside, and the lung is collapsed. When a patient comes into the accident dispensary with a stab wound in the chest, the instrument used in making the stab should be left in place until provision has been made to close the opening and prevent collapse of the lung. As you would suspect, a collapsed lung is of no use in respiration.

Alterations in Rate of Respiration. The rate of respiration varies with age. In the newborn it is 40; in the infant, 30; in a 5-year-old child, 25; and in an adult, between 14 and 18 per minute. One case is reported in which a young lady had a normal rate of 3 per minute. The rate is increased in fever due to any cause. Usually it is increased in acidosis and after hemorrhage.

Modified Respiratory Movements. Normally, both the diaphragm and the external intercostal muscles are used in inspiration. In some individuals the diaphragm (abdominal type) predominates; in others the external intercostals (costal type) predominate. A record of a good balance between costal and abdominal factors is shown in Figure 317. Normal breathing is called *eupnea.*

Difficult respiration is called *dyspnea.* Rapid respiration is called *hyperpnea.* The inability to breathe when in the recumbent position is called *orthopnea.* Temporary cessation of breathing is called *apnea.*

Respiration may be periodic in the terminal stages of many diseases. The most common type of periodic respiration is called *Cheyne-Stokes respiration.* In this type there is a period of apnea lasting several seconds; then respiration begins, at first, very short and shallow; then each becomes a bit deeper until a maximum is reached; and then it tapers off until apnea occurs again. Each time the period of apnea occurs, you think that the patient has expired. This type of respiration indicates a respiratory center that is badly damaged by anoxia or toxins. Figure 318 is a record of Cheyne-Stokes respiration in a very ill patient.

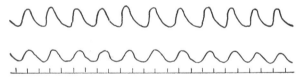

FIG. 317. Respiratory movements in a normal subject. The upper line indicates the movements of the thoracic walls; the lower line indicates the movements of the abdominal walls. (Minnesota Med.)

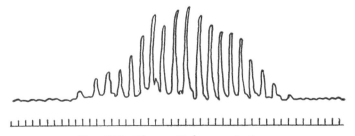

FIG. 318. Cheyne-Stokes respiration.

In asthma there is prolongation of the expiratory phase of respiration, and the ratio of inspiration to expiration is altered, since there is difficulty in getting air out of the lungs. In Figure 319, taken from an asthmatic patient, the prolongation of expiration is evident in the thoracic record. Wheezing in asthmatic patients is due to air being forced out through constricted bronchioles.

Figure 320 is a record taken on a patient suffering from lobar pneumonia. It is evident that the external intercostal muscles and the diaphragm are not working in unison. The external intercostal muscles begin to contract just as the diaphragm begins to relax. This dissociation or asynchronism is noted occasionally in seriously ill patients; the significance is not understood.

Morphine has a depressing effect on the respiratory center. The

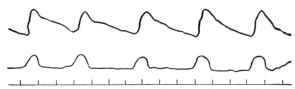

Fig. 319. Respiratory movements in asthma. Prolongation of expiration is noted in the thoracic record. (Minnesota Med.)

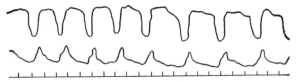

Fig. 320. Respiratory movements in lobar pneumonia. Asynchronism is noted; the thoracic inspiration begins just as the diaphragmatic expiration begins. (Minnesota Med.)

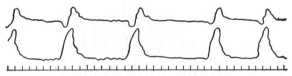

Fig. 321. Respiratory movements in morphine addict. The rate is very slow; the patient failed to recover. (Minnesota Med.)

slow rate in a morphine addict who had taken an overdose of the drug is illustrated in Figure 321. We had to keep this patient up and walking about until some of the drug was eliminated. Respiratory failure due to overdose of morphine may occur if the respiratory center is not stimulated vigorously. When an injection of morphine is given to any patient it should be charted at once; otherwise it may be repeated by another nurse, and a serious depression of respiration might ensue.

If morphine is given to a woman in labor just before delivery the respiratory center of the newborn may be so depressed that it cannot function, and respiration cannot be established. The question of sedation and anesthesia is a vital one in obstetrics; in the Reed method, mothers go through childbirth without medication.

A cough is a sudden, violent expulsion of air after a deep inspiration and temporary closure of the glottis to build up pressure in the lower respiratory passages. A cough results from the stimulation of the mucous membrane in the respiratory tract.

A sneeze is a violent expiration; air is expelled through the nose. Usually it is due to stimulation of the endings of the trigeminal

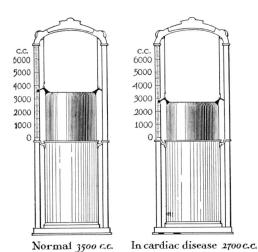

Normal *3500 c.c.*   In cardiac disease *2700 c.c.*

Fig. 322. (*Left*) Vital capacity of 3,500 cc. in a normal individual. (*Right*) Vital capacity of 2,700 cc. in a patient with heart disease; the congested pulmonary capillaries encroach upon the space normally occupied by alveolar air.

nerve in the nasal mucosa by irritating substances or particles of pollen to which the individual is sensitive.

YAWNING is a prolonged, deep inspiration which indicates mental or physical weariness or even boredom.

A SIGH is a prolonged inspiration, followed by a deep expiration.

HICCOUGH is due to spasmodic contraction of the diaphragm, which causes a sudden inspiration. A sudden closure of the glottis shortens inspiration and gives origin to the characteristic sound. Often it is due to irritation of the stomach. Persistent hiccough may indicate cancer of the stomach.

After injury to the phrenic nerves the diaphragm is paralyzed, and the external intercostal muscles bear the full responsibility of inspiration. Respiration is costal in type in such cases.

Sometimes during the course of administration of an anesthetic, the external intercostal muscles cease to contract during inspiration. When this occurs the patient is said to have "paradoxical" respiration, and it indicates too deep a level of anesthesia.

Vital capacity is reduced in heart disease, because a large amount of blood accumulates in the pulmonary circuit, and the dilated vessels encroach on the space normally occupied by alveolar air. Reduced vital capacity is illustrated by diagram in Figure 322. Vital capacity is reduced in any condition in which there is muscular weakness, since the patient is not capable of the great muscular effort required in testing vital capacity.

Oxygen use is increased if the thyroid gland is overactive, and it is reduced if the gland is underactive.

Observing Patients' Respiratory Rates. It is important that nurses observe and count respiratory rates when patients are unaware of it. This may be done while the nurse apparently is counting the pulse. If a patient knows that his respiration is being observed he may try to alter it voluntarily, or he may be unable to breathe normally while being watched. Respiration seems bound to change when we become conscious of it.

Artificial respiration is administered routinely by anesthetists during the course of all lung and heart operations and often during long abdominal operations. It is administered during resuscitation after drowning, electric shock, asphyxiation and in infantile paralysis.

In the operating room an anesthetist compresses the bag of the anesthetic machine by hand, to administer artificial respiration by way of a catheter in the trachea or a mask over the nose and the mouth, attached to the gas machine. Artificial respiration is easy

Fig. 323. Arm-lift, back-pressure method of giving manual artificial respiration (after Holger Nielson). From *top* to *bottom*, the operations are: placing hands for arm lift; the arm lift; placing hands for back pressure; applying back pressure. (Gordon, A. S., *et al.*: A critical survey of manual artificial respiration, J.A.M.A. 147:1444)

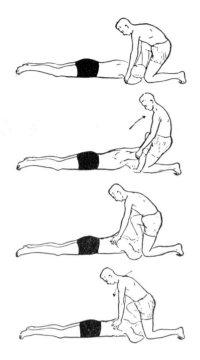

to manage by this method, and there should be a portable gas machine in all emergency stations for the administration of oxygen by artificial respiration.

If no gas machine is at hand, or while waiting for a rescue squad, artificial respiration is administered by the back pressure—arm lift method, which is approved by the American Red Cross. This is for use by the general public when dealing with cases of asphyxia or apnea from other causes.

The patient is placed in a prone position, with elbows bent, arms overhead, with one hand upon the other. A cheek is placed on the hands, the face turned slightly to one side.

The operator kneels on one knee at the head of the patient and puts the foot of the opposite leg near the elbow. He places his hands on the patient's back in such a way that the thumbs just touch each other, the "heels" of the hands being just below a line running between the armpits. He rocks slowly forward, elbows straight, until his arms are approximately vertical, exerting steady pressure upon the chest. This causes expiration or the passage of air out of the lungs. Then the operator begins to rock backward slowly and slides his hand to the patient's arms just above the elbows. He raises the arms until resistance and tension are felt at the patient's shoulders. This brings about inspiration or the entrance of air into the lungs. Then he drops the arms. This completes a full cycle. This method is an improvement over older methods because, as stated above, it not only aids expiration but also inspiration.

The cycles are repeated 12 times a minute; the expansion and the compression phases each are 2 seconds in duration, and the release period 1 second, making 5 seconds for each cycle. Another advantage is that this method can be continued a long time without exhaustion of the operator. It can be performed by a child, if need be.

Oxygen must be brought to the alveoli quickly, so artificial respiration must be applied speedily after an emergency. Good pulmonary ventilation is needed, and the supply of blood to heart and brain must be kept up. The above method fulfills these requirements. It is easy to administer, does not permit aspiration of vomited stomach contents, and there is no danger of dislocating the shoulder, fracturing ribs or vertebrae.

The arm-lift, back-pressure method cannot be applied if patients are trapped under debris, if they have extensive burns or if they have broken vertebrae, ribs or arms. It is shown in Figure 323.

Some cases have been reported in which spontaneous breathing occurred after 5 hours of artificial respiration by the manual method. The length of time that artificial respiration is administered depends on the condition of the heart. As long as heart action continues, artificial respiration is continued.

Various mechanical devices, such as pulmotors, have been developed for the administration of artificial respiration. The best ones available at the present time are the intermittent positive pressure devices. The lungs are inflated by positive pressure, which rises gradually and does not exceed 25 cm. of water pressure. The pressure then falls rapidly and reaches zero at the end of expiration.

Poliomyelitis. In poliomyelitis the muscles of respiration may be involved. Death will result unless respiration is maintained. The Drinker respirator (iron lung) is used in the treatment of such patients. Figure 324 is a photograph of a Drinker respirator.

Asphyxiation (Oxygen lack, carbon dioxide excess). In asphyxiation by illuminating gas, carbon monoxide enters the alveoli

Fig. 324. Drinker machine for artificial respiration.

and diffuses into the blood. Hemoglobin unites with carbon monoxide, forming a stable compound. Since such hemoglobin is no longer available to transport oxygen, the tissues suffer from oxygen lack. The administration of oxygen by artificial respiration is essential. If the concentration of oxygen dissolved in the plasma is raised sufficiently, carbon monoxide can be driven off, and hemoglobin then becomes available for the transport of oxygen again.

The Initial Respiration. As soon as a baby is born, it should be held with the head down to allow mucus to drain from the respiratory passages. It may not breathe spontaneously. If this is the case, the baby is spanked gently, since stimulation of the skin may start respiration. If this is ineffective the baby may be placed alternately in warm and cool water, in an attempt to start respiration by stimulating receptors for temperature and thus influence the respiratory center. Sometimes it is necessary to blow very gently into the baby's mouth through sterile gauze. Great care must be used if this is done, since it is easy to rupture the lung and produce internal pneumothorax.

Hyperventilation. In some hospitals, hyperventilation is induced as a part of postoperative treatment. It consists of the administration of a high percentage of carbon dioxide for several minutes twice each day. This increases the depth of the respiratory movements. Some surgeons believe that the incidence of postoperative pneumonia is decreased by such periods of hyperventilation.

Oxygen Therapy. Often it is necessary to administer oxygen to patients. The simplest means is to administer oxygen from a tank by means of a nasal catheter. A second method is to place the patient in an oxygen tent.

Caisson Disease. High barometric pressures are used in caisson work (under rivers, in driving piles, etc.). As pressure increases more gas is dissolved in the plasma. If workmen are decompressed too rapidly, excess nitrogen is released in the form of bubbles in the blood. The bubbles lodge in capillaries in muscles, around joints and in the lungs. The result is pain in muscles and joints, paralysis of muscles, dyspnea (chokes) and congestion. This condition is called *caisson disease, divers' palsy,* or *bends.* If decompression is carried out gradually such symptoms do not occur.

The release of bubbles of gas in the blood may cause difficulty if aviators ascend above 25,000 feet in planes which are not pressurized. The condition in aviators is called *decompression sickness,* and the symptoms are comparable with caisson disease.

Mountain Sickness (Altitude sickness). A condition called *mountain sickness* may be experienced at high altitudes by many individuals. The disagreeable symptoms—headache, nausea, vertigo and severe muscular weakness—are due to anoxia. People who are acclimatized by dwelling at high altitudes do not experience such symptoms unless they attempt severe muscular exercise.

Hemoptysis. This refers to spitting of blood from respiratory passages beyond the nose. *Epistaxis* refers to bleeding from the nose.

Breath Sounds. If one listens over the chest with a stethoscope, the breath sounds may be heard. Each inspiration is accompanied by a rustling sound which is thought to be due to the sudden expansion of the alveoli. It is heard only during inspiration and over healthy lungs.

On listening over the course of the primary bronchi, a louder sound is heard during both inspiration and expiration. This is known as the *bronchial murmur* and is due to air going in and out of the primary bronchi. Breath sounds vary with pulmonary diseases.

Air conditioning refers to the controlling of the temperature, the moisture content and the proper circulation of air in a room or building.

SUMMARY

1. Movements of respiration
    A. Inspiration: 4 events
    B. Expiration: 4 events
2. Pressure changes with respiratory movements
    A. Intrapulmonic pressure; below atmospheric during inspiration, above atmospheric during expiration and equal to atmospheric in any position of rest of the thorax
    B. Intrapleural pressure: always below atmospheric normally
3. Volume changes with respiratory movements
    A. Recorded by means of a spirometer; called a spirogram
    B. Information derived from spirogram: rate, tidal volume, minute volume of respiration, ratio of inspiration to expiration, inspiratory reserve, expiratory reserve, vital capacity, oxygen use, maximal breathing capacity and ventilatory equivalent
    C. Bronchospirometry
    D. Residual volume; minimal air; dead-space air; not measured by spirometer
4. Control of respiration
    A. Nervous control: co-ordination, gradation. In eupnea, inspiration active and expiration passive
        a. Voluntary control; limited
        b. Reflex control
            (1) By afferent impulses from lungs; Hering-Breuer reflexes
            (2) By afferent impulses from aortic and internal carotid areas
                (A) Chemoreceptors; stimulated by oxygen lack
                (B) Baroceptors: stimulated by sudden, marked changes in arterial blood pressure
            (3) By afferent impulses from respiratory passages: Nose—sneeze; larynx, trachea and bronchi—cough; protective reflexes

(4) By afferent impulses from other areas of the body: incidental reflexes

B. Chemical control: carbon dioxide tension

C. Integration of nervous and chemical control and influence of temperature of blood

5. Chemistry of respiration

A. Composition of inspired, expired and alveolar air

B. Diffusion of gases: from higher to lower concentrations, due to molecular movement

C. Transport of gases in the blood

a. Oxygen carried in 2 ways: dissolved in plasma and in combination with hemoglobin

b. Carbon dioxide carried in 4 ways: in solution in plasma, as sodium acid carbonate, as potassium acid carbonate in erythrocytes and as a carbamino compound with hemoglobin

6. Maintenance of acid-base balance

A. Reaction of the blood; slightly alkaline

B. Physicochemical factors: buffers of the blood; 4 pairs; alkaline reserve. Activity of buffers under different conditions and in response to varying amounts of acid and base

C. Physiologic factors

a. Pulmonary ventilation; carbon dioxide effects on respiratory center; hypercapnia and acapnia

b. Renal excretion of acid and base

(1) Production of ammonia and conservation of fixed base

(2) Changing ratio of disodium and monosodium phosphates

(3) Retention or elimination of sodium acid carbonate

7. Muscular exercise

A. Changes in respiration

B. Changes in circulation

C. Changes in the blood

D. Changes in body temperature

E. Changes in kidney function

F. Changes in metabolism; oxygen debt

SITUATION AND QUESTIONS

The respiratory rate is considered one of the vital signs in caring for an ill person. Therefore, it is one of the important procedures taught to student nurses.

1. In counting the respiratory rate, the student nurses found that the rate in the adult was usually between: _____(a) 10 to 12 per minute; _____(b) 12 to 16 per minute; _____(c) 14 to 18 per minute; _____(d) 20 to 26 per minute.

2. Respirations are usually counted by observing the rise and fall of the chest wall. The main muscle action for enlarging the thoracic cavity is: _____(a) contraction of the diaphragm; _____(b) relaxation of the diaphragm; _____(c) relaxation of the intercostal muscles; _____(d) contraction of the pectoralis major.

3. Since there is some amount of voluntary control of respiration, nurses record respiratory movements unobserved by the patient. The stimulus which keeps us breathing and limits voluntary control is: _____(a) nitrogen; _____(b) oxygen; _____ (c) carbon dioxide; _____(d) equal parts of all 3.

4. The reflex regulation of respiration is important. The reflex which cuts short inspiration is: _____(a) aroused in the baroceptors; _____(b) the Hering-Breuer reflex; _____(c) protective reflex from the larynx; _____(d) incidental reflex from the skin.

5. In times of stress accessory muscles of respiration are brought into action. Forced expiration is brought about by: _____(a) relaxation of diaphragm; _____(b) relaxation of abdominal muscles; _____(c) contraction of pectoralis muscles; _____ (d) contraction of the abdominal muscles.

6. One respiratory cycle includes an inspiration and an expiration. The amount of air moved in and out of the lungs with one normal respiratory cycle is called: _____(a) inspiratory reserve air; _____(b) vital capacity; _____(c) tidal volume; _____(d) minimal air.

14. Anatomy of the Digestive System

INTRODUCTION

The function of the digestive system is to prepare food for absorption into the blood or the lymph so that it may be utilized by the cells of the body. The food is broken into small particles, mixed with saliva so that it may be tasted and then easily swallowed. In the stomach further digestion takes place, and the homogeneous chyme (partially digested food, saliva and gastric juice) is moved on to the small intestine where digestion is completed and selective absorption begins.

Absorption continues throughout the length of the small intestine, and any unabsorbed residue is finally passed along to the large intestine. In this last portion of the digestive system additional water is absorbed, bacteria flourish, and the residue is excreted as feces.

As long as food material remains in the lumen (the space within the wall) of the digestive tract it is not really "inside the body"; it becomes part of the body only after it has been absorbed from the lumen of the gut. It is evident that secretion of digestive juices, movement of food material along the alimentary tract and absorption are prerequisites for making food available to the body after it is eaten.

Let us consider briefly how it is possible for the protein and the

580

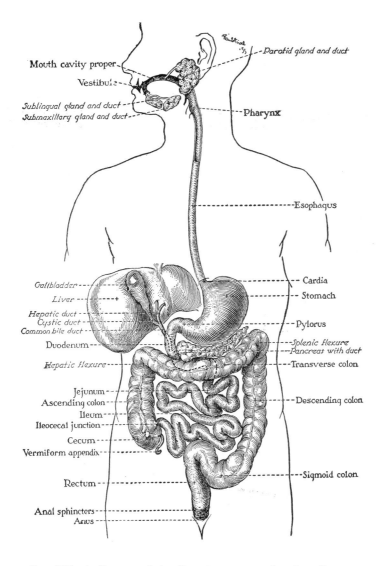

Mouth cavity proper
Vestibule
Sublingual gland and duct
Submaxillary gland and duct
Parotid gland and duct
Pharynx

Esophagus

Gallbladder
Liver
Hepatic duct
Cystic duct
Common bile duct
Duodenum
Hepatic flexure
Jejunum
Ascending colon
Ileum
Ileocecal junction
Cecum
Vermiform appendix
Rectum
Anal sphincters
Anus

Cardia
Stomach
Pylorus
Splenic flexure
Pancreas with duct
Transverse colon
Descending colon
Sigmoid colon

FIG. 325. A diagram of the digestive system, showing alimentary canal and accessory organs. The liver and gallbladder have been turned upward and to the right.

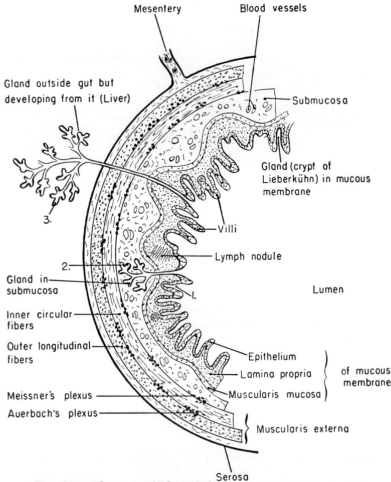

Mesentery   Blood vessels

Gland outside gut but
developing from it (Liver)

Submucosa

Gland (crypt of
Lieberkühn) in mucous
membrane

3.

Villi

Lymph nodule

2.

Gland in
submucosa

Lumen

Inner circular
fibers

Outer longitudinal
fibers

Epithelium

Lamina propria

of mucous
membrane

Meissner's plexus

Muscularis mucosa

Auerbach's plexus

Muscularis externa

Serosa

FIG. 326. The general plan of the gastro-intestinal tract, showing glands in 3 locations: (1) gland in mucous membrane; (2)
gland in submucosa; (3) gland outside tract. (Modified from Ham,
A. W.: Histology, ed. 2, Philadelphia, Lippincott)

starch in a grain of wheat to become part of the body. The wheat
is ground, mixed with chemicals to purify it, the flour separated
by chemical and physical processes and retained while the waste is
rejected. The flour is made into bread, the bread is eaten, broken
into small pieces and digested. The protein is broken down into
amino acids, and the starch to simple sugars during digestion.

These useful products of digestion are absorbed selectively into the blood and transported to all parts of the body and utilized by the cells. Really, the wheat is subjected to two milling processes, one in making it into flour and the second in making the flour available to the body.

It is the purpose of the author in the present chapter to consider the machinery of the mill in the body; that is, the anatomy of the organs that produce digestive juices, move food material along the alimentary tract and absorb it selectively. In order for any individual to be in good health, each part of the digestive system must do its work correctly.

COMPONENTS OF THE DIGESTIVE SYSTEM

The digestive system comprises the alimentary tube and its accessory organs: tongue, teeth, salivary glands, liver and pancreas. Figure 325 is a diagram of the parts of the digestive system.

ALIMENTARY TUBE

The alimentary tube is a long, muscular tube lined with mucous membrane, extending from the lips to the anus. The total length is about 27 ft. of which 1½ ft. are above the diaphragm. Each part of the tube is called by a different name, for example, mouth, pharynx, esophagus, stomach, small intestine and large intestine. Each part has its own special anatomic characteristics and performs its own particular functions, yet contributes an essential part to the single purpose of making food available to the cells of the body.

General Structural Plan of the Walls of the Alimentary Tube. There are 4 main layers in the wall of the alimentary tube: mucous membrane or mucosa, submucosa, external muscular layer and serosa or adventitia. The general plan is shown by diagram in Figure 326.

MUCOUS MEMBRANE OR MUCOSA. The innermost layer of the wall of the alimentary tube consists of 3 components: the epithelial lining, the lamina propria and the muscularis mucosae (muscle of the mucosa).

Epithelial Lining. The epithelium varies in structure according to the function of the part of the digestive tube it lines, so that it is protective, secretory and absorptive, respectively, in the esophagus, the stomach and the small intestine. It is of the stratified squamous type in the oral cavity, the pharynx and the esophagus; columnar in the stomach, the small intestine and the large intestine; and then stratified squamous again in the anal region.

Although glands are abundant in the epithelium, they are unable to produce enough secretion and of the proper composition to meet all the requirements of digestion. Therefore, secretions from the glands of the epithelium are supplemented by secretions from glands in 3 additional locations: in the lamina propria, in the submucosa and entirely outside the alimentary tract but connected by ducts (salivary glands, liver and pancreas). The glands of the epithelium, as well as the supplementary glands, are all derived from the lining of the alimentary tract in embryonic life. Glands in the various locations are illustrated in Figure 326.

Lamina Propria. This is a layer of connective tissue that supports the epithelium and connects it with the underlying muscularis mucosae (or the submucosa, in some locations) by means of fibers. There are glands in the lamina propria in some parts of the digestive tract. There is lymphatic tissue scattered here and there in the lamina propria; one such nodule is shown in Figure 326. Lymphocytes and plasma cells (which may possibly be the source of gamma globulin) are abundant in the lamina propria.

Blood vessels and lymphatic vessels are present in the lamina propria.

Muscularis Mucosae. This layer consists of 2 thin layers of smooth muscle with varying amounts of elastic tissue interspersed. The inner layer of smooth muscle is arranged in a circular sheet, and the outer in a longitudinal sheet. These thin sheets of smooth muscle in the mucous membrane make possible localized movements in the mucosa and enable it to be thrown into folds in some parts of the alimentary tract.

THE SUBMUCOSA is the second main layer of the wall of the alimentary tube. It serves to connect the mucous membrane with the outer muscular layer (muscularis externa). It is composed of loose connective tissue, in which there are elastic fibers. This layer can be "pulled up" to form cores in the folds of mucous membrane. Networks of large blood vessels are abundant in this layer. Nerve fibers and ganglion cells are interwoven to form a submucous plexus called *Meissner's plexus,* in which are found components of both divisions of the autonomic system.

EXTERNAL MUSCULAR LAYER OR MUSCULARIS EXTERNA. The third main layer of the wall of the alimentary tube is composed of 2 very substantial sheets of smooth muscle, an inner circular and an outer longitudinal sheet. The function of this layer of the gut wall is to mix thoroughly the contents of the lumen with the digestive juices and to move them along.

A plexus of nerve fibers and ganglion cells called the *myenteric* or *Auerbach's plexus* is found between the 2 sheets of smooth muscle. This plexus resembles the submucous plexus in that both divisions of the autonomic system are represented in it.

Serosa or Adventitia. The outermost main layer of the gut wall is fibrous in nature above the diaphragm and serous below the diaphragm. The serosa below the diaphragm is really visceral peritoneum.

Peritoneum. It seems pertinent to discuss the peritoneum briefly at this time. The peritoneum is a double-walled sac which lines the abdominal cavity (parietal peritoneum) and is invaginated by, or reflected over, the viscera (visceral peritoneum). Mesenteries are extensions of peritoneum from the abdominal wall which suspend the viscera and help to hold them in place. Other parts of the peritoneum that connect 2 organs in the abdominal cavity are called *ligaments.* The greater omentum is a special ligament, arranged

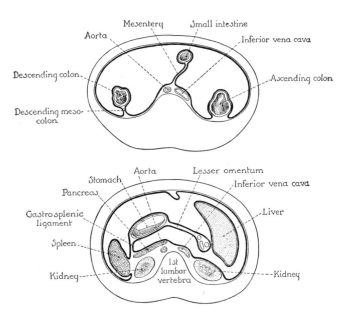

Fig. 327. Reflections of the peritoneum as seen in transverse section. (*Top*) The level indicated in Figure 328 by the line a-a. (*Bottom*) The level indicated in Figure 328 by the line b-b. (Redrawn from Morris)

like an apron of fat, that connects the stomach and the transverse colon. A second special ligament is the lesser omentum, which connects the stomach and the first part of the duodenum with the liver. The complicated reflections of the peritoneum, as seen in transverse and sagittal sections, are illustrated in Figures 327 and 328.

There is a small amount of fluid between the parietal and the visceral layers of peritoneum which permits them to glide over each other without friction.

ANATOMY OF ORGANS OF THE DIGESTIVE TUBE

Mouth. The vestibule of the mouth is the portion between the lips and the cheeks externally and the teeth internally. The mouth proper is the portion posterior to the teeth.

THE LIPS are composed of striated muscle (orbicularis oris) and fibro-elastic connective tissue. The outer surface is covered with skin. The red, free margins of the lips are covered with modified skin. The epithelium is covered with a layer of dead cells; the connective tissue papillae of the derma contain so many capillaries

FIG. 328. Reflections of the peritoneum as seen in sagittal section. Lines a-a and b-b indicate the levels of the sections shown in Figure 327. Certain structures shown in Figure 327 lie to the right or left of the plane of the above drawing.

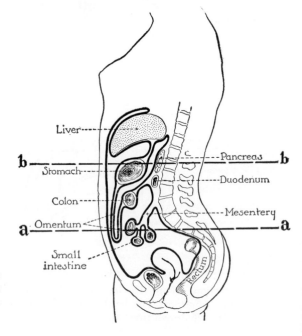

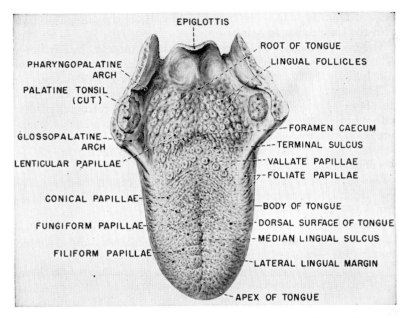

EPIGLOTTIS

ROOT OF TONGUE

PHARYNGOPALATINE
ARCH

LINGUAL FOLLICLES

PALATINE TONSIL
(CUT)

GLOSSOPALATINE
ARCH

FORAMEN CAECUM

TERMINAL SULCUS

LENTICULAR PAPILLAE

VALLATE PAPILLAE

FOLIATE PAPILLAE

CONICAL PAPILLAE

BODY OF TONGUE

FUNGIFORM PAPILLAE

DORSAL SURFACE OF TONGUE

MEDIAN LINGUAL SULCUS

FILIFORM PAPILLAE

LATERAL LINGUAL MARGIN

APEX OF TONGUE

FIG. 329. The surface of the human tongue as viewed from above. The palatine arches and tonsils have been cut through transversely. (Redrawn after Spalteholz) (Shapiro, H. H.: Maxillofacial Anatomy, Philadelphia, Lippincott)

that they give red color to the lips. This portion of the lips is not keratinized to the same extent as typical skin; consequently, it must be moistened frequently (or protected by cold cream or lipstick) to avoid cracking. There is a transition from modified skin to mucous membrane on the inner surface of the lips. In this region the dermis of the skin is replaced by the lamina propria typical of mucous membranes. Glands of the mucous type are present in the lamina propria.

THE CHEEKS are lined with mucous membrane in which the epithelium is of the stratified squamous nonkeratinizing type, typical of wet epithelial surfaces. The superficial cells are easily rubbed off by food particles and replaced by new cells from below. Glands are present in the epithelium. The lamina propria consists of dense fibro-elastic connective tissue which merges with the submucosa. The submucosa consists of connective tissue in which there are elastic fibers and numerous blood vessels. Strands of fibro-elastic tissue extend through the submucosa to connect the lamina propria with the underlying muscle.

The main substance of the cheek is striated muscle (buccinator). When the jaws are closed, the relaxed mucous membrane is thrown into folds by means of its connections with the muscle layer.

THE TONGUE is composed of interlacing bundles of striated muscle fibers, arranged in longitudinal, vertical and horizontal planes, with fibro-elastic connective tissue between. The mucous membrane on the under surface is thin; it forms a fold, called the *frenum lingulae*, that extends from near the tip of the tongue to the floor of the mouth.

One of the first requests that the physician of old used to make was "Stick out your tongue." If the tongue was coated, the physician knew that all was not well with the alimentary tract. The appearance of the tongue is of diagnostic importance in such diseases as scarlet fever and pernicious anemia, but such a simple examination seems to have gone out of style.

The mucous membrane on the dorsum of the tongue is thick, and that over the anterior two thirds (or body of the tongue) is studded with papillae, as shown in Figure 329. The papillae are of 3 types: filiform, fungiform and vallate.

The filiform (meaning "threadlike") papillae, which are arranged in parallel rows, are tall and narrow. They give the tongue a roughness that is important in licking ice-cream cones and lollipops. Probably you have noticed when your dog or cat licks your hand that the tongue feels like sandpaper; this roughness is due to the filiform papillae.

The fungiform papillae are not abundant; they have narrow bases and expanded tops like mushrooms.

The vallate papillae, which one author describes as castles surrounded by moats, are arranged in a V-shaped line, between the body and the root (posterior third) of the tongue. Taste buds are found in the fungiform and vallate papillae (p. 351). Figure 330 illustrates the filiform and fungiform types of papillae.

The root of the tongue or the pharyngeal portion contains masses of lymphatic tissue which constitute the lingual tonsil (p. 532).

The tongue is important in mastication (chewing), deglutition (swallowing) and speaking. The hypoglossal nerve is motor to the muscles of the tongue. The trigeminal nerve supplies receptors of touch, temperature and pain in the tongue. The facial and the glossopharyngeal nerves carry impulses from the taste buds, which give rise to taste sensations.

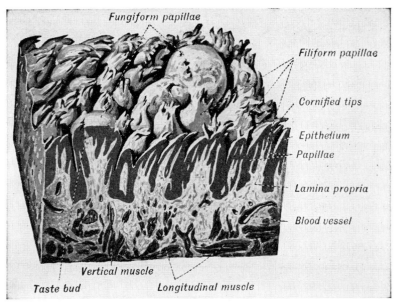

Fungiform papillae

Filiform papillae

Cornified tips

Epithelium

Papillae

Lamina propria

Blood vessel

Vertical muscle

Taste bud   *Longitudinal muscle*

FIG. 330. Surface of dorsum of tongue, drawn through a combined study with binocular microscope and of sections. × 16. (After Braus.) (Maximow, A. A., and Bloom, William: Textbook of Histology, ed. 6, Philadelphia, Saunders)

TEETH. During one's lifetime a person has 2 sets of teeth. The first set is called the *milk* or *deciduous* teeth. These begin to erupt (called *dentition*) at about 6 months of age, and one appears about each month thereafter until all 20 have erupted. The deciduous teeth are lost between 6 and 13 years of age.

The second set of teeth is called the *permanent set*. These appear between 6 and 17 years (except the wisdom teeth). There are 32 in the permanent set. They are named from their shape or function. Beginning at the mid-line and progressing laterally, in each jaw, the teeth are called: central incisor, lateral incisor, canine, 2 bicuspids or premolars, and 3 molars.

The incisors are shaped like chisels and serve to cut food.

The canines are shaped like dog's teeth; they tear and shred food.

The bicuspids crush and tear food.

The molars crush and grind food.

The last molar tooth in each jaw is called a *wisdom tooth;* the 4 wisdom teeth may erupt between 17 and 25 years of age or may

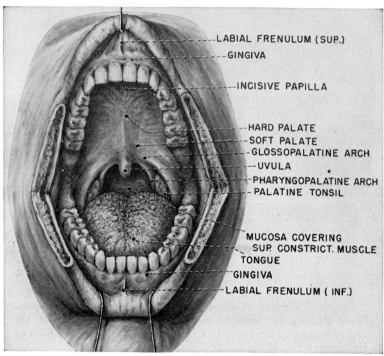

FIG. 331. The palate or roof of the mouth, teeth, tongue and palatine tonsils are shown. The hard palate is formed by the palatine processes of the maxillae and the horizontal plates of the palatine bones; it separates the mouth from the nasal cavity. The soft palate is composed of muscular tissue. The uvula is the fleshy mass hanging from the soft palate above the root of the tongue. The glossopalatine and the pharyngopalatine arches are called the pillars of the fauces (passage from mouth to pharynx). The palatine tonsils lie between the palatine arches. The gingivae are the gums; they are composed of fibrous tissue covered with mucous membrane. They cover the alveolar processes of the maxillae and the mandible and surround the necks of the teeth. (Redrawn after Spalteholz) (Shapiro, H. H.: Maxillofacial Anatomy, Philadelphia, Lippincott)

never erupt at all. The teeth are shown in Figure 331.

The 2 chief parts of a tooth are the crown and the root.

The crown or portion beyond the gum is covered with enamel, which is the hardest substance in the body. The bulk of the tooth

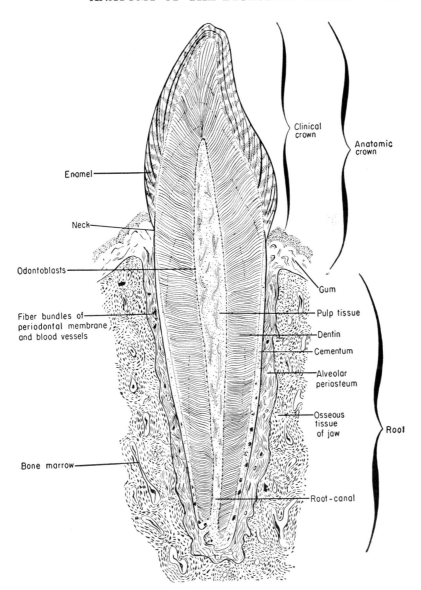

Fig. 332. Longitudinal section of canine tooth in situ.
Semidiagrammatic.

is composed of dentin, which is calcified connective tissue. The central cavity in the shell of dentin is called the *pulp cavity* and is filled with soft, pulpy connective tissue. Blood vessels and nerves (branches of the trigeminal) enter the tooth by way of the root canal. The parts of a tooth are shown in Figure 332.

The roots of the teeth fit into sockets in the alveolar processes, which are projections from the mandible and the maxillae. The roots are covered with cementum and are separated from the bone of the sockets by a strong connective tissue membrane called the *periodontal* membrane.

The teeth are laid down in the embryo, so the diet of the mother should contain an abundance of calcium and vitamin D during pregnancy to ensure proper development of teeth. The diet of the young child influences the permanent set of teeth, so it, too, should include abundant calcium and vitamin D in order to prevent dental caries.

SALIVARY GLANDS. There are 3 pairs of salivary glands which pour their secretions into the mouth: parotid, submaxillary and sublingual. In addition, buccal glands are scattered throughout the mucous membrane of the mouth.

The parotid glands lie below and in front of the ears, between the mastoid processes of the temporal bones and the rami of the mandible. The location is shown in Figures 325 and 333. The duct (Stensen's) passes through the buccinator muscle and pours its secretion into the vestibule of the mouth opposite the upper second molar tooth, on each side.

The submaxillary glands lie in contact with the inner surface of the mandible and the ducts (Wharton's) open into the floor of the mouth beside the frenum lingulae, behind the lower incisors (Fig. 333).

The sublingual glands lie beneath the mucous membrane of the floor of the mouth and open either by means of several ducts in the floor of the mouth or by larger ducts which join the ducts of the submaxillary glands.

The secretions from the salivary glands may be thin and watery (produced by serous cells) or thick and viscid (produced by mucous cells), according to the type of stimulus which arouses them and the particular type of cell responding.

Branches of the external carotid arteries bring an abundant blood supply to the salivary glands. Both divisions of the autonomic nervous system supply the salivary glands.

THE ROOF of the mouth (Fig. 331) is formed by the bony hard

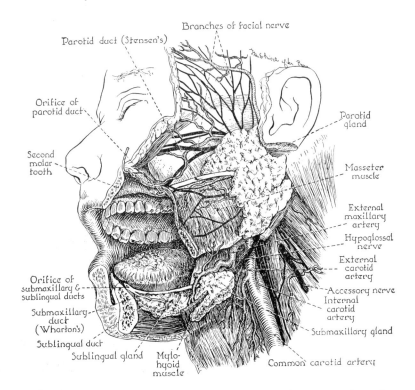

Fig. 333. Salivary glands, their ducts and orifices. Branches of the facial, the accessory and the hypoglossal nerves are shown. Common, external and internal carotid arteries are shown. (After Bonamy and Broca)

palate and the anterior portion of the soft palate. The hard palate is formed by the palatine processes of the maxillae and the horizontal plates of the palatine bones. It is covered with thick muco-periosteum. The epithelium is of the stratified squamous keratinizing type, which is protective in function, since it bears the constant thrusts of the tongue. The lamina propria is continuous with the periosteum of the underlying bones. The upper surface of the roof of the mouth is the floor of the nasal cavity.

The soft palate is attached to the posterior margin of the hard palate and is movable. It is drawn up, during the act of swallowing, to close the nasopharynx and prevent food from entering the

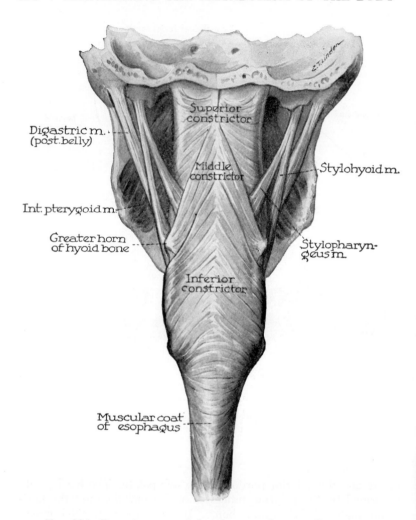

Fig. 334. Posterior view of the pharynx, showing the constrictor muscles. (Thorek, Philip: Anatomy in Surgery, Philadelphia, Lippincott)

nasal cavity. The lower or posterior margin is free and forms an arch from one side of the pharynx to the other, with the uvula projecting from the middle of the arch, as shown in Figures 300 and 301. The soft palate is composed of interlacing striated muscle

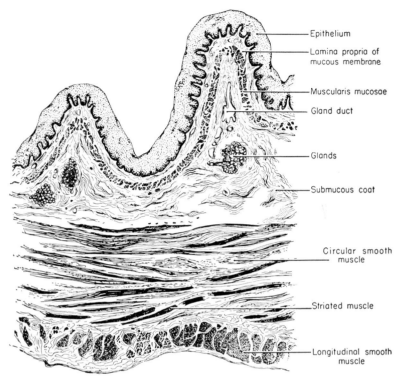

Epithelium

Lamina propria of
mucous membrane

Muscularis mucosae

Gland duct

Glands

Submucous coat

Circular smooth
muscle

Striated muscle

Longitudinal smooth
muscle

FIG. 335. Cross section of esophagus, through middle third. ×18.

fibers, covered with mucous membrane. The passage from the mouth to the pharynx is called the *fauces*. The roof of the mouth is illustrated in Figure 331.

Pharynx (Throat). The pharynx (p. 530) is a muscular tube lined with mucous membrane. There is a fibrous membrane, called the *pharyngeal aponeurosis*, under the mucous membrane, and beneath the aponeurosis is a thick layer of skeletal muscle. There are longitudinal fibers in the inner muscular layer and circular fibers (the pharyngeal constrictors) in the external layer. Some of these are shown in Figures 113 and 334. The constrictor muscles of the pharynx are concerned with swallowing. When the bolus of food enters the pharynx it is grasped by the constrictor muscles and moved on into the esophagus. Other muscles raise the pharynx during swallowing, draw the sides laterally to increase its width

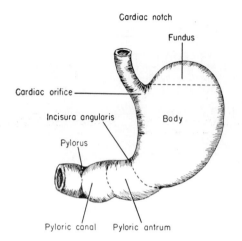

Cardiac notch

Fundus

Cardiac orifice

Incisura angularis

Body

Pylorus

Pyloric canal   Pyloric antrum

Fig. 336. Diagram of the parts of the stomach. (From Grant, J. C. B.: A Method of Anatomy, ed. 5, Baltimore, Williams & Wilkins.)

and aid the soft palate in closing the nasopharynx. As a result, the bolus of food is directed downward and forced into the esophagus.

Esophagus or Gullet. The esophagus is a collapsible tube, about 10 in. long, which lies back of the trachea. It begins at the end of the laryngopharynx and passes through the mediastinum and the diaphragm to the stomach.

The mucous membrane is composed of stratified squamous, non-keratinizing epithelium anchored firmly to the lamina propria. The lamina propria contains some glands (called *cardiac glands*), a few muscle fibers and a small amount of lymphatic tissue. In the submucosa there are a few esophageal mucous glands. The external muscular layer is composed of striated muscle in the upper third, mixed striated and smooth in the middle third and smooth muscle (circular and longitudinal sheets) alone in the lower third of the esophagus. The striated muscle that is present in the walls of the esophagus is not under the control of the will; it is supplied by autonomic fibers which travel in the vagus nerves. The adventitia is composed of fibrous connective tissue. A section is shown in Figure 335.

The stomach is an expanded portion of the alimentary tube that serves as a reservoir during digestion of food. It lies in the upper part of the abdomen, on the left side, just below the diaphragm (Fig. 7).

THE CARDIAC ORIFICE is the opening between the esophagus and the stomach; it is guarded by the cardiac sphincter. The part of

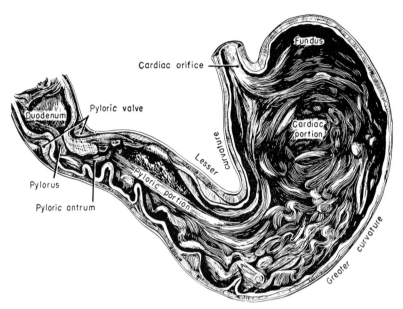

FIG. 337. Interior of the stomach, showing rugae. (Adapted from Lewis, W. H.: Gray's Anatomy of the Human Body, ed. 26, Philadelphia, Lea & Febiger)

the stomach which lies above the horizontal line drawn through the cardiac orifice is called the *fundus*. Two thirds of the remainder of the stomach is called the body. Beyond this are the pyloric antrum and the pyloric canal, marked off from the body by the incisura angularis (Fig. 336). The opening between the stomach and the small intestine is called the *pylorus;* it is guarded by the pyloric sphincter, which is made up of a fold of the middle coat of the muscularis externa. The medial border of the stomach is called the *lesser curvature,* and the lateral border the *greater curvature.*

THE EPITHELIUM of the mucous membrane is of the simple columnar type. When the stomach is empty the mucous membrane is thrown into folds called *rugae* (Fig. 337). The mucous membrane is studded with millions of simple tubular glands; those in the fundus and the body of the stomach are called *peptic glands.* There are 3 kinds of cells in the walls of the simple tubular glands: chief cells, which produce pepsin; parietal cells, which produce

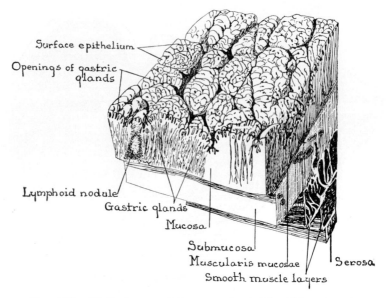

Surface epithelium

Openings of gastric glands

Lymphoid nodule

Gastric glands

Mucosa

Submucosa

Muscularis mucosae

Smooth muscle layers

Serosa

Fig. 338. All the layers of the stomach. ×17. (After Braus)

hydrochloric acid; and mucous neck cells, which produce mucus. In addition to the tubular glands, there are surface mucous glands. The openings of the gastric glands are indicated in Figure 338.

THE LAMINA PROPRIA is riddled with glands.

THE MUSCULARIS MUCOSAE is composed of an inner circular and outer longitudinal sheet.

THE SUBMUCOSA is composed of loose connective tissue, in which blood vessels are abundant. In the pyloric region, there are coiled mucous glands in the submucosa that produce a large amount of mucus.

THE MUSCULARIS EXTERNA of the stomach is composed of 3 layers of smooth muscle: an inner oblique, a middle circular and an outer longitudinal layer.

THE SEROSA is composed of visceral peritoneum. The various layers of the wall of the stomach are illustrated in Figure 338.

The blood supply is derived from branches of the celiac artery; drainage is by way of gastric veins. Lymphatic vessels are abundant. Both divisions of the autonomic system supply efferent fibers to the stomach and visceral afferent fibers conduct impulses from the stomach to the central nervous system.

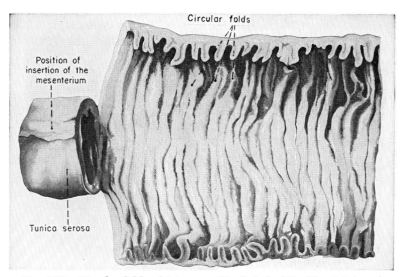

Fig. 339. Circular folds of jejunum. (Spalteholz, W.: Hand Atlas of Human Anatomy, Philadelphia, Lippincott)

The small intestine is about 1 in. in diameter and 20 ft. long and extends from the pylorus to the ileocecal orifice. It is arranged in coils in the abdominal cavity and is divided into 3 parts: duodenum, jejunum and ileum.

The duodenum is about 10 to 12 in. in length; it forms a C-shaped concavity in which the head of the pancreas lies. The bile and pancreatic ducts open into the duodenum about 3 in. from the pylorus.

The jejunum forms the next two fifths of the small intestine and extends from the duodenum to the ileum.

The ileum forms the remainder of the small intestine. It joins the large intestine at right angles; the ileocecal sphincter guards the entrance.

The wall of the small intestine contains the usual 4 main layers characteristic of the alimentary tract. However, an increase in epithelial surface is needed for absorption, and this is obtained by 2 variations: circular folds and villi.

The circular folds are like ridges in the mucosa, with cores of submucosa, as shown in Figure 339.

The villi are small projections of mucous membrane; they contain cores of lamina propria which may be thought of as trees on the

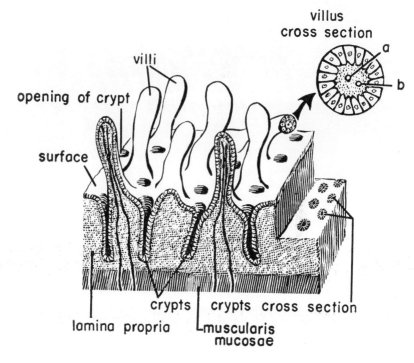

FIG. 340. Three-dimensional drawing of the mucous membrane of the small intestine. The villi are projections of epithelium containing cores of lamina propria. The glands (crypts of Lieberkühn) are located in the lamina propria. Vascular and lymphatic capillaries extend into the villi (*a* and *b* in the enlarged drawing shown by the arrow). (Modified from Ham, A. W.: Histology, ed. 2, Philadelphia, Lippincott)

ridges (Fig. 340). They give the appearance of velvet to the intestinal lining. The villi are highly specialized for absorption. The epithelium is composed of tall columnar cells, among which numerous goblet cells are present.

The lamina propria of the mucous membrane is composed of loose connective tissue. As stated above, it forms the cores of the villi, and each villus contains a vascular capillary, a lymph vessel (called a *lacteal*) and nerve fibers. There is an abundance of lymphatic tissue in the lamina propria. This may appear as solitary nodules or in groups of nodules called *Peyer's patches*. The intestinal glands, which are called the *crypts of Lieberkühn,* are found in the lamina propria. They dip down from the surface between villi to reach almost to the muscularis mucosae, like wells between the trees (villi), and their function is to secrete enzymes. The muscularis mucosae is present but possesses no distinguishing characteristics in the small intestine.

The submucosa is composed of loose connective tissue and contains blood and lymph vessels. The only glands in this layer are Brunner's glands in the duodenum; they secrete mucus that is passed along ducts in the muscularis mucosae to empty into the crypts of Lieberkühn.

The muscularis externa consists of an inner circular and outer longitudinal layer, and it thins out as it approaches the large intestine.

The serosa is composed of visceral peritoneum.

Arteries pass to the wall of the intestine by way of the mesenteries; they give branches to the serosa and then pass through the mucularis externa to which they give branches also. The main vessels in the submucosa give origin to capillary networks around the tubules of the glands in the mucous membrane and likewise send capillaries into the villi. The blood drains into veins that eventually enter the portal system. Lymphatic vessels begin as capillaries (lacteals) in the villi and enter the mesenteric lymph nodes in which the lymph is filtered on its way to the thoracic duct. Visceral afferent nerves conduct impulses from the intestine to the central nervous system, and efferent fibers from Auerbach's and Meissner's plexuses supply the smooth muscle of the intestinal wall.

The large intestine is about 2½ in. in diameter and 4½ ft. long and extends from the ileocecal sphincter to the anus. The parts of the large intestine are the cecum, the colon and the rectum.

THE CECUM is a blind pouch about 2 to 3 in. long which hangs down at the junction of the ileum and the colon. The ileocecal valve lies at the upper border of the cecum and prevents the return of feces from the cecum into the small intestine. The vermiform appendix arises from the cecum about an inch below the ileocecal valve. It is a twisted and coiled tube whose walls contain all the layers of the intestine, with an abundance of lymphatic tissue in the lamina propria.

THE COLON (Fig. 325) is subdivided into the ascending, the transverse, the descending and the sigmoid portions.

The ascending colon extends from the cecum to the under surface of the liver, where it turns left to form the right or hepatic flexure.

The transverse colon crosses the upper part of the abdominal cavity from right to left and turns downward to form the left or splenic flexure.

The descending colon extends from the splenic flexure to the brim of the pelvis, where it turns toward the mid-line to become the sigmoid colon.

The sigmoid (pelvic) colon extends from the descending colon at the level of the pelvic brim to the rectum. It descends along the left pelvic wall, then passes transversely across the pelvis from left to right, to the right pelvic wall, where it bends upon itself, passes again to the left to join the rectum in the mid-line, at the level of the second or third sacral vertebra. It is evident that the sigmoid colon is really "S-shaped" as the name implies. Patients are placed on the left side when receiving an enema, so that gravity may assist in filling the sigmoid colon.

THE RECTUM extends from the sigmoid colon to the anus (opening of the large intestine to the exterior). It descends along the hollow of the sacrum and the coccyx to the tip of the coccyx and is about 5 to 7 in. long. The rectum is made up of the rectum proper and the anal canal.

The rectum proper extends from the sigmoid colon to the pelvic floor. There are 3 transverse folds in the rectum proper, which appear as creases on its outer surface. In the interior the transverse folds appear as shelves or horizontal folds. The mucous membrane, the submucosa and the greater part of the circular muscular layers are present in the folds.

The anal canal extends from the pelvic floor to the anus. The anal canal passes through the narrow space between the 2 medial borders of the levator ani muscles, which compress it to a mere slit.

THE WALL of the large intestine contains the 4 main layers which are characteristic of the alimentary tube. There are no villi in the mucous membrane as there are in the small intestine. Goblet cells are abundant in the *epithelium.* The glands (crypts of Lieberkühn) in the *lamina propria* are deeper than in the small intestine; they secrete mucus. Solitary nodules of lymphatic tissue are present in the lamina propria. There is lymphatic tissue, also, in the submucosa of the cecum and the rectum. Many networks of small veins are present in the lamina propria and the *submucosa.* In the

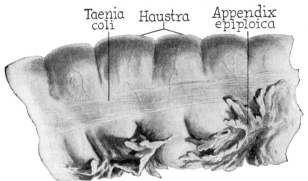

FIG. 341. Portion of descending colon, showing haustra, taeniae coli and epiploic appendages.

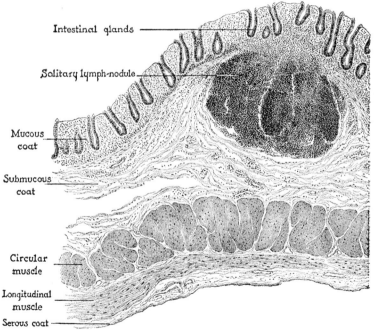

FIG. 342. Longitudinal section of large intestine (ascending colon), showing the general arrangement of the coats and a solitary lymph nodule. ×30.

rectum these veins may become dilated and form internal hemor-rhoids.

The muscularis externa differs from that in other parts of the alimentary tube in that the longitudinal muscle layer is arranged in 3 flat bands called *taenia coli* (Fig. 341). These bands are not as long as the intestine; consequently, the latter is gathered (shirred) into small sacs called *haustra,* which are characteristic of the large intestine.

The serosa consists of visceral peritoneum. This forms little pouches containing fat, which hang from the large intestine and are called *appendices epiploicae.* A section of the wall of the large intestine is shown in Figure 342.

THE STRUCTURE of the rectum differs from that of the remainder of the large intestine in that the mucous membrane is arranged in 5 to 10 vertical folds, called *rectal columns* (Fig. 343). There are 3 sphincters which guard the exit of the alimentary tube:

1. The internal sphincter is a thickening of the circular muscular layer of the muscularis externa and is not under the control of the will.

2. The levatores ani, which exert a sphincterlike action, are composed of skeletal muscle and are under the control of the will.

3. The external sphincter is a cylinder of skeletal muscle around the lower two thirds of the anal canal, attached directly to the skin

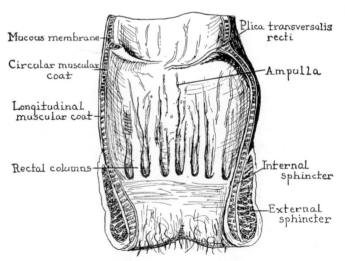

FIG. 343. Interior of rectum and anal canal. (After Spalteholz)

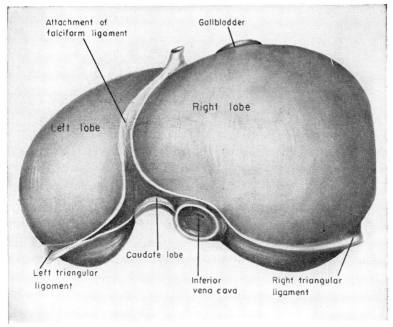

FIG. 344. The superior surface of the liver. (From model by His) (Adapted from Lewis, W. H.: Gray's Anatomy of the Human Body, ed. 26, Philadelphia, Lea & Febiger)

and to the coccyx by means of a tendon. The external sphincter is under the control of the will.

The blood supply to the wall of the large intestine is derived from branches of the superior and the inferior mesenteric arteries. The blood that leaves the large intestine enters the portal system. Lymphatic drainage is abundant.

Visceral afferent fibers conduct impulses from the large intestine to the central nervous system. Both divisions of the autonomic system supply efferent fibers to the wall of the large intestine.

REMAINING ACCESSORY ORGANS

Two accessory organs, the liver (and biliary apparatus) and the pancreas remain to be discussed.

The liver is the largest organ of the body, weighing about 3 pounds in an adult. It lies mostly in the right hypochondrium (p. 612). The superior surface fits under the dome of the diaphragm. The inferior surface is molded over the stomach, the duodenum, the right colic flexure, the right kidney and the right suprarenal

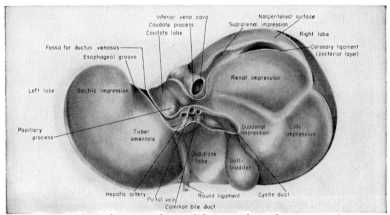

FIG. 345. Inferior surface of liver. The tuber omentale is a prominence which rests against the front of the lesser omentum and fits into the lesser curvature of the stomach. (From model by His) (Adapted from Lewis, W. H.: Gray's Anatomy of the Human Body, ed. 26, Philadelphia, Lea & Febiger)

gland. Some of the structures with which the posterior surface comes in contact are the vertebral column, the pillars of the diaphragm and the inferior vena cava. The superior surface is illustrated in Figure 344, and the inferior surface in Figure 345.

The liver consists of 4 lobes; the 2 main lobes are the right and the left, separated by the falciform ligament. The right lobe is subdivided into right lobe proper, quadrate and caudate lobes.

The liver is almost completely covered with peritoneum. Under this there is a covering of fibro-elastic tissue called *Glisson's capsule,* which accompanies the blood vessels into the interior of the liver. The porta is a fissure which extends transversely across the left portion of the right lobe. At the porta there is a tree trunk of connective tissue, continuous with the capsule, which extends up into the substance of the liver. The "tree" branches extensively and furnishes internal support for the liver. It also provides pathways by which branches of the portal vein, the hepatic artery, the bile ducts and the lymphatic vessels can reach all parts of the liver.

At the porta, the portal vein and the hepatic artery enter the tree of connective tissue and branch with each branching of the tree. Lymphatic vessels and bile ducts, which have tributaries in every branch of the tree, leave the liver at the porta. The hepatic artery supplies the liver with arterial blood; hence, it supplies a large part of the oxygen used by the liver. The portal vein brings venous blood that has traversed the walls of the intestinal tract and

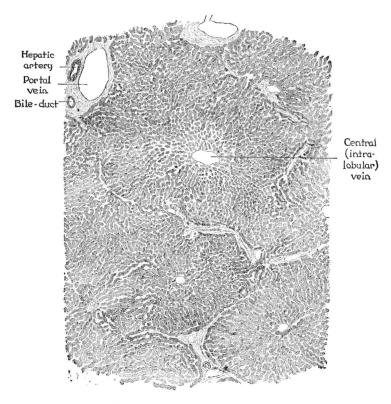

Hepatic
artery

Portal
vein

Bile-duct

Central
(intra-
lobular)
vein

FIG. 346. Section of liver, showing the general
arrangement of the lobules, the interlobular and
the intralobular vessels. ×120.

is rich in absorbed food. Blood leaves the liver by way of the hepatic veins, which are not found in the branches of the tree of connective tissue. These veins begin in the central veins of the liver,
which unite to form the sublobular and then the hepatic veins,
which, in turn, empty into the inferior vena cava.

A unit of liver substance is called a *liver lobule*. The lobules
are separated by a small amount of interlobular connective tissue
in which are found terminal branches of the hepatic artery, the
portal vein and the beginnings of bile ducts and lymphatic vessels.
Figure 346 illustrates the lobular arrangement of the liver.

The substance of liver lobules is composed of branching cords of

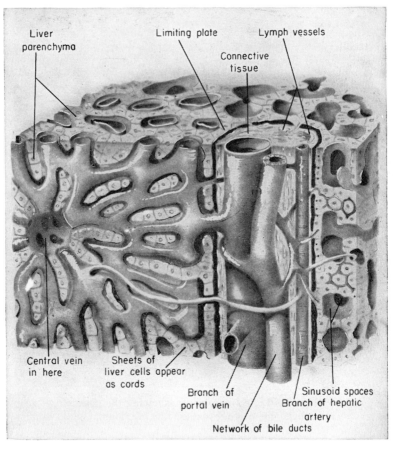

FIG. 347. Stereogram of a portion of a liver lobule.
(After Hans Elias)

epithelial cells that radiate from the center of the lobule to its periphery as shown in Figure 347. There are sinusoids or large vascular capillaries between the cords of cells that receive blood from both the hepatic artery and the portal vein. The blood then flows on to the central veins. The cords are at least 2 cells thick, as shown in Figure 348.

A large amount of blood can be trapped in the sinusoids of the

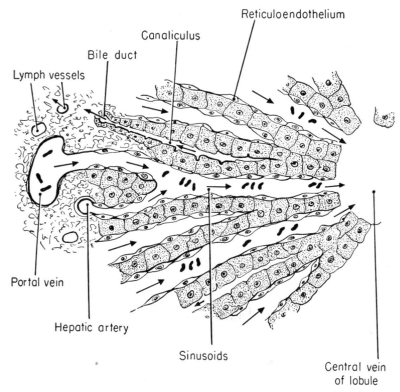

FIG. 348. Drawing (at high-power magnification) to show how blood from the portal vein and the hepatic artery (at left) flows into sinusoids, lined by reticuloendothelium, that lie between liver cords, and empties into the central vein (right). The way that bile travels in the opposite direction in canaliculi to empty into bile ducts in portal areas is also shown. (Adapted from Ham, A. W.: Histology, ed. 2, Philadelphia, Lippincott)

liver and this can influence the circulating blood volume and cardiac output. In other words, the liver is an important reservoir. The left portion of the liver receives blood from the upper gastro-intestinal tract, the pancreas, the duodenum and the stomach. The right portion of the liver receives blood from the jejunum and the ileum.

The sinusoids are lined with reticuloendothelial cells (p. 32), called *Kupffer's cells*, which engulf foreign material that gains access to the blood stream.

The biliary apparatus begins between the cords of liver cells as bile capillaries. They unite with other bile capillaries to form larger ducts, and finally all bile is collected into one large duct from each lobe. The bile ducts from the right and the left lobes unite to form the hepatic duct. The cystic duct from the gallbladder unites with the hepatic duct to form the common bile duct. This duct and the main pancreatic duct usually join before emptying into the duodenum at the ampulla of Vater through the sphincter of Oddi (Fig. 349, labeled *duodenal papilla*).

THE GALLBLADDER is a sac of smooth muscle lined with mucous membrane and is located on the under surface of the liver. It has the shape and the size of a small pear. The wall of the gallbladder contains 4 layers of tissue.

The mucous membrane is composed of columnar epithelium and lamina propria. This layer is thrown into folds in the empty organ.

The second layer is composed of smooth muscle.

The third layer is composed of connective tissue, in which blood vessels and lymphatic vessels are abundant.

The outer layer or serosa is composed of visceral peritoneum.

The functions of the gallbladder and the mechanism of its emptying are discussed on page 634.

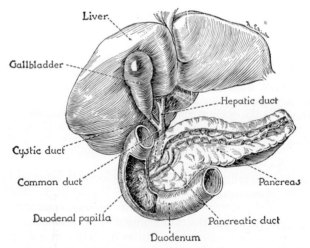

FIG. 349. Gallbladder, showing location. Bile ducts, pancreatic ducts and the entrance of the ducts into the duodenum are shown.

The Pancreas. The location of the pancreas is shown in Figures 7 and 325. It consists of a head, a body and a tail. The head rests in the concavity of the duodenum; the body extends toward the spleen and the tail is in contact with the spleen.

The pancreas is composed of lobules in which the secretory units are acini (alveoli) or single rows of epithelial cells arranged around a lumen. The acinar (alveolar) cells are concerned with the production of pancreatic juice that is emptied into the duodenum through pancreatic ducts. Of these ducts, the main one usually unites with the common bile duct (Fig. 349), while the accessory duct may open into the duodenum independently.

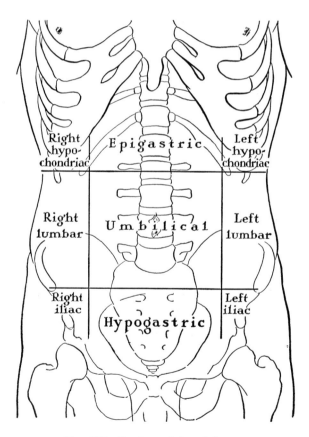

FIG. 350. Regions of the abdomen.

There are groups of irregular cells scattered here and there throughout the pancreas, as shown in Figure 395. These are called the *islands of Langerhans* and are concerned with the production of insulin and glucagon.

SURFACE PROJECTIONS OF DIGESTIVE ORGANS

The abdomen is divided arbitrarily into 9 regions for purposes of location of the viscera on the surface. The regions are shown in Figure 350. The location of the various viscera is given in the table.

Right hypochondrium	*Epigastrium*	*Left hypochondrium*
Greater part of the right lobe of the liver, hepatic flexure of the colon and part of the right kidney	Greater part of left lobe and part of right lobe of liver with gallbladder, part of stomach, part of duodenum, pancreas, upper end of spleen, parts of kidneys and suprarenal glands	Part of stomach, part of spleen, tail of pancreas, splenic flexure of colon, part of left kidney and, sometimes, part of left lobe of liver
Right lumbar	*Umbilical*	*Left Lumbar*
Ascending colon, part of right kidney and, sometimes, part of ileum	Greater part of transverse colon, part of duodenum, part of jejunum and ileum, part of mesentery and greater omentum, part of kidneys and ureters	Descending colon, part of jejunum, part of left kidney
Right iliac	*Hypogastrium*	*Left iliac*
Cecum and appendix, termination of ileum	Ileum; bladder in children; bladder, if distended, in adults; uterus when pregnant; sigmoid flexure	Sigmoid colon, jejunum and ileum

PRACTICAL CONSIDERATIONS

MOUTH

Harelip and cleft palate are discussed on page 138.

Ankyloglossia (tonguetie) is the condition in which the frenum linguae is abnormally short, and free movements of the tongue are not possible. This interferes with sucking during infancy and with speech later.

Stomatitis is a condition characterized by inflammation of the soft tissues of the mouth. It is accompanied by pain and salivation and often by fetor (offensive odor) of the breath.

Parotitis is inflammation of the parotid glands; mumps is a common type of parotitis. Parotitis occurs occasionally as a postoperative complication; this type is called *surgical parotitis.*

Ludwig's angina is an acute streptococcic infection of the floor of the mouth. The tissues of the floor are swollen and indurated (hardened). There are constitutional symptoms, such as fever, nausea, malaise; the condition may be fatal.

ESOPHAGUS

Strictures from corrosive or caustic substances may occur in the esophagus.

Varices. The veins of the esophageal wall may become dilated and tortuous; such dilatations are called *esophageal varices.*

Cancer of the esophagus is fairly common.

Heartburn. So-called "heartburn" is a burning sensation in the esophagus associated with the stimulation of the mucosa of the upper part of the esophagus by acid contents regurgitated from the stomach.

"Belching" is the act of expelling gas from the stomach into the esophagus and the mouth after a meal. It is brought about by reverse waves which originate in the cardiac region of the stomach.

STOMACH

Ulcer formation may occur in the gastric mucous membrane. The most frequent site is the posterior wall at the pyloric end, along the lesser curvature. Gastric resection (excision of part of the stomach) is advised for gastric ulcers, since they frequently become the site of gastric cancer.

Gastro-enterostomy is an operative procedure in which the canal of the jejunum is made continuous with the stomach. Food may enter either the duodenum or the jejunum, after such an operation for ulcer or cancer.

Cardiospasm is a condition in which the cardiac sphincter is constricted and fails to relax properly during swallowing. The subject complains that the food "sticks in his throat."

Pyloric stenosis of the hypertrophic type is a condition which sometimes occurs in young male infants, in which the pyloric sphincter is in a state of persistent spasm, and hypertrophy of the sphincter results. The condition has to be treated surgically.

"Laparotomy" is the making of an incision in the abdominal wall, such as is done in abdominal operations.

Small Intestine

Peritonitis. Inflammation of the peritoneum is called *peritonitis*. It is accompanied by rigidity of the muscles of the abdominal wall, tenderness over the abdomen, paralysis of the intestine, vomiting and pain.

Colic. Spasmodic contraction of the muscularis externa produces typical colic. The pain is like that felt in a cramp of one of the voluntary muscles.

Inflammation of the mucous membrane of the intestinal wall is sometimes called *intestinal influenza* or *intestinal grippe*.

Ulcers of the mucous membrane of the duodenum near the pylorus are common.

Intestinal obstruction may be due to: (1) hernial-sac incarceration or retention (p. 197); (2) foreign bodies, especially at the ileocecal junction; (3) stricture from an ulcer, peritonitis or tumor; (4) volvulus, a knotting or twisting of the intestine; (5) intussusception or telescoping of one part of the intestine into another portion of it; and (6) bands that arise from adhesions. Any intestinal obstruction is exceedingly serious, since it upsets the water and salt balance of the body and cuts off the blood supply to a part of the intestinal wall.

Paralytic ileus is a condition in which the bowel is paralyzed. It may occur after any abdominal or pelvic operation and has the same effect as other types of obstruction. In some cases the condition is asociated with a low concentration of potassium in the body fluids.

Ileostomy refers to the surgical formation of a fistula or an artificial anus through the abdominal wall into the ileum. This may be necessary in patients who suffer from cancer of the colon or the rectum.

Large Intestine

Appendicitis is quite common. Since the appendix is a blind tube, wastes accumulate which cannot be moved by peristaltic contractions. Muscular rigidity, pain and vomiting are common. The chief danger is that of rupture, followed by peritonitis. If the appendix becomes inflamed, it should be removed (appendectomy) before it ruptures.

Distention of the Colon is extreme in congenital megacolon. Only one bowel movement in several months may occur.

Colostomy refers to making an artificial anus or opening from the colon to the exterior.

Hemorrhoids are dilatations of the veins in the rectal mucous membrane.

Cancer may be found in any part of the colon but is more common within 2 to 3 in. of the anus.

An enema of soapsuds is called a *cleansing enema*. The patient should be turned on the left side, to facilitate filling of the sigmoid colon.

Sigmoidoscopy refers to the visual inspection of the sigmoid colon by the aid of special instruments.

LIVER

Cirrhosis is a condition in which parts of the liver undergo structural changes as a result of destruction and regeneration of some of the liver lobules. Often there is interference with the portal circulation in cirrhosis, and collateral circulation is established (by way of the azygos vein) to relieve portal congestion. Evidence of this is seen in the prominent veins on the surface of the abdomen.

Jaundice (icterus) occurs in disease of the liver or the biliary apparatus when bile enters the blood stream instead of being eliminated into the intestine.

GALLBLADDER

Acute cholecystitis is inflammation of the lining of the gallbladder and usually is accompanied by obstruction of the cystic duct.

Empyema of the gallbladder is suppurative cholecystitis or formation of pus in the gallbladder.

Cholelithiasis refers to the presence of stones in the gallbladder.

PANCREAS

Pancreatitis is inflammation of the pancreas.

Cancer of the pancreas occurs occasionally.

Diabetes mellitus (p. 741) is the condition in which the islands of Langerhans are abnormal.

SUMMARY

1. Components of the digestive system
   A. Alimentary tube
      a. General structural plan
         (1) Mucous membrane; consisting of epithelium, lamina propria and muscularis mucosae

(2) Submucosa

(3) External muscular layer or muscularis externa

(4) Serosa or adventitia; special description of peritoneum

2. Anatomy of organs of the digestive tube

A. Mouth: lips, cheeks, tongue, teeth, salivary glands (parotid, submaxillary, sublingual) and roof of the mouth (hard and soft palates)

B. Pharynx

C. Esophagus: extent; characteristics of each of the four layers

D. Stomach

a. Gross description; names of parts

b. Microscopic structure

(1) Epithelium (gastric glands); lamina propria (glands); muscularis mucosae (two layers)

(2) Submucosa: coiled glands in pyloric region

(3) Muscularis externa (three layers)

(4) Serosa: peritoneum

E. Small intestine

a. Parts: duodenum, jejunum and ileum

b. Microscopic structure

(1) Great increase in epithelial surface for absorption (circular folds and villi); cores of villi formed of lamina propria; lymphatic tissue; crypts of Lieberkühn in lamina propria

(2) Brunner's glands in submucosa

(3) Muscularis externa: two layers; this is noted as it approaches large intestine

(4) Serosa: peritoneum

F. Large intestine

a. Parts

(1) Cecum; ileocecal valve; appendix

(2) Colon: ascending, hepatic flexure, transverse colon, splenic flexure, descending colon and sigmoid colon

(3) Rectum; rectum proper and anal canal

b. Microscopic structure: characteristics of each of the 4 main layers

3. Remaining accessory organs

A. Liver

a. Size, location, surfaces and lobes

b. Capsule; connective tissue tree; arrangement of branches of the hepatic artery, portal vein, lymphatic capillaries, bile capillaries. Central veins and hepatic veins

      c. Lobules; cords of cells. Sinusoids. Reticuloendothelial cells

      d. Biliary apparatus: bile capillaries, bile ducts, hepatic duct, cystic duct, gallbladder and common bile duct

      B. Pancreas: location, parts, lobules, acinar (alveolar) cells, ducts and islands of Langerhans

    4. Surface projections of digestive organs

SITUATION AND QUESTIONS

Joseph Coop, a 25-year-old male, was admitted to the hospital with the chief complaint of hematemesis. He also complained of severe midepigastric pain. These symptoms plus the observation made by the physician that the patient seemed rather emotional and tense led to the tentative diagnosis of a peptic ulcer.

    1. Peptic ulcers invade the lining of the wall of the stomach. This lining is called: _____(a) serosa; _____(b) mucosa; _____(c) submucosa; _____(d) smooth muscle.

    2. Perforation of a peptic ulcer may occur. This is a dangerous complication, as the contents of the stomach are emptied into the abdominal cavity and may produce a generalized infection of the lining of the abdominal wall and covering of the viscera. This serous membrane is the: _____(a) pleura; _____(b) perineum; _____(c) mesentery; _____(d) peritoneum.

    3. In preparation for surgery a gastric suction tube was passed through the esophagus into the stomach. The name of the sphincter guarding the opening from the esophagus into the stomach is the: _____(a) cardiac; _____(b) pyloric; _____(c) ileocecal; _____(d) semilunar.

    4. A subtotal gastrectomy was performed with an anastomosis of the remaining upper portion of the stomach with the middle section of the small intestine. This section of the small intestine is the: _____(a) cecum; _____(b) ileum; _____(c) duodenum; _____(d) jejunum.

    5. Good oral hygiene is important in the postoperative care of this patient to prevent surgical parotitis. The parotid gland is: (a) an endocrine gland; _____(b) located sublingually; _____ (c) a salivary gland; _____(d) known to have no enzyme function.

15. Physiology of the Digestive System

INTRODUCTION

Foods are substances which can be changed into simple components by digestive processes, absorbed from the lumen of the small intestine, transported by the blood or the lymph and used by the cells of the body to furnish energy. Foods build new tissue characteristic of each particular organ, repair worn-out parts of organs, help maintain excitability and conductivity of nervous tissue, contractility of muscular tissue and play an essential role in general growth and nutrition.

Foods are not useful to cells as eaten; they must be split into simpler components. This is accomplished by a battery of enzymes, each secreted at the opportune time, in essential amounts and composition, and accompanied by events which assure the proper pH for digestion. The means of controlling the production of various

618

enzymes is truly remarkable. Moreover, the food and its derivatives must be moved from one part of the alimentary tract to another and retained in some parts for a relatively long time. The movements involved in digestion are performed by smooth muscle, with few exceptions; the control of these movements is as remarkable as that of the secretions.

When the derivatives of the food have been properly digested, they are presented to the mucosa of the small intestine for absorption; any residue is moved along into the large intestine and excreted from the body.

After the simple components have been absorbed, the various cells of the body withdraw whatever they need from the blood. Enough is burned to give energy for work and to keep the body warm. Some of the remainder is stored temporarily and doled out as needed to keep the blood sugar at a normal level. If we eat more than we need, the reserve may be stored as adipose tissue to be used as need arises when the intake of food is curtailed. The various uses of foodstuffs depend on an abundant supply of oxygen to cells and on the presence of hormones (p. 718) to regulate the distribution according to the needs of the body. By the processes of digestion and resynthesis in cells, protein and fat from any source can be changed into protein and fat characteristic of the human body. After serving the body in whatever capacity assigned, the food we eat eventually is oxidized, and the waste products are excreted, and the energy utilized.

For example, the orange juice, the prunes, the buttered toast, the poached egg and the milk which you have for breakfast (before it leaves the body as heat, carbon dioxide, water and nitrogenous waste) may repair your liver, give you energy to write an examination and care for patients and even may be incorporated into hemoglobin in some of your erythrocytes for a time.

Your digestive system serves you well, from a few hours after birth until death, in spite of the abuse you frequently give it. Normally, you have little difficulty if you give the alimentary tract reasonable care; otherwise, difficulty with either the chemistry or the mechanics of the digestive system can make you a very miserable individual.

FOODS

The discussion of foods here is very limited, since it is presented thoroughly in textbooks of chemistry.

Foods may be divided into 2 general classes: inorganic and organic. The former comprises inorganic salts and water, and the latter comprises carbohydrates, fats, proteins and accessory foodstuffs or vitamins.

INORGANIC

Inorganic salts in foods are combinations of the following cations: sodium, potassium, calcium, iron, copper, magnesium and manganese and the following anions: chloride, bicarbonate, phosphate, sulfate and iodide. Proper amounts of inorganic salts are needed to maintain osmotic relationships, excitability, conductivity, contractility, acid-base balance and for the coagulation of blood. Salts are lost each day in the urine and the feces and need to be replaced. Any marked departure from the normal amounts of various salts gives rise to pathologic conditions in the body (Addison's disease, p. 736, and tetany, p. 733).

Water is essential to growth and nutrition. Water plays many important roles (p. 60). Since it is so essential for all cellular reactions, the need for a balance between intake and output is evident (p. 685).

ORGANIC

Carbohydrates are organic compounds containing carbon, hydrogen and oxygen, the latter 2 in the same proportion as in water, that is, 2:1. There are 3 groups of carbohydrates.

MONOSACCHARIDES or simple sugars, such as glucose (dextrose), levulose (fructose) and galactose, are soluble in water. Glucose is the form in which carbohydrate is present in the blood.

DISACCHARIDES or double sugars are also water-soluble and comprise sucrose (cane sugar or table sugar), lactose or milk sugar and maltose or malt sugar.

POLYSACCHARIDES are multiple sugars, such as glycogen (animal starch, which is stored in the liver and the muscles), dextrin, plant starch and cellulose.

Fats are organic compounds composed of carbon, hydrogen and oxygen. They are organic salts or esters of glycerol and organic acids. The organic acids common in food and body fat are: palmitic, stearic and oleic. We know of no "essential" fatty acids specifically required by human beings, but in rats it has been demonstrated that 3 unsaturated fatty acids are essential in the diet: linoleic acid, linolenic acid and arachidonic acid. This means that rats are unable to synthesize these fatty acids; if they are lacking, serious difficulties arise.

Neutral fats are insoluble in water, so in order to facilitate digestion, fat is emulsified or separated into small droplets by bile and is then suitable for enzyme attack.

Two important substances are related to fats: cholesterol and lecithin.

PURE CHOLESTEROL is a white, crystalline substance. It is found in every living cell where it serves probably as a framework in which the other constitutents of protoplasm can undergo essential metabolic changes. Cholesterol is important in the maintenance of normal permeability of cell membranes, which is a protective function. It is resistant to the action of enzymes.

LECITHIN is widely distributed in both fluids and tissues of the body. It is especially abundant in white matter (nerve fibers) of the nervous system. It is probably important in the transport and the metabolism of fats.

Proteins are organic compounds composed of carbon, hydrogen, oxygen and nitrogen; some contain sulfur and phosphorus. Proteins are large molecules, composed of enormous numbers of amino acids. The proteins are in a constant state of change. The proteins in the plasma, the liver and the cells of the tissues form a large protein pool, in which the proteins of all parts of the body are in dynamic equilibrium. A protein may be in the protoplasm of the liver today, in the plasma tomorrow, in a muscle fiber the next day and a component of an enzyme on the fourth day, and so on. The circulating plasma is a means of exchange between various tissues.

Proteins are important in the growth or formation of new protoplasm, the repair of tissues and in resistance to infection; they are needed in extra amounts when one is recovering from an operation, during pregnancy and during lactation. If the protein in the diet is inadequate for the needs of the body, the condition of hypoproteinemia or low concentration of protein in the plasma exists.

The proteins which enable one to maintain a good state of nutrition at any age are called *adequate* or *complete* proteins. Most animal proteins are adequate proteins. This means that they contain the 10 indispensable or essential amino acids, which the body cannot synthesize. These acids are: lysine, tryptophane, histidine, phenylalanine, leucine, isoleucine, threonine, methionine, valine and arginine. Most plant proteins lack one or more of the essential amino acids, so one must be certain to include milk, meat, cheese, fish and eggs in the diet.

Some residues of amino acids, after nitrogen is split off, may be converted to glucose (called antiketogenic amino acids); this is a part of normal metabolism in health, but in an untreated diabetic patient such glucose is lost to the body. The residues of other amino acids (called ketogenic), after nitrogen is split off, are converted to beta-oxybutyric acid and form a part of normal metabolic processes in health, but in the untreated diabetic patient, these residues make ketosis worse (p. 741).

The classes of proteins are: simple, conjugated and derived. Albumin is an example of a simple protein, hemoglobin is a conjugated protein, and derived proteins are represented by proteoses, peptones and peptids. In digestion, proteins are split into amino acids with the incorporation of water.

VITAMINS

Vitamins, which are organic compounds present in many natural foodstuffs, are required for growth and other processes. They produce no energy but play a role in transformations of energy and in the regulation of metabolism.

It has been known for a long time that dietary diseases developed under certain conditions, such as in sailors who used to spend months on sailing vessels, without access to fresh foods. Methods of prevention have been known almost as long; English sailors used to be required to drink lime juice on long voyages; as a result they were called "limeys."

The acquiring of accurate scientific knowledge about vitamins was begun in 1906. Most of the vitamins now known take part in enzymatic or oxidative reactions. Some act as catalysts, which means that they speed up reactions and enable them to take place at body temperature; in the absence of catalysts, the same reactions would require a much longer time and a much higher temperature. Some vitamins are precursors (forerunners) of enzymes. Some work as assistants to enzymes. Vitamins aim at various targets; some act on epithelial tissues, some on bone, and some aid the absorption of foods from the lumen of the intestine.

We receive most of the vitamins needed by the body from the food we eat. A few vitamins are synthesized by bacterial action in the large intestine and are absorbed into the blood.

If the supply of vitamins is insufficient, difficulties arise. There are 6 main causes of vitamin deficiency: (1) a low intake, as a result of loss of appetite or the use of special diets in the treatment of obesity, hypertension, allergy, peptic ulcer or as a result of a limited diet after an operation; (2) failure of absorption, as in prolonged vomiting or diarrhea, the absence of bile salts from the intestine (which affects the absorption of the fat-soluble vitamins) or the use of mineral oil as a laxative or in low-calorie salad dressings (mineral oil dissolves the fat-soluble vitamins and carries them out with it in the feces); (3) in liver disease, in which there may be a failure to convert precursors to active vitamins or a failure to store the vitamins; (4) during an increased demand for vitamins, as during fever, pregnancy or lactation; (5) destruction or excretion in the gastro-intestinal tract, such as after sulfonamide drugs, which inhibit bacterial activity in the gut; (6) lack of proper substrate or substance on which to act. Certain amino acids must be present for some vitamins to be effective.

FAT-SOLUBLE VITAMINS

Vitamin A. SOURCES. Vitamin A occurs in many forms. In animal tissues it is found in fish-liver oils, but carotenoid pigments of plants are precursors, which means that they are transformed into vitamin A in the body. Such pigments are present in green leafy plants and yellow vegetables. Beta carotene has the greatest vitamin-A activity of the carotenoid pigments. The conversion to A probably takes place in the epithelial cells of the wall of the intestine, and the thyroid hormone is involved in some way in the conversion.

FUNCTIONS. Vitamin A is concerned with growth (bone, teeth), epithelial tissues, synthesis of visual purple for night vision, and it plays some role in reproduction.

RESULTS OF DEFICIENCY. The skin becomes dry and rough, there is suppression of activity of sweat glands, and the epithelial linings of the respiratory, the alimentary and the genito-urinary tracts become keratinized.

Vitamin D. SOURCES. It occurs in many forms. Calciferol or D_2 is not a natural product but is formed by irradiation of ergosterol; 7-dehydrocholesterol or D_3 is present in fish-liver oils. Cod-liver oil is a rich source.

FUNCTIONS. Vitamin D is required for normal growth, absorption of calcium and phosphorus from the intestine and the utilization of calcium and phosphorus in development of bone. It is linked in some way with phosphatase enzyme systems and, perhaps, with the parathyroid glands.

RESULTS OF DEFICIENCY. Rickets occurs when vitamin D is deficient. In this condition cartilage cells are not replaced by osteoblasts in locations where ossification should take place. Bones are misshapen, epiphyses are enlarged, and there is delayed closure of the fontanels and retarded eruption of teeth.

Vitamin E. Sources. Vitamin E occurs in the form of alpha, beta and gamma tocopherol. It is present in wheat germ, cottonseed, corn and palm oils, egg yolk and green leaves.

Functions. Vitamin E bears some unknown relation to muscle metabolism. It is essential for reproduction in rats.

Results of Deficiency. The most common deficiency is muscular dystrophy, together with primary fibrositis, aching limbs and fibrillar nodules on arms and legs in the region of the joints.

Vitamin K. Sources. Vitamin K is not a natural vitamin; it is synthesized by bacteria in the large intestine. Menadione is synthetic vitamin K.

Functions. Vitamin K is required by the liver in the synthesis of prothrombin.

Results of Deficiency. When vitamin K is deficient the prothrombin concentration of the blood is low, and there is a tendency to hemorrhage.

Water-Soluble Vitamins

B Complex. Thiamine. *Sources.* Yeast, whole-grain cereals, dry peas, beans, soybeans, nuts, pork, liver and egg yolk all supply thiamine. Some of the factors of the B complex are synthesized by the bacteria in the large intestine.

Functions. It is important in the metabolism of carbohydrate. An important derivative is pyrophosphate, known also as cocarboxylase, which is a coenzyme or prosthetic group of decarboxylase.

The results of deficiency usually are a part of a multiple vitamin deficiency—beriberi characterized by anorexia, loss of weight, debility, peripheral neuritis and edema. The heart usually is enlarged. The blood levels of pyruvic and lactic acid are high.

Riboflavin. *The sources* are the same as for thiamine. Widely distributed in nature, it is present in all cells of plants and animals. It is phosphorylated by enzymes in the cells in the intestinal mucosa before absorption.

Functions. It is the prosthetic group of a large number of distinct enzymes. It accepts H atoms from specific substrates and passes them on to other molecules. It is important in carbohydrate metabolism.

Results of Deficiency. This is one of the most common vitamin deficiencies in man. It is characterized by glossitis, cheilosis and seborrheic dermatitis.

NIACIN. *Sources.* See thiamine. It is present in plant and animal tissues as the amide.

Functions. It appears as coenzyme I (also called *cozymase* and *diphosphopyridine nucleotide* or DPN) and coenzyme II (also called *triphosphopyridine nucleotide* or TPN). Probably as many as 40 reactions are now known to involve these molecules.

Results of Deficiency. Pellagra, which is the most deleterius of the vitamin deficiencies in North America, is the chief result. It is characterized by three "d's": dementia, dermatitis and diarrhea.

PANTOTHENIC ACID. *The sources* are widely distributed. Also, it is synthesized in the intestine by bacterial action.

Functions. Coenzyme A is involved in acetylation of aromatic amines in the liver and in the brain.

Results of Deficiency. It is not recognized in man.

PYRIDOXINE. *Sources.* See thiamine. It is synthesized by some bacteria.

Functions. It is involved in protein metabolism and is the prosthetic group for transaminase and codecarboxylase. It serves in tryptophane metabolism.

Results of deficiency are not recognized in man.

BIOTIN. *Sources.* Some is synthesized in the large intestine by bacteria. See also the sources of thiamine.

Functions. It serves in carbon-dioxide fixation. It is condensed with pyruvic acid and serves in enzymatic deamination of various amino acids.

The results of deficiency are dermatitis, loss of hair, loss of muscular control, anorexia and loss of weight, and lassitude.

INOSITOL. *Sources.* It is synthesized in the intestinal tract.

Functions. A lipotropic agent, it helps to prevent fatty liver. It may play a role in amylase activity.

The results of deficiency are fatty liver and baldness.

PTEROYLGLUTAMIC ACID. *The sources* are green leafy vegetables and liver.

Functions. It is a hemopoietic agent, but does not relieve neurologic disturbances associated with pernicious anemia.

Results of Deficiency. Anemia.

VITAMIN B_{12}. *The sources* are green leafy vegetables and liver. The "intrinsic factor" may facilitate its absorption from the intestinal tract.

Functions. It acts as a hemopoietic agent and aids in growth. It improves all disturbances associated with pernicious anemia.

Results of Deficiency. Anemia.

PARA-AMINOBENZOIC ACID. *Sources.* See thiamine.

Functions. In man, its functions are undecided, but it plays a part in the growth of animals.

The results of deficiency are not recognized in man.

CHOLINE. *Sources.* See thiamine.

Functions. Essential for normal nutrition, it has a lipotropic action and aids in the synthesis of phospholipid. In transmethylation it furnishes labile methyl groups.

Results of Deficiency. Lack of growth, anorexia, emaciation, dehydration and fatty livers will result.

Vitamin C. SOURCES: As ascorbic acid, it is found in vegetables and citrus fruits.

FUNCTIONS. It is concerned in normal production of supporting tissues of mesenchymal origin (dentin and collagen).

The results of deficiency are scurvy; failure to deposit intercellular cement substance; abnormal collagen, with a tendency to hemorrhage and slow wound healing.

Vitamin P, Citrin. SOURCES. It is found with C. Citrin is present in lemon peel; as rutin, it is found in buckwheat.

FUNCTIONS. It is necessary for maintenance of normal permeability of capillaries.

The results of deficiency are decreased capillary resistance, specifically in man.

DIGESTION

Attention already has been called to the necessity for changes in the food as eaten, before it can be of use to the body. The types of activity that occur in the alimentary tract are: (1) mechanical: a grinding of the food, mixing it with juices, moving it along, spreading it over the surface of the small intestine to favor absorption and elimination of the residue; and (2) chemical: splitting to simple components.

The latter change is due to digestive enzymes, which are catalytic substances formed by living cells and having specific actions in bringing about chemical changes. Each enzyme acts on only one type of foodstuff and requires a certain pH for its activity. The ending *ase* indicates an *enzyme*, for example, *lipase* refers to an enzyme that "digests fats," *protease*, one that "digests proteins" and *amylase*, one that "digests starches." The names of the enzymes, the method by which their production is controlled, the foodstuff on which they act and the products produced by their activity are presented in tabular form, to facilitate a review of the facts which are treated more fully in textbooks of chemistry.

Digestive Juices

Glands	How Activated	Secretes	Acts Upon	Products of Digestion
Salivary (saliva)	Reflexly	Salivary amylase (ptyalin)	Starch, dextrins, glycogen	Maltose
Gastric (gastric juice)	1st phase— reflexly	Parietal cells; HCl	Activates pepsinogen	
	2nd phase— hormonal gastrin	Chief cells gastric protease (pepsinogen)	Protein	Proteoses, peptones, amino acids
	3rd phase— probably hormonal, but uncertain	Rennin—probably only in stomach of young	Soluble caseinogen	Paracasein, precipitated by calcium
Alveolar or acinar cells of pancreas (pancreatic juice)	Reflexly	Juice rich in enzymes —see below		
	Hormonal a. Secretin	Watery juice, rich in NaHCO₃	Neutralizes acid chyme	
	b. Pancreozymin	Thick juice, rich in enzymes		
		Pancreatic amylase (amylopsin)	Starches, dextrins and glycogen	Maltose, lactose and sucrose
		Pancreatic lipase (steapsin)	Emulsified fats	Fatty acids and glycerol
		Pancreatic protease (trypsinogen, chymotrypsinogen and carboxypeptidase)	Proteins, proteoses and peptones	Peptones and amino acids
Intestinal (crypts of Lieberkühn) intestinal juice (or succus entericus)	Reflexly hormonal	Aminopolypeptidase (erepsin)	Peptones	Amino acids
	a. Secretin	Lactase	Lactose	Galactose and glucose
	b. Enterocrinin	Maltase	Maltose	Glucose
		Sucrase	Sucrose	Glucose and fructose
		Enterokinase	Activates trypsinogen and chymotrypsinogen	Trypsin and chymo-trypsin
Liver (bile)	Production of bile-secretin Emptying of gallbladder- cholecystokinin	No enzymes	Fats	Emulsified fats

DIGESTION IN THE MOUTH

Mechanical Change. The food is ground into small particles and mixed thoroughly with saliva in the mouth. The movement is called *chewing* or *mastication*. The tongue, the teeth and the muscles of mastication are used to pulverize the food.

Chemical Change. Saliva is produced by the salivary glands. The secretion begins when one thinks about food, sees it, smells it or hears it talked about, and secretion continues when food is taken into the mouth.

The first part of the secretion is called the *psychic secretion;* the optic, the olfactory and the cochlear nerves are the usual afferent paths. The continuation of secretion while actually eating is due to stimulation of the nerves of taste. The efferent pathway may be either division of the autonomic system; each division supplies one type of secretory (that is, either serous or mucous) cell in the salivary glands. The center for the reflex secretion of saliva is in the medulla. Saliva dissolves food and enables the taste buds to be stimulated.

SALIVA consists of a mixture of the secretions from the 3 pairs of salivary glands and mucus from the surface epithelial cells. It contains 99.4 per cent of water, together with mucin, salivary amylase, inorganic salts, sloughed epithelial cells and disintegrating leukocytes. The thin, watery type of saliva is produced by serous cells in the salivary glands and the thick, viscid type by mucous cells in the same glands. The type produced is determined by the nature of the stimulus, that is, solid or liquid food. The *serous* type of cells is found in the parotid, the *mucous* type in the sublingual, and *both* serous and mucous in the submaxillary glands.

The functions of saliva are to dissolve food and aid mastication, speech and deglutition (swallowing). It coats the food with mucus, which makes it slippery. The digestive action is to change cooked starch, dextrin and glycogen to maltose by means of salivary amylase.

DIGESTION IN PHARYNX AND ESOPHAGUS

Mechanical Change. The food is carried from the mouth to the stomach by the act of deglutition. For convenience of description, this is divided into 3 stages.

THE FIRST STAGE of deglutition consists of collecting the bolus or mass of food on the dorsum of the tongue. Then a sudden elevation of the tongue throws the mass into the pharynx. The first stage of deglutition is under voluntary control.

THE SECOND STAGE of deglutition is the passage of the bolus through the pharynx. The air passages must be shut off. The nasopharynx is closed by the elevation of the uvula and the soft palate, the larynx is pulled up under the root of the tongue, and the glottis is closed. The bolus is grasped by the constrictors of the pharynx and passed along into the esophagus. Figure 351 indicates the changes that occur in the position of the soft palate and the larynx during deglutition.

If only liquid is swallowed, the constrictors of the pharynx are not involved. The second stage is involuntary, although skeletal muscles of the pharynx are striated. Respiration is inhibited reflexly during the passage of food through the pharynx.

THE THIRD STAGE is the passage through the esophagus. The muscle in the upper portion of the esophagus in man is striated but not under the control of the will. The muscle in the lower portion of the esophagus is smooth. It exhibits waves of contraction called *peristaltic* (meaning "to send around") waves. A typical peristaltic wave is preceded by relaxation. The function of peristaltic waves is to move food along the alimentary tract in a caudal direction. The cardiac sphincter relaxes as a peristaltic wave in the esophagus approaches.

Deglutition is a very complicated reflex; it is guided by a center in the medulla. The afferent nerves are the trigeminal, the glosso-

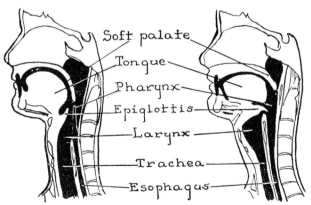

FIG. 351. Deglutition. Diagram showing elevation of soft palate and larynx and closure of glottis during deglutition. (After Tigerstedt)

pharyngeal and the vagus. The efferent nerves involved are the masticator, the glossopharyngeal, the vagus, the accessory and the hypoglossal.

Chemical Change. The only secretion produced by glands in the pharynx and the esophagus is mucus, which facilitates swallowing of a bolus of food by making it slippery. No enzymes are produced in this portion of the alimentary tract.

DIGESTION IN THE STOMACH

Mechanical Change. Waves of contraction are present in the pyloric portion of the stomach and occur at a rate of about 3 per minute. The waves begin as shallow ripples near the cardia and become deeper as they move toward the pyloric antrum. As digestion proceeds, small amounts of food are passed through the pylorus whenever the first part of the duodenum is empty. There is a definite pressure gradient from the pyloric antrum to the duodenum, which is important in the emptying of the stomach. After an ordinary meal it takes from 5 to 7 hours for the stomach to become empty. Carbohydrates leave the stomach first, and fats are the slowest to leave.

Chemical Change. SECRETION OF GASTRIC JUICE. There are 3 phases in the production of gastric juice.

Cephalic Phase. This is stimulated by the sight, the smell, the taste or, indeed, even by the thought of food. Since the receptors and the afferent nerves that lead to the first phase of secretion are in the head, this is called the *cephalic phase.* The vagus nerves are the efferent pathways in this reflex secretion of gastric juice.

The cephalic phase is especially important since it assures the presence of some gastric juice as soon as food enters the stomach. Sometimes it is called *the appetite juice.* The importance of presenting a patient with a tray attractively arranged with appetizing food is obvious.

Gastric Phase. This phase is due to the presence of food in the stomach and is thought to act in one of two ways—by distending the pyloric region mechanically and by chemical stimulation due to the presence of partially digested proteins. Both factors act as stimuli for the mucosa in the pyloric region of the stomach to produce a hormone called *gastrin.* Gastrin enters the blood stream and is carried to the glands in the fundus and the body of the stomach where it stimulates the production of gastric juice. This phase involves both hormone and nervous factors; that is, the vagus nerves must be intact for the above sequence of events to transpire.

FIG. 352. Section of frozen stomach of rat during digestion to show stratification of food given at different times. Food was given in three portions and colored differently. (Redrawn after Grützner: Pflüger's Arch. ges. Physiol. **106**:463)

Intestinal Phase. The presence of chyme (liquid food and juice as it leaves the stomach) in the duodenum stimulates further production of gastric juice. The mechanism is not well understood, but it is thought that the control is of the hormonal type.

COMPOSITION OF GASTRIC JUICE. Gastric juice is strongly acid due to the presence of hydrochloric acid; mucus and gastric protease also are present.

The principal digestive action in the stomach is the splitting of proteins to the proteose and peptone stage. This is accomplished after the protease, which is secreted in an inactive form, is activated by hydrochloric acid.

Since food is layered as it enters the stomach (Fig. 352), salivary digestion continues in the center of the stomach contents until all of the food is mixed thoroughly with gastric juice and the acidity inhibits activity of salivary amylase.

The mucus of the gastric juice helps to neutralize the hydrochloric acid.

DIGESTION IN THE SMALL INTESTINE

Mechanical Change. Three types of movement occur in the small intestine: rhythmic segmentation, peristalsis and pendular movements.

RHYTHMIC SEGMENTATION. This consists of a squeezing and mixing of intestinal contents by means of localized rhythmic contractions of the circular muscle. The contractions are most pronounced in the duodenum and the jejunum and serve to mix the contents thoroughly and spread them over the surface of the mucosa. Rhythmic segmentation is myogenic in origin. This means that the activity is an inherent property of the smooth muscle and in no way dependent on the nerve supply.

PERISTALSIS. Peristaltic waves may begin in any part of the small intestine and move along for short or long distances. The waves that travel for short distances are called *peristaltic waves;* those that travel longer distances are called *peristaltic rushes*. Peristaltic waves and rushes may not move contents the entire distance they travel.

When one begins to eat, and food enters the stomach, marked activity begins in the ileum. This is a reflex and is called the *feeding reaction*. The existence of this reflex is one important reason for not giving food by mouth immediately after operations on the small intestine, as the increased activity might lead to rupture of fresh sutures.

The first chyme reaches the ileocecal sphincter within 2 to 4 hours after eating a meal.

Peristalsis is dependent on extrinsic nerves. The vagus nerves (cranial autonomic or parasympathetic) are primarily motor to the smooth muscle in the wall of the small intestine and inhibitory to the smooth muscle of the sphincters. The thoracolumbar (sympathetic) nerves are primarily inhibitory to the smooth muscle of the small intestine and motor to the smooth muscle of the sphincters.

PENDULAR MOVEMENT. This refers to a swaying to and fro of the small intestine. The function is unknown.

Alvarez has suggested that there is a gradient in the intestinal muscle which normally keeps the material moving caudally. He found an underlying metabolic gradient; more oxygen is used by the cells in the wall of the duodenum than in the ileum, and more carbon dioxide is produced in the former. The rate of rhythmic contraction is more rapid in the upper parts of the small intestine. In case of inflammation along the tract, the normal gradient may be reversed, and vomiting may occur; or the gradient may be steepened, and diarrhea may occur.

Chemical Change. Three secretions are emptied into the small intestine: pancreatic juice, bile and intestinal juice.

PANCREATIC JUICE enters the small intestine within 1 to 2 minutes after one begins to eat a meal. This secretion is a reflex, due to stimulation of the nerves of taste, and the vagus nerves form the

---

FIG. 353. Diagrams to illustrate the secretion of saliva, gastric juice and pancreatic juice. The emptying of the gallbladder is shown also. (A) Reflex control of salivary secretion. (B) 1. Cephalic phase, reflex. 2. Gastric phase, possibility of both reflex and hormonal control. 3. Intestinal phase, hormonal control. (C) Hormonal control of pancreatic secretion through secretin. (D) Hormonal control of gallbladder evacuation through cholecystokinin.

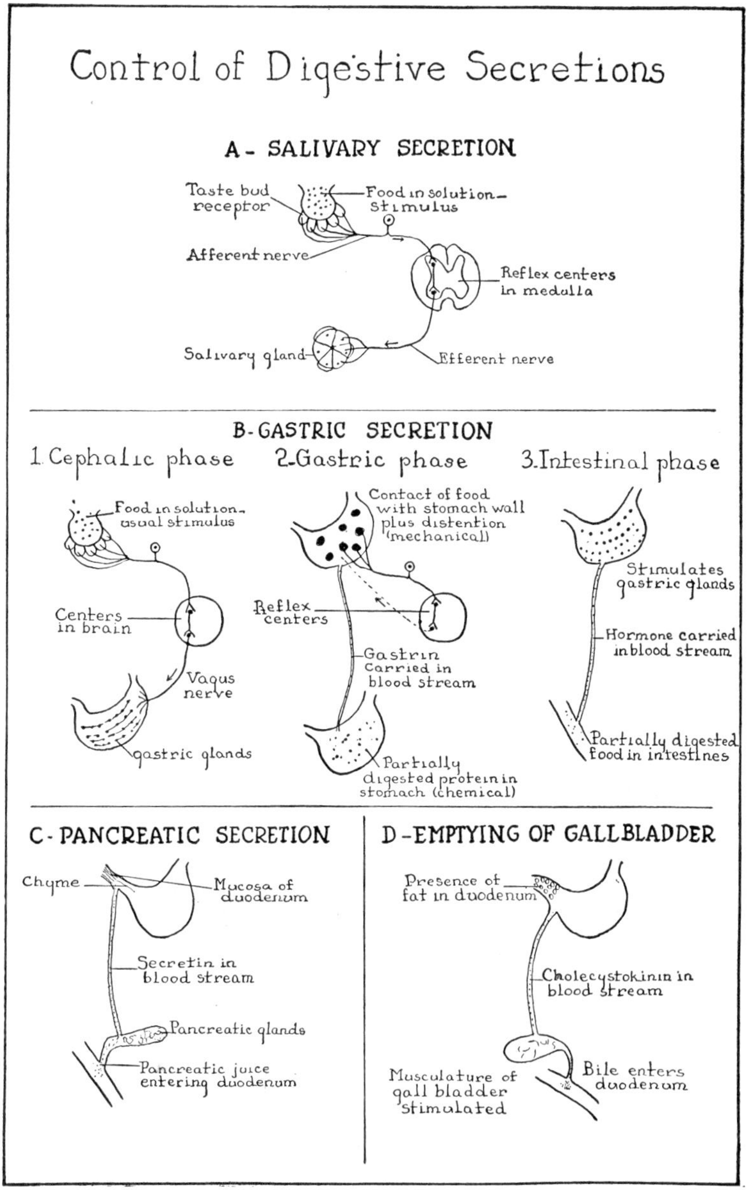

FIGURE 353 *(Caption on facing page)*

efferent pathway. The flow is greatly increased when acid chyme begins to enter the duodenum from the stomach. The acid chyme reacts with a substance in the duodenal mucosa and produces several hormones, two of which are concerned with the production of pancreatic juice.

The first hormone is secretin, which is carried from the duodenal mucosa by means of the blood to the acinar (alveolar) cells of the pancreas, where it stimulates the flow of a thin, watery juice, rich in sodium bicarbonate. Secretin also stimulates the production of bile by the liver and of intestinal juice by the glands of the small intestine.

The second hormone is pancreozymin, which also is carried by the blood to the acinar (alveolar) cells, where it stimulates a flow of thick, viscid pancreatic juice, rich in enzymes.

Pancreatic juice contains sodium bicarbonate, amylase, protease and lipase. The *sodium bicarbonate* partially neutralizes the hydrochloric acid of the chyme, as intestinal digestion requires a less acid reaction than the gastric digestion for optimum activity.

Pancreatic *amylase* digests uncooked starch, dextrin and glycogen to maltose. Pancreatic *protease,* secreted in the inactive form of trypsinogen and chymotrypsinogen, is activated by enterokinase to trypsin and chymotrypsin, which digest proteins, proteoses and peptones to peptones and amino acids. Pancreatic *lipase* (steapsin) splits emulsified fats to fatty acids and glycerol.

BILE is produced by the liver. The production is stimulated by secretin, as mentioned above. Bile is stored temporarily in the gall-bladder and is emptied when chyme enters the duodenum.

The third hormone produced by the action of chyme on the duodenal mucosa is cholecystokinin. It is carried by the blood to the gallbladder where it stimulates the smooth muscle to contract and empty its concentrated bile into the duodenum just when it is needed. The constituents of the bile (p. 638) that are important

FIG. 354. Diagram of digestion. (A) Carbohydrates: polysaccharides hydrolyzed to disaccharides by amylase; disaccharides hydrolyzed to monosaccharides by disaccharases. (B) Fats: emulsified by bile, then hydrolyzed to glycerol and fatty acids by lipases. (C) Proteins: HCl supplies the proper pH for protein digestion. The protein is hydrolyzed to amino acids by the gastric, the pancreatic and the intestinal proteases. Although the chemical union is between the nitrogen of the NH_2 group and the carbon of the COOH group, it is indicated in the diagram as between H and O for simplicity, in consideration of the addition of H_2O.

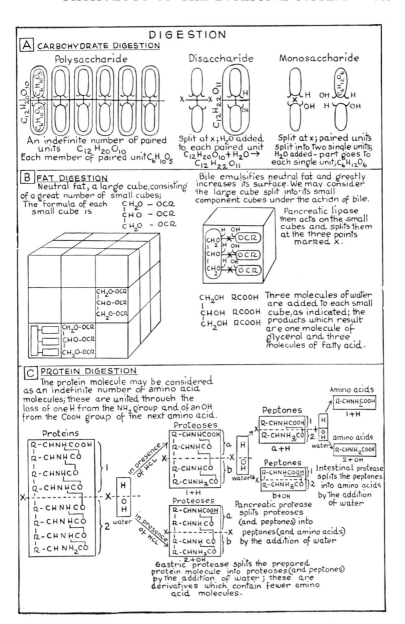

FIGURE 354 (*Caption on facing page*)

in digestion are the bile salts; they emulsify fats and so prepare them for digestion by pancreatic lipase.

INTESTINAL JUICE OR SUCCUS ENTERICUS. Intestinal juice is produced by the glands of the small intestine (crypts of Lieberkühn) when chyme enters the duodenum. The production of intestinal juice is stimulated by the hormone secretin, and also by enterocrinin (a *fourth hormone* produced by duodenal mucosa).

Intestinal juice contains the following enzymes: (1) a protease (erepsin), which completes protein digestion to the amino acid stage; (2) enterokinase, which activates trypsinogen; (3) sucrase, which splits sucrose to glucose and fructose; (4) maltase, which splits maltose to 2 molecules of glucose; and (5) lactase, which splits lactose to glucose and galactose.

Enterogastrone is produced by the action of fats on the duodenal mucosa. It is carried by the blood stream to the stomach, and there it inhibits contractions of the smooth muscle of the wall of the

GASTRO-INTESTINAL HORMONES

HORMONE	WHERE PRODUCED	AGENTS STIMULATING PRODUCTION	ACTION
Gastrin	Gastric mucosa of pyloric region	Distention and protein derivatives	Stimulates production of gastric juice by gastric glands in fundus and body of stomach
Secretin	Duodenal mucosa	Acidity of duodenal contents	Stimulates production of watery pancreatic juice, bile and intestinal juice
Pancreozymin	Duodenal mucosa	Chyme	Stimulates production of enzyme-rich pancreatic juice
Enterogastrone	Mucosa of small intestine	Soaps, fatty acids, fats and certain sugars	Inhibits secretion of gastric juice and motility of stomach
Cholecystokinin	Mucosa of small intestine	Fats, fatty acids, dilute HCl and peptone	Stimulates emptying of gallbladder
Enterocrinin	Duodenal mucosa	Chyme	Stimulates production of intestinal juice

stomach and also inhibits the secretion of gastric juice. The term used to designate such an inhibiting hormone is *chalone* (meaning "to relax").

Figure 353 illustrates the mechanisms of secretion of some of the digestive juices.

Figure 354 is a diagram of digestion of the 3 foodstuffs.

The gastro-intestinal hormones are arranged in tabular form on the facing page.

DIGESTION IN THE LARGE INTESTINE

Mechanical Change. The movements of the large intestine are very sluggish. About 3 or 4 times daily "mass movements" occur that transport the contents along to the sigmoid colon, where the feces accumulate. Mass movements are prone to occur after meals and represent the "gastrocolic reflex." Advantage can be taken of this reflex after breakfast to establish the habit of emptying the bowel each morning.

The sacral autonomic nerves (parasympathetic) are the nerves of "emptying"; that is, they bring about contraction of the smooth muscle in the wall of the colon, with relaxation of the sphincters of the rectum. The thoracolumbar autonomic nerves (sympathetic) are the nerves of "retention"; that is, they cause relaxation of the smooth muscle of the wall of the colon, with contraction of the sphincters of the rectum.

Chemical Change. No enzymes are secreted by the glands of the large intestine. The only secretion produced in this portion of the alimentary tube is mucus, and this aids in moving the fecal contents along to the rectum.

Functions. BACTERIAL ACTION. The large intestine is filled with bacteria, which act on the undigested residues. They produce fermentation of carbohydrate, during which organic acids are produced. The bacteria also produce putrefaction of proteins. Some of the split products are eliminated with the feces, and others are absorbed. Those that are absorbed are phenol, indol and skatol; these are conjugated with other substances in the liver and then excreted by way of the urine.

Bacteria that inhabit the large intestine synthesize vitamin K, which is then absorbed, provided that bile is present in the intestine. Some components of the vitamin B complex are produced by intestinal bacteria, and these likewise are absorbed and used by the body.

DEFECATION (emptying of the rectum). The sigmoid colon is

filled with feces by the mass movements of the large intestine. The rectum remains empty until just before defecation. As the feces enter and stretch the rectum the desire to defecate is aroused. If unheeded, the desire disappears (due to adaptation of stretch receptors), and the feces remain in the rectum and become hard and dry, and defecation then becomes difficult and painful.

The contractions of the smooth muscle in the walls of the rectum are accompanied by relaxation of the internal and the external sphincters and the contraction of the voluntary muscles of the abdominal walls and the pelvic floor. The levator ani muscles assist in expelling the last of the fecal contents.

VALUE OF THE LARGE INTESTINE AS AN EXCRETORY ORGAN. The feces contain from 65 to 67 per cent water, from 5 to 9 per cent nitrogen, from 12 to 18 per cent fatty acids and lecithin and from 11 to 22 per cent ash. The ash contains calcium (from 10 to 20 times as much as is excreted in the urine), potassium (also excreted in the urine), iron (excreted only in the feces), magnesium (an equal amount excreted in the urine), bismuth (excreted only in the feces) and mercury (also excreted in the urine). In the feces there are present a large amount of mucus, bile pigments, large numbers of bacteria, the undigested cellulose and the epithelial cells that have been sloughed off the mucosa of the intestine.

LIVER

FUNCTIONS OF THE LIVER

The liver, one of the wonders of the body, performs a great variety of functions.

Production of Bile. Bile, which is considered both a secretion and an excretion, is produced continuously by the liver. Bile (in the gallbladder) contains 90 per cent water; the remaining constituents are mucus, bile pigments, cholesterol, bile salts, lecithin and inorganic salts. Mucus is added to bile during its stay in the gallbladder. The bile pigments are "excreted" by the liver. These are the products of disintegration of hemoglobin from worn-out erythrocytes; bilirubin is the chief one of the bile pigments. The bile salts are "secreted." They emulsify fats in the intestine. During the temporary storage of bile in the gallbladder it becomes concentrated, due to the absorption of water.

Conversion of Glucose to Glycogen and Storage of the Latter. As portal blood brings glucose to the liver, it is converted to glycogen and stored temporarily in the liver cells. As the concentration of glucose in the blood begins to decrease, glycogen is changed back to glucose and released to the blood. This process goes on until the next meal is taken.

Storage of Various Substances. The liver is important as a storehouse for protein, iron, copper and vitamins A, D and B_{12} (same as the antiamenic factor).

Deamination. Amino acids are deaminized (nitrogen removed) and then the nitrogen is converted to urea (which is the chief nitrogenous waste product) in the liver.

Desaturation. Fatty acids are desaturated (double bonds are created between adjacent carbon atoms) in the liver. This makes them more available for oxidation by the cells of various tissues.

Phagocytosis. The reticuloendothelial cells (Kupffer cells) that line the sinusoids of the liver possess remarkable phagocytic powers. They engulf worn-out erythrocytes and foreign materials, such as dyes.

Production of heparin, which is an anticoagulant, takes place in the liver.

Production of Plasma Proteins. Most of the plasma proteins, such as albumin, fibrinogen and prothrombin, are produced in the liver.

ABSORPTION

Absorption is the transfer of the products of digestion through the epithelial cells of the villi into the blood or the lymph. The processes involved in absorption are osmosis and diffusion. However, these physical processes cannot account for all the intricacies of absorption, so investigators ascribe much that goes on to the "special vital activity" of the epithelial cells of the mucosa.

One reason that absorption is so difficult to study is that secretion by all the glands of the intestine goes on simultaneously with absorption; this complicates the study greatly. Materials used in manufacturing the various secretions are taken from the blood and returned again to the blood after they have served their function in the lumen of the digestive tract. Absorption of these digestive secretions is going on at the same time that the products of digestion of foods are being absorbed.

Stomach. There is very little absorption from the stomach; alcohol, a small amount of water, some sugar and a few drugs are thought to be absorbed in this portion of the alimentary tract.

The Small Intestine is the Great Absorbing Organ. Water and inorganic salts are absorbed throughout the length of the small intestine. Carbohydrates are absorbed as monosaccharides directly into the vascular capillaries in the villi (Fig. 355). Proteins are absorbed as amino acids, also into the vascular capillaries in the villi (Fig. 355). There seem to be 2 pathways for fat absorption. The first is by way of the blood; some neutral fat is absorbed by this channel (vascular capillaries in the villi). The second pathway is by way of the lymph, and this involves a resynthesis. Fatty acids and glycerol enter the epithelial cells of the mucosa separately, and, during their passage through the epithelial cells, they are resynthesized, and the neutral fat (called chyle) then enters the lymphatic capillaries (lacteals) in the villi (Figs. 356 and 357). It is possible that some lipids may enter the lymph without being hydrolyzed in the intestinal lumen. Bile salts aid in ferrying fatty acids into epithelial cells.

Villi are in constant motion, due to the activity of the smooth muscle fibers in the muscularis mucosae. About 85 per cent of all the absorption that takes place along the alimentary tube occurs in the villi of the small intestine.

It is thought that only water is absorbed in the large intestine;

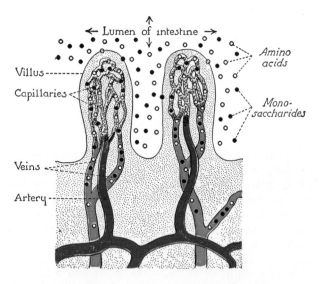

FIG. 355. Diagram of absorption of carbohydrate and protein; monosaccharides and amino acids enter the capillaries of the villi.

consequently, it is very difficult to feed a patient by nutrient enemas. If the material in the nutrient enema is transported backward through the large intestine until it enters the small intestine, then it can be absorbed readily. Owing to the efficiency of the ileocecal sphincter, this method of feeding is highly unsatisfactory, since entrance to the small intestine from the colon is rare.

FIG. 356. Diagram of absorption of fat. Glycerol enters the epithelial cells as such; fatty acids combine with alkali to form soap, or dissolve in bile, and thus enter the epithelial cells. Within the cells, the fatty acids are freed, and they unite with the glycerol to form neutral fat, which enters the lacteals. Some neutral fat is absorbed directly into the blood; thus there are two pathways for the absorption of fat.

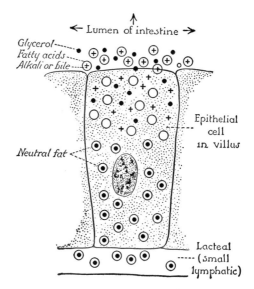

FIG. 357. Lacteals or lymphatic capillaries in intestine of rat; filled with dye. (After Ranvier)

METABOLISM

Metabolism refers to all the changes in foodstuffs from the time they are absorbed from the small intestine until they are excreted as waste products from the body. Metabolism consists of 2 phases: *anabolism* (meaning "a building up") and *catabolism* (meaning "to throw down"). In other words, during the phase of anabolism, protoplasm is built up, while during the phase of catabolism, protoplasm is broken down by oxidative processes with the release of energy, as heat and work, or the storage of energy, in the form of "high energy bond" phosphate.

The processes of metabolism are carried out by means of enzymes within the cells. Many of the cellular enzymatic reactions depend on the presence of vitamins and are regulated by hormones.

CARBOHYDRATE METABOLISM

In considering carbohydrate metabolism, it is necessary to call attention to the regulation of the blood sugar concentration, the synthesis of tissue glycogen, the oxidation of carbohydrate and the relation of various endocrine glands to carbohydrate metabolism.

Regulation of Blood Sugar Concentration. Sugar (glucose) is added to the blood by 3 sources: absorption from the small intestine, breakdown of liver glycogen (glycogenolysis) and formation of glucose from noncarbohydrate sources (gluconeogenesis), such as amino acids, lactic acid, citric acid, pyruvic acid and glycerol.

Sugar is removed from the blood by 3 channels: formation of tissue glycogen (in liver and muscles), conversion to fat and storage in adipose tissue, and oxidation by tissues.

The blood glucose level varies continually within rather narrow limits and is determined by the balance between the processes adding glucose to and those taking glucose from the blood. Glucose oxidation supplies more than one half of the energy of the body and is the only source of energy in the brain.

Tissue Glycogen. Glycogen is synthesized in liver and in muscles. The synthesis of tissue glycogen in general (glycogenesis) requires the aid of adenosine triphosphate (ATP) which supplies the energy needed by releasing it from the energy-rich bonds. By this means, ATP is an essential phosphorylating agent in formation of glycogen.

The formation of muscle glycogen depends practically entirely on glucose from the blood. When this muscle glycogen is broken

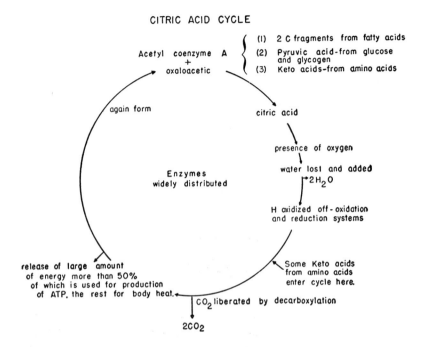

FIG. 358. Citric acid cycle. Fats, carbohydrates and proteins ultimately are oxidized by way of the citric acid cycle. Water and
carbon dioxide are produced and a large amount of energy is liberated; some of this keeps the body warm and the remainder is stored
temporarily in the high-energy phosphate bonds of ATP.

down during muscle contraction, it yields lactic and pyruvic acids.
About four fifths of these acids are rebuilt to muscle glycogen during recovery from activity. The portion that escapes into the blood
is transported to the liver and there converted to glucose and
liver glycogen. Some may be eliminated in the urine. It is evident
that muscle glycogen can contribute to blood glucose only indirectly through the assistance of the liver.

The breakdown of liver glycogen yields glucose that enters the
blood stream.

Carbohydrate oxidation in the tissues involves 2 stages. The
first is the breakdown of tissue glycogen with the formation of lactic and pyruvic acids. The second stage is the oxidation of pyruvic
acid (and lactic acid, which is converted to pyruvic) to acetyl

coenzyme A, and then the oxidation to carbon dioxide and water in the reactions of the citric (tricarboxylic) acid cycle, with the release of utilizable energy as ATP. Since the citric acid cycle is of fundamental importance in the oxidation of all types of foodstuffs, a diagram of it is presented in Figure 358.

Relation of Endocrine Glands to Carbohydrate Metabolism. PANCREAS. Insulin, which is produced by the beta cells of the islands of Langerhans, is concerned with the utilization of carbohydrate in general. Insulin is essential to the phosphorylation of glucose by ATP (under the action of hexokinase). This reaction must take place before glucose can be converted to glycogen, to fat or be oxidized. Insulin inhibits gluconeogenesis.

Glucagon, which is produced by the alpha cells of the islands of Langerhans, promotes the breakdown of liver glycogen.

ANTERIOR LOBE OF THE PITUITARY GLAND. A hormone of the anterior lobe of the pituitary tends to inhibit the action of hexokinase in the phosphorylation of glucose.

ADRENAL CORTEX. One of the hormones of the adrenal cortex stimulates gluconeogenesis from amino acids and promotes the production of liver glycogen.

ADRENAL MEDULLA. The hormones of the adrenal medulla (epinephrine and nor-epinephrine) promote a rapid breakdown of liver glycogen to glucose, and of muscle glycogen to lactic and pyruvic acids.

It is evident that carbohydrate metabolism is exceedingly complex and that there must be a balance between various glands of internal secretion for a normal rate of carbohydrate utilization. Figure 359 is a diagram of carbohydrate metabolism.

In summary, when glucose enters the blood from the intestine:

1. Some glucose may be oxidized at once to carbon dioxide and water, with the release of energy to maintain body temperature and to enable one to do muscular work.

2. Another portion of glucose is synthesized to liver glycogen. When the blood sugar level falls, this is changed back to glucose and released to the blood and eventually is oxidized.

3. Another portion of glucose is changed to fat, and stored as adipose tissue. There are fat depots in the subcutaneous tissues, around the kidneys, in the mesenteries, in the greater omentum, in the mediastinum and in the cervical, the axillary and the inguinal regions.

4. Some glucose can be transformed into amino acids by the addition of nitrogen.

CARBOHYDRATE   METABOLISM

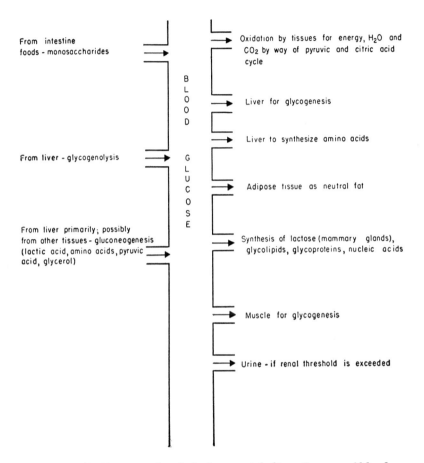

FIG. 359. Diagram of carbohydrate metabolism. Sources of blood glucose are indicated on the left and means of utilizing glucose are indicated on the right.

5. If there is a large intake of carbohydrate within a short period of time, such as eating a generous amount of candy at one sitting, some of the glucose may be eliminated by the kidneys (alimentary glycosuria), since the "factories" which normally handle carbohydrate are flooded by the sudden large intake, and the excess spills over into the urine.

Carbohydrates are very easy to burn, and they serve as a source of ready energy. Each gram of carbohydrate releases 4 large calories of heat when it is oxidized. (A large calorie, written *Cal.*, is the amount of heat required to raise the temperature of 1 kg. (2.2 pounds) of water from 15° to 16° C).

FAT METABOLISM

The lipids in the blood are in the form of neutral fat (as chylomicrons), cholesterol, cholesterol esters of the fatty acids and phospholipids.

The sources of the lipids in the blood are (1) absorption from the small intestine, (2) mobilization of depot fat and (3) synthesis in the liver. It was stated above that glucose could be converted to fat and stored in fat depots, so that either fat or glucose can give origin to depot fat. Phospholipids and cholesterol esters are especially important in the transport of fatty acids in the blood. Both phospholipids and cholesterol are essential constituents of the protoplasm of every cell and are maintained even during starvation.

Fat forms the bulk of stored energy-producing food in the body; it is in the form of neutral fat. Depot fat is in a continuous state of change; it is continually laid down and remobilized. It is in general characteristic for a given animal species but may be modified by diet to some extent.

The liver plays an essential role in fat metabolism. It desaturates some fatty acids, hydrogenates some unsaturated fatty acids, shortens and lengthens the carbon chains of fatty acids. It is particularly concerned with lipid synthesis. It produces changes in the composition of lipids and is responsible for the first stages of oxidation of fatty acids. Fatty acids undergo beta oxidation, which means that 2 carbon units are split off at a time. These 2 carbon units condense in the liver to form aceto-acetic acid, which is the primary ketone body.

Aceto-acetic acid and its companion, beta-hydroxybutyric acid, leave the liver by way of the blood and are carried to the muscles, where they are oxidized. The oxidation progresses along the citric acid cycle, in which the ketone bodies are burned to carbon dioxide and water, with the release of a large amount of energy as ATP. Oxalo-acetic acid, which is derived from carbohydrate (or amino acid) metabolism by way of acetyl coenzyme A, is necessary for the oxidation of ketone bodies in the citric acid cycle. Before the details of this interaction were known, it was stated that "fats burned in the flame of carbohydrates."

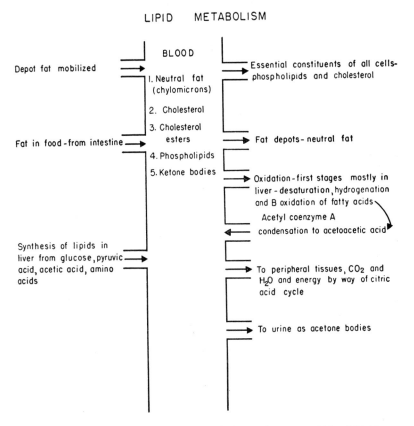

LIPID   METABOLISM

Fig. 360. Diagram of lipid metabolism. Sources of blood lipids are indicated on the left, and the means of utilizing lipids are indicated on the right.

It is recognized that if carbohyrate is not available for oxidation (as during starvation or on a high-fat diet) or if the oxidation of carbohydrate is abnormal (as in diabetes mellitus), then more ketone bodies than usual are produced by the liver. In fact, the the rate of production greatly exceeds the capacity of the muscles to oxidize them, and the ketone bodies accumulate in the blood and appear in the urine in large amounts. This condition is called *ketosis*.

The liver normally contains about 5 per cent of total lipids, which are chiefly phospholipids and neutral fat, with a small amount of cholesterol and its esters. In some conditions a "fatty" liver is present, in which the total lipids constitute about 30 per cent of the weight of the liver. In this case, the turnover of phospholipid in the liver is low. The increase in lipids is due to cholesterol esters and neutral fat. Fatty livers are found on high-fat diets, in untreated diabetes mellitus, when there is a deficiency of choline and the essential unsaturated fatty acids and with excessive intakes of cholesterol, cystine, biotin, thiamine and other vitamins of the B complex.

When fatty acids are oxidized they release 9 Cal. of heat per gram of fat.

Figure 360 is a diagram of fat metabolism.

Protein Metabolism

Proteins are the chief organic components of protoplasm. Each animal species and each type of tissue is characterized by its own specific kinds of proteins. The enzymes and many of the hormones that regulate the chemical processes of the body are protein in nature.

There are 3 sources of amino acids in the blood: absorption from the small intestine, synthesis by liver and tissue cells and catabolism of tissue protein. The amino acids in the blood constitute a pool that can be drawn upon for all purposes of protein metabolism.

Each tissue of the body takes from this amino acid pool in the blood the specific amino acids, in the proper proportions needed, to synthesize the kinds of protein required for growth, maintenance and proper function of that tissue.

Amino acids in excess of the requirements for the formation of structural tissue proteins, enyzmes and hormones, are deaminized in the liver to form ammonia and keto acids. The ammonia is converted to urea and excreted in the urine. The liver converts some of the keto acids (called *ketogenic amino acids*) to ketone bodies and others (called *antiketogenic acids*) to glucose. Then the ketone bodies and the glucose are metabolized along the lines of fat and carbohydrate substances, respectively. By whichever path metabolism advances, the ultimate fate is oxidation to carbon dioxide and water, with the release of utilizable energy, by way of acetyl coenzyme A and the citric acid cycle.

Ribonucleic acids, which alone are present in the cytoplasm, regulate the synthesis of cytoplasmic proteins. Desoxyribonucleic acids, which are present only in the nucleus, control the synthesis of the proteins of the chromosomes.

There are several proteolytic enzymes present in tissues that are

PROTEIN   METABOLISM

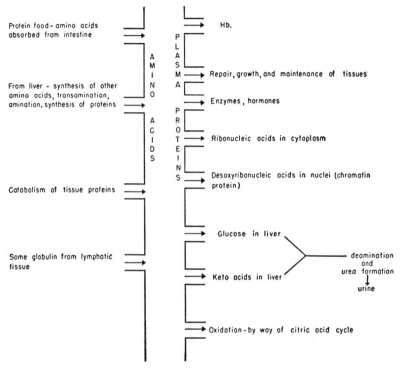

FIG. 361. Diagram of protein metabolism. Sources of amino acids and plasma proteins are indicated on the left, and the means of utilizing amino acids are indicated on the right.

concerned with the breakdown of tissue proteins to amino acids. Anabolism and catabolism of protein in tissues and liver are affected by hormones of the thyroid and the anterior pituitary glands.

The liver not only deaminizes amino acids but also transfers N from one amino acid to another (transamination) and adds N to keto acids (amination), derived from carbohydrate and fat metabolism. The amino acid nitrogen in the body is shifting continually from one amino acid to another, being added to the pool, then withdrawn from the pool and incorporated into tissue, liver or plasma protein, then split and again returned to the pool. Figure 361 is a diagram of protein metabolism. In addition to urea, nitrogenous waste products comprise uric acid, creatinine and hippuric acid.

It has been found by the use of radioactive isotopes containing radioactive oxygen, carbon, hydrogen or nitrogen that any type of food can be changed into another in the body. The common meeting ground for the 3 foodstuffs is pyruvic acid. Some of the factors that determine the course to be followed by any particular food are hormones, enzymes, vitamins, the acid-base balance and the type and the amount of food eaten.

METABOLISM OF THE INDIVIDUAL AS A WHOLE

In the normal body it is probable that a mixture of the 3 foodstuffs is being oxidized so long as one eats a mixed diet. If a mixed diet is not eaten, or if the metabolic processes are disturbed, the type of food which is being burned can be determined by the "respiratory quotient." This is the ratio of the carbon dioxide produced to the oxygen used, that is CO_2/O_2. On a mixed diet, the ratio is 0.83; on carbohydrate it is 1.00; on fat, 0.70; and on protein, 0.80.

BASAL METABOLISM

Basal metabolism refers to the energy output required to keep an individual alive; that is, to maintain his body temperature and to keep his respiration and circulation going. It is related to one's surface area, being about 1,000 Cal. per square meter of body surface per day. This is about 38 to 40 Cal. per square meter per hour for men, and 36 to 38 for women. Variations of plus or minus 10 per cent are permitted in the normal range. This means that on the basis of 40 Cal. for men, the limits are 36(40–4) and 44(40+4) Cal. per square meter per hour. Basal metabolic rates are commonly reported as follows: minus 6 per cent or plus 8 per cent, for example.

The basal metabolic rate varies with age, being higher in the young, with a maximum at 3 to 6 years of age. It varies, also, with the state of nutrition, being low in undernutrition. It is lower in women than in men. It varies with pathologic conditions (abnormal thyroid activity) and with the type of diet.

The basal metabolic rate is determined by the "indirect" method; this means that only the oxygen use is determined. Each liter of oxygen used is equivalent to a certain number of calories, and a respiratory quotient of 0.83 is assumed. The individual must be in a resting state, and the test is done about 14 hours after the last meal. If these conditions are fulfilled, the basal metabolic rate can be determined when pulmonary function tests (p. 551) are performed.

The total caloric requirement is determined especially by one's occupation. For the sedentary student a maximum of 2,400 Cal. is sufficient; for a carpenter, 3,200; a stone mason, 4,400; and a lumberman, 6,000 to 8,000 Cal. daily, supply the needs. Difficulty arises when one who follows a sedentary occupation takes in the amount of food needed by a lumberman.

The protein requirement is about 1 gm. per kg. of body weight per day; this means that from 10 to 15 per cent of the caloric value of the diet should be derived from protein food. Carbohydrates should furnish 50 to 60 per cent of the caloric requirement, and fat should furnish the remainder, or 30 to 35 per cent. The intake of water is regulated by one's thirst; if the kidneys are normal, any excess water is excreted. A mixed diet takes care of the inorganic salt requirement, with the exception of sodium chloride. Wide variations exist in the intake of sodium chloride, and if the kidneys are normal, any excess is excreted.

PRACTICAL CONSIDERATIONS

Factors that influence movements and secretions of the alimentary tube are:

1. Impulses from higher centers, such as the cerebral cortex and the hypothalamus that can exert pronounced effects on the activity of the digestive system;

2. Disease in some part of the alimentary tract, in the gallbladder, the urinary bladder, the pelvic viscera or peritoneum that can inhibit activity in the tract. A full colon and rectum tend to inhibit movements of the upper part of the intestinal tract and of the stomach;

3. Emotions, during which epinephrine is released, that can have the same inhibitory effect on the stomach and the intestine as stimulation of the thoracolumbar division of the autonomic system. Both motility and secretory activity are curtailed. Do not permit yourself and those about you to become upset during or immediately after a meal.

Borborygmus refers to the rumbling of gas in the bowel, or "flatus." It may accompany gas pains, which are relieved only by the passage of gas.

Hypoproteinemia refers to a low concentration of proteins in the plasma.

Nausea. The word *nausea* means "sea-sickness"; the term has been in use for 3,000 years. It is a feeling of discomfort, accompanied by salivation, aversion to food, weakness, trembling and perspiration. Usually it precedes vomiting. Nausea is common in the early months of pregnancy, in gastro-intestinal disturbances from various causes, disease of the inner ear (especially of the semicircular canals), gastritis and flying at high altitudes without oxygen.

Vomiting. Morning sickness of pregnancy often is accompanied by vomiting. Brain tumors usually are accompanied by a projectile type of vomiting. Upsets or infections of the digestive system are accompanied by vomiting. In the act of vomiting, there is compression of the stomach by the muscles of the abdominal wall against the liver and the diaphragm. The cardiac sphincter relaxes, and the contents of the stomach are ejected. Emetics are substances which are given to produce vomiting when the stomach needs to be emptied, in cases where the individual has taken poison or some other harmful substance.

Diarrhea. In this condition there are frequent bowel movements, and the fecal material is liquid, since it is moved so rapidly through the alimentary tube that absorption cannot occur. Usually it is due to the intake of spoiled food or infection in the digestive system. Laxatives and cathartics may lead to diarrhea.

Vomiting and diarrhea can become very serious conditions if they persist for a few days. One loses large volumes of liquid and salts in both conditions. Normally, about 8,200 cc. of fluid is poured into the alimentary tube from the blood in a day (in the form of digestive juices). The following amounts of juices are secreted each day: saliva, 1,500 cc.; gastric juice, 2,500 cc.; bile, 500 cc.; pancreatic juice, 700 cc.; and intestinal juice, 3,000 cc. As stated previously, this is taken back into the blood by absorption, so that it is not lost to the body. If either vomiting or diarrhea occurs, the patient becomes dehydrated due to the loss of part of the digestive juices. If vomiting persists for a couple of days, alkalosis occurs, since a large amount of HCl is lost in the vomitus. If diarrhea persists, with a loss of pancreatic, as well as intestinal juices, acidosis occurs due to the loss of $NaHCO_3$. These conditions are especially serious in infants.

Celiac Disease. This is a chronic disturbance in nutrition, seen most frequently in children 2 to 3 years of age. The abdomen is distended, and there is diarrhea, with large, frothy, foul-smelling stools.

Colitis refers to inflammation of the mucosa of the colon. The acute form is accompanied by diarrhea. The mucous form is characterized by diarrhea in which there is much mucus in the stools. In the ulcerative form the mucosa is studded with ulcers.

Constipation often is due to hemorrhoids or to irritative lesions in the pelvic organs.

Feeding Other than by Mouth. Patients who cannot take food by mouth may be fed by gavage, which means that liquid food is given by a Rehfuss tube passed through the nose or the mouth and the esophagus into the stomach. Nutrient enemas are not satisfactory. Intravenous feeding is very common; glucose and amino acids, with vitamins and salts, are administered by vein. After occlusion of the esophagus by accident, a patient can feed himself by gastric fistula (a permanent opening through the abdominal wall into the stomach).

Gastric expression refers to the withdrawal of stomach contents after a test meal or injection of histamine (which stimulates the parietal cells to secrete HCl). The contents are analyzed for acid and enzymes. If no acid is present, the patient is said to have *achlorhydria;* this is the finding in pernicious anemia. Less than the normal amount of acid is called *hyposecretion* and occurs in cancer of the stomach. If there is an unusually high content of acid, the patient is said to have *hyperacidity* or hypersecretion; this usually indicates ulcer.

Gastric lavage refers to repeatedly washing out the stomach, as after one has taken poison or an overdose of sleeping pills.

Relief of Distention. In order to prevent paralytic ileus, suction tubes are introduced into the intestine after operations on some part of the digestive system. Gas and fluid are sucked out through the tube to prevent distention; consequently, these patients must be supplied with fluid, salts and food by vein to prevent dehydration. A Miller-Abbott tube is a double-lumen tube about 8 ft. long that is introduced through the nose. A balloon is attached, so that it may be inflated through one lumen and stimulate peristalsis. Gas and fluid are aspirated through the larger lumen, and distention is relieved. The Wangensteen is another type of tube, used for the same purpose.

Barium Meal. A thick barium solution is given, and the esophagus is examined by fluoroscope while the patient is swallowing the barium. Then roentgenograms are taken at intervals for examination of stomach and small intestine. For examination of the large intestine by x-ray pictures, a barium enema is given. The barium solution coats the lining of the gastro-intestinal tract mak-

654 MAINTAINING THE METABOLISM OF THE BODY

ing it visible by fluoroscope and outlining it as shown by use of x-rays. Barium is x-ray opaque. The rate of movement through the alimentary tube is determined, and ulcers, masses and other pathology are noted.

Liver Function Tests. The liver performs such a variety of functions that no one test can give information about the liver as a whole. The dye test gives information about the reticuloendothelial (Kupffer) cells of the liver, as they remove the dye from blood and the liver cells excrete it into the bile. Tests for presence of bilirubin or bile pigments in the blood give information about the ability of the liver to excrete bile pigments; the icterus index is a good test for this function.

The cephalin-cholesterol flocculation test gives information about the function of the liver in the production of plasma proteins. The plasma protein concentration can be determined and indicates the ability of the liver to produce such proteins.

The concentration of cholesterol and the cholesterol esters also gives information about the liver in connection with fat metabolism. Needle biopsies are taken from the liver, making possible a microscopic examination of liver structure during life.

Hepatitis is a condition in which there is impairment of liver function. Cirrhosis of the liver is the result of malnutrition, and not of alcoholism, as formerly supposed.

Graham-Cole Test; Gallbladder Visualization. Dyes are given which are excreted by the liver into the bile. These enter the gallbladder and are concentrated there, and, since they are opaque to x-rays, they outline the gallbladder and make it visible. Then a meal of fat is given, and a second roentgenogram of the gallbladder, taken later, indicates whether or not it has emptied properly.

Abnormal Metabolism. In some individuals there is a disturbance in carbohydrate metabolism, called *diabetes mellitus,* in which they are unable to burn glucose at the normal blood sugar level. They lose large amounts of glucose in the urine. Glucose made from amino acids and other noncarbohydrate substances, likewise is lost in the urine.

Ketosis is present in diabetes mellitus; this is because the liver produces keto acids faster than they can be utilized by the muscles. When ketosis exists, the patient is sluggish mentally, and acetone can be smelled on his breath. Large amounts of acetone bodies carry out sodium in the urine. This not only decreases the alkaline reserve but also leads to dehydration, since whenever sodium is lost, water is lost also.

The ketogenic diet is used by some physicians in the treatment of epilepsy since it is believed that the nervous system is less irritable and convulsions are less likely to occur in ketosis. If ketosis becomes severe, coma results.

Obesity or overweight is due to an excessive intake of food, beyond the needs of the body. The excess is stored as adipose tissue. For weight control, the caloric intake should be reduced, yet the diet can be balanced and contain essential salts and vitamins. Peculiar diets are usually not satisfactory, and "reducing pills" may be harmful.

Altered Basal Metabolism. The thyroid gland plays a role in the regulation of the metabolic rate. If it is overactive the basal metabolic rate is elevated beyond the normal limits, and, if the thyroid is underactive, the basal rate is depressed below the normal limit.

The type of diet can influence the metabolic rate; a high protein diet stimulates metabolism more than other types of diets.

A low external temperature stimulates metabolism and a high temperature likewise is accompanied by a high metabolic rate.

Stool Examinations. The color of the stool is important. If no bile enters the intestine, the stools are clay-colored. If old blood, from the upper part of the gastro-intestinal tract is present, the stools have the color and the consistency of tar (ulcer or cancer of stomach). Fresh blood appears as red streaks in the stools and is due to hemorrhoids or cancer of the rectum.

The stools should be examined for eggs or segments of parasites in certain types of disturbances of the gastro-intestinal tract.

SUMMARY

1. Foods
    A. Inorganic salts and water
    B. Organic
        a. Carbohydrates: monosaccharides, disaccharides and polysaccharides
        b. Fats; essential fatty acids: linoleic, linolenic and arachidonic. Cholesterol and lecithin
        c. Proteins; adequate proteins contain essential amino acids. Simple, conjugated and derived
    C. Accessory foods; vitamins
        a. Need for vitamins
        b. Causes of vitamin deficiency: 6 types of causes
        c. Fat-soluble vitamins: A, D, E and K; sources, functions and results of deficiency

d. Water-soluble vitamins: B complex, C and P; sources, functions and results of deficiency

2. Digestion

A. Digestion in the mouth

a. Mechanical change: mastication

b. Chemical change: production of saliva, functions of saliva; composition; action of salivary amylase

B. Digestion in pharynx and esophagus

a. Mechanical change: deglutition; 3 stages

b. Chemical change: production of mucus; no digestive action

C. Digestion in stomach

a. Mechanical change: contractions; emptying of stomach

b. Chemical change: secretion of gastric juice; cephalic, gastric and intestinal phases. Composition of gastric juice; digestive action on proteins

D. Digestion in small intestine

a. Mechanical change

(1) Rhythmic segmentation

(2) Peristalsis; slow and fast

(3) Pendular movement

b. Chemical change

(1) Production of secretions

(A) Pancreatic juice; secretin and pancreozymin. Digestive actions: amylase, protease and lipase; function of sodium bicarbonate

(B) Bile; production, storage, emptying of gall-bladder and function in digestion

(C) Intestinal juice; secretin and enterocrinin

E. Digestion in large intestine

a. Mechanical change: mass movements

b. Chemical change: mucus only

c. Functions of large intestine

(1) Bacterial action; fermentation, putrefaction and synthesis of vitamins

(2) Defecation

(3) Value of large intestine as an excretory organ

3. Functions of the liver

A. Production of bile; both an excretion and a secretion

B. Conversion of glucose to glycogen and the reverse

C. Storage of various substances: minerals, vitamins

D. Deamination; transamination; amination; formation of urea

E. Desaturation, synthesis and hydrogenation

F. Phagocytosis

G. Production of heparin

H. Production of plasma proteins

4. Absorption

   A. Processes involved

   B. Water and inorganic salts

   C. Carbohydrates

   D. Proteins

   E. Fats

5. Metabolism

   A. Carbohydrate

      a. Regulation of blood sugar concentration

      b. Tissue glycogen: liver and muscles. Products of breakdown

      c. Oxidation: via pyruvic acid and citric acid cycle

      d. Effects of endocrine glands

   B. Fat metabolism

      a. Form of lipids in blood

      b. Sources of lipids in blood

      c. Role of liver in lipid metabolism

      d. Ketosis

      e. Fatty livers

   C. Protein metabolism

      a. Sources of amino acids in blood

      b. Channels of removal from blood

      c. Deamination and production of urea

      d. Conversion of keto acids to glucose and ketone bodies

      e. Transamination

      f. Amination

   D. Metabolism of individual as a whole; respiratory quotient

   E. Basal metabolic rate

   F. Caloric requirement; requirement for each foodstuff

SITUATION AND QUESTIONS

After discharge from the hospital, Mr. Coop received specific instructions with regard to his diet, work and other activities.

1. After a time, Mr. Coop found that some fatty foods were included in his diet. What substance is necessary for the emulsification of fats? _____(a) Lipase; _____(b) Secretin; _____(c) Bile; _____(d) Steapsin.

2. Fats are a very vital constituent of the diet because they: _____(a) are an available source of energy; _____(b) are used for building and repair of tissues; _____(c) constitute

the framework of protoplasm; _____(d) break down to fatty acids which are necessary to maintain an acid-base balance.

3. What hormone is produced by the intestinal mucosa when fat enters the small intestine? _____(a) Gastrin; _____(b) Pancreozymin; _____(c) Secretin; _____(d) Cholecystokinin.

4. What are the end-products of fat metabolism? _____(a) Fatty acids and glycerol; (b) Adipose tissue; _____(c) Urea; _____(d) Carbon dioxide and water.

5. Fats, along with other food materials, are moved along the digestive tract by waves of contraction called: _____(a) deglutition; _____(b) peristalsis; _____(c) rhythmic segmentation; _____(d) pendular movements.

16. Anatomy of the Excretory System

INTRODUCTION

The cells of the body use oxygen that is supplied by the lungs and raw materials (foodstuffs) supplied by absorption from the small intestine. These substances are brought to the cells by the blood and the tissue fluid and are used not only for growth, maintenance and repair of tissues but also as a source of energy, which keeps the body alive, active and at a normal temperature. In the process of oxidation, not only is energy released, but waste products are produced also. The latter diffuse from cells into tissue fluid and then enter the blood.

One of the waste products is volatile, like smoke from a furnace, and this (carbon dioxide) is eliminated in expired air by means of the lungs. Another waste product is water, and this is eliminated by several channels (p. 685). Some other waste products (salts of heavy metals), like ashes in the furnace, are eliminated by way of the large intestine. The remaining waste products (some inorganic salts and nitrogenous waste products) require special organs (the kidneys) for their elimination.

Waste products are formed continuously and must be eliminated continuously. The kidneys are the special organs that remove ni-

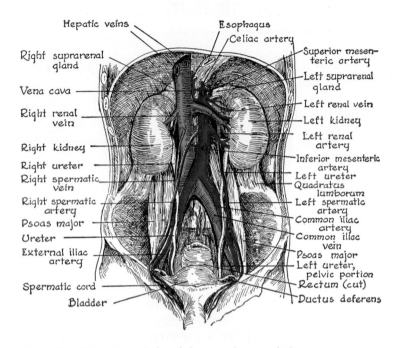

FIG. 362. Dissection of the abdomen, showing kidneys in position and course and relations of ureters and urinary bladder.

trogenous waste products from the blood and concentrate them in a fluid called *urine*. In addition to the kidneys, a duct system (ureters) is necessary to carry urine from the kidneys to the urinary bladder where it is stored temporarily and another duct (urethra) to carry urine from the bladder to the exterior. The anatomy of the kidneys and the duct system will be described in the present chapter, and the function of the various parts of the kidneys will be discussed in the following chapter.

KIDNEYS

LOCATION

The kidneys are located in the posterior part of the abdominal cavity, one on either side of the vertebral column, behind the peritoneum. The kidneys are surrounded by masses of adipose tissue and loose areolar connective tissue. They rest on the psoas major and the quadratus lumborum muscles and on part of the diaphragm.

The location is shown in Figure 362, and the surface projections in Figure 8.

FIXATION

Since the kidneys are not held in place by any special folds of peritoneum or distinct ligaments, their fixation depends to a large extent on pressure of neighboring structures and the renal fascia. In the adipose tissue that surrounds the kidneys there is a supporting layer of fibrous tissue called the *renal fascia*.

GROSS STRUCTURE

The kidney is bean-shaped. The lateral border is convex, and the medial is concave. In the central portion of the concave border there is a deep longitudinal fissure called the *hilum*, where vessels and nerves enter and leave and from which the ureter leaves. The

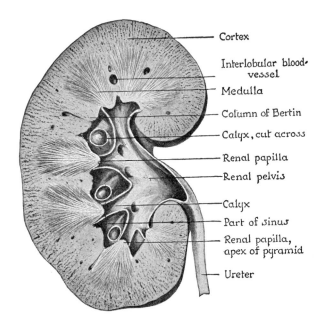

Cortex

Interlobular blood-vessel

Medulla

Column of Bertin

Calyx, cut across

Renal papilla

Renal pelvis

Calyx

Part of sinus

Renal papilla, apex of pyramid

Ureter

FIG. 363. Longitudinal section of kidney, showing divisions of renal substance and relations of renal pelvis and calyces. The renal column is labeled *Column of Bertin*. Striations on pyramids indicate course of collecting tubules toward papillae.

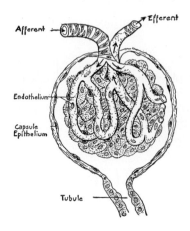

Fig. 364. Diagram of a glomerulus and capsule. The afferent vessel of the glomerulus is larger than the efferent vessel; the tuft of capillaries is surrounded by the capsule of epithelium; the beginning of the tubule is shown. (Redrawn from Winton and Bayliss)

kidney is covered with a fibrous capsule that strips off easily after the kidney is removed from the body.

LONGITUDINAL SECTION

If the kidney is sliced through vertically, from the convex to the concave border, and laid open in longitudinal halves, it will be noted that the hilum expands into a central cavity called the *renal sinus,* in which lie a funnel-shaped sac, called the *renal pelvis,* and calyces, which look like cups. Each kidney has from 4 to 13 calyces or cup-shaped tubes, each of which surrounds one or more renal papillae. The renal calyces and pelvis form the upper expanded end of the ureter.

The kidney is composed of an inner medulla and an outer cortex. The medulla is light in color and consists of striated cone-shaped masses called *renal pyramids.* The bases of the pyramids are placed toward the outer edge of the kidney, and the apices converge to the renal sinus where they form the papillae that project into the calyces.

The cortical substance or cortex of the kidneys is of a darker color than the medulla and is granular and soft. It arches over the bases of the pyramids and dips in between the adjacent pyramids toward the renal sinus. The parts that dip in between the pyramids are called *renal columns.* The structures named above are illustrated in Figure 363.

MICROSCOPIC STRUCTURE

The unit of structure in the kidney is called a *nephron,* of which

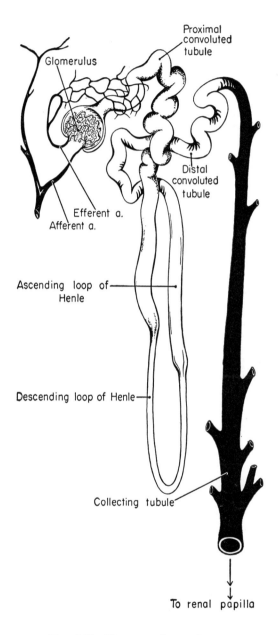

FIG. 365. Diagram of a nephron.

there are over a million in each human kidney. Each nephron consists of a renal corpuscle and renal tubules.

A renal corpuscle consists of a glomerulus and a surrounding glomerular capsule (capsule of Bowman).

A GLOMERULUS is a tuft of capillaries, such as is seen in Figure 364. The artery that brings blood to the glomerulus is called the *afferent arteriole*. This breaks up into capillary loops, and then all the capillary loops unite to form the efferent arteriole which drains blood from the glomerulus. Note that this vessel is not called a vein, even though it drains blood from capillaries.

THE GLOMERULAR CAPSULE is the blind end or beginning of a renal tubule that is invaginated by the glomerulus. The inner layer of the capsule closely surrounds the capillary loops of the glomerulus; fluid is filtered from these capillaries into the space between the inner and the outer layers of the capsule.

A renal tubule is called by different names in its devious and tortuous course. It begins in the glomerular capsule, then becomes the thick-walled *proximal convoluted* tubule, and then the loop of Henle, with descending and ascending limbs, the walls of which are thin. The next portion of the tubule is called the *distal convoluted* tubule and has thick walls. It is the end of the nephron. The distal convoluted tubule empties its contents into a branch of a straight collecting tubule that serves merely as a duct from any gland. The straight collecting tubule opens at the apex of a renal pyramid, through a papilla, into a calyx. Many nephrons drain into each collecting tubule. The parts of a renal tubule are shown in Figure 365. The total length of all the tubules in the human kidneys is about 75 miles.

The epithelium differs in the different parts of the tubule in accordance with the work that each part has to perform. The cells in the parietal part of the glomerular capsule are squamous in type. In the proximal convoluted tubule there are large cuboidal cells. In the usual condition, the cells are high, and the lumen of the tubule appears as a cleft. When the kidney is very active (as during diuresis) the cells are low and flattened, the brush border is high, and the lumen is large. The epithelium of the descending limb of the loop of Henle is of the squamous type. In the ascending limb the cells are cuboidal; in the distal convoluted tubule the epithelial cells are lower, and the lumen is larger than in the proximal convoluted tubule. There is no brush border in the distal tubule. In the small collecting tubules the cells are cuboidal; in the larger collecting tubules the cells are columnar. Throughout the tubule the epithelial cells are supported by a basement membrane.

The types of epithelium in the various parts of a tubule are illustrated in Figure 366.

RELATION OF MICROSCOPIC TO GROSS STRUCTURE

All of the glomeruli are confined to the cortex. The proximal convoluted tubules are in the cortex also, close to the glomeruli. Each tubule then follows a straight course into the medulla, as the descending limb of the loop of Henle, then loops back and returns as the ascending limb to the cortex and touches its glomerulus between the afferent and the efferent arterioles, where it forms part of a thick structure called the *macula densa*.

The distal convoluted tubules lie in the cortex. They join the straight collecting tubules that extend from the cortex down through the medulla to open through the tips of the papillae of the pyramids. The striations of the pyramids are the collecting tubules converging to the apices.

Thus, the cortex is made up of glomeruli and all of the convoluted portions of the tubules. The loops of Henle and their descending and ascending limbs and the straight collecting tubules make up the medulla.

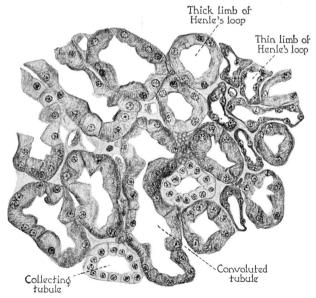

FIG. 366. Types of epithelium in kidney tubules.

Blood Supply

The renal artery enters the hilum and divides and subdivides many times until its smallest branches form the afferent arterioles of the glomeruli. These break up into capillary loops, which in turn unite and drain into the efferent arterioles of the glomeruli. The efferent arterioles divide into second sets of capillaries around the convoluted tubules. The blood is drained from the second sets of capillaries into small veins that unite and form larger and larger veins, until they finally form the renal vein. A diagram of the blood supply of a nephron is shown in Figure 367.

The cells in the middle layer (media) of the afferent arteriole are specialized and are called *juxta-glomerular cells;* they lie in close contact with the macula densa.

Nerve Supply

The kidneys are supplied with visceral afferent fibers that transmit impulses from the kidneys to the central nervous system. The blood vessels of the kidneys are supplied with vasoconstrictor fibers from the thoracolumbar division of the autonomic system. The cells of the tubules have no nerve supply.

THE EXCRETORY DUCTS

The ureters are tubes about 10 or 11 in. long that convey urine from the kidneys to the urinary bladder. Here it is stored temporarily until it is emptied to the exterior through another tube called the *urethra.*

Ureters

Each kidney empties its urine into a ureter, the upper end of which is expanded into the renal pelvis and lies in the renal sinus. Urine leaves the straight collecting tubules through openings in papillae, that give the papillae the appearance of sieves. From the papillae the urine enters the minor calyces, which unite to form the major calyces, and these, in turn, unite to form the renal pelvis.

The ureters lie behind the parietal peritoneum; they descend along the posterior abdominal wall to the pelvic brim. After crossing the brim of the pelvis, the ureters pass along the lateral wall of the pelvis and follow a downward and medial course along the pelvic floor to reach the urinary bladder (Fig. 362).

The wall of a ureter consists of 3 layers of tissue: mucous membrane, muscle and adventitia.

Mucus Membrane. The epithelium of the mucous membrane

is of the transitional type (p. 27) and it rests on a lamina propria. The mucous membrane usually is arranged in longitudinal folds.

The muscular layer consists of an inner longitudinal and an outer circular sheet of smooth muscle, which is the reverse of the arrangement of that in the wall of the intestine. In the lower third of the ureter there is a third sheet of muscular tissue, an outer longitudinal layer.

The adventitia or outer layer of the ureter wall consists of fibrous connective tissue, with some elastic fibers. A section of the wall of a ureter is shown in Figure 368.

The ureters enter the bladder by passing obliquely through the muscle. There is no valve, but a fold of the mucous membrane

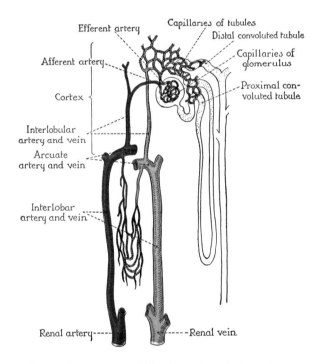

FIG. 367. Diagram of blood supply to kidney showing the renal artery and its branches, the afferent artery of glomerulus, the capillaries of glomerulus, the efferent artery of glomerulus, the capillaries about the tubules, the tributaries to the renal vein and the renal vein.

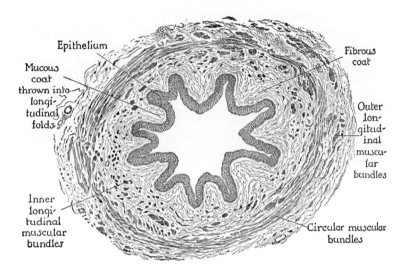

Fig. 368. Cross section of lower third of ureter, showing 3 muscular layers. Adventitia is not labeled. ×25

of the bladder serves to keep urine from returning to the ureters during contractions of the urinary bladder.

The blood supply is derived from branches of the spermatic or ovarian arteries, and the blood drains into the corresponding veins. There are visceral afferent and visceral efferent nerve fibers from both divisions of the autonomic system.

Urine is transported along the ureters to the urinary bladder by means of peristaltic contractions.

URINARY BLADDER

The urinary bladder is a thick-walled, muscular sac that lies behind the pubis, below the parietal peritoneum. The location is shown in Figure 362. The bladder serves as a reservoir for urine, and it is emptied periodically.

The urethra takes its exit from the lowest portion of the bladder. The triangular area between the urethral opening and the entrance of the ureters is called the *trigone* of the bladder.

The epithelium of the bladder mucosa is of the transitional type; its appearance in the collapsed and distended conditions is illustrated in Figures 130 and 369. The lamina propria contains some elastic fibers.

The muscular coat consists of an inner longitudinal, middle cir-

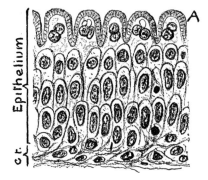

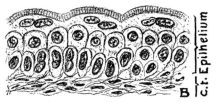

FIG. 369. Transitional epithelium from bladder. (*Left*) Contracted condition. (*Right*) Distended condition.

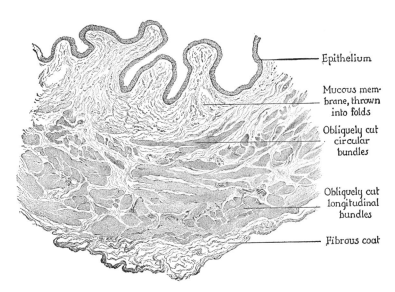

Epithelium

Mucous membrane, thrown into folds

Obliquely cut circular bundles

Obliquely cut longitudinal bundles

Fibrous coat

FIG. 370. Cross section of bladder wall, showing the various layers. ×12.

cular and outer longitudinal layer of smooth muscle; the entire muscular coat is called the *detrusor muscle*. The middle layer is thickest and forms an internal sphincter at the exit of the urethra (Fig. 370).

The blood supply is derived from the hypogastric arteries, and the drainage is into the hypogastric veins.

The nerve supply consists of visceral afferent and visceral efferent fibers. The thoracolumbar supply is the nerve of "retention," which means that it relaxes the wall of the bladder and contracts the sphincter. The sacral supply is the nerve of "emptying"; to accomplish this it must contract the smooth muscle of the wall and relax the sphincter. The nerve supply is illustrated in Figure 371.

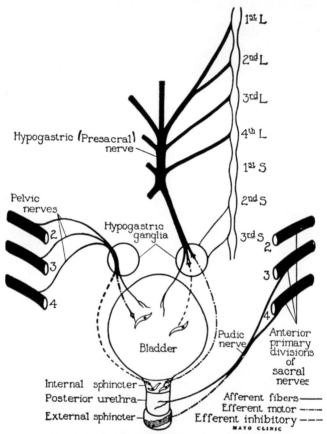

FIG. 371. Diagrammatic representation of innervation of the bladder and the urethra in man. On the left, the nerves of "emptying" are shown; these are motor to the bladder wall and inhibitory to the sphincter. On the right, the nerves of "retention" are shown; these are inhibitory to the bladder wall and motor to the sphincter. Both bladder wall and urethra are supplied with afferent fibers. (After Learmonth) (Best, C. H., and Taylor, N. B.: Physiological Basis of Medical Practice, ed. 5, Baltimore, Williams & Wilkins)

Micturition

This refers to the emptying of the urinary bladder. The 3 layers of muscle of the bladder wall, called the *detrusor muscle,* act as a unit in emptying the bladder. When about 300 cc. of urine have accumulated in the bladder, stretch receptors in the wall are stimulated by distention, and afferent impulses are sent over visceral afferent nerve fibers to the central nervous system which arouse a desire to empty the bladder. Then there is a removal of voluntary control, which is essential to the release of a chain of reflexes. The act of micturition is actually started by a relaxation of the voluntary muscles of the perineum.

The first reflex appears as a series of rhythmic contractions of the detrusor muscle that become more and more powerful. These contractions of the wall of the bladder are accompanied by a relaxation of the internal sphincter of the bladder.

As urine passes along the urethra other receptors are stimulated which call forth additional reflexes. Further rhythmic contractions of the wall of the urinary bladder occur, and these are accompanied by a relaxation of the external sphincter of the urethra. These additional contractions of the wall assure complete emptying of the bladder.

Although the emptying of the urinary bladder is reflex in nature, it is initiated by an effort of the will and a voluntary removal of restraint. It can be stopped at various stages. The external sphincter of the urethra can be closed voluntarily, but it is opened as a part of a chain of co-ordinated reflexes.

If the urinary bladder is not emptied when the desire to do so first is noted, it will be distended further. Micturition can be inhibited voluntarily until about 700 cc. of urine has accumulated. By this time a sensation of pain may be aroused, and micturition becomes urgent.

URETHRA

The urethra is the tube that conveys urine from the urinary bladder to the exterior. It differs in men and women. In men it is common to the excretory and the reproductive systems, but in women it belongs only to the excretory system.

Female Urethra. In women the urethra is only 1 to 1½ in. long; this should be kept in mind when catheterizing (p. 675). The posterior wall of the urethra is united firmly with the anterior wall of the vagina, and, sometimes, as a result of injury, there is an opening from the urethra into the vagina. This distressing condition is called a *urethrovaginal fistula.*

The urethral orifice is in the vestibule (p. 778); as shown in Figure 412, it appears as a small slit. The wall of the urethra is composed of mucous membrane and a muscular layer. An external sphincter of striated muscle surrounds the orifice.

The male urethra is made up of 3 portions: the prostatic, the membranous and the cavernous portions.

THE PROSTATIC portion is about 1 in. long and extends from the urinary bladder to the pelvic floor. During its course it is completely surrounded by the prostate gland. When this gland enlarges, as it commonly does in elderly men, it compresses this portion of the urethra and makes micturition difficult indeed.

THE MEMBRANOUS portion of the urethra extends through the pelvic floor or body wall, from the apex of the prostate gland to the bulb of the urethra, and is about ½ in. long.

THE CAVERNOUS portion of the urethra is in the penis (p. 762) and is between 5 and 6 in. long. It extends from the bulb of the urethra to the external orifice and is surrounded by the corpus cavernous urethrae (p. 762). The parts of the male urethra are shown in Figure 397. A section of the cavernous portion is shown

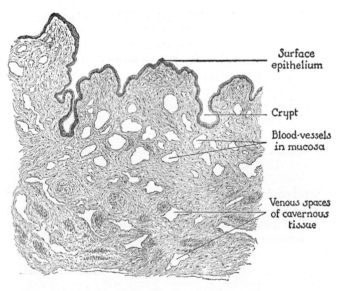

Surface epithelium

Crypt

Blood-vessels in mucosa

Venous spaces of cavernous tissue

FIG. 372. Cross section of wall of male urethra, cavernous portion, showing crypts and blood spaces in the mucosa. ×35.

in Figure 372. The 3 portions are common to the excretory system (for transport of urine) and to the reproductive system (for transport of semen, p. 763).

PRACTICAL CONSIDERATIONS

Floating Kidney. Sometimes the kidney is not held in place securely by the adjacent organs and it may slip from the normal position. This condition is called *floating kidney* and is more common on the right side than on the left. There is usually pain, due

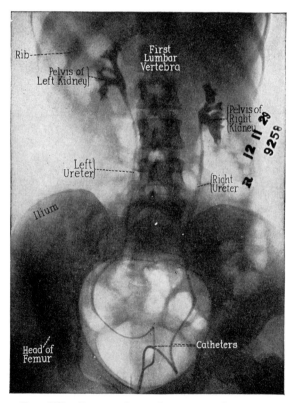

Fig. 373. Retrograde pyelogram. Sodium iodide has been injected through catheters, which are shown still in position. The pelves of the kidneys and the ureters are shown. The right kidney is a little lower than the left, which is normal.

to twisting of the ureter, and it may cause temporary obstruction to the flow of urine until the kink is straightened by movement of the kidney.

Pyelitis is an infection of the renal pelvis that may follow infection of the bladder, since it is easy for infection to spread along the mucous membrane of the ureters from that of the bladder.

Kidney stones (renal calculi) may form in the pelves of the kidneys and cause pain, hematuria (blood in the urine) and pyuria (pus in the urine). The presence of stones in the kidneys is diag-

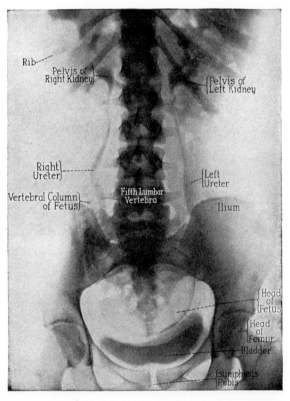

Fig. 374. Intravenous urogram. Visualization of the urinary tract 15 minutes after the injection of the dye. The patient was pregnant; the head of the fetus is shown compressing the urinary bladder. (Dr. Vastine: Woman's College Hospital)

nosed by means of x-ray pictures. When a stone passes along a ureter the pain is exceedingly severe and is called *renal colic.* Stones may consist of uric acid, calcium oxalate or calcium phosphate.

Bladder Difficulties. In an unconscious patient the bladder may distend to the level of the umbilicus. In a conscious patient retention of urine may occur also, due to obstruction of the urethra by enlargement of the prostate gland, infection of the urethra or damage to the spinal cord or the nerve supply of the bladder. There is danger of rupture of the bladder when it is distended so greatly.

Cystitis is an infection of the mucosa of the bladder. Pain and frequency (urgency to empty the bladder every few minutes) are noted in cystitis.

Catheterization of the bladder refers to emptying it by insertion of a tube or catheter through the urethra into the bladder. It is done to relieve distention or for continuous drainage in incontinent patients. It is done also when a "catheterized" specimen is requested for analysis. In women, the urine eliminated spontaneously may be contaminated by vaginal discharge; therefore, it is frequently essential to draw a specimen by catheter to rule out such a possibility. If urine from each kidney separately is desired for analysis, catheters are inserted into each ureter, in turn, by way of the urethra and the bladder, and specimens are collected directly from each ureter.

Enuresis refers to involuntary emptying of the bladder after the age of 3 years. Usually it is due to faulty training but may indicate bladder pathology, emotional instability or feeblemindedness.

Incontinence refers to inability to control the elimination of urine and feces. Often it indicates disorder of the nervous system.

A cystoscopic examination is one in which the interior of the bladder is examined visually. In certain conditions it is necessary to wash out the bladder, and such a procedure is called a bladder *irrigation.*

Dysuria is difficult or painful urination.

Prostate Gland. Anything that happens to the prostate gland in men gives rise to urinary symptoms.

A pyelogram is an x-ray picture of the pelvis of the kidney taken after the administration of a dye opaque to x-rays (Fig. 373). Of course, the dye used for this test must be excreted by the kidney. Visualization of ureters and the urinary bladder is illustrated in Figure 374. Figure 375 shows the appearance of the

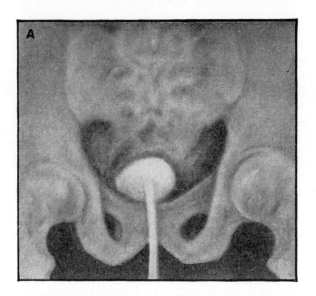

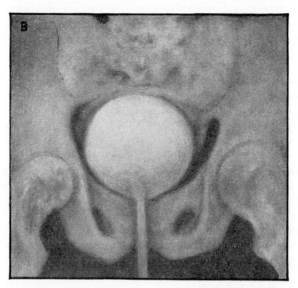

Fig. 375. Cystograms of male bladder, showing bladder containing about 20 cc. of sodium iodide solution (*top*) and 500 cc. (*bottom*). (Redrawn from Morris)

urinary bladder when distended with different amounts of fluid.

Urethra. Occasionally, there is a reflex spasm of the urethral sphincter that prevents emptying of the bladder, since it interferes with the normal chain of reflexes. *Urethritis* may be followed by stricture (narrowing) of the urethra due to adhesions. When this condition exists, frequency and dribbling of urine are noted due to incomplete emptying of the bladder during micturition.

SUMMARY

1. Kidneys
   A. Location
   B. Fixation
   C. Gross structure: hilum, capsule
   D. Longitudinal section: renal sinus, renal pelvis, calyces, renal papillae, cortex, medulla, renal pyramids and renal columns
   E. Microscopic structure: nephron
      a. Renal corpuscle: glomerulus and glomerular capsule; afferent and efferent arterioles
      b. Renal tubule: proximal convoluted tubule, loop of Henle and distal convoluted tubule
      c. Collecting tubules
   F. Relation of microscopic to gross structure
      a. Cortex: glomeruli, proximal convoluted tubules and distal convoluted tubules
      b. Medulla: loops of Henle and collecting tubules
   G. Blood supply: 2 sets of capillaries; juxta-glomerular cells
   H. Nerve supply
2. Excretory ducts
   A. Ureters: location, course, structure of walls, entrance into bladder, blood and nerve supply and function
   B. Urinary bladder
      a. Location; function
      b. Trigone
      c. Structure of wall: transitional epithelium, lamina propria and 3 layers of smooth muscle; internal sphincter
      d. Blood supply
      e. Nerve supply
      f. Micturition: reflexes
   C. Urethra
      a. Function
      b. Differs in men and women
         (1) Female urethra; short; orifice; external sphincter

(2) Male urethra: long; 3 portions—prostatic, membranous and cavernous; common to excretory and reproductive systems

SITUATION AND QUESTIONS

Mrs. Betty Dilto was admitted to the hospital ward. The nurse prepared her for surgery that was to be performed the following morning. One of the routine studies done before surgery is a urinalysis.

1. Miss Mack inserted a catheter into Mrs. Dilto's urinary bladder for the purpose of obtaining a urine specimen. The urinary bladder is located: _____(a) on the posterior abdominal wall; _____(b) between the vagina and the urethra; _____(c) behind the symphysis pubis;_____(d) behind the peritoneum.

2. The urinary bladder receives urine; _____(a) by peristaltic waves from the ureters; _____(b) drop by drop from the urethra; _____(c) directly from the kidneys by way of the hilum; _____(d) by force of gravity through the ureter.

3. In catheterizing a female patient, Miss Mack must remember that: _____(a) the female urethra is approximately 8 in. long; _____(b) the urethral orifice is located between the clitoris and the vagina; _____(c) there is a sphincter of smooth muscle near the end of the urethra; _____(d) the female urethra is common to the excretory and the reproductive systems.

4. The stimulus that initiates the act of emptying the bladder is: _____(a) stretching of the bladder wall; _____(b) increased pressure within the bladder; _____(c) concentration of urine; _____(d) change of chemical constituents of urine within the bladder.

5. The efferent pathway of the nervous system involved in emptying the bladder is: _____(a) cranial nerves; _____(b) thoracolumbar division of the autonomic nervous system; _____(c) somatic efferent nerves; _____(d) craniosacral division of the autonomic nervous system.

UNIT 4. MAINTAINING THE
METABOLISM OF THE BODY

17. Physiology of the Excretory System and Water and Salt Balance

INTRODUCTION

We stated in the previous chapter that carbon dioxide, water, nitrogenous waste products and inorganic salts are substances to be excreted from the body. Some of these are excreted by more than one channel, but nitrogenous waste products are excreted almost exclusively by the highly specialized kidneys.

The glomeruli of the kidneys are so made that they present an extensive capillary surface through which more than 150 L. of tissue fluid pass by filtration each day. This arrangement makes it possible to remove waste products from the plasma and get them into the lumens of the kidney tubules.

However, many substances that have filtered into the glomerular capsules as tissue fluid are useful to the body and must be taken back into the blood, along with most of the water. Consequently, it is the function of the cells of the tubules to reabsorb all but about 1½ L. of the water that filters into the glomerular capsule, as well as those solutes or dissolved substances that are useful to the body. At the same time, the cells of the tubules must reject the waste products that are not useful to the body and retain enough water in the tubules to keep such products in solution. In other words, the cells of the tubules so modify the large amount of glomerular filtrate or tissue fluid that they make it into 1½ L. of urine in which waste products are concentrated.

The production of urine is not the only function performed by the kidneys. The amount of water that they can eliminate is not limited to that needed to keep waste products in solution but can vary widely beyond this amount. This means that in health one's kidneys can produce either very dilute or very concentrated urine, and this flexibility or adjustability in elimination of water makes it possible for the kidneys to play a very important role in maintaining water balance. They serve as a "spillway" for water not needed by the body.

The amount of inorganic salts, particularly sodium chloride, excreted by the kidneys can vary widely also, and this indicates the essential function of the kidneys in the maintenance of salt balance. The kidneys also have the ability to manufacture ammonia and to substitute it for sodium and in this way to help maintain the acid-base balance of the body.

In summary, the kidneys contribute a generous share to homeostasis or maintenance of the constancy of the internal environment by removing and excreting waste and by conserving useful substances and returning them to the plasma. Without normally functioning kidneys it would be impossible to preserve the normal composition of the plasma and the tissue fluid.

CHANNELS OF EXCRETION

The substances to be eliminated from the body, namely water, carbon dioxide, nitrogenous waste (urea, ammonia, creatinine, hippuric acid, uric acid) and inorganic salts, are eliminated by 4 channels: kidneys, skin, lungs and large intestine.

The kidneys eliminate water, nitrogenous waste and inorganic salts.

The skin eliminates water and small amounts of nitrogenous waste and inorganic salts.

The lungs eliminate water and carbon dioxide.

The large intestine eliminates water, and some inorganic salts, together with bile pigments and wastes from the digestive tract.

In the present chapter the function of the kidneys in the manufacture of urine and the maintenance of water and salt balance will be considered.

CHARACTERISTICS OF URINE

Urine is a watery solution of nitrogenous waste and inorganic salts that are removed from the plasma and eliminated by the kidneys. The color usually is amber but varies with the amount produced. The reaction is acid on a mixed diet and alkaline on a vegetable diet. The specific gravity usually is between 1.016 and 1.020, but may vary from 1.002 to 1.040 in normal kidneys, according to whether the urine is very dilute or very concentrated. The quantity of urine is about 1½ L. daily. An increase in daily output that is persistent is called *polyuria,* and a temporary increase is called *diuresis.* A decrease below the average amount is called *oliguria.*

The composition varies with the waste products to be removed and with the need for maintenance of homeostasis. About 95 per cent of urine is water. The average amount of solids excreted per day is about 60 Gm.; of this, about 25 Gm. consist of inorganic salts and 35 Gm. consist of organic substances. The composition of urine of an adult man on a mixed diet is as follows:

Inorganic constituents		Organic constituents	
NaCl	15.000 Gm.	Urea	30.000 Gm.
K	3.3	Creatinine	1.0
SO_4	2.5	Uric acid	0.7
PO_4	2.5	Hippuric acid	0.7
NH_3	0.7	Indican	0.01
Mg	0.1	Acetone bodies	0.04
Ca	0.3	Undetermined	2.945
Fe	0.005		
Other	0.2		

Abnormal constituents that may be present in urine are listed on page 690.

PRODUCTION OF URINE

The chief function of the kidneys is to produce urine; consequently, each part of the nephron performs a specific function.

The glomerulus is a tuft of capillaries to which blood is brought by an afferent arteriole and from which blood is drained by an efferent arteriole of smaller diameter. This anatomic arrangement favors the maintenance of a high blood pressure throughout the capillary loops in the glomerulus. The pressure of glomerular (tissue) fluid in the glomerular capsule is low, and the walls of the capillaries and the inner layer of the capsule are thin and permeable. Consequently, the glomerulus is an ideal filtering apparatus, and filtration of water and dissolved substances (except plasma proteins) from the vascular capillaries into the capsule of Bowman takes place throughout the length of the glomerular capillaries. In other words, glomerular (or tissue) fluid can be produced along the entire length of glomerular capillaries. More than 1,500 L. of plasma circulates through the glomerular capillaries daily, and from this more than 150 L. of protein-free plasma is filtered daily.

The amount of filtrate produced depends upon the permeability of the capillary walls and the inner layer of the glomerular capsule, the pressure of blood in the glomerular capillaries, the amount of blood flowing through the kidneys and the colloid content of the plasma. The factors that influence the production of tissue fluid in general are discussed on pages 401 and 411.

The cells of the tubules convert tissue fluid to urine. Conditions are well suited for reabsorption of some of the constituents of the glomerular filtrate by the tubular cells, which then transfer these constituents back to the blood.

The tubular cells are supplied with blood from the efferent arterioles of the glomeruli; this blood has lost about 10 per cent of its fluid (to the glomerular filtrate) and salt content in the passage through the glomerular capillaries. As a result, there is a higher plasma protein or colloid content in the capillary blood bathing the tubular cells. This means a higher colloid osmotic pressure than usual. The blood pressure is lower in the tubular capillaries than in the glomerular capillaries. Because of these factors, reabsorption of fluid back into the blood of the tubular capillaries by osmosis occurs readily.

Selective Reabsorption

Reabsorption of Water. An enormous amount of water is reabsorbed by the cells of the tubules. All but about 1½ L. of the water that filters through the walls of the glomerular capillaries is reabsorbed in this way and returned to the plasma. This is the first step in changing glomerular filtrate to urine.

Threshold Substances. These are substances, such as glucose, that are useful to the body; they are reabsorbed selectively by the cells of the tubules. Threshold substances are absorbed in different amounts, according to the normal plasma levels. Most of the threshold substances have "renal thresholds," and when these are exceeded in the blood, the threshold substances are excreted. For example, if one eats a large amount of candy in a short period of time, the body is flooded with glucose, and some of it appears in the urine (alimentary glycosuria). Amino acids, sodium and chloride are reabsorbed readily by the tubular cells and are representative of threshold substances; amino acids are reabsorbed completely from the glomerular filtrate, but sodium and chloride are absorbed only in such amounts as to keep the concentration in the plasma normal.

Nonthreshold Substances. These are substances that are not useful to the body. Urea, uric acid and creatinine are examples of nonthreshold substances. These are not actively absorbed by the tubular cells, but a certain amount may diffuse back into the blood passively from the tubular lumen. The concentration of nonthreshold substances always is much higher in the urine than in the plasma, a fact that indicates a lack of selective reabsorption on the part of the tubular cells.

Synthesis of Ammonia and Hippuric Acid. The cells of the renal tubules can synthesize ammonia and hippuric acid. While the glomerular filtrate is passing along through the lumens of the tubules, the tubular cells substitute ammonia for some of the sodium and also substitute monosodium phosphate for disodium phosphate. In these two ways the tubular cells help to conserve sodium for the body.

Excretion by Tubular Cells. The tubular cells can excrete certain foreign substances from the plasma. Dyes, such as phenolsulfonphthalein and Diodrast, are excreted by tubular cells. This means that the cells actively remove these dyes from the capillary blood that is bathing them and transport them through the cells into the lumen of the tubules, despite the fact that water and threshold substances are moving through the cells in the opposite direction after reabsorption. Other substances that are excreted by tubular cells are penicillin and para-aminohippuric acid. Physicians often give the latter along with penicillin, and, since there is some competition between them for the excretory transport medium of the tubular cells, it is hoped that the cells will be so occupied with excretion of para-aminohippuric acid that they will excrete penicillin more slowly. When this occurs a high blood level of penicillin persists for a longer time than if no para-aminohippuric acid is given.

In summary, the function of the kidneys is to preserve the normal composition of the circulating blood. This is accomplished by filtration in the glomeruli and selective reabsorption of so-called threshold substances by the tubular cells. Seven eighths of the filtered water that is reabsorbed is taken from the lumens of the proximal convoluted tubules, and the remaining one eighth is reabsorbed along the remainder of the tubules. Glucose, sodium and chloride are absorbed by the cells of the proximal convoluted tubules. Ammonia is synthesized by the cells in the distal convoluted tubules. In this region, also, the change from disodium phosphate to monosodium phosphate in the urine occurs. This means that the urine becomes acid in the distal convoluted tubules and some sodium is conserved. Because of the reabsorption of water, waste products are concentrated in the urine as it passes along through the lumens of the tubules.

EFFECTS OF HORMONES ON URINE PRODUCTION

The "salt and water hormone" of the adrenal cortex is called aldosterone. It is important in the reabsorption of sodium and water and in the excretion of potassium by the renal tubular cells.

The *antidiuretic hormone* of the posterior lobe of the pituitary gland (p. 723) increases the reabsorption of water and the excretion of sodium chloride. The production of this hormone depends on the hypothalamus, since there are receptors (called *osmoreceptors*) in the arteries supplying the hypothalamus that are sensitive to the concentration of sodium chloride in the blood. When the concentration of salt is high in the blood, the receptors in the hypothalamus are stimulated, impulses are sent to secretory cells in the posterior lobe of the pituitary gland and more antidiuretic hormone is secreted. This is carried by the blood, and it increases the reabsorption of water by the kidney tubules, which, in turn, dilutes the sodium chloride in the blood. In this indirect way, the production of urine is under the control of the central nervous system.

WATER BALANCE

Amount of Water in the Body. Water is the most abundant constituent of the body. It makes up about 70 per cent of the entire body weight.

The functions of water are discussed on page 60. It is important (1) as a solvent, (2) in all the chemical reactions that occur in the tissues, (3) in the regulation of body temperature and (4) in the excretion of waste products.

INTAKE

The exogenous source of water refers to water taken into the body as beverage and as a constituent of food.

The endogenous source is the metabolic process of all cells; water is a waste product in the metabolism of all 3 types of foodstuffs.

The amount of water taken in the form of beverage varies widely. In one individual studied, the intake varied from 880 to 2,440 cc. on different days, at rest. When the same individual worked, his intake varied from 2,225 to 4,550 cc. daily. On an average mixed diet, one takes from 700 to 1,200 cc. daily as part of the food eaten (even meat has a high water content). The endogenous source contributes about 300 cc. daily (water of metabolism).

Thirst is important in the regulation of exogenous intake of water. It is related to the concentration of dissolved substances in the plasma and the general state of supply in the cells of the body. Habit is important, also, in regulation of exogenous intake. Some individuals make a habit of drinking a certain number of glasses or cups of beverage each day, regardless of thirst.

OUTPUT

Water is excreted by all 4 channels of excretion.

Lungs. It is lost by way of the lungs in saturating the expired air. The amount lost by this channel varies with the humidity of the air inspired, with the depth and the rate of breathing and with the temperature of the inspired air.

Large Intestine. The amount of water lost by way of the large intestine is small; the average daily amount is about 150 cc. If there is diarrhea, the water lost by this channel may become very great.

Skin. The loss by way of the skin may be divided into the insensible loss and the loss by perspiration. The insensible loss varies from 300 to 800 cc. daily; it goes on throughout the day and we are unaware of it. The rate of loss is fairly constant for any individual.

The loss of water in perspiration is purely an emergency mechanism required in the regulation of the body temperature. It varies with exercise, external temperature and body temperature. We perspire more (1) when we exercise, (2) when the environmental temperature is high and (3) when the body temperature is high, as in fever. Loss of water by perspiration is a safety factor in temperature regulation but a hazard when the body supply of water is low, as there is no way to decrease this loss even if we are totally deprived of water.

Kidneys. The amount of water lost by the kidneys varies greatly and depends on the available supply of body water. The kidneys act as a spillway for water not lost through other channels and not needed by the body. If the supply of water is low, the waste products are excreted in a small amount of water, and the urine is very concentrated, with a specific gravity approaching 1.040. If the supply of water is overabundant, as in drinking a large amount of water within a few minutes, a very dilute urine can be produced, in which the specific gravity approaches 1.002. The "obligatory" loss of water by the kidneys depends on the waste to be excreted; sufficient water must be excreted to keep the waste products in solution. The amount lost by this channel, therefore, depends on the intake, respiration and perspiration. If abnormal conditions arise, such as vomiting and diarrhea, the amount of water lost by the kidneys is curtailed immediately.

BALANCE BETWEEN INTAKE AND OUTPUT

In health, the balance between intake and output of water is perfect, so there is no edema, water intoxication or dehydration. One suffers no harmful effects, from taking either a small or a large amount of water, provided that there is enough to regulate body temperature and excrete waste products. This is possible only if the kidneys are normal.

SALT BALANCE

The functions of inorganic salts are discussed on page 60. Some of their functions are the maintenance of osmotic relationships, acid-base balance, conductivity of nerves, contractility of muscles, transport of gases and aiding in the coagulation of the blood.

Intake. With the exception of sodium chloride, which is voluntarily added to food as it is cooked or served, one takes in enough inorganic salts on a mixed diet to satisfy requirements.

Output. Inorganic salts are excreted by 3 channels: kidneys, skin and intestine. Calcium, magnesium and phosphorus are excreted by kidneys and large intestine. Sulfur, sodium, potassium and chloride are excreted chiefly by the kidneys, but the skin excretes a small amount of sodium chloride in the perspiration.

The amount of sodium chloride excreted by the kidneys varies. In health, an individual probably runs into difficulty with salt balance only when he perspires profusely and loses more chloride than he takes in.

Water and sodium chloride "move" together. If a patient is in difficulty in connection with water balance, he is quite likely to be in difficulty with salt balance, also.

FLUID COMPARTMENTS OF THE BODY

The water of the body is divided into 3 fluid compartments for

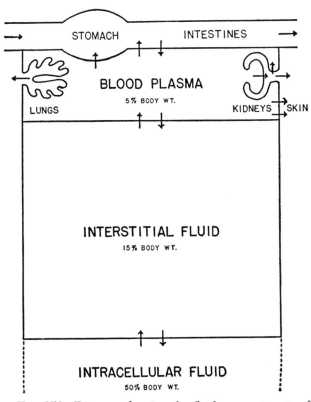

FIG. 376. Diagram showing the fluid compartments of the body. The intracellular fluid compartment is not completed; it is about 2½ times as large as the other two compartments combined. (Gamble, J. L.: Bull. Johns Hopkins Hosp.)

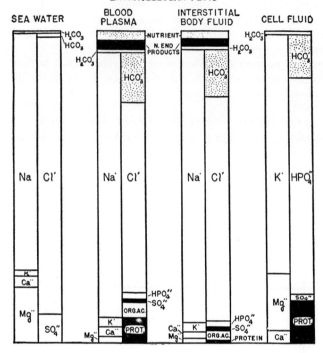

Fig. 377. The comparative compositions of blood plasma, interstitial and intracellular fluids. The potential base or cations are indicated in the left column in each diagram; the anions are indicated in the right. The same 4 cations are present in sea water, blood plasma and interstitial fluid, but in differing amounts. There are important differences in the anions. The acid-base composition of blood plasma usually is expressed as milliequivalents per liter; the total base is equal to 155 mEq./L., and the sum of the anions is the same. To convert the individual ions from milligrams per 100 cc. to mEq./L., multiply the former by 10, and divide by the atomic weight times the valence. For example: The concentration of chloride is about 370 mg./100 cc. of serum; $370 \times 10 = 3,700$; divide this by 35, and the result is about 106 mEq./L. Calcium concentration is about 10 mg./100 cc. of serum; $10 \times 10 = 100$; divide this by 40×2; the result is about 1.25 mEq./L. (Gamble, J. L. Bull. Johns Hopkins Hosp.)

purposes of discussion. These compartments are shown in Figure 376. Water enters the blood from the small and the large intestines, after being taken in as beverage, as a component of food and by reabsorption of digestive juices. It leaves the body by way of the lungs, the large intestine, the kidneys and the skin.

Vascular Compartment. The first compartment is the vascular compartment, occupied by the blood plasma. The water in this compartment forms about 5 per cent of the body weight. In this compartment there is a rapid circulation of fluid, and it is under pressure in the blood vessels. The composition of the fluid in the vascular compartment (plasma) is shown in Figure 377.

Interstitial Fluid Compartment. The second compartment comprises the interstitial or tissue fluid, lymph, aqueous humor, pericardial fluid, pleural fluid, peritoneal fluid and cerebrospinal fluid. The fluid in this compartment forms about 15 per cent of the body weight.

The fluid in the vascular compartment and that in the interstitial fluid compartment together make up the "extracellular" fluid, which is concerned with the transport of nutritive products to all parts of the body, transport of waste products from cells to organs of excretion, osmotic relationships, water balance, salt balance and acid-base balance.

The composition of fluid in the interstitial fluid compartment is based on the analyses of lymph and cerebrospinal fluid. As is evident in Figure 377, the chief difference between plasma and interstitial fluid is in protein content; the interstitial fluid contains very little protein compared with plasma. The barrier between these two compartments is the capillary wall, which is permeable to all the solutes of plasma except protein. Blood pressure supplies the filtering force that moves fluid from the vascular into the interstitial fluid compartment. The force that pulls it back into the vascular compartment from the interstitial compartment is the osmotic force of the plasma proteins.

Intracellular Fluid Compartment. The third fluid compartment comprises the intracellular fluid, which is a constituent of the protoplasm of cells. This is the water in which cellular oxidations occur. The intracellular fluid forms about 50 per cent of the body weight. The total amount of fluid in the 3 fluid compartments, therefore, makes up about 70 per cent of the entire body weight.

There are several differences in composition between the extracellular and the intracellular fluids. Sodium and chloride are present in higher concentration in the former than in the latter, while potassium and phosphates are present in higher concentration in the latter. Protein is more abundant inside the cells than in the fluid bathing the cells. In order to make possible such differences in composition, there must be a highly selective barrier between the interstitial and the intracellular compartments, and the cell membrane with its special properties constitutes such a barrier.

Water moves from one compartment to another freely, but certain salts are more restricted in their movements.

PRACTICAL CONSIDERATIONS

TESTS FOR KIDNEY FUNCTION

Specific Gravity. Normal kidneys are able to vary the specific gravity of urine from 1.002 to 1.040. This ability is tested by the Mosenthal and the concentration-dilution tests. In the former, the daily variation in specific gravity and volume of urine is determined; in the latter, the differences in specific gravity of urine on a "dry" diet and after the intake of a large amount of water within a short period of time are determined.

If the kidneys are diseased, the variation in specific gravity of urine is limited. In fact, the specific gravity may be "fixed" and remain about 1.010 regardless of variations in intake of water. These tests of flexibility of specific gravity are easy to perform, and the information derived is valuable, since lack of ability to concentrate the urine is one of the earliest signs of kidney damage.

Color. If bile pigments are present, the urine is deeply colored. Urine may become cloudy on standing; in acid urine this is due to urates, and in alkaline urine it is due to phosphates. The cloudiness may also be due to pus or mucus.

Abnormal constituents include blood, pus, albumin, sugar, acetone bodies and indole and skatole.

BLOOD. The presence of blood in the urine is called *hematuria*. It may be due to contamination from vaginal discharge, cystitis, tuberculosis of the kidney or tumor along the passages. Whenever blood is found in the urine, additional examinations are imperative to determine the origin of the blood.

PUS. The presence of pus in the urine is called *pyuria*. It may be due to infection of the bladder or of the renal pelvis. Additional tests are needed.

ALBUMIN. The presence of albumin in the urine is called *albuminuria*. It may indicate contamination with vaginal discharge, cystitis or infection along the canals, and these sources should be ruled out as possible causes. *Orthostatic albuminuria* also must be ruled out. This is a condition in which albumin is present in specimens of urine collected during the day, when the patient is in the upright position; the specimens collected after resting in bed are free of albumin. This is purely a circulatory phenomenon; in the standing position there is enough pressure on the left renal vein to cause a disturbance in filtration. There is no disease of the kidneys present. If all other causes for albuminuria, such as those listed above, have been ruled out, then it is safe to conclude that there is pathology of the kidneys in the form of glomerulonephritis (primarily involvement of glomeruli) or nephrosis (primarily involvement of tubules).

SUGAR. The presence of sugar in the urine is called *glycosuria;* it may be *alimentary glycosuria,* due to a large intake of sugar. It may be due to emotional upsets, such as during examinations (epinephrine causes excessive glycogenolysis, with marked elevation of blood sugar to above renal threshold concentration). If glycosuria is found in a pregnant or lactating woman, lactosuria must be ruled out. When all other causes have been ruled out, diabetes mellitus may be suspected, and additional tests (glucose tolerance) are imperative.

ACETONE BODIES. The presence of acetone bodies in the urine is called *acetonuria* or ketosis. It should be kept in mind that a small amount of acetone bodies is present in the urine of normal individuals. If the amount is increased, it may indicate too little carbohydrate in the diet (fad reducing diets), too low a calorie intake or partial starvation, complete starvation, or diabetes mellitus. The amount of ketone bodies is increased in any condition in which a larger proportion of fat than normal is being burned.

INDOLE AND SKATOLE. The amount of indole and skatole present in the urine indicates the amount of putrefaction in the large intestine. This may be increased in constipation.

Special Clearance Tests. The dye phenolsulfonphthalein (commonly called P.S.P.) is used to test the excretory function of the tubular cells. One cubic centimeter of dye is injected intramuscularly or intravenously, after the bladder has been emptied. Water is given by mouth. The bladder is emptied at the end of 1 hour (if dye is given intramuscularly) or 30 minutes (if dye is given intravenously), and again at the end of 2 hours, or 1 hour, respectively. The amount of dye that is eliminated in the 2 specimens is determined. Normal kidneys eliminate 60 to 80 per cent of the injected dye within the specified time. Impaired kidneys eliminate less than this amount.

There are other special tests, called *clearance* tests, that are done in certain hospitals. By means of these special tests the following information can be derived: (1) the rate of glomerular filtration (inulin clearance), (2) the maximal absorptive function of the tubular cells (glucose Tm), (3) the maximal excretory function of the tubular cells (Diodrast Tm) and (4) the amount of plasma flowing through the kidneys in a given time (Diodrast clearance).

MICROSCOPIC EXAMINATION OF URINE

When a drop of abnormal urine (which has been centrifuged) is examined, erythrocytes, tiny stones (renal calculi) and casts may be noted. The casts are tiny masses of material that have hardened in the tubular lumens, and they assume the shape of the lumen. The presence of casts indicates kidney injury.

DIURESIS

Diuresis refers to a temporary increase in the production of urine, which may be produced by administration of a drug known as a *diuretic.*

Water diuresis follows the intake of a large amount of water within a short period of time. Most of the water will be eliminated by normal kidneys within 2 hours after it has been taken in.

Dilution diuresis follows dilution of the plasma proteins by intravenous injection of a large amount of sucrose or sodium sulfate. Immediately after injection, the filtration rate is increased, causing a dilution type of diuresis.

Tubular diuresis is due to the presence of large amounts of waste products in the glomerular filtrate. Urea, glucose in a diabetic patient, sucrose and sodium sulfate act as tubular diuretics.

UREA is a natural diuretic. When one eats a large amount of protein, the diuretic effect of urea is noted.

GLUCOSE in an untreated diabetic is a waste product and is responsible for the polyuria of such patients.

SUCROSE OR SODIUM SULFATE act as tubular diuretics after they are filtered by the glomeruli.

Waste products in the lumens of the tubules hold enough water in the lumens (by osmosis) to keep themselves in solution and cause diuresis by opposing reabsorption of water.

Caffeine produces a dilatation of the vessels of the kidneys and, since more blood flows through the kidney vessels, more urine is produced.

Digitalis, which is used in the treatment of heart disease, has a diuretic effect since it improves the blood flow through the kidneys.

CHARACTERISTICS OF THE URINE IN CERTAIN DISEASES

In untreated **diabetes mellitus** a large amount of urine is produced (polyuria), which is pale in color, has a high specific gravity and contains glucose and a large amount of acetone bodies.

In **diabetes insipidus** a very large amount of urine is produced (as much as 30 L. per day), which is pale in color, has a very low specific gravity and contains neither glucose nor a large amount of acetone bodies.

In **glomerulonephritis** there are both hematuria and albuminuria. In the acute stage the urine volume is low, and the specific gravity is high, while in the chronic stage there is usually polyuria, with low specific gravity (fixed around 1.010). There will be other alterations in the body as a result of the kidney impairment, such as retention of waste products (uremia, acidosis), low plasma protein with edema and depletion of salt.

In **tubular nephritis** (commonly called *nephrosis*) polyuria, hematuria and albuminuria may be present. The specific gravity of the urine is low. Other alterations in the body are edema and probably acidosis, since the kidneys cannot manufacture ammonia. It is difficult to find conditions in which injury is confined to glomeruli alone or to tubules alone; sooner or later all parts of the nephrons are involved.

SUPPRESSION OF URINE PRODUCTION

The production of urine may be suppressed completely for a few days (anuria) during an attack of acute nephritis. Hot packs are applied in an attempt to increase elimination through the skin, to tide the patient over the acute stage. In some hospitals "artificial kidneys" are used for a few hours each day during the attack. Both hot packs and artificial kidneys are temporary measures, and if the kidneys do not recover sufficiently to begin to function within a few days, death results. The danger of anuria is uremia, due to the retention of nitrogenous waste products. This condition is accompanied by dyspnea, high blood pressure, convulsions, diarrhea and vomiting. Much is being attempted along the lines of "medical management" to tide patients over periods of temporary suppression of urine production.

DISTURBANCES OF WATER AND SALT BALANCE

Disturbance in water and salt balance involve changes in volume and composition of extracellular fluid, and, if prolonged, changes in intracellular fluid occur also.

A decrease in extracellular fluid volume (dehydration) follows prolonged vomiting, diarrhea or profuse perspiration, as well as deprivation of water. As soon as a decrease in extracellular fluid occurs, there is impairment of circulation; this means less blood flow to the kidneys. If the kidneys are not supplied abundantly with blood, they cannot perform their functions properly, so waste

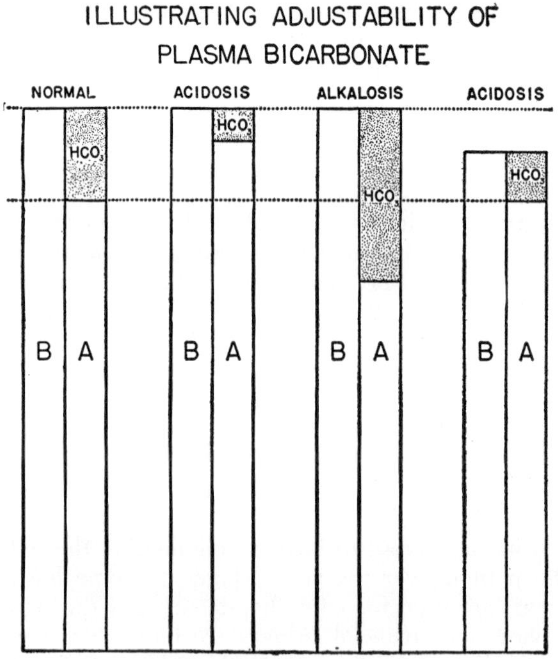

ILLUSTRATING ADJUSTABILITY OF PLASMA BICARBONATE

FIG. 378. Diagram illustrating the adjustability of plasma acid carbonate. The concentration of acid carbonate is determined by the extent to which the total fixed base concentration exceeds the sum of the concentration of all the other anions. The acid carbonate is decreased in acidosis, whether mild or severe; it is increased in alkalosis. (Gamble, J. L.: Internat. Clinics Ser. **46**:2)

products begin to accumulate. If the condition is not permitted to continue, and if dehydration is corrected, the changes in composition are corrected automatically as soon as the kidneys can function again.

In prolonged vomiting, one loses water in saliva and gastric juice, together with HCl in gastric juice. In this condition, then, alkalosis ensues, in addition to dehydration. In diarrhea, there is loss of water in pancreatic juice, bile and intestinal juice, together with a loss of $NaHCO_3$, so acidosis ensues, in addition to dehydration. The same condition can result when Miller-Abbott or Wangensteen suction tubes are in use, unless care is taken to replace the fluid withdrawn.

In kidney disease there is retention of nitrogenous waste, sulfates and phosphates. Albumin is lost in the urine, and water accumulates in the subcutaneous tissues in the form of edema. This water is lost to the vascular compartment as surely as if it had left the body.

In diabetes mellitus there is dehydration due to the polyuria.

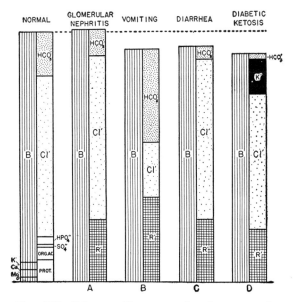

FIG. 379. Diagram illustrating the changes in the composition of plasma in certain conditions. (Gamble, J. L.: Internat. Clinics Ser. 46:2)

In addition, the excess amounts of acetone bodies to be eliminated carry out sodium with them (eliminated as sodium salts). Dehydration leads to renal impairment, with all the difficulties which accompany that. Whenever the kidneys are impaired, not only do waste products accumulate in the blood and lead to acidosis, but also the production of ammonia is impaired. This leads to further acidosis due to loss of sodium.

When a person perspires excessively he may suffer from lack of sodium chloride, especially if he drinks plenty of water but does not replace the sodium chloride lost. There are cramps, lassitude, apathy, stupor, headache, weakness, nausea and vomiting. All of these symptoms can be prevented by taking extra salt or salt tablets with water, or by drinking dilute salt solution instead of water.

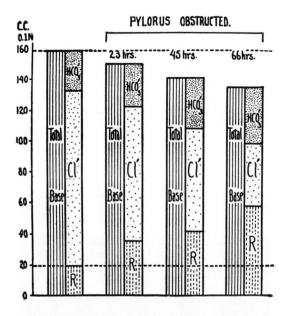

FIG. 380. Diagram illustrating the changes in the composition of the plasma in pyloric obstruction that has continued through 66 hours, in other words, changes that follow prolonged vomiting. (Gamble, J. L., from Best, C. H., and Taylor, N. B.: Physiological Basis of Medical Practice, ed. 5, Baltimore, Williams & Wilkins)

There is a deficiency of sodium chloride in Addison's disease (p. 736).

It is evident that there are many conditions in which disturbances in water balance and salt balance may occur. Some of the more common disturbances are illustrated in Figures 378, 379 and 380. A disturbance in salt balance seldom is found without a disturbance in water balance and vice versa. In most cases, if the disturbance in volume is corrected the disturbance in composition will be corrected automatically, if the kidneys are normal. Whenever there is a disturbance in water and salt balance, the functions of the various cells of the body (nervous system, heart muscle, smooth muscle, skeletal muscle, liver, etc.) are not performed properly.

The extent of the disturbances can be ascertained by determinations of sodium, potassium, chloride, pH and bicarbonate of the plasma. These same determinations can be made in order to follow the results of treatment.

Water Intoxication. It is possible to produce water intoxication in an individual whose kidneys are impaired. This condition is accompanied by headache, vertigo, vomiting, muscle cramps and edema, and really is due to decrease in salt concentration of the extracellular fluid. Death may occur in coma or convulsions, since there is edema of the brain and an increase in intracranial pressure.

SUMMARY

1. Channels of excretion
2. Characteristics of urine: color, reaction, specific gravity, quantity, composition
3. Production of urine
    A. Filtration in glomerulus; factors which influence filtration
    B. Selective absorption in tubules: water, threshold and non-threshold substances
    C. Synthesis of ammonia and hippuric acid
    D. Excretion by tubular cells
    E. Effects of hormones on urine production: salt and water hormone of adrenal cortex; antidiuretic hormone of posterior pituitary gland
4. Water balance
    A. Amount of water in the body
    B. Intake; exogenous and endogenous sources
    C. Output: 4 channels of excretion; factors involved in each
    D. Balance between intake and output

5. Salt balance
   A. Intake
   B. Output
6. Fluid compartments
   A. Vascular; amount and composition
   B. Interstitial fluid compartment: amount and composition; comparison with composition of plasma
   C. Intracellular fluid compartment: amount and composition; differences between extracellular and intracellular fluids

SITUATION AND QUESTIONS

An experiment on urine production in a mammal was demonstrated to the class in the physiology laboratory. From this experiment the students were able to arrive at the following conclusions:

1. The hormone from the posterior lobe of the pituitary gland may influence urine production by exerting its effects on the: _____(a) afferent arteriole; _____(b) glomerulus; _____ (c) renal tubules; _____(d) renal pelvis.

2. Epinephrine may influence urine production by: _____ (a) changing the blood flow and pressure in the glomerulus; _____(b) changing the permeability of the capillary walls of the glomerulus; _____(c) changing the pressure within the capsule of Bowman; _____(d) changing the rate of reabsorption in the kidney tubules.

3. The primary function of the kidney tubules is to: _____ (a) return plasma proteins to the blood; _____(b) reabsorb urea from the filtrate passing through the lumen; _____(c) reabsorb water, glucose and chloride from the filtrate passing through the lumen; _____(d) act as a filter to prevent plasma proteins from leaving the blood.

4. When sugar is found in the urine, it indicates probably that the: _____(a) kidney tubules are damaged; _____(b) glomerular walls have been damaged and, therefore, are more permeable to glucose; _____(c) the hormone pituitrin is not being secreted in normal amounts; _____(d) the glucose level in the blood is above threshold so that the tubules cannot absorb all that is presented to them. _____ __

5. If an excess amount of water is eliminated by the kidneys, the fluid compartment of the body most rapidly affected is the: _____(a) vascular compartment; _____(b) interstitial compartment; _____(c) intracellular compartment; _____ (d) subarachnoid compartment.

18. Regulation of Body Temperature

INTRODUCTION

The maintenance of a fairly constant body temperature in man is another example of homeostasis in which many activities are correlated to accomplish one purpose. As long as one is alive, heat is produced. The amount produced in health varies greatly in accordance with variations in activity of skeletal muscles and is influenced also by the type of food eaten, temperature of the surroundings and the condition of certain endocrine glands. If an adult man rested for 24 hours and took no food, he would produce about 1,700 Cal. of heat. If he were moderately active he would produce about 3,000 Cal., and if he did heavy work he would produce about 7,000 Cal. Not only are there such wide variations in health, but the variations may be equally wide in infectious diseases and glandular disturbances. Whatever the amount of heat produced in the body, the co-operation of the circulatory system is needed to distribute the heat throughout the body.

Since heat is produced continuously during life, it must be lost continuously. If there were no heat loss, the temperature of the body under basal conditions would rise by 1.8° F per hour; with moderate activity it would rise by 3.6° F per hour. It is evident that not only must there be continued loss of heat, but the amount lost must vary also in accordance with changes in heat production. Most of the heat loss takes place through the skin and is regulated by the amount of blood flowing through the cutaneous vessels and also by the activity of the sweat glands.

In order to maintain a balance between heat production and heat loss, fine adjustments are needed. A device somewhat like a thermostat is required, but the regulating mechanism in the body differs from a thermostat in that heat production cannot be "turned off completely," no matter how hot the external environment becomes. Heat production in the body cannot drop below the *basal* level.

The mechanisms for temperature regulation are so efficient in health that only when one does exceedingly heavy work or when the environmental conditions interfere with heat loss does the body temperature depart from the normal range. Since one adjusts so well to both external and internal "threats," a departure from normal body temperature has come to be one of the cardinal signs of disease. The first thing that a mother does if a child's behavior suddenly alters is to take his temperature, and she immediately reports to her physician if the temperature is elevated.

Temperature is taken several times a day in hospitalized patients, and physicians usually examine the temperature charts before they make their daily calls on their patients.

The close observation of temperature in ill individuals is most important, since the "optimum" body temperature for man extends over a limited range. Enzymes that take part in all functions of cells in the body require specific temperatures, and the heat-sensitive enzymes are inactivated irreversibly at high body temperatures.

CLASSES OF ANIMALS WITH RESPECT TO TEMPERATURE REGULATION

There are 2 classes of animals with respect to temperature regulation: homiothermal and poikilothermal.

The homiothermal group comprises mammals and birds, which are said to be "warm-blooded." This means that a relatively constant body temperature is maintained under widely varying cli-

matic conditions. In other words, homiothermal animals possess
regulatory mechanisms for adjusting heat production and heat loss.
The poikilothermal group comprises fish, amphibia and reptiles, which are said to be "cold-blooded." This means that the
body temperature fluctuates with the surroundings, since these
animals possess no regulatory mechanisms for heat production and
heat loss. With every change in environmental temperature there
is a corresponding change in the rate of oxidation, and every activity is conditioned by the "weather."

Hibernating animals are homiothermal during their waking
months and poikilothermal during their sleeping period.

HEAT PRODUCTION

Heat production cannot be decreased below the basal level even
when the temperature of the external surroundings is so high that
life is in danger. In fact, heat production increases in proportion
to the temperature of the external environments. Thus, it adds an
internal threat to the external threat.

On the other hand, heat production increases also when one is
exposed to a cold environmental temperature, but it cannot be increased to such an extent that it protects an individual against
extreme cold, and he can "freeze" to death.

Thus, heat production cannot be decreased below the basal level
nor can it be increased unduly or it will coagulate the proteins of
protoplasm and irreversibly inactivate enzymes that are essential
to every metabolic process that normally occurs in cells.

SOURCES OF HEAT

Heat is produced by the oxidation of foodstuffs in all the cells of
the body, but since a great part of the body is composed of skeletal muscles, most of the heat is produced by oxidations in them.
Heat is produced during the secretory activities of glands. Since
the liver is the largest gland in the body, it contributes a generous
share of the heat so produced.

Heat is produced by activity in nervous tissue, but this is a small
amount compared with equivalent weights of skeletal muscle. Heat
that is produced in any tissue is distributed by means of the circulating blood. This prevents overheating in any one organ.

The body can gain heat from external objects or from the sun's
rays, shining directly on the body or reflected from sand or snow.
Any object which has a higher temperature than that of the skin
can contribute heat to the body (heating pads, hot-water bottles).

Any factor that alters metabolism or the rate of oxidation of the cells influences heat production. Such factors are activity of muscles, intake of food, hormones, body temperature and external temperature.

Activity of Muscles. SKELETAL MUSCLES. When skeletal muscles are relaxed, as during rest or sleep, heat production is lowest. The maintenance of tone in skeletal muscles is accompanied by an increase in heat production, since some motor units are active. Severe muscular exercise and hard work are accompanied by maximal heat production in muscles. Under such conditions only 25 per cent of the energy liberated by chemical changes in the muscles can be converted to mechanical work, and the balance is converted to heat.

During muscular activity heat production rises from the basal level of about 40 to 500 Cal. per square meter of body surface per hour.

Heat production in skeletal muscles depends on connection with the central nervous system. If the external temperature begins to drop, reflexes are set up to increase heat production. "Shivering" is the outstanding reflex that involves skeletal muscles.

SMOOTH MUSCLES. The activities associated with digestion and absorption of food are accompanied by increased heat production in the smooth muscles of the gastro-intestinal tract.

HEART MUSCLE. Heat is produced by cardiac muscle during each systole.

The intake of food is associated with increased heat production. Part of this is due to the activity of the smooth muscles of the gastro-intestinal tract and to the marked activity of the glands that produce digestive juices in large amounts.

The epithelial cells of the small intestine produce heat during their activities connected with absorption of foodstuffs and reabsorption of digestive juices.

Each type of foodstuff stimulates metabolic processes, but protein excels in this respect. One requirement for basal metabolic tests is that no food should have been eaten during the preceding 14 hours. The reason is to avoid the increased heat production associated with digestion and absorption of food.

Hormones. An output of epinephrine stimulates heat production (and decreases heat loss) temporarily. Since this is true, one should be free from emotional strain during a basal metabolic test.

Thyroxin (p. 728) stimulates the rate of oxidation in all cells of the body. In fact, a determination of the basal metabolic rate is a commonly used test for thyroid activity. When the thyroid gland is overactive, it is possible to have an enormous increase in heat production (80 Cal. per square meter per hour).

Body Temperature. As the body temperature rises, heat production rises. Each degree rise in rectal temperature is accompanied by a 7 per cent increase in heat production. It is evident that a basal metabolic determination is of no value if one's temperature is elevated (as in fever).

External Temperature. The production of heat is increased by both high and low external temperatures. In the warm environment all chemical processes are speeded up; in the cold environment, the output of epinephrine, together with shivering, increases heat production. In extreme cold the activities of the cells are depressed.

HEAT LOSS

The channels of heat loss are the skin, the lungs and the excreta.

Excreta. The amount lost by way of excreta is small (except in diuresis or diarrhea) and depends on taking in food and beverages that are below body temperature and excreting waste at body temperature.

Lungs. The amount of heat lost by the lungs depends on the temperature and the humidity of inspired air. If one is inhaling warm air, saturated with moisture, the amount of heat lost by the lungs is very small.

The skin is the channel through which about 85 per cent of heat is lost under the usual conditions in a temperate climate, but in a hot dry climate practically 100 per cent of the heat is lost through the skin.

The physical processes by which heat is lost are: conduction, radiation, convection and vaporization (evaporation of water). By means of "partitional calorimetry," the amount of heat lost by each of these means under different conditions of external temperature, humidity and air movement has been determined.

CONDUCTION refers to the transfer of heat from one molecule to another by contact. Man loses heat by conduction to the air that is in contact with the skin (if it is cooler than the skin), to clothing, to air in the respiratory system, to food and beverages ingested (below body temperature), by stepping on cold floors with bare feet, by sitting on cold stone or metal seats, by lying on cold ground, by swimming in cold water and even by lying on an operating table.

Therefore, loss of heat by conduction can occur through the skin, the lining of the gastro-intestinal tract and the lining of the respiratory system. Since man protects himself by clothing, the loss of heat by conduction through the skin may not be great. The protective value of clothing is almost exactly proportional to the thickness of the layer of still air trapped in the meshes or between the layers of clothing, since air is a poor conductor of heat. Woolen clothing greatly reduces heat loss by having a wealth of meshes in which air is trapped. The fur covering of animals is of great importance because of the air that can be trapped in the fur. The warmest covering for a bed on a cold night is a feather comforter or puff, since a generous amount of air is trapped between the feathers, and one's body heat is not lost so rapidly.

RADIATION is the transfer of infrared or heat waves through the air to objects in the room or to the walls of the room, without physical contact. A gradient of temperature is essential, and one can lose heat by radiation only if the surroundings are cooler than the body. Under ordinary conditions, in a temperate climate, one loses about 60 to 65 per cent of body heat by radiation. The loss by radiation is increased at low temperatures and it ceases if the external temperature rises to about 95° F. (35° C.).

CONVECTION refers to replacing the layer of air next the body (which has been warmed by conduction and radiation) by a layer of cool air. In order to lose heat by convection, movement of air is essential.

Convection plays a role in loss of heat by the lungs, in that there is constant movement of air in and out of the respiratory passages. Heat is lost by convection from the skin when the body moves or when air moves over the body. Under ordinary conditions one loses from 10 to 15 per cent of the body's heat by convection.

Loss of heat by convection becomes important when one sits in a breeze, in the path of a fan or rides in an open car. Under the above conditions, loss of heat by convection may be increased to about 40 per cent. Loss of heat by this means increases when one swims in cool water (by movement of arms and legs) and during vigorous exercise, if one moves the extremities rapidly.

VAPORIZATION refers to loss of heat when water evaporates or changes from the liquid to the vapor state. Each gram of water that evaporates (at body temperature) requires 0.58 Cal. of heat. In temperature climates a person loses about 20 to 30 per cent of his heat by vaporization of water.

Part of this is lost by saturating the expired air with water vapor from the lining of the respiratory tract, but, as stated previously, the amount lost in this way depends on the condition of the inspired air. The amount of water lost by vaporization from the lungs is about 300 cc. daily.

The greater part of heat loss by vaporization is through the skin. A continuous loss of heat through the "insensible" loss of water (p. 685) occurs, since one loses from 300 to 800 cc. of water daily by this means.

The loss of heat by evaporation of perspiration ("sensible" loss) varies with the temperature and the relative humidity of the external air. The relative humidity is the ratio between the actual moisture and the maximal amount of moisture which the air could hold at that temperature. It is a measure of the degree of saturation of air with water vapor. The optimum or best relative humidity for human comfort is between 40 and 60 per cent, since this enables one to lose heat by vaporization.

When the external temperature exceeds that of the body, evaporation is the only method of heat loss available to the body, since loss by conduction, radiation and convection are now impossible. One's ability to survive at high external temperatures depends on the ability to lose heat by evaporation of perspiration. The maximal rate of sweat secretion is about 1.7 L. per hour (for short periods of time). This means a loss of about 1,000 Cal. of heat

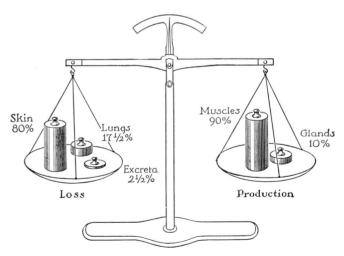

Fig. 381. Balance between heat loss and heat production.

per hour. A person can endure a temperature of 250° F. if the air is dry and if he can perspire freely. If sweat does not evaporate but is wiped away or runs down over the body, no heat is lost at all by this means.

It must be emphasized again that the amount of heat lost by each physical process depends on the condition of the body and the environment.

MECHANISMS INVOLVED IN MAINTAINING A BALANCE BETWEEN HEAT PRODUCTION AND HEAT LOSS

In order to maintain a fairly constant body temperature there must be a balance between heat production and heat loss. Figure 381 is a diagram of the factors involved in maintaining such a balance. If one of these factors changes, other factors must be adjusted to maintain the balance. For example, the effect of muscular activity on body temperature depends on the extent to which the heat loss can be increased to compensate for the increase in heat production, and heat loss, in turn, depends on the environment.

The skin is the most important organ in the body with respect to regulation of heat loss. Each of the physical processes listed above is concerned with loss of heat through the skin. The amount of heat lost depends on the blood flow through the cutaneous vessels, the activity of the sweat glands and the pilomotor muscles.

Blood Flow Through the Skin. The blood brought to the skin loses heat to the enviroment. The amount of blood flowing through the skin can be varied markedly; it can be decreased to almost zero or increased to as much as 12 per cent of the total blood flow. In the fingers the blood flow can be changed from about 1 cc. to 90 cc. per 100 Gm. of tissue per minute. The blood flow through the hands and the feet is particularly significant since these are the most important areas for dissipation of heat. Not only can the blood flow through arterioles, capillaries and venules be varied, but there are also arteriovenous anastomoses in the extremities through which blood can be shunted from arteries to veins without going through capillaries. This makes possible a great increase in the amount of blood flowing through the area concerned.

In cold surroundings the blood flow to the skin is decreased greatly by vasoconstriction; in warm surroundings the blood flow is greatly increased by vasodilatation and the opening of arteriovenous anastomoses. The amount of blood flowing through the skin, in turn, determines the amount of heat that it is possible to lose by conduction, radiation and convection.

Sweat Glands. The second means of adjustment is by way of sweat glands. These are inactive in cold surroundings. In hot environments, the sweat glands are active, and the amount of heat lost by evaporation of sweat is great if the relative humidity is low.

Pilomotor Muscles. The third means of adjustment is less important in man than in lower animals. In cold surroundings, the smooth muscles around the bases of hair follicles contract, and the hair or the fur stands on end. The nearest approach to this in man is the appearance of "gooseflesh" when one feels cold. When hair stands on end more air can be trapped, and insulation against cold is more effective. In warm surroundings the pilomotor muscles are relaxed, the hair lies flat, and a minimal amount of air is trapped.

Figure 382 shows the means by which heat is lost in temperate, cold and hot-dry climates.

NERVOUS CONTROL OF TEMPERATURE REGULATION

It has been shown that in response to changes in the temperature of the environment, alterations in the blood-flow through the skin and in the activity of the sweat glands occur. The skin not only contains plexuses of blood vessels and sweat glands but it also contains warm and cold receptors that play an important role in the regulation of temperature. In addition to peripheral temperature receptors, there are temperature-sensitive receptors in the hypothalamus that are affected by the temperature of the blood flowing through them.

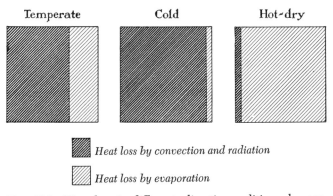

FIG. 382. Heat loss in different climatic conditions, by convection, radiation, and evaporation from the skin.

The sequence of events that come after exposure to cold is as follows: The cold receptors in the skin are stimulated, and afferent impulses are transmitted to the central nervous system, which set into operation a chain of reflexes. (1) There is vasoconstriction of the blood vessels in the skin; since less blood flows through the skin, less heat is lost by conduction, radiation and convection. (2) Sweat glands are inhibited. (3) Pilomotor muscles are stimulated, and the erection of hair tends to conserve heat by trapping a greater layer of air between hairs.

If, despite these adjustments, the body temperature begins to fall, the central receptors bring about reactions to increase heat production. (4) The tone of skeletal muscles is increased. (5) Shivering may occur (coarse adjustment). (6) The output of epinephrine is increased (fine adjustment). If a balance cannot be achieved between heat loss and heat production by the above responses on exposure to cold, the body temperature will begin to decline.

When exposed to external heat, the chain of events begins with stimulation of warm receptors in the skin. When the afferent impulses reach the central nervous system, reflexes are set into operation to increase heat loss and to decrease heat production. The sequence of events is: (1) The cutaneous vessels are dilated, and the increased blood-flow through the skin makes possible an increase in loss of heat from the skin, provided that the external temperature is still below that of the skin. (2) The sweat glands are stimulated. (3) Pilomotor muscles are relaxed. (4) Skeletal muscles are relaxed to decrease heat production to a minimum.

If an individual undergoes repeated exposures to heat, he shows some acclimatization, in that sweating begins at lower levels of body temperature than before, the sodium chloride content of sweat decreases, and the output of adrenocorticotrophic hormone (p. 722) by the anterior pituitary increases. This, in turn, increases the output of the "salt and water" hormone by the adrenal cortex (p. 735), and the reabsorption of sodium chloride from the lumens of the kidney tubules increases.

CENTER OF INTEGRATION

The hypothalamus is the center of integration for the regulation of body temperature. There is a center in the anterior portion of the hypothalamus that protects against overheating, or regulates heat loss. In the posterior portion of the hypothalamus there is a heat-conservation center that regulates heat production and protects against overcooling.

The hypothalamus receives afferent impulses from peripheral temperature receptors and apparently contains central receptors that are sensitive to the temperature of blood flowing through the hypothalamus. The hypothalamus sends efferent impulses to both the visceral efferent system and the somatic efferent system. The visceral activities are the vasomotor changes, secretion of sweat and pilomotor activities. The somatic activities are shivering and, in dogs, panting.

PHYSIOLOGIC VARIATIONS IN BODY TEMPERATURE

The range of temperature found in a large number of healthy, young adults was 96.5° to 99.3°, with an average of 98.1° F.

There is a daily or diurnal variation in body temperature, which is established at about 1 year of age. The temperature is lowest in the early morning, after several hours of rest in bed, when one is inactive and not digesting food. The temperature is highest in the late afternoon and the early evening, after a day of activity and after the evening meal. If the temperature is taken every hour over a 24-hour period, as much as 3° F variation may be found, but the usual variation between the early morning and late afternoon is about 1° F.

There is some variation in basal temperature with the menstrual cycle. Ovulation is thought to occur at the low point of the monthly temperature curve (p. 743).

ABNORMAL VARIATIONS IN BODY TEMPERATURE

Temperature regulation is poorly developed in premature babies, infants and elderly persons.

High External Temperatures

Heat Exhaustion. When one is subjected to high external temperatures, one may perspire so much that heat exhaustion supervenes. This is possible because temperature regulation has priority over the maintenance of water and salt balance, and sweating continues even though it produces severe dehydration and marked salt loss. Heat exhaustion is characterized by the following: severe muscle cramps, pallor, low blood pressure, vertigo, weakness, nausea, vomiting and fainting. The symptoms are due to chloride depletion and can be prevented by taking enough sodium chloride and water to make up for the excessive loss by perspiration.

Heat Stroke. This is seen most frequently in elderly persons in poor health who indulge in alcoholic beverages. When first exposed to excessive heat these individuals perspire, and the loss of water leads to a decrease in plasma volume, with decrease in cardiac output. This means a decreased blood flow through the skin. As the cutaneous blood supply becomes inadequate, sweat secretion diminishes and then ceases completely as circulatory failure supervenes.

When the main pathway of heat loss, namely evaporation of sweat, is closed, the body temperature rises with explosive suddenness, and the general condition of the patient becomes very critical. The skin is dry and flushed. As the body temperature rises to dangerously high levels the patient becomes comatose. The absence of sweat is the most striking characteristic of heat stroke. Death occurs if the body temperature rises to about 111° F, due to coagulation of protein of protoplasm and irreversible inactivation of enzymes.

Low External Temperatures

If the body is subjected to excessive cold, or if there is too great a loss of heat through insufficient clothing or by immersion in cold water, the body temperature falls markedly. As the body temperature falls, there is a feeling of exhaustion and an uncontrollable desire to sleep.

The respiration becomes slow, the blood pressure falls, the dissociation of oxyhemoglobin decreases, and coma occurs. One case is reported in which there was recovery after the body temperature had fallen to 64° F. The patient was a woman who went to sleep in the street in very cold weather, while intoxicated. The body was stiff when found, but there was a faint sound, which was interpreted as a heart sound, about 12 times a minute. By means of excellent care, recovery took place, but amputation of both legs and of several fingers later was necessary, since the tissues had been irreparably damaged, probably due to the formation of crystals of ice within the cells.

Fever

Fever is an elevation of body temperature. It may be due to an infection, a reaction to a foreign protein, drugs, diathermy, injury to the brain or lesions in the upper portion of the spinal cord.

The typical onset of fever due to an infectious disease is as follows: (1) The patient feels cold, is pale, has a dry skin and gooseflesh. (2) He cannot seem to get warm, even with extra clothing. (3) If he goes to bed and lies under several blankets, even with hot water bottles and heating pads, he still feels cold. (4) His teeth chatter, and he has such a severe chill (shivering) that he may shake the bed. (5) If his oxygen use were measured during the chill it would be found to be about 3 times as great as normal, which means that he is producing a large amount of heat. (6) In spite of increased heat production and minimal heat loss, the feeling of cold persists during the chill. (7) The extra heat is being stored in the body, and, at the end of the chill, the body temperature is elevated, having risen 3° or more during the chill. The events during a chill are shown by diagram in Figure 383.

The heat production of the body is increased during the course of the fever. It is increased about 7 per cent for each degree rise in body temperature. However, the heat loss keeps pace with heat production during the course of the fever, so it seems as if the thermostat is set at a higher level during the course of fever.

There is a specific destruction of body protein during fever; the nitrogen minimum (amount in the diet required to maintain nitrogen balance) is much higher during fever than it is normally. One needs a high caloric intake during the course of a fever; a daily intake of about 4,000 Cal. is advised. The percentage of carbohy-

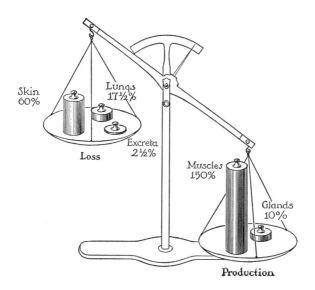

Fig. 383. Disturbed balance in chill, at the onset of fever, when heat production exceeds heat loss.

drate is kept high to prevent the excessive use of fat, with the appearance of ketosis.

At the end of a fever that is permitted to run its course, the temperature may fall suddenly to the normal range. This sudden drop is called a *crisis*. It is the opposite of a chill, in that heat loss is increased markedly over heat production. The skeletal muscles are relaxed, the skin is flushed, and perspiration is profuse. The temperature returns to normal in the course of a few hours. The events that take place during such a crisis are illustrated by diagram in Figure 384. When the return to normal temperature occurs slowly it is called *lysis*.

The significance of fever is unknown. It is possible that bacteria do not grow as well at the higher temperature, and perhaps the body forms antibodies more readily at the elevated temperature. Phagocytosis is increased during fever. The patient can be made more comfortable by sponge baths. At the present time, the use of antibiotics prevents an infectious disease from running its course, and yet "fever therapy" is used in the treatment of some diseases.

PRACTICAL CONSIDERATIONS

Taking the Temperature. Nurses learn to take the body tem-

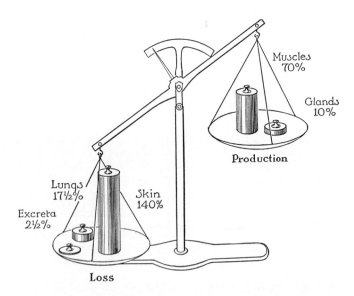

FIG. 384. Disturbed balance at the crisis, when heat loss exceeds heat production.

perature as one of the first routines. The temperature may be taken in the mouth, the rectum or the axilla.

THE MOUTH temperature is most variable. It is influenced by hot food or beverages, cold food or beverages, smoking, mouth breathing, talking, and evaporation of sweat from the face. The thermometer should be left in place for 3 minutes (under the tongue) in spite of instructions to the contrary on the thermometer.

THE RECTAL temperature is about 0.5° to 0.7° F higher than that of the mouth and is the best guide to the internal temperature of the body. The thermometer should be inserted to a depth of 2 in. and left in place 3 minutes. Rectal temperatures are taken in preference to oral temperatures in small children, very ill patients and delirious patients.

AXILLARY temperatures are about 1° F lower than mouth temperatures. The thermometer should be left in place in the axilla for about 10 minutes.

Temperatures of 101° to 105° are found after severe muscular exercise and during infectious diseases, in which the temperature regulating mechanisms are efficient, but the thermostat is set at a higher level. The temperature during fever therapy may rise to 106° F. During heat stroke temperatures of 106° to 112° F are found, but in this condition the temperature regulating mechanisms are impaired. Below 94° F, there is also an impairment of temperature regulation, and the ability to regulate temperature is lost completely when the body temperature falls to 82° F.

"Dehydration fever" is seen occasionally in children with low plasma volumes. It seems due to depression of sweat glands and responds readily to administration of water and sodium chloride.

Sedation and Anesthesia. With excessive sedation, the body temperature falls. During anesthesia, the reflexes are depressed or absent, and temperature is not maintained at the normal level. The muscular relaxation under curare predisposes to a fall in body temperature. In order to lower the temperature, as during refrigeration anesthesia for amputations and operations on the heart, narcosis and ice packs are necessary.

Defective Regulation. Temperature regulation is defective in newborn babies; it is especially poor in premature babies. In infants, a fit of screaming can cause a marked rise in body temperature, and warm and cold baths can alter the temperature more than in adults.

In elderly persons the temperature usually is subnormal. The body is less active, the circulation feeble, and there is less power of compensation for changes in external temperature. These individuals are intolerant of extremes of external temperature.

Voluntary Aid in Temperature Regulation. It has been found that dressing in thin, white clothing is best for comfort in the desert. Permeability of clothing to moisture is important in order to permit loss of heat by evaporation of sweat.

Woolen clothing makes one very comfortable in cold surroundings.

When a person lives in a hot, moist climate he takes a long siesta each afternoon. This decreases heat production by decreasing the period of activity during the day. Lying sprawled out enables one to lose more heat than lying curled up, since the surface available for heat loss changes with posture.

Since the hands and the feet are so important in dissipation of heat, one can be more comfortable without gloves and with open shoes in a hot environment.

Air conditioning refers to making rooms cooler during hot weather. It is not satisfactory to have too great a difference between the inside and the outside temperatures. The following differences seem to be most satisfactory: outside 95°, inside 80° F; outside 90°, inside 78° F; and outside 80°, inside 75° F.

Drafts are especially bad. A draft on some part of the body has a tendency to cause vasoconstriction in the skin and vasodilatation in the nasal mucous membrane and may predispose one to colds.

One air-conditioning engineer stated, "If women would dress in winter in clothes that are comparable in warmth with those of men, they would be comfortable in a room at 72° F instead of 76°, and if men would take off their vests, coats and collars in hot weather, buildings would not have to be cooled below 83° F. A reconciliation of the double comfort standard would simplify greatly the problem of the engineer and would reduce the expense of heating and cooling buildings."

Beneficial results occur in operating and recovery rooms that are air conditioned. In nurseries, the weight loss of infants during the first few days of life has been reduced by air conditioning. Allergic patients are benefited greatly by proper air conditioning, because the air is washed free of pollen, yeasts and other disturbing contaminants.

SUMMARY

1. Classes of animals with respect to temperature regulation
   A. Homiothermal: constant body temperature
   B. Poikilothemal: varying body temperature

   C. Hibernating
  2. Heat production
     A. Limitations
     B. Sources
        a. Oxidations: muscles, glands and nervous tissue
        b. Gain from sun's rays or hot external objects
     C. Factors which influence heat production
        a. Activity of muscles: skeletal, smooth, cardiac
        b. Intake of food; motility and secretory activity; dynamic
action of foodstuffs
        c. Hormones: epinephrine; thyroxin
        d. Body temperature
        e. External temperature
  3. Heat loss
     A. Channels: skin, lungs and excreta
     B. Loss of heat from skin
        a. Conduction
        b. Radiation
        c. Convection
        d. Vaporization
  4. Mechanisms involved in a balance between heat production
and loss
     A. Blood flow through the skin
     B. Activity of sweat glands
     C. Pilomotor muscles
  5. Nervous control of temperature regulation
     A. Thermal receptors in skin; cold and warm receptors
     B. Hypothalamus
     C. Chain of reflexes when exposed to cold; to heat
     D. Center of integration: visceral efferent and somatic efferent
  6. Physiologic variations in body temperature
     A. Diurnal variation
     B. Variation with menstrual cycle
  7. Abnormal variations in body temperature
     A. Exposure to high external temperatures
        a. Heat exhaustion
        b. Heat stroke
     B. Exposure to low external temperatures
     C. Fever
        a. Causes
        b. Onset; chill
        c. Changes during course of fever
        d. Termination; crisis

SITUATION AND QUESTIONS

One of the first symptoms Mr. Lloyd experienced before his attack of pneumonia was a "chill." After being admitted to the hospital, the nurse explained that he had a fever and that his temperature-regulatory mechanisms were temporarily out of balance.

1. During a chill: _____(a) heat production exceeds heat loss; _____(b) heat loss exceeds heat production; _____ (c) heat loss and heat production are equal; _____(d) heat production temporarily stops completely.

2. The center for temperature regulation is in the: _____(a) cerebellum; _____(b) medulla; _____(c) midbrain; _____(d) hypothalamus.

3. On the fifth day, Mr. Lloyd's temperature dropped by crisis. Most of the heat lost during the crisis was by: _____(a) conduction; _____(b) convection; _____(c) radiation; _____ (d) evaporation.

4. After Mr. Lloyd's temperature returned to normal, the nurses continued to take his temperature for 3 consecutive days. It was shown that there is a diurnal variation in man's body temperature of about: _____(a) 1°; _____(b) 0.1°; _____(c) 5°; _____(d) 10°.

~~~~~~

19. Anatomy and Physiology of the Endocrine System

~~~~~~

INTRODUCTION

Some of the glands of the body lose connection with the epithelial surface from which they originate (Fig. 12) and become islands of epithelial tissue surrounded by connective tissue. As a result, such glands pour their secretions into the blood instead of on the original epithelial surface, as do the sweat glands of the skin and the glands of the alimentary tube.

717

The glands that have severed connection with the epithelial surface are called *ductless* glands, glands of *internal secretion* or *endocrine* glands. In addition to the glands that are derived from surface epithelium, some endocrine glands are derived from the nervous system, and a third group is derived from mesoderm (p. 790).

The glands of the **first group** (from epithelial surfaces) comprise the anterior lobe of the pituitary, the thyroid, the parathyroids and the islet cells of the pancreas. They produce hormones that are protein in nature.

The glands of the **second group** (from nervous system) comprise the medulla of the adrenal gland, which produces an amine as its hormone, and the posterior lobe of the pituitary, whose hormones are polypeptides.

The glands of the **third group** (from mesoderm) comprise the cortex of the adrenal gland and the secretory cells of the gonads (ovaries and testes). The internal secretions or hormones of this group are steroid in nature.

The glands of the endocrine system are relatively simple structures, consisting of clumps or cords of secretory cells that lie between wide capillaries or sinusoids and are supported by delicate connective tissue of the reticular type. In some of the glands the hormone is stored temporarily. An example of this is the so-called *colloid* (thyroglobulin) in the thyroid gland.

The glands of the endocrine system do not form an anatomic system in which they are in continuity, as is true of the organs which comprise other systems. The individual glands are located in widely separated regions of the body and form a system only from a functional standpoint.

The products which the endocrine glands make are called *hormones* (derived from words that mean "I arouse"). Hormones are specific organic substances manufactured by secretory cells of endocrine glands under physiologic conditions and carried by the blood to various parts of the body to perform their particular functions.

The general functions that are performed by hormones are: (1) chemical integration or correlation of many activities, in which some hormones act rapidly (such as epinephrine) and others act very slowly (such as thyroxin); (2) regulation of growth of the skeleton, the muscles, the viscera and even mental growth; (3) differentiation or morphogenesis, such as the maturation of the gonads, development of the secondary sexual characteristics and reproduction; (4) regulatory functions, in that they do not initiate new processes but may augment those already going on, such as catalyzing enzyme reactions; and (5) homeostasis or the maintenance of a constant internal environment, by controlling the intermediate metabolism of carbohydrates, fats and proteins, salt and water balance and the blood sugar level.

In performing the functions listed above, some of the hormones are essential to life (adrenal cortical hormones) and others are not (gonadal hormones). Hormones may act for short or long periods of time.

There are certain basic principles to be kept in mind, so far as functions of hormones are concerned. The function of one affects the functions of others, in that one may reinforce another, and 2 or more may act in sequence. One hormone may sensitize tissues to the action of another.

The production of each hormone is regulated in a particular way; for example, by the level of the blood sugar (insulin), by the level of sodium chloride in the blood (antidiuretic hormone), by the level of blood calcium (parathormone), by the nervous system (epinephrine) or by the blood level of a hormone from another gland. An example of the last is a trophic or regulatory hormone, such as the thyrotrophic hormone of the anterior lobe of the pituitary which regulates the production of thyroxin by the thyroid gland. The glands whose activities are regulated by trophic hormones are called *target organs*. The blood level of a hormone from a target gland reciprocally controls the production of the corresponding trophic hormone.

The role of the anterior lobe of the pituitary in the production of trophic hormones reminds one of the role of a superintendent of nurses in a hospital. The superintendent makes out a schedule for each floor, assigning the number of nurses, maids, orderlies, and so on. In order to do this efficiently, she must receive daily reports from each floor. Each nurse, maid and orderly on the floor has particular tasks to do.

In order to have mental and physical health and to preserve homeostasis, a delicate and intricate balance must be maintained in the endocrine system. Too little secretion by any one gland not only leaves its own particular function undone but also affects the functions of other hormones. Too much secretion by any one gland, such as occurs in adenomata or tumors of glands, likewise disturbs its own function and those of other hormones. This applies to all the components of the endocrine system, which comprises the pituitary (also called *hypophysis cerebri*), the thyroid, the parathyroids, the adrenals, the gonads, the islands of Langerhans of the pancreas and the mucosa of the stomach and the duodenum, which produces several hormones.

METHODS OF STUDY

Various methods of study have been used in determining the functions of the endocrine glands. (1) The histology of the gland, or microscopic structure under different conditions, contributes to knowledge of the gland. (2) The effects of lack of a particular hormone are determined by removal of the gland in animals, by depression of its secretion by x-rays or radioactivity and by observation of patients in which spontaneous hypofunction of the gland in question occurs. (3) Information is gained by administration of a hormone to normal individuals, to normal animals and to patients or animals who lack it. (4) Information is gained also by chemical analyses of glands, blood, urine and by the synthesis or manufacture of hormones.

THE PITUITARY GLAND

GENERAL DESCRIPTION

The pituitary gland lies at the base of the brain (Fig. 163) attached to the floor of the third ventricle, behind the optic chiasm, in the sella turcica of the sphenoid bone. It is surrounded by a capsule of fibrous connective tissue.

The pituitary gland is composed of 2 lobes: anterior and posterior.

The anterior lobe comprises 3 subdivisions: pars distalis, pars tuberalis and pars intermedia, all of which arise from the roof of the mouth.

The posterior lobe, which is derived from the nervous system, together with the tuber cinereum (an area of gray matter that extends from the optic chiasm to the mammillary bodies and forms part of the floor of the third ventricle) and the infundibulum (stalk from tuber cinereum to posterior lobe), comprises the neurohypophysis.

Blood is supplied to the pituitary gland by branches from the internal carotid arteries and from the circle of Willis. The veins that drain the gland empty into the cranial venous sinuses.

Nerves pass to the anterior lobe from the carotid plexus, which, in turn, is composed of nerve fibers from the superior cervical ganglion of the lateral chain of thoracolumbar ganglia. The posterior lobe receives millions of nerve fibers from the hypothalamus.

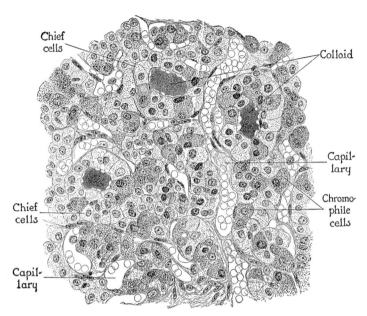

Chief cells

Colloid

Capillary

Chromophile cells

Chief cells

Capillary

FIG. 385. Section of the anterior lobe of the pituitary gland. ×250.

STRUCTURE

The anterior lobe is composed of thick, irregular branching cords of epithelial cells supported by delicate reticular fibers. Between the cords of cells there are wide vascular channels called *sinusoids*, lined with reticuloendothelial cells, rather than with ordinary endothelium.

There are 3 types of cells (chromophobes, eosinophilic cells, basophilic cells) with respect to staining reactions, and it is thought that the cells change from one type to another at times. In the pars intermedia of the anterior lobe there are some follicles (secretory sacs) that contain a material called *colloid*. A section of the anterior lobe is shown in Figure 385.

The posterior lobe is composed of innumerable nerve fibers and modified neuroglia cells called *pituicytes*.

HORMONES AND THEIR FUNCTIONS

Anterior Lobe. There are at least 6 hormones produced by the anterior lobe of the pituitary: growth hormone, follicle-stimulating hormone, luteinizing hormone (female) or interstitial-cell stimulating hormone (male), thyrotrophic hormone, adrenocorticotrophic hormone and lactogenic or luteotrophic hormone. A seventh hormone, intermedin, produced by the pars intermedia of the anterior lobe, is of no importance in man but causes an expansion of pigment-containing cells or melanophores in frogs and undoubtedly plays a part in protective coloration.

THE GROWTH HORMONE is concerned with the growth of bones, viscera and muscles. It causes a retention of nitrogen, which is used in building body protein. It controls the growth of bones by acting on the cartilage cells in the epiphyseal disks of the long bones.

THE FOLLICLE-STIMULATING HORMONE (FSH) is one of the gonadotrophic hormones. It acts on the ovaries to stimulate development of ovarian follicles and the production of follicular hormone which is called *estrogen*. In the male, this gonadotrophic hormone also is called *FSH*. It stimulates spermatogenesis and the development of the seminiferous tubules (p. 758).

THE LUTEINIZING HORMONE (LH) is a second gonadotrophic hormone that stimulates the formation of the corpora lutea of the ovaries and the production of *progesterone* (corpus luteal hormone). In the male, this gonadotrophic hormone is called the *interstitial-cell stimulating* hormone (ICSH). It stimulates the production of the male hormone, *testosterone,* by the interstitial cells of the testes (p. 759).

One of the hormones produced by the placenta during pregnancy performs functions like LH and is called the *anterior-pituitarylike* (APL) hormone (p. 743).

THYROTROPHIC HORMONE stimuates the growth and the secretory activity of the thyroid gland. It is thought to be produced in larger amounts than normal in exophthalmic goiter (p. 725).

THE ADRENOCORTICOTROPHIC HORMONE (ACTH) controls the growth and the secretory activity of the adrenal cortices.

THE LACTOGENIC OR LUTEOTROPHIC HORMONE controls the production of milk by the mammary glands after they have been acted upon by estrogen and progesterone (p. 804). This hormone is concerned, also, with the secretion of estrogen and progesterone by the ovaries.

The factors that control the production of the growth hormone and the lactogenic or luteotrophic hormone by the anterior lobe of the pituitary gland are unknown at present. The production of the gonadotrophic, the thyrotrophic and the adrenocorticotrophic hormones is influenced by the blood levels of estrogen, progesterone, thyroxin and adrenal cortical hormones, respectively.

In summary, the functions of the hormones of the anterior lobe of the pituitary gland are to control the growth of all parts of the body, to control the growth and the production of internal secretions of the gonads, the thyroid, the adrenal cortex and the secretion of milk by prepared mammary glands. The anterior lobe of the pituitary gland is called the *master gland*, since it controls the activity of several other glands.

Posterior Lobe. There are 3 hormones produced by the posterior lobe of the pituitary gland: pitressin, antidiuretic hormone and pitocin. The 3 hormones are present in the extract of the posterior lobe in a mixture called *pituitrin.*

PITRESSIN stimulates the smooth muscle of the blood vessels, including the coronaries, and that of the wall of the alimentary tube.

THE ANTIDIURETIC HORMONE (ADH), which has not been separated from pitressin in commercial preparations, stimulates the reabsorption of water by the cells of the distal convoluted tubules of the kidneys. Its production is under nervous control. It is probable that there are osmoreceptors in the hypothalamus that are sensitive to the concentration of sodium chloride in the plasma. When the concentration of sodium chloride is high in the plasma, impulses from the osmoreceptors stimulate an increased production of ADH by the secretory cells of the posterior lobe of the pituitary gland. This increases the reabsorption of water by the cells of the tubules and dilutes the plasma. In this way, it serves to lower the concentration of sodium chloride. This hormone also promotes the excretion of sodium chloride by the kidneys.

PITOCIN stimulates the contraction of uterine muscle.

In summary, the functions of the hormones of the posterior lobe of the pituitary gland are to influence water balance by controlling the reabsorption of water in the distal convoluted tubules of the kidneys, to influence salt balance by promoting excretion of sodium chloride and to influence the activity of uterine muscle and possibly other smooth muscle. Pitressin probably plays no part in the daily maintenance of arterial blood pressure despite its action on smooth muscle of the arterioles.

PATHOLOGY

Hypofunction of the Anterior Lobe. If there is hypofunction of the anterior lobe in young children, there is failure to grow (dwarfism). The simultaneous lack of the trophic hormones leads to a failure of growth and secretory activity of the thyroid, the cortex of the adrenal glands and the gonads. It is impossible to have hypofunction of the anterior lobe of the pituitary gland alone,

FIG. 386. Effects of pituitary disease, showing a pituitary giant and dwarf; the woman is of normal height. (Boyd, William: An Introduction to Medical Science, ed. 4, Philadelphia, Lea & Febiger)

since other glands are involved, as well. This is the Lorain-Levi type of dwarfism, in which the individuals remain like children throughout life, but there is no mental retardation.

Sometimes there is atrophy of the anterior lobe in adult women as a result of postpartum (after delivery) occlusion of blood vessels that supply the pituitary gland. All of the hormones of the anterior lobe are decreased or absent. The condition is called *Simmonds' disease*. It is characterized by premature senility, with weakness, emaciation, mental lethargy, somnolence and skin changes characteristic of old age, together with loss of teeth, pubic hair and axillary hair. It is a rapid deterioration in both physical and mental life.

Hyperfunction of the Anterior Lobe of the Pituitary Gland. This occurs when there is a tumor or adenoma of the anterior lobe. The growth hormone is produced in more than normal amounts. If this condition begins before puberty, gigantism results, in which there is overgrowth of the whole body. Such individuals may grow to be more than 8 ft. tall (Fig. 386).

If hyperfunction of the anterior lobe occurs after the epiphyses of the long bones have closed, only the face, the hands and the feet are affected, and these become larger. The condition is called *acromegaly* (Fig. 387). The lower jaw becomes prominent, and

FIG. 387. Acromegaly, showing protrusion of lower jaw, heavy lips and "spade" hands. (Karsner, H. T.: Human Pathology, ed. 7, Philadelphia, Lippincott)

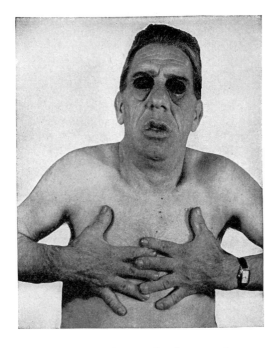

the lower teeth separate; as the face enlarges the features become coarser. The skin is greasy and moist, and pigmentation may be increased. Headaches due to increased intracranial pressure, and even visual disturbances due to pressure on the optic chiasm, may occur.

Hypofunction of the Posterior Lobe. The symptoms noted in this condition are due to lack of the antidiuretic hormone. There is an output of from 10 to 30 L. of urine per day. The urine is very dilute and contains no sugar. This fact is responsible for the name "diabetes insipidus." There is great thirst, and since the water that is taken is usually below body temperature, and urine is excreted at body temperature, much heat is lost, and the body temperature falls. This is an example of unusual loss of body heat by way of excreta.

Hyperfunction of the posterior lobe is not recognized clinically.

Hypofunction of Both Anterior and Posterior Lobes. When there is hypofunction of both lobes, the condition that follows is called *dystrophy adiposo genitalis* or *Fröhlich's syndrome.* The outstanding characteristics are obesity of the feminine type of distribution (mammary glands, buttocks and thighs) and sexual infantilism.

If the condition occurs before puberty, dwarfism results. If it occurs after puberty, in a male patient, he becomes effeminate and lacks the male secondary sexual characteristics. In a female the obesity is marked, and the patient may weigh more than 300 pounds. There is usually polyuria and a high carbohydrate tolerance. The double lesions are in (1) the anterior lobe of the pitui-

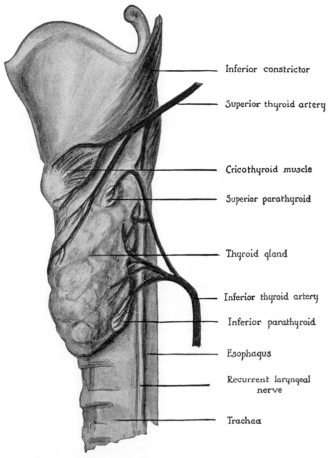

Inferior constrictor

Superior thyroid artery

Cricothyroid muscle

Superior parathyroid

Thyroid gland

Inferior thyroid artery

Inferior parathyroid

Esophagus

Recurrent laryngeal nerve

Trachea

FIG. 388. Thyroid and parathyroid glands.

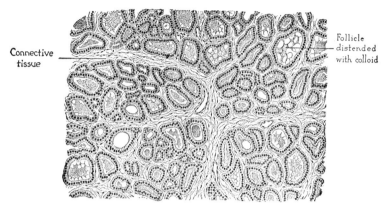

Connective tissue

Follicle distended with colloid

FIG. 389. Section of the thyroid gland. The follicles, which are lined with simple cuboidal epithelium, show varying degrees of distention with colloid material. ×100.

tary and (2) either the posterior lobe of the pituitary or the hypothalamus.

THE THYROID GLAND

GENERAL DESCRIPTION

The thyroid gland lies in the anterior middle portion of the neck, just below the larynx, as shown in Figure 388. It consists of 2 lateral lobes united by a strip called the *isthmus*. It is covered by a capsule that consists of connective tissue and is part of the deep fascia of the neck. Partitions from the capsule extend into the gland as septa and divide it into lobules.

The thyroid gland is supplied with blood through branches of the external carotid and either the subclavian or its thyrocervical trunk. The veins that drain the thyroid gland empty into the internal jugular or the innominate veins. The blood supply is very abundant.

The thyroid gland receives nerves from the lateral chain of sympathetic ganglia and twigs from the vagus and the glossopharyngeal nerves.

The thyroid gland originates as an outgrowth from the pharynx.

STRUCTURE

The thyroid gland is composed of follicles (sacs), each of which is formed normally by a single layer of cuboidal epithelial cells, bound together by connective tissue. The follicles contain a homogeneous material called *colloid*. The epithelium varies with the condition of the gland; it may change from a low cuboidal to a high columnar as the gland becomes more active. The microscopic structure is shown in Figure 389.

HORMONE AND ITS FUNCTIONS

The hormone produced by the thyroid gland is called *thyroxin;* it contains about 65 per cent iodine. The thyroid gland takes up iodide from the food, converts it to organic iodine which is then combined with protein to form thyroglobulin.

Thyroglobulin is stored as colloid in the follicles; the molecules are very large and cannot enter the blood in this form. They are split by a proteolytic enzyme into thyroxin which enters the blood and is carried combined with proteins of the plasma to all parts of the body. Consequently, an estimation of the "protein-bound iodine" of the plasma is a measure of the amount of thyroxin in the blood.

The production of thyroxin is controlled by the thyrotrophic hormone of the anterior lobe of the pituitary gland. There is a reciprocal relationship between the level of thyroxin in the blood and the production of thyrotrophic hormone by the anterior lobe. For example, a high concentration of thyroxin in the blood inhibits the production of thyrotrophic hormone. The thyrotrophic hormone stimulates growth of the follicular cells and also activates the enzyme in the stored colloid so that more thyroxin becomes available to enter the blood.

Thyroxin performs many functions: (1) It regulates the rate of oxidation and heat production in all cells of the body and varies the rate of metabolism to meet the physiologic needs. (2) It is concerned with growth and differentiation of organs. (3) It plays a part in mental development. (4) Its presence is essential to the attainment of sexual maturity. (5) It plays some part in the distribution and the exchange of water, salts and protein. (6) It influences the production of glucose from amino acids (gluconeogenesis). (7) It decreases the amounts of fatty acids, cholesterol and phospholipids in plasma and thus is concerned with the mobilization of fats.

PATHOLOGY

Iodine Deficiency. If the iodine intake is insufficient, a simple or "colloid goiter" occurs. This is called *adolescent goiter* also, since commonly it is noted at the age of puberty in girls. The gland is enlarged due to an increase in the number and the size of epithelial cells, but there is not an increased amount of colloid in the follicles. Usually the gland, because of its increased size, makes enough thyroxin so there are no symptoms of hypofunction, and the only evidence of pathology is the enlargement of the gland. In some individuals the gland may be so large that it exerts pressure on the trachea and leads to choking sensations.

Hypofunction of the Thyroid Gland. When the thyroid gland is underactive in an infant, a condition called *cretinism* develops. The first signs of cretinism appear at about 6 months of age, when it is noted that both the mental and physical development are slow. Thereafter the infant does not sit up, walk and talk at the usual age. The mental development is so retarded that the child may become an idiot. The physical growth is so retarded that the child remains a dwarf.

The teeth are poorly developed, and ossification of bones is delayed. The tongue is large and protrudes from the mouth. The skin is thickened and dry. There is poor tone in the skeletal muscles. The secondary sexual characteristics do not develop. The body temperature is low, the blood pressure low, the heart rate slow, and the basal metabolic rate is about 25 per cent below the normal range. A typical cretin is shown in Figure 390.

When pronounced hypofunction of the thyroid gland appears in an adult the condition is called *myxedema*. A myxedematous patient undergoes a complete change of personality and mental ability and becomes slow, lethargic and stupid. The hair falls out, and the skin becomes thick and dry. Obesity is common. The heart dilates, but there is no evidence of cardiac failure, and digitalis therapy has no effect on cardiac function. The cholesterol of the blood is elevated, and the basal metabolic rate is low.

A mild state of hypothyroidism may exist. In this, the individual is obese and sluggish, and there may be amenorrhea, with sterility. It is difficult to hold the attention of such an individual who seems unable to concentrate on any phase of mental activity.

Hyperfunction of the Thyroid Gland. Hyperthyroidism is seen in 2 forms: exophthalmic goiter (Graves's disease) and adenomatous goiter with hyperthyroidism. In exophthalmic goiter apparently there is too much thyrotrophic hormone produced with overactivity of the thyroid gland secondarily. The symptoms and signs are: a moderate or no enlargement of the thyroid gland, polyphagia (increased appetite) and diarrhea with weight loss, very high basal metabolic rate (+100 per cent), the skin is flushed and moist (a

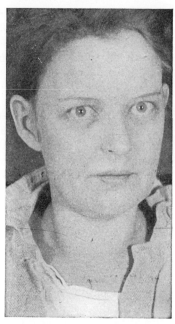

Fig. 390. (*Left*) Cretinism. At the time the photograph was taken, the patient was 42 years of age, weighed 88 pounds and was 45 inches tall. The I.Q. was 12. She was slow in development; she walked at 6 years. The skin was dry and the hair dry and coarse; the nose was flat, tongue large and abdomen prominent. The patient died 4 months after the photograph was taken; no thyroid tissue could be found. (Minnesota School for the Feeble Minded)

Fig. 391 (*Right*) Exophthalmic goiter. The patient's thyroid was diffusely enlarged; hyperthyroidism had been present for about 4 years. Exophthalmos and increased lid space are noted. The pulse rate is 134; the left ventricle is enlarged; the basal metabolic rate is plus 69 per cent. (Minneapolis General Hospital)

means of increasing heat loss to keep pace with heat production and maintain a normal temperature), tachycardia and palpitation (consciousness of heart's beating), a high concentration of protein-bound iodine and low cholesterol in the blood and marked nervousness with frequent emotional disturbances.

The eye signs are: a widening of the space between the lids, so that the white of the eye can be seen above and below the iris (Fig. 391), and the eyes protrude. This last sign is responsible for the name "exophthalmic" goiter.

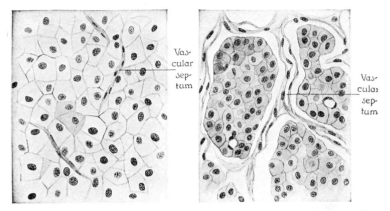

Vas-
cular
sep-
tum

Vas-
cular
sep-
tum

FIG. 392. Section of the parathyroid glands. On the left, the cells are arranged in uniform masses; on the right, the cells are arranged in lobules, separated by vascular septa. ×200.

In the adenomatous type of hyperthyroidism, an excess of thyroxin is produced. The thyroid gland in this condition is usually enlarged for many years before any signs of hyperthyroidism are evident. The basal metabolic rate is not as high as in the exophthalmic type of goiter, and the eyes are normal. The other signs and symptoms of hyperthyroidism are present.

THE PARATHYROID GLANDS

GENERAL DESCRIPTION

The parathyroid glands are located on the posterior surface of the thyroid gland (Fig. 388). They lie beneath the capsule and actually may be embedded in the substance of the thyroid gland. Usually there are 4 parathyroid glands.

The parathyroid glands receive blood by way of branches of the external carotid, the subclavian or the thyrocervical trunk, and the veins drain into the internal jugular or innominate veins.

The nerve supply is from the vagus and the glossopharyngeal nerves.

The parathyroid glands originate from the pharynx.

Structure. The cells of the parathyroid glands are arranged in clumps or irregular cords with large capillaries between. There are 2 types of cells present, and it is thought that the chief cells secrete the hormone. The microscopic structure is shown in Figure 392.

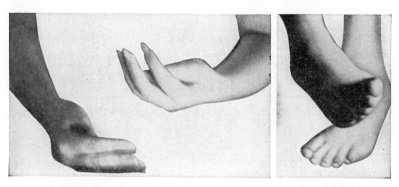

FIG. 393. The hands and feet of a patient with tetany, showing the typical position of the hands (*main d'accoucheur*) and the feet assumed in carpopedal spasm. (Grollman, Arthur: Essentials of Endocrinology, ed. 2, Philadelphia, Lippincott)

HORMONE AND ITS FUNCTIONS

The hormone produced by the parathyroid glands is called *parathormone*. The amount produced is regulated by the level of the blood calcium.

Parathormone is concerned with the regulation of calcium and phosphorus metabolism; it controls the level of calcium and inorganic phosphorus in the blood. The balance between these elements in the diet, the bones and the excreta must be maintained. It is not known whether this hormone acts on the cells of the bone (osteoclasts) to destroy bone and free calcium, or whether it acts on the tubular cells of the kidney in which it may regulate the excretion of phosphates.

PATHOLOGY

Hypofunction of the Parathyroid Glands. The most striking change is noted in the nervous system, where there is an increased excitability of the peripheral nerves, the ganglia and the central nervous system. This, in turn, affects the skeletal muscles, in which twitching, spasms and convulsions occur. The condition is called *tetany*, and it exhibits, in addition to the above, numbness and tingling of the extremities, stiffness in the hands, the feet and the hips, cramps of the extremities, the characteristic carpopedal spasm (Fig. 393) and spasm of the laryngeal muscles, which may lead to death by asphyxiation.

In tetany, the ionized calcium in the blood is below the normal level, and this is responsible for the change in excitability of the nervous system. The inorganic phosphate in the blood is higher than usual. The amount of phosphate in the urine is decreased. There may be disturbances in the gastro-intestinal tract, such as vomiting and bloody diarrhea. The body temperature is elevated, due to the increased activity of the skeletal muscles with no corresponding increase in heat loss. This condition may follow removal of parathyroids by mistake during thyroidectomy for hyperthyroidism.

Hyperfunction of the Parathyroid Glands. The excretion of phosphates in the urine is increased and leads to a decrease in the amount in the plasma. The calcium level in the blood is high, and an increased amount of calcium is excreted by the kidneys. In fact, the concentration of calcium is so high in the urine that kidney stones are of frequent occurrence. The high level of calcium in the blood leads to hypotonicity of the skeletal muscles which are unusually pliable and exceedingly weak.

There may or may not be bone disease. If there is bone disease, spontaneous fractures are frequent, the teeth fall out, and bone deformities occur. The bones may show cysts filled with fluid (osteitis fibrosa cystica).

ADRENAL GLANDS (SUPRARENAL)

GENERAL DESCRIPTION

The adrenal glands are located above the kidneys. Figures 8 and 362 show the location of these glands. Each consists of an outer portion called the *cortex* and an inner portion called the *medulla.*

The blood supply to the adrenal glands is very abundant. They receive blood by way of branches from the inferior phrenic (superior suprarenal), the aorta (middle suprarenal) and the renal (inferior suprarenal) arteries. The blood is collected into the suprarenal veins; the right empties into the inferior vena cava, and the left into the renal vein.

The nerve supply consists of preganglionic fibers from the thoracolumbar division by way of the splanchnic nerves and also twigs from the vagus and the phrenic nerves.

The cortex arises from mesoderm, and the medulla has the same origin as the ganglia of the thoracolumbar division of the nervous system.

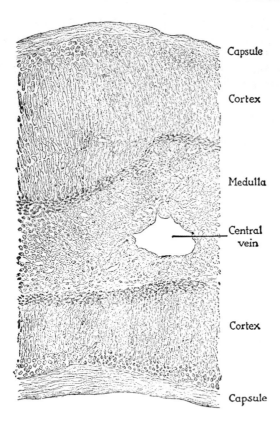

Capsule

Cortex

Medulla

Central
vein

Cortex

Capsule

Fig. 394. Section of the suprarenal gland, including the entire thickness of the organ. The general arrangement of the cortex and medulla is shown. ×27.

STRUCTURE

The cells of the adrenal cortex are arranged in 3 layers which differ in relation to the blood vessels.

In the **outer layer** (zona glomerulosa) the free edge of each cell adjoins a capillary.

In the **middle layer** (zona fasciculata) the cells lie in straight cords between lines of straight capillaries.

In the **inner layer** (zona reticularis) the cells form networks with sinusoids between them.

The cells of the medulla are arranged in groups; they are in contact on all sides with sinusoidal venules. The microscopic structure of the adrenal gland is illustrated in Figure 394.

HORMONES AND THEIR FUNCTION

The adrenal cortex produces 3 types of hormones, and all are steroid in nature.

SALT AND WATER HORMONES. Aldosterone represents the first type of adrenal cortical hormones. It acts on the cells of the renal tubules and plays an essential role in the reabsorption of water and sodium chloride and in the elimination of potassium chloride. Synthetic desoxycorticosterone acts in the same manner. Thus, aldosterone is important in mineral and water metabolism.

SUGAR HORMONES. The second group of hormones is called the *sugar* hormones, or the corticosterone group (in which there is an oxygen on the eleventh carbon atom). Cortisone is a member of this group. This group is concerned with the preservation of carbohydrate reserves of the body. They stimulate gluconeogenesis (production of new glucose, that is, from a noncarbohydrate source) from amino acids. They also stimulate the deposition of glycogen in the liver and mobilize fat from depots and stimulate its oxidation in the liver.

The corticosterone group also is involved in the body's response to stress. In some way the members of this group reduce the rate at which the cells that build intercellular substances (fibroblasts, osteoblasts and chondroblasts) proliferate. As a result, both the quantity and the quality of intercellular substance that such cells make and keep in repair are affected.

During stress there is a reduction in the size of the thymus and the spleen and in lymphatic tissue, in general, and also a reduction in the rate of mitosis in lymphatic tissue. The eosinophils in the circulating blood are decreased in number.

In conditions of stress, the cortical hormones are used more rapidly, and this lowers the blood level so more ACTH is produced. There is also an increased output of epinephrine during stress, and this, in turn, stimulates the production of more ACTH (in a manner unknown at present). The function of these hormones and their roles in conditions of stress are the source of much speculation at present.

GONADAL-LIKE HORMONES. The members of the third group of adrenal cortical hormones are identical with the gonadal hormones and are represented by adrenosterone. Both male (testosterone) and female (estrogen and progesterone) are produced by the adrenal cortex. The amount of the male hormone is much greater than the amount of the female hormones. These hormones increase the retention of nitrogen and lead to increase in growth of tissues and muscular vigor. Their normal function in the human body is not yet evident.

Summary of the Functions of the Adrenal Cortical Hormones. These hormones are concerned with the regulation of mineral metabolism in which they maintain homeostasis, despite wide fluctuations in intake.

They help to preserve the carbohydrate reserves of the body by stimulating gluconeogenesis from amino acids and the deposition of glycogen in the liver. In some way, through an influence on lymphatic tissue, they play a role in the response of the body to stress.

The adrenal cortical hormones are essential to life. One can meet the demands of everyday living if the adrenal cortical hormones are produced in normal amounts. Otherwise, one becomes rather inflexible and cannot withstand stress. This shows up as an inability (1) to adjust to varying intakes of water and salt, (2) to react normally to infections and (3) to respond normally to exercise, exposure to cold and mild degrees of hypoglycemia.

The adrenal medulla produces epinephrine and nor-epinephrine and thereby constitutes an important link between the nervous system and the endocrine system. The secretory activity of the cells of the adrenal medulla is under the control of the thoracolumbar division of the autonomic nervous system.

EPINEPHRINE is believed to be produced especially during such emergencies as emotional crises, hypoglycemia, mild hypoxia and hypotension. It induces constriction of arterioles (except those of the skeletal muscles and heart muscle); it increases the rate and the force of the heart beat. It dilates the bronchioles by relaxing the smooth muscle in their walls. It increases the blood sugar by increasing the breakdown of glycogen in the liver. In general, the effects are the same as stimulation of the thoracolumbar division of the autonomic nervous system, and the function of epinephrine is to reinforce these activities and prolong them. In addition, it stimulates the production of ACTH, which, in turn, stimulates the production of adrenal cortical hormones. Epinephrine as it appears on the market is really a combination of epinephrine and nor-epinephrine; therefore, the effects ascribed above to epinephrine are really due to a mixture of the 2 hormones.

PATHOLOGY

Hypofunction of the adrenal cortex leads to a condition known as *Addison's disease.* This is characterized by many signs

and symptoms: (1) gastro-intestinal disturbances, which are mani-
fested as nausea, vomiting and diarrhea; (2) alterations in salt and
water balance, resulting in a fall in plasma sodium, chloride and
bicarbonate, with a rise in potassium; (3) alterations in the circulatory system, which lead to a decrease in plasma volume with fall
in blood pressure and secondary impairment of kidney function
(the last leads to oliguria and accumulation of nitrogenous waste
in the blood); (4) a disturbance in carbohydrate metabolism is
indicated by a low blood sugar, decrease in gluconeogenesis and
low liver glycogen; (5) there is pigmentation of the skin (the color
varies in different patients from yellow to black, and the change
is called *bronzing* of the skin); (6) the patient is acutely prostrated
by any minor infection and has no capacity to adapt to even minor
changes in either the external or the internal environments; in other
words, there is no ability to withstand any form of stress. Muscle
weakness or asthenia is marked.

Hyperfunction of the Adrenal Cortex. Tumors of the adrenal
cortex lead to an increased production of hormones that resemble
sex hormones. If the tumor appears in a young child, there is
somatic and sexual precocity. The arms and the legs are short,
the trunk is elongated, the muscles bulge, the shoulders are broad,
and the hips are narrow. Full sexual development may occur in
children of 2 to 4 years of age. If an adrenal cortical tumor appears in an adult woman, she undergoes masculinization, with
change in voice, growth of hair and muscularity.

There is a condition called *Cushing's syndrome* that is characterized by an excessive production of the corticosterone type of
hormones. In this there is wasting and weakness of the muscles
of the limbs, with obesity of the face, the neck and the trunk. The
eye slits are narrow, and the mouth is fishlike. The skin is thin,
and the growth of body hair is profuse. The bones become porous.
There are some signs of diabetes mellitus, hypertension and edema.
The accessory reproductive organs undergo atrophy.

Hypofunction of the medullae of the adrenal glands is not
recognized clinically.

Hyperfunction of the medullae of the adrenal glands accompanies the presence of tumors known as *pheochromocytomata.*
There are 2 types of disorder.

In the first, there are recurrent attacks of extreme, but transient,
hypertension, due to periodic release of large amounts of the hormone epinephrine. The systolic blood pressure rises above 300
mm. Hg during such attacks.

In the second type of disorder there is sustained hypertension, and the condition is like malignant hypertension. The individual is in very poor general health. There is loss of weight and a marked increase in the basal metabolic rate.

GONADAL HORMONES

GENERAL DESCRIPTION

The cells that produce the gonadal hormones are in the ovaries (p. 765) and the testes (p. 755). The ovaries are supplied with blood by way of the ovarian artery and branches from the uterine arteries. The testes are supplied by the spermatic arteries. The veins empty into the inferior vena cava on the right and into the renal vein on the left side. The nerve supply is derived from both divisions of the autonomic system. The gonads develop from mesoderm.

The structure of growing ovarian follicles and corpora lutea is described on page 765. The structure of the testes is described on page 758.

HORMONES AND THEIR FUNCTIONS

The ovaries produce ova and 2 hormones: estrogen or follicular hormone and progesterone or corpus luteal hormone.

ESTROGEN is concerned with the development of the secondary sexual characteristics at the age of puberty. It also induces changes (1) in the uterine mucosa for the reception of the fertilized ovum (p. 775), (2) in the mammary glands and (3) in the mucosa of the vagina.

The production of estrogen is controlled by the follicle-stimulating hormone of the anterior lobe of the pituitary gland.

PROGESTERONE is produced by the cells of the corpus luteum, under the control of the luteinizing and luteotrophic hormones of the anterior lobe of the pituitary gland. Progesterone prepares the uterus for implantation of the fertilized ovum and the nourishment and the development of the embryo in the early stages of its growth. It supplements the action of estrogen on the mammary glands.

IN SUMMARY, the ovarian hormones are responsible for the development of the secondary sexual characteristics, the reception, the implantation and the early nourishment of the fertilized ovum (if the ovum is not fertilized, menstruation occurs) and the secretion of milk by the mammary glands. Much information of value regarding these hormones has been derived by a study of estrus cycles of lower animals.

The interstitial cells of the testes of vertebrates produce an

internal secretion called *testosterone*. The production of this hormone is under the control of the ICSH of the anterior lobe of the
pituitary gland. Testosterone is responsible for the development of
the secondary sexual characterisitics of the male and for the development and the maintenance of the accessory organs of reproduction.

PATHOLOGY

Hypofunction of the Ovaries. If the ovaries are removed before puberty, or if the anterior lobe of the pituitary gland is underactive, the secondary sexual characteristics fail to develop at the
age of puberty. The menstrual cycles never are established. If
the ovaries are removed after the age of puberty, the uterus, the
vagina and the external genitalia undergo atrophy.

Hypofunction of the Testes. If the testes are removed before
puberty, or if the gonadotrophic hormones of the anterior lobe of
the pituitary gland are lacking, the secondary sexual characteristics
fail to develop. The voice remains high-pitched, and there is no
growth of hair on the face and the trunk. There is a deposit of fat
around the hips and in the pectoral and the gluteal regions. The
epiphyses close late; consequently, the individual is tall. The legs
are disproportionately long in comparison with the trunk. The
accessory reproductive organs remain small, and the individual is
sterile, which means that reproduction is impossible.

If the testes are removed after puberty, there is atrophy of the
accessory reproductive organs.

Hyperfunction of the gonads is not recognized clinically.

ISLET CELLS OF THE PANCREAS

GENERAL DESCRIPTION

The pancreas is located in the epigastrium and the left hypochondrium (Figs. 7, 325 and 350), behind the stomach and in
contact with the posterior abdominal wall. It consists of a head,
a body and a tail and extends from the duodenum to the spleen.

The pancreas performs a dual function; it produces an external
secretion (pancreatic juice, p. 632) and 2 internal secretions (insulin and glucagon). Insulin is produced by the beta cells, and
glucagon is produced by the alpha cells of the islands of
Langerhans.

The pancreas receives blood by way of branches from the splenic,
the superior mesenteric and the hepatic arteries. The blood from

the pancreas is drained into the splenic and the superior mesenteric veins and then enters the portal vein. The nerve supply is derived from both divisions of the autonomic system.

The pancreas originates from the duodenum.

Structure. The islet cells are groups of pale cells, separated from the surrounding acinar or alveolar cells by thin reticular membranes. There are between 20,000 and 1,750,000 islands in the human pancreas. Two types of cells are noted in the islands—alpha and beta. A section of pancreatic tissue is shown in Figure 395.

HORMONES AND THEIR FUNCTIONS

Glucagon (alpha cells) causes a breakdown of liver glycogen, with an increase in blood sugar. It is present in all preparations of insulin, and its effects are noted for only about 10 minutes after the injection of insulin. It is a glucose mobilizer.

Insulin. The better-known hormone insulin is produced by the beta cells, and its production is controlled essentially by the level of glucose in the blood. The vagus nerves are thought to be partly responsible for the production of insulin.

Insulin performs many functions. It lowers the blood sugar by (1) increasing the oxidation of glucose by the tissues, (2) stimulating the formation and the storage of glycogen in the liver, (3)

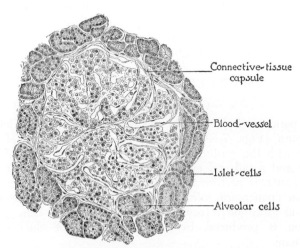

FIG. 395. Section of the pancreas, showing details of the islands of Langerhans. ×190.

decreasing gluconeogenesis from amino acids and (4) stimulating the formation of fat from glucose.

The effects of insulin are antagonized by several hormones: (1) *epinephrine* stimulates the breakdown of glycogen in the liver and produces hyperglycemia; (2) *adrenal cortical hormones* (corticosterone group) stimulate gluconeogenesis; and (3) *thyroxin* stimulates gluconeogenesis. The anterior lobe of the pituitary gland probably antagonizes the effects of insulin indirectly by stimulating the production of adrenal cortical hormones and thyroxin.

Pathology

Hypofunction of the Islet Cells (Beta Cells). Hypofunction of the beta cells of the islands of Langerhans leads to the condition known as *diabetes mellitus.* This has a high incidence and requires medical care for a long time. It is frequent in late middle life, occurs more often in women than in men and is influenced by heredity and obesity. It is transmitted as a mendelian recessive character. Nine out of every 10 adults who develop diabetes mellitus are obese.

Many Disturbances in Metabolism Occur in Diabetes Mellitus. *Carbohydrate.* So far as carbohydrate metabolism is concerned, there is impaired oxidation of glucose by tissues, and the blood sugar rises, and sugar appears in the urine. Glycogen is not formed and stored in the liver normally. No glucose is converted to fat and stored in the fat depots.

Protein metabolism is disturbed in that gluconeogenesis is increased, and, since glucose is not utilized normally, the glucose formed from amino acids also is lost in the urine.

Fat metabolism is disturbed. The glycerol portion is converted to glucose and lost in the urine. An excessive amount of fatty acids is burned, and the blood and the urine are flooded with acetone bodies, which means that ketosis is present.

The degree of ketosis is a particularly critical factor in the survival of untreated diabetics. Since acetone bodies are carried out in the urine as sodium salts, the alkaline reserve is depleted, and acidosis supervenes. When a person loses sodium he loses water also, and this leads to dehydration. Dehydration, in turn, leads to circulatory impairment and failure of kidney function.

In addition to the hyperglycemia, the glycosuria, the ketosis, the acidosis and the dehydration, the individual is always thirsty (polydipsia) and always hungry (polyphagia).

The skin of the untreated diabetic is in poor condition, and injuries heal slowly and with difficulty. Ulcers are common, and gangrene may necessitate amputation of some of the toes. A diabetic ulcer, with gangrene of a toe, is illustrated in Figure 396.

The worst complication in diabetes mellitus is the change in the walls of arteries (arteriosclerosis) that is associated with the disturbance in fat metabolism. The arterial change progresses despite proper treatment of the diabetes mellitus and may produce disastrous results in the eyes (cataract), the kidneys, the extremities, the heart and the brain.

Death of untreated diabetics usually is due to diabetic coma with severe ketosis and acidosis.

Hyperfunction of the beta cells is due to an adenoma or tumor. It is characterized by attacks of weakness, profuse perspiration and trembling. The attacks occur when meals are delayed, or when unusual exertion is undertaken. In the early stages, the symptoms are relieved by the taking of food or sugar.

Before leaving the subject of internal secretions we wish to point out that the thymus and the pineal body are not glands of internal secretion. The placental hormones are discussed on page 743. It is advisable for the student to review the gastro-intestinal hormones.

PRACTICAL CONSIDERATIONS

PITUITARY GLAND

Tumors of the pituitary gland cause headaches due to increased intracranial pressure. When the gland is enlarged it is quite likely

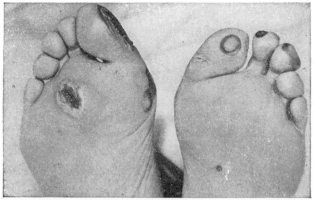

FIG. 396. Gangrene of the feet in untreated diabetes mellitus. (Williams, J. R.: North Carolina M. J. 4:129)

to exert pressure on the optic chiasm and produce disturbances of vision.

ACTH is used for the treatment of rheumatoid arthritis. It stimulates the production of the hormones of the adrenal cortex. It leads to temporary improvement, but there are likely to be undesirable effects, since the production of all types of adrenal cortical hormones is stimulated, which means that there may be an inversion of secondary sexual characteristics and hypertension.

Pregnancy Tests. Both of the gonadotrophic hormones are present in the blood and the urine of women. During pregnancy, there is an increase in the amount of a hormone that has the same effects as the luteinizing hormone. It is called the *anterior-pituitary-like* (APL) hormone. It is produced by chorionic tissue (p. 796), and it makes possible the Aschheim-Zondek and the Friedman tests for pregnancy. The injection of urine from a pregnant patient into immature female mice or rabbits produces characteristic changes in the ovaries. When these changes are noted it indicates pregnancy and makes possible an early diagnosis before pregnancy can be diagnosed by physical examination.

There is another test for early pregnancy that depends on the effects of estrogen and progesterone on the basal body temperature. There is a variation in the daily basal temperature with the menstrual cycle. The basal temperature is taken before one arises, after a good night's sleep, with no food or activity during the preceding 12 hours. The highest basal temperature, 99° to 100° F, together with the highest rate of basal metabolism, occurs about 7 days before the menstrual flow begins. The lowest basal temperature and the lowest basal metabolic rate occur about 15 days before the menstrual flow, or about 8 days before the highest temperature. At the low point of the monthly basal temperature curve, ovulation occurs, just at the peak of estrogen production.

As the corpus luteum develops, the basal temperature rises, reaching a peak within 24 hours after ovulation. If fertilization of the ovum occurs, the basal temperature remains high; if fertilization does not occur, the corpus luteum regresses, progesterone production ceases, and the basal temperature falls just before the menstrual flow begins.

If a woman has been following her basal temperature curve accurately enough to know her characteristic monthly pattern, she can detect pregnancy even before a menstrual period is missed. This is because the basal temperature does not fall as usual just before the period is due. (Of course infection, such as a cold, must be ruled out, if the temperature remains up.)

Basal temperature studies have proved to be exceedingly important in both sterility and fertility clinics and are useful as a measure of ovarian activity.

Posterior Lobe Preparations. PITUITRIN is used in the treatment of postpartum hemorrhage, to keep the uterine muscle contracted and stop the bleeding. It has been used also after incomplete abortions to complete the emptying of the uterus. It is used to relieve gas pains by stimulating the contraction of the smooth muscle of the intestinal tract and eliminating the gas. Pituitrin is effective in the control of diabetes insipidus and can be used in the form of a spray on the nasal mucosa.

PITRESSIN has both pressor and antidiuretic properties. It can be used in the treatment of diabetes insipidus.

PITOCIN is used for its effect on uterine muscle. One has a choice so far as posterior lobe preparations are concerned. However, pituitrin is readily available and can be used wherever either pitressin or pitocin are indicated, as it contains both factors.

THYROID GLAND

The activity of the thyroid gland may be tested by determining the basal metabolic rate, the level of cholesterol in the blood or the level of protein-bound iodine in the blood.

Iodine relieves the condition of colloid goiter; it may be administered as iodides in salt or drinking water. Individuals who eat plenty of sea food get enough iodine in the diet, but the inland sections of the United States lack iodine in the soil, so the vegetables raised in these districts lack iodine. The situation usually is controlled by adding iodide to the water supply or using iodized salt.

When iodides are administered to patients suffering from hyperthyroidism, the activity of the proteolytic enzyme in the colloid of the follicles is reduced, and less thyroxin is released daily from the stored thyroglobulin, thus alleviating the condition to some extent. For this reason, hyperthyroid patients often are given a short course of iodide treatment to improve them before they undergo surgery (removal of part of the thyroid gland).

Thiouracil and related substances decrease the production of thyroxin and thereby relieve the symptoms of hyperthyroidism. However, the only treatment of permanent value in toxic hyperthyroidism (thyrotoxicosis) is thyroidectomy. Care must be taken not to remove the parathyroid glands by mistake during thyroidec-tomies.

Radioactive iodine is administered to individuals who have cancer of the thyroid gland. This is concentrated in the gland and destroys some of the tissue, thereby decreasing the production of the hormone.

Thyroid extract or dried thyroid gland is used in the treatment of myxedema and cretinism. Substitution therapy is excellent, and hypothyroidism can be relieved and recurrence prevented if the therapy is continued. The results are some of the most gratifying in the practice of medicine. The dilated heart, characteristic of the myxedematous patient, decreases in size when thyroid therapy is begun, but does not respond to digitalis therapy.

PARATHYROID GLANDS

Parathormone is not satisfactory to use in the treatment of tetany, since patients develop a tolerance for it, and the dose must be increased frequently. Calcium lactate, vitamin D to increase calcium absorption from the intestine, and diets adequate in both calcium and phosphorus are satisfactory in the treatment of tetany.

The only satisfactory treatment for hyperparathyroidism is sur-gery.

ADRENAL GLANDS

Cortex. HYPOFUNCTION. For patients with hypofunction of the adrenal cortex, diets containing a high content of sodium chloride and low potassium and plenty of carbohydrate are beneficial. Aldosterone corrects the salt and water disturbance but not the disturbance in carbohydrate metabolism. Its prolonged use leads to hypertension.

CORTICOSTERONE in the form of cortisone is used in the treatment of rheumatoid arthritis. Marked improvement is noted almost im-mediately, but the condition is not cured. The expense of the treatment, together with some undesirable effects that accompany long periods of administration, leave much to be desired.

HYPERFUNCTION. The only satisfactory treatment for hyperfunc-tion of the adrenal cortex is surgical removal of the tumor.

Medulla. THE HORMONE of the adrenal medulla (mixture of epinephrine and nor-epinephrine) is used in the treatment of bronchial asthma, urticaria (hives), cardiac failure, circulatory collapse and with local anesthetics in operations on eye, nose and throat. It constricts blood vessels and decreases bleeding, causes the blood to coagulate faster and delays the absorption of the local anesthetic. It may stimulate the production of ACTH by the anterior lobe of the pituitary gland.

Since this is one of the drugs used most frequently by nurses, the effects of an injection of epinephrine will be listed in detail. (1) It constricts arterioles of the splanchnic area, the skin (leading to paleness) and the kidneys. (2) It dilates the arterioles of skeletal muscles and heart muscle. (3) It increases the rate and the force of the heart beat, and may cause cardiac irregularities. (4) It raises the blood pressure. (5) It relaxes muscles of the bronchi so that breathing is easier. (6) It increases the breakdown of glycogen in the liver, which leads to hyperglycemia. (7) It increases the basal metabolic rate (and oxygen use) by about 20 per cent for 30 minutes. (8) It makes the blood coagulate more rapidly than usual.

The effects of epinephrine are more marked in the presence of hyperthyroidism, since thyroxin increases the sensitivity of tissues to epinephrine.

HYPERFUNCTION. The only satisfactory treatment for hyperfunction of the adrenal medulla is surgical removal of the tumor (pheochromocytoma).

GONADS

Estrogens have not proved to be satisfactory in the treatment of amenorrhea. The synthetic product, diethylstilbestrol, is used in the treatment of the menopause, but some of the effects are undesirable.

Progesterone therapy has been disappointing in the treatment of habitual abortion. (The excretory product of progesterone is called *pregnanediol.*)

Testosterone. The most pronounced effect that follows testosterone therapy is a psychological one. (The excretory product of testosterone is called *androgen.*)

ISLET CELLS OF THE PANCREAS

Hypofunction. A commonly used test for hypofunction of the beta cells of the islets is the glucose tolerance test. In performing this test, the fasting blood sugar is determined, and then a definite amount of glucose is given (dependent upon the body weight), and the blood sugar is determined at definite intervals thereafter for about 2 hours. The variations in blood sugar, after the ingestion of glucose, give information with respect to the production of insulin.

Insulin is used in the treatment of diabetes mellitus. It is not a cure but it enables carbohydrate, fat and protein metabolism to approach the normal pattern.

Insulin dosage and diet must be adjusted carefully from time to time. If an overdose is administered, convulsions occur when the blood sugar falls to a low level. If the dose is too small, acidosis and diabetic coma may occur. This means that the patient becomes unconscious, and the accumulated acetone bodies lead to serious disturbances in water balance and acid-base balance.

Insulin is given by the hypodermic route, since it is destroyed by the digestive enzymes if given by mouth. It is combined with protamine or protamine and zinc to slow its absorption and prolong its effects. There are fewer hypoglycemic reactions, and the blood sugar level remains more nearly constant throughout the day and the night with the new preparations.

Some cases of diabetes mellitus do not respond to insulin therapy as expected. It may be that in these individuals the anterior lobe of the pituitary gland, the adrenal cortex or the thyroid gland is at fault. The adrenal medulla also is at fault in some instances. Liver disease alters the effects of insulin.

Pregnancy. Diabetic women occasionally have difficulty during pregnancy. The disease of the arteries may lead to degeneration of the placenta, with toxemia, or there may be a hormone imbalance or lowered renal threshold for glucose in pregnant diabetic women. Some of these patients have been carried through pregnancy normally by controlling the levels of estrogen and progesterone in the blood, in addition to controlling the blood sugar level by insulin and diet.

Mental Disorders. Insulin has been used in the production of shock for the treatment of certain mental disorders. The very low level of glucose in the blood caused by an excessive dose of insulin alters the activity of the cells of the central nervous system. Many individuals who undergo insulin shock therapy show some improvement in mental activity after a course of treatments.

Alloxan. It has been found that the beta cells of the islets can be selectively destroyed by an injection of alloxan. This makes it possible to study experimental diabetes mellitus easily because the animal is not deprived of the external secretion of the pancreas as is the case after complete removal of the pancreas.

GLANDULAR THERAPY

It should be kept in mind that the administration of hormones is not without undesirable effects. It is possible to produce inhibi-

ENDOCRINE SYSTEM IN VERTEBRATES

ENDOCRINE GLAND AND HORMONE	PRINCIPAL SITE OF ACTION	PRINCIPAL PROCESSES AFFECTED
Pituitary gland (a) Anterior lobe Growth	General	Growth of bones, viscera and muscles; nitrogen retention
Follicle-stimulating (FSH)	Ovaries	Development of follicles; with LH, secretion of estrogen and ovulation
	Testes	Development of seminiferous tubules, spermatogenesis
Luteinizing (LH) or interstitial cell stimulating (ICSH)	Ovaries	Development of corpora lutea and secretion of progesterone (see FSH)
	Testes	Development of interstitial tissue and secretion of testosterone
Thyrotrophic (TTH)	Thyroid	Growth of thyroid and production of thyroxin
Adrenocortico-trophic (ACTH)	Adrenal cortex	Growth of adrenal cortex and secretion of adrenal cortical steroids
Lactogenic or luteo-trophic	Mammary glands and ovaries	Secretion of milk by mammary glands and secretion of estrogen and progesterone
Intermedin	Chromatophore cells in skin of amphibia	Expansion of pigment cells and dispersion of pigment granules; function unknown in man
(b) Posterior lobe Pitressin (pressor and ADH)	Arterioles and cells of kidney tubules	Blood pressure Reabsorption of water; water balance
Pitocin	Uterine muscle	Contraction; parturition, possibly
Thyroid gland Thyroxin	General	Metabolic rate; morphogenesis; physical and mental growth; intermediate metabolism
Parathyroid glands Parathormone	General	Metabolism of calcium and phosphorus
Adrenal glands (a) Cortex Aldosterone (like desoxycorticosterone)	Kidney tubules	Reabsorption of sodium chloride and elimination of potassium
Corticosterone	General	Carbohydrate metabolism; quantity and quality of intercellular substance; lymphatic tissue in response to stress

ENDOCRINE GLAND AND HORMONE	PRINCIPAL SITE OF ACTION	PRINCIPAL PROCESSES AFFECTED
Adrenosterone and estrogen and progesterone	General	Like testosterone, estrogen and progesterone
(b) Medulla Epinephrine	Heart muscle and smooth muscle	Pulse rate and blood pressure; same effects as stimulation of thoracolumbar division of autonomic nervous system
Ovaries Estrogen	General	Development of secondary sexual characteristics
	Mammary glands	Development of duct system
	Accessory reproductive organs	Maturation and normal cyclic function
Progesterone	Mammary glands	Development of alveolar tissue
	Uterus	Preparation for implantation; maintenance of pregnancy
Testes Testosterone	General	Development of secondary sexual characteristics
	Accessory reproductive organs	Maturation and normal function
Islet cells of pancreas Insulin	General	Utilization of carbohydrate
Placenta (chorionic tissue) APL (anterior-pituitarylike)	Same as LH	Same as LH
Estrogen	Same as estrogen	Same as estrogen
Progesterone	Same as progesterone	Same as progesterone
Alimentary tract Gastrin	Glands in fundus and body of stomach	Production of gastric juice
Secretin	Pancreas, liver and intestine	Production of watery pancreatic juice, (rich in $NaHCO_3$) bile and intestinal juice
Pancreozymin	Pancreas	Production of pancreatic juice rich in enzymes
Enterogastrone	Stomach	Inhibits secretion and motility
Cholecystokinin	Gallbladder	Contraction and emptying
Enterocrinin	Small intestine	Stimulates production of intestinal juice

tion of the very glands that are supposed to be stimulated by such therapy. For example, ovarian hormones inhibit production of gonadotrophic hormones by the anterior lobe of the pituitary gland. This, sooner or later, leads secondarily to a failure of ovarian function. Because of the interrelation of the glands of the endocrine system, all of the possible effects of glandular therapy should be considered carefully before it is begun.

SITUATION AND QUESTIONS

When Miss Griffin reported to duty, she found that a new patient had been admitted. Her diagnosis was listed as tumor of the pituitary gland. Miss Griffin, remembering that this gland was referred to as the "master gland," began to consider all of the possible symptoms which might be presented by this patient.

1. Because of the location of the pituitary gland, one of the symptoms most likely to result from pressure would be: _____(a) ringing in the ears; _____(b) blurring of vision; _____(c) slurring of speech; _____(d) disturbance of gait.

2. If the thyroid gland should be affected because of the thyrotrophic hormone: _____(a) spontaneous fractures would occur; _____(b) general body metabolism would be disturbed; _____(c) there may be an increased absorption of water by the kidney tubules; _____(d) there might be periodic episodes of high blood pressure.

3. The adrenal cortices might not function properly because the production of their hormones is influenced by the substance produced by the anterior lobe of the pituitary gland. This substance is: _____(a) cortisone; _____(b) epinephrine; _____ (c) pituitrin; _____(d) corticotrophic hormone (ACTH).

4. The follicle-stimulating hormone of the anterior lobe of the pituitary gland stimulates the production of the following hormone: _____(a) Gonadotrophic hormone; _____(b) Testosterone; _____(c) Estrogen; _____(d) Adrenosterone.

5. The parathyroid glands are not directly influenced by the pituitary gland; therefore, there would be no disturbance in the new patient's: _____(a) mental and physical growth; _____ (b) salt and water metabolism; _____(c) calcium and phosphorus metabolism; _____(d) renal tubular function.

UNIT 5

THE REPRODUCTIVE SYSTEM

UNIT 5. THE REPRODUCTIVE SYSTEM

20. Anatomy and Physiology of the Reproductive System

INTRODUCTION

The ability to reproduce is one of the properties that characterize living matter. Under suitable conditions various forms of life are capable of reproducing themselves from one generation to the next. One-celled organisms reproduce by division of the parent cell into 2 so-called *daughter* cells. In higher forms of life a new individual can be produced only by the union (fertilization) of an ovum of a female and a spermatozoon of a male.

The union of an ovum and a spermatozoon may take place after

753

they have left the body, as is the case in fishes. In birds the union takes place in the body of the female; then the fertilized ovum leaves the body and develops outside, if kept at the proper temperature.

In mammals the young are born alive since the fertilized ovum remains in the uterus of the female until ready for independent existence. We find, as we study the development of a new human being, that this is the greatest of the innumerable miracles in human life.

In both men and women, the organs of the reproductive system may be divided into 2 groups: (1) the gonads (testes and ovaries), which perform the double function of producing germ cells (spermatozoa and ova) and hormones (testosterone, estrogen and progesterone) and (2) a series of ducts for the transportation of germ cells. In the male, a part of the duct system (penis) is modified for the transfer of germ cells into the body of the female. In the female a part of the duct system (uterus) is modified for the nutrition and the growth of the new individual.

The differentiation of the sexes is a remarkable process. During the first few weeks of intra-uterine life there is no structural difference to indicate whether the developing individual is going to be a male or a female. After this, differentiation begins and, normally, the reproductive organs are completely differentiated, but immature, at birth. At puberty, which is initiated by the hormones of the anterior lobe of the pituitary gland, the organs of reproduction become functionally mature. This occurs between 12 and 14 years in girls and at about 16 years in boys, in temperate climates. It occurs earlier in warmer and later in colder climates.

As puberty advances into adolescence, the secondary sexual characteristics appear gradually. These characteristics comprise the pitch of the voice (dependent on the growth of the larynx), the growth of the external genitalia, broadening of the pelvis in girls (making it suitable for childbearing), distribution of hair on face and trunk, development of mammary glands and establishment of the menstrual cycles.

Adolescence lasts until the late 'teens in girls and until the early twenties in boys.

MALE REPRODUCTIVE SYSTEM

The male reproductive system consists of a pair of male gonads or testes and a system of excretory ducts with their accessory structures. The ducts are the epididymis, the ductus deferens and the ejaculatory ducts. The accessory structures are the seminal vesicles, the prostate gland, the bulbo-urethral glands and the penis.

The 2 testes are suspended outside of the abdominal cavity in a sac (Figs. 397 and 398) called the *scrotum* (meaning "leather"), which lies between the thighs. In early fetal life the testes lie in the abdominal cavity, one below and in front of each kidney. During growth of the fetus the testes move downward through the future inguinal canal and usually enter the scrotum a short time before birth.

The scrotum may be considered an evagination of the body wall. The location of the testes in the scrotum is exceedingly important, since spermatogenesis (described below) can occur only at the scrotal temperature, which is lower than that inside the abdominal

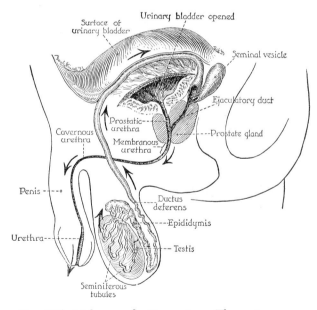

FIG. 397. Male reproductive system. The various organs of the male reproductive system are shown. The path of the spermatozoon from the time it leaves the testis until it leaves the body is indicated. The prostatic, the membranous and the cavernous portions of the urethra are shown.

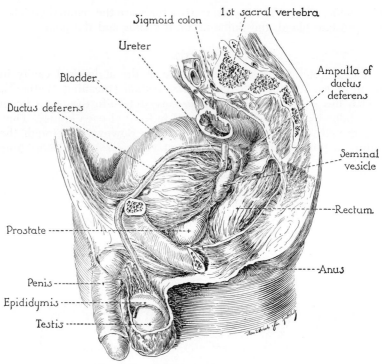

FIG. 398. Male reproductive system.

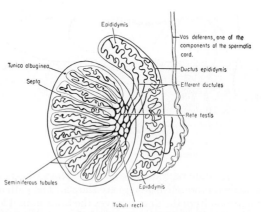

FIG. 399. Diagram showing the parts of the testis and the epididymis. (Modified from Ham, A. W.: Histology, ed. 2, Philadelphia, Lippincott)

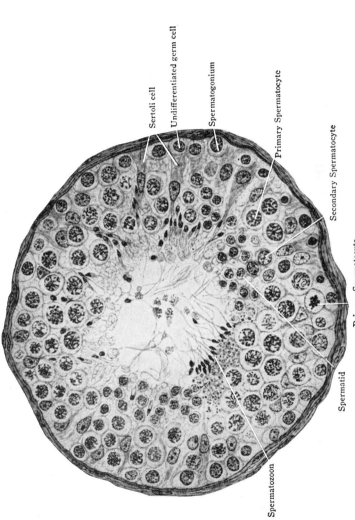

Sertoli cell

Undifferentiated germ cell

Spermatogonium

Primary Spermatocyte

Secondary Spermatocyte

Primary Spermatocyte

Spermatid

Spermatozoon

Fig. 400. Cross section of a seminiferous tubule, showing various stages of spermatogenesis. ×550. (After Stieve) (Hotchkiss, R. S.: Fertility in Men, Philadelphia, Lippincott)

cavity. If the testes fail to descend but remain in the abdomen, spermatogenesis does not occur.

Each testis is an oval, white body about 1½ in. long. It is covered with a serous membrane (the peritoneum) called the *tunica vaginalis*. Beneath this is a tough, white fibrous covering called the *tunica albuginea*. The substance of the testis is seminiferous tubules, bound together with connective tissue.

Each testis is made up of about 250 lobules, and the cavity of each lobule contains the beginning of from 1 to 3 seminiferous tubules. The total length of tubules in the 2 testes is almost 1 mile. The seminiferous tubules empty into spaces called the *rete* (meaning "a net") *testis*, and these spaces, in turn, drain into 15 to 20 tubules called *efferent ducts*. These pass through the tunica albuginea and empty into the epididymis, as shown in Figure 399.

The germinal epithelium that forms the walls of the seminiferous tubules consists of many layers of epithelial cells, which are spermatogenetic (sperm-producing) cells. These are supported by connective tissue stroma.

The changes that the spermatogenetic cells undergo, as they move toward the lumens of the seminiferous tubules, are called *spermatogenesis*. Cells in different stages of development are called by different names. The youngest cells are called *spermatogonia* (Fig. 400). The next are the primary spermatocytes, which undergo a modified mitosis (called *reduction division* or maturation) in which the number of chromosomes is reduced by one half (to 24). The resulting cells are called *secondary spermatocytes*. Each of these undergoes ordinary mitosis, forming 2 spermatids.

Spermatids undergo a transformation during which they become spermatozoa, with head, middle piece and tail, after which they are released from the testis. The stages of development are shown in Figure 401.

The acquisition of the tail endows a spermatozoon with motility and makes it possible for it to pass through the duct system of the male and then through the vagina, the uterus and the uterine tube of the female to join an ovum.

Spermatozoa that have just escaped from the testis are not capable of fertilizing an ovum. They remain for a time in the duct system of the male and undergo a process called *ripening* before they are ejected.

In the human testes, spermatogenesis begins at the age of puberty and continues throughout life. It is influenced by temperature and vitamin E and is controlled by FSH produced by the anterior lobe

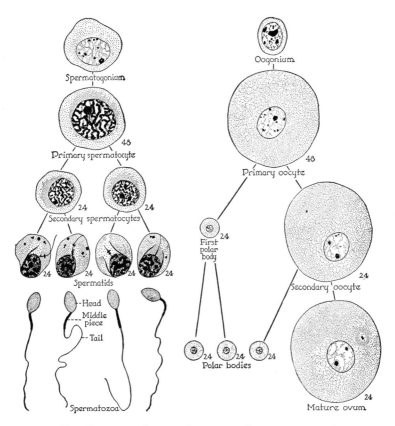

Fig. 401. Diagram of gametogenesis with maturation. The various stages of spermatogenesis are indicated on the left; 1 spermatogonium gives rise to 4 spermatozoa. On the right, the oogenesis of the ovum is indicated; from each oogonium, 1 mature ovum and 3 abortive cells are produced. In maturation, the chromosomes are reduced to one-half the number characteristic for the general body cells of the species, as indicated. In man, the number in the body cells is 48, and that in the mature spermatozoon and ovum is 24.

of the pituitary gland. The seminiferous tubules undergo gradual involution with advancing age but apparently never completely cease to function until death.

The interstitial tissue fills the spaces between the seminiferous tubules. There are clumps of endocrine cells in the connective tis-

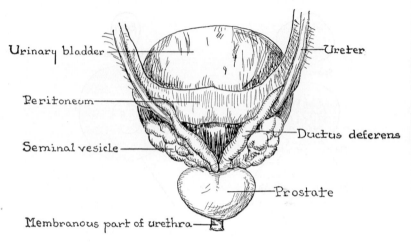

Urinary bladder — Ureter

Peritoneum —

— Ductus deferens

Seminal vesicle —

— Prostate

Membranous part of urethra —

Fig. 402. Posterior view of the urinary bladder, the ductus deferens, the seminal vesicles and the prostate gland. (After Gray)

sue that have large nuclei, centrioles and granules in their cytoplasm, and they produce testosterone.

The blood supply is derived from the internal spermatic arteries, and the drainage is into the internal spermatic veins. These vessels form part of the spermatic cord (Fig. 108). Lymph vessels accompany the blood vessels in the spermatic cord.

The testes are supplied with nerve fibers from both divisions of the autonomic system. Visceral afferent fibers transmit impulses to the central nervous system.

DUCT SYSTEM

The duct system comprises the epididymis, the ductus deferens and the ejaculatory duct that transport spermatozoa from each testis.

Epididymis. Efferent ducts from the rete testis combine to form the epididymis (Fig. 399) of each testis. An epididymis is attached to the posterior surface of each testis and is greatly convoluted. It becomes the ductus deferens.

The ductus deferens is a duct that passes from the epididymis to the ejaculatory duct (for ejection of spermatozoa). A ductus deferens is shown in Figures 397 and 398. The ductus deferens passes from the scrotum, through the muscles and the fascia of the abdominal wall by way of the inguinal canal, and enters the abdominal cavity and, eventually, the pelvic cavity. Each ductus deferens,

FIG. 403. Diagram of a cross section of the prostate gland, showing the distribution of the mucous, the submucous and the main glands and where their ducts open. (Redrawn and slightly modified from Grant, J. C. B.: A Method of Anatomy, ed. 4, Baltimore, Williams & Wilkins)

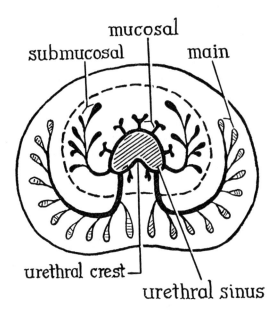

mucosal

submucosal   main

urethral crest

urethral sinus

together with blood vessels, lymphatic vessels, nerves and coverings, makes up a spermatic cord.

Each ductus deferens passes in front of and medial to a ureter and then turns sharply downward to reach the space between the posterior surface of the bladder and the rectum. In its course it enlarges into an ampulla, again becomes narrow, and finally joins with the duct of the seminal vesicle to form an ejaculatory duct (Fig. 397).

Ejaculatory Duct. Each ejaculatory duct is formed by the union of a ductus deferens with a duct from a seminal vesicle (an epithelial-lined sac with secretory functions) on the same side. The 2 ejaculatory ducts enter the posterior surface of the prostate gland and continue through the substance of this gland for less than an inch before they end in the prostatic portion (Fig. 397) of the urethra (p. 672).

ACCESSORY STRUCTURES OF THE DUCT SYSTEM

The accessory structures of the duct system of the male comprise the seminal vesicles, the prostate gland, the bulbo-urethral glands and the penis.

The right and the left seminal vesicles (Figs. 397, 398 and

402) are sacs that lie behind the bladder and in front of the rectum, lateral to the ductus deferens of the same side. The function of the seminal vesicles is to secrete a substance that is important in maintaining the motility of the spermatozoa by helping to provide optimal conditions. The duct from the seminal vesicle joins with the ductus deferens to form an ejaculatory duct.

The prostate gland surrounds the proximal part of the male urethra as it emerges from the urinary bladder. Its location is shown in Figures 397, 398 and 402. The urethra enters the base of the prostate gland near its anterior surface and descends almost vertically through it; the 2 ejaculatory ducts also pass through the prostate gland to join the prostatic urethra.

The prostate gland is composed of glandular and muscular tissue. The glandular tissue consists of 15 to 30 branched tubular glands whose ducts open separately into the prostatic urethra. The glands are arranged in 3 sets: mucosal, submucosal and the main prostatic glands that form the bulk of the prostatic secretion. The general plan is illustrated in Figure 403.

It is the mucosal glands that form adenomata in elderly men and cause difficulty in urination by enlarging the prostate and compressing the prostatic urethra. The smooth muscular tissue forms a thick ring around the urethra and serves as an internal sphincter for the urinary bladder. This muscle also supplies part of the force for ejaculation.

The prostatic secretion is important in stimulating and maintaining motility of the spermatozoa; it is added to the material from the ejaculatory ducts in the prostatic urethra.

The bulbo-urethral glands (Cowper's glands) are 2 small glands that lie on either side of the membranous urethra. They drain into the bulb of the urethra by means of ducts. They produce an alkaline secretion that probably aids in neutralizing acid urine, thus helping to provide an optimal condition for the spermatozoa.

The penis is an external genital organ through which the urethra passes to the exterior. It is composed of 3 cylindrical bodies of erectile tissue (full of spaces which may be distended with blood). Two of these, called the *corpora cavernosa,* are located side by side in the dorsal half of the penis. The third, called the *corpus cavernosum urethrae,* conducts the urethra in its substance. It lies ventral to the corpora cavernosa and expands into the glans (the conical body which forms the distal end of the penis).

Each cavernous body is surrounded by a sheath of connective tissue that contains collagen and elastic fibers. The 3 cavernous

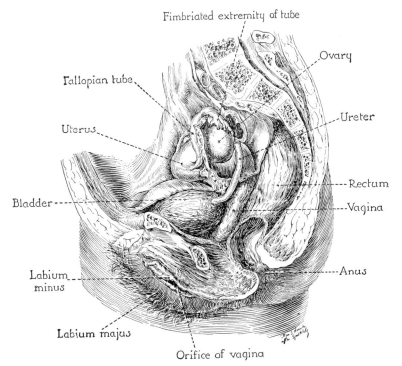

Fimbriated extremity of tube

Ovary

Fallopian tube

Ureter

Uterus

Rectum

Bladder

Vagina

Anus

Labium minus

Labium majus

Orifice of vagina

Fig. 404. Female reproductive system.

bodies are bound together by elastic connective tissue and covered by skin, the epithelium of which is very thin. The substance of the cavernous bodies is a network of connective tissue and smooth muscle, with spaces between. The organ is flaccid when these spaces are empty and becomes turgid when they are filled. The amount of blood in the spaces is controlled by vasodilator fibers in the sacral autonomic nerves and varies with sexual activity.

The urethra opens at the apex of the glans penis. There is a fold of skin called the *prepuce* over the glans that is removed in circumcision. The scrotum and the penis are called the *external genitalia* of the male.

SEMEN

The spermatozoa, together with the secretions from the epididymis, the seminal vesicles, the prostate gland and the bulbo-urethral glands, compose the semen. The secretions of the epididymis favor

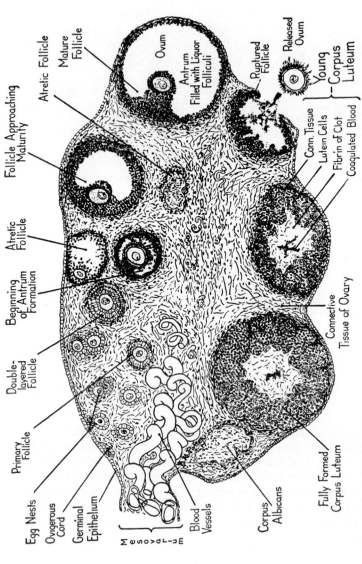

FIG. 405. Schematic diagram of an ovary, showing the sequence of events in the origin, the growth and the rupture of an ovarian (graafian) follicle and the formation and the retrogression of corpus luteum. For proper sequence, follow clockwise around ovary, starting at the mesovarium. (Patten, B. M.: Human Embryology, New York, Blakiston Division of McGraw-Hill)

Atretic Follicle

Mature Follicle

Ovum

Antrum Filled with Liquor Folliculi

Follicle Approaching Maturity

Ruptured Follicle

Released Ovum

Young Corpus Luteum

Atretic Follicle

Conn. Tissue

Luten Cells

Fibrin of Clot

Coagulated Blood

Beginning of Antrum Formation

Double-layered Follicle

Connective Tissue of Ovary

Primary Follicle

Egg Nests

Ovigerous Cord

Germinal Epithelium

Mesovarium

Blood Vessels

Corpus Albicans

Fully Formed Corpus Luteum

the so-called *ripening* of the spermatozoa after they have left the testes; the other secretions are produced during ejaculation.

Semen is ejected by means of contraction of the smooth muscle of the prostate gland and the contraction of the bulbocavernosus muscle which compresses the cavernous portion of the urethra. Each cubic centimeter of semen contains at least 100 million spermatozoa, and there are at least 2 cc. with each ejaculation. The spermatozoa are highly motile in fertile men. Only one spermatozoon can fertilize an ovum. Spermatozoa contain hyaluronidase, an enzyme that disperses the covering of the shed ovum and clears the way for the penetration of the spermatozoon into the ovum.

FEMALE REPRODUCTIVE SYSTEM

The female reproductive system consists of a pair of female gonads or ovaries, a system of ducts (uterine tubes, uterus and vagina) with their associated structures (external genitalia) and the mammary glands.

OVARIES

The ovaries (Fig. 404) are small bodies that lie near the lateral walls of the pelvis; they are not connected with the uterine tubes directly. The tissue (germinal epithelium) involved in the production of ova forms a single layer on the outer surface of the ovary. The connective tissue of the ovary is called the *stroma*.

The follicles (small secretory sacs or cavities) of the ovary are found in the outer zone or cortex of the ovary, and each follicle contains an ovum surrounded by a single layer of epithelial cells. By means of a series of changes (Fig. 405) some of the primary follicles become mature (graafian) follicles. As a follicle matures, the ovum within it grows, the follicle moves toward the surface, becomes greatly distended with fluid and actually bulges from the surface of the ovary.

Two courses are open to mature follicles: the mature follicle can undergo involution without shedding its ovum or the follicle ruptures, and the ovum is shed on the surface of the ovary near the end of the uterine tube.

Unlike the spermatozoa, ova are incapable of independent movement. They are drawn into the end of the uterine tube by ciliary activity of the epithelial lining of the tube and are moved along toward the uterus by ciliary activity and peristaltic contractions of the wall of the uterine tubes. In its passage, 2 courses are possible for each ovum: it may be fertilized (united with a spermatozoon) in the tube or, if it is not fertilized, it moves along to the uterus, which it enters and there disintegrates.

Ovulation. The discharge of an ovum by rupture of the wall of a mature ovarian follicle is called *ovulation*. Usually it occurs at intervals of 28 days, from puberty to the menopause. The maturation of the ovum begins before ovulation but is completed after the ovum is shed.

After the ovum is shed, the edges of the follicle close, and there is some bleeding into the follicle. The follicular cells enlarge, and there is an accumulation of a yellow pigment in their cytoplasm. The entire follicle becomes filled and is now called a *corpus luteum*.

Two possible courses are open to the corpus luteum: (1) if the shed ovum is not fertilized, the corpus luteum continues to grow for about 2 weeks and then regresses, eventually becoming a small, white, ovarian scar called a *corpus albicans;* or, (2) if the ovum is fertilized, the corpus luteum becomes very large, forming the corpus luteum of pregnancy. It persists until sometime between the third and the sixth months of pregnancy, when it degenerates completely and leaves a large scar on the ovary.

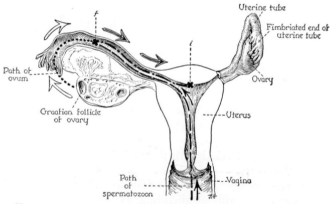

Fig. 406. Female reproductive system. The various organs of the female reproductive system are shown. The path of the ovum from the ovary into the uterine tube is indicated. The path of the spermatozoon in the female genital tract is indicated. The usual site of fertilization in the uterine tube is marked with a cross and by the letter *f*. The path of the fertilized ovum from the uterine tube into the uterus and the site of implantation are shown; the latter is marked with a cross and by the letter *i*.

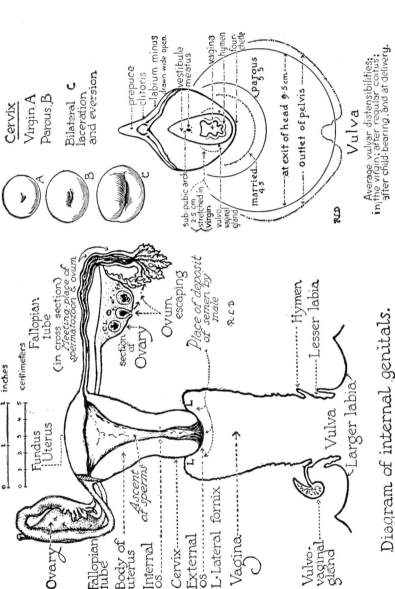

Diagram of internal genitals.

Fig. 407. Organs of the female reproductive system; the ovary and tube on the left side of the drawing are shown in the true position; on the right side they are spread out and cut in two to show the inside structure. All parts are labeled. (Robert L. Dickinson, New York)

The ovum is capable of being fertilized for only a day or two after ovulation.

Fate of the Ova Which are not Shed. Several hundred thousand follicles with ova in them are present in the ovaries at birth. About two thirds of these disappear by degeneration before the age of puberty. Only about 400 follicles reach maturity and discharge ova between puberty and the menopause. The remainder disappear by the age of 50. Thus, most of the primary follicles degenerate either as they are at birth or after some degree of useless development. The death of a follicle by involution is called *atresia,* and such follicles are called *atretic* follicles.

Menopause. The ovaries function for about 30 years, both in producing ova and in secreting hormones. They finally become exhausted and cease to function, and the menstrual cycles cease. Ova are no longer shed, and the period of possible child bearing is over. There is atrophy of the ovaries, the duct system and the accessory organs.

The blood supply of the ovaries is derived from the ovarian arteries and the ovarian branches of the uterine arteries. The veins form a plexus (uterine and ovarian) and then drain into the ovarian veins.

Nerve Supply. Nerves reach the ovaries from both divisions of the autonomic system. Visceral afferent fibers carry impulses to the central nervous system.

Duct System

The duct system comprises the uterine tubes, the uterus, the vagina and the associated structures (external genitalia).

Uterine Tubes. These are called *oviducts* and *fallopian tubes* and are shown in Figures 404, 406 and 407. The tubes penetrate the uterine wall and open into its cavity. Their function is to convey shed ova from the ovaries to the uterus.

The uterine tubes are in contact with the ovaries but are not continuous with them. Each tube lies in the upper part of the broad ligament of its own side and is about 4½ in. long. The free end of the uterine tube is trumpet-shaped and forms the infundibulum; the margins are fringed, and the fringe is called the *fimbria.* The next portion of the tube is called the *ampulla.*

There are 3 layers in the walls of the tube; the outer is serous (peritoneum), the middle is muscular, and the inner is mucous membrane. Some of the epithelial cells of the mucous membrane are secretory, and others are ciliated; the mucous membrane is

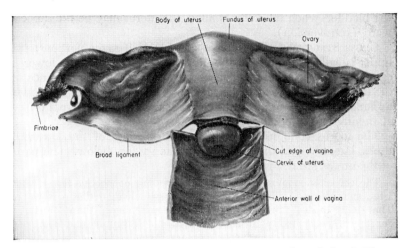

FIG. 408. Female reproductive organs as seen from behind. The posterior wall of the vagina has been opened and spread out. (Schaeffer, J. P.: Morris' Human Anatomy, ed. 11, New York, Blakiston Division of McGraw-Hill)

thrown into folds. Ciliary movement and peristaltic contractions transport the ovum to the uterus. The average time required for an ovum to reach the uterus is about 5 days.

The uterus is a hollow, muscular, pear-shaped organ. The lower portion is embedded in the pelvic floor between the bladder and the rectum. The upper portion of the uterus is free and movable and rests on the upper surface of the urinary bladder (Fig. 404). The uterus is connected with the surrounding structures and walls of the pelvis by means of ligaments. The principal ligaments are the broad and the round (Fig. 408).

Each broad ligament is a transverse fold of peritoneum that extends from the lateral border of the uterus across the pelvis to the pelvic wall and floor. It encloses the round and the ovarian ligaments, the uterine tube, the blood vessels and the nerves of its side. The round ligament passes from the lateral border of the uterus, in front of and below the entrance of the uterine tube of that side, through the broad ligament to the lateral pelvic wall, then through the inguinal canal in a course similar to that of the ductus deferens in the male and merges with the tissue of the external genitalia (labium majus).

In the standing position, the uterus is tilted forward, with the upper portion resting on the upper surface of the urinary bladder (anteversion). The position of the uterus changes with the size of the bladder; when the latter is filled, the uterus may be tilted backward (retroversion).

GROSS STRUCTURE. The uterus consists of 2 main portions: the upper is called the *body* of the uterus (Fig. 407), and the lower is called the *cervix*. The portion of the body above the entrance of the uterine tubes is called the *fundus*. The distal end of the cervix terminates in thick prominent lips that surround the external orifice of the uterus (external os).

The uterus contains 3 openings: the openings of the 2 uterine tubes, laterally, and the opening into the vagina, below. The parts of the uterus are shown in Figure 407.

The cervix is composed of dense, collagenous, connective tissue, with a few smooth muscle fibers. It must become widely dilated at parturition. The ability to dilate probably is due to the softening of the intercellular substance, associated with an increased blood supply and increased tissue fluid content. The mucous membrane contains tall columnar cells that secrete mucus.

MICROSCOPIC STRUCTURE. The wall of the uterus is composed of 3 main layers: the serosal covering (peritoneum), the myometrium (muscle) and the mucous membrane (called *endometrium*). The serosa merges with the peritoneum of the broad ligament.

The myometrium consists of smooth muscle. It is very thick and forms the main part of the uterine wall. The size of the uterus is capable of great change; its capacity is about 2 to 5 cc. before pregnancy and between 5,000 and 7,000 cc. at term. It weighs about 60 Gm. at puberty and about 1,000 Gm. at the end of pregnancy, which is an increase of more than 16 times. The increase in size is due to both hyperplasia (increase in the number of cells, that is, by the addition of new cells) and hypertrophy (increase in size of original cells). The nuclei of the cells become larger, and there is an increase in the amount of cytoplasm in each cell.

The change in size of the uterus during pregnancy truly is remarkable. It is due in part to hormones, both estrogen and progesterone, and in large measure to the distention by the growing fetus, which is a very effective stimulus to growth. There is also some stretching of the uterine wall, so the elastic and fibrous components of the wall are involved, as well as the smooth muscle. The shortening of the elastic fibers is a large factor in the retraction of the uterus after delivery.

The endometrium consists of a special mucous membrane that rests on a lamina propria of connective tissue. The lamina propria, called the *endometrial stroma*, is filled with glands and is continu-

FIG. 409. Section of endometrium, showing glands cut in various planes. (A) Gland opening on surface of endometrium. (B) Gland. (C) Muscle bundles invading mucosa. (D) Muscular tissue. (E) Blood vessel. ×40.

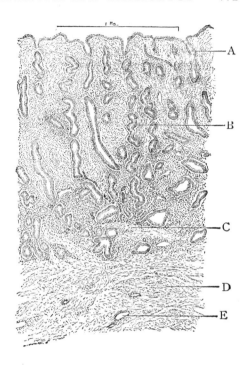

ous with the underlying myometrium. The epithelium consists of 2 layers; one is very thick and is called the *superficial* or functional layer, and the other is thin and is called the *basilar* layer. The free surface of the mucous membrane consists of a single layer of columnar epithelial cells. The glands are of the tubular type and extend almost to the myometrium, as illustrated in Figure 409.

Cyclic Changes of the Endometrium. In a nonpregnant woman, the functional layer of the uterine mucosa undergoes cyclic changes (called *menstrual cycles*) that are closely related to changes in the ovaries. The cycles recur from puberty to menopause, at intervals of 25 to 35 days.

Menstruation is the discharge of blood associated with the shedding of the functional layer of uterine mucosa. The menstrual blood is peculiar in that it does not coagulate.

The changes in the mucosa have been observed directly in pieces of endometrium of monkeys that have been implanted into the anterior chambers of their eyes. The following description is based on such observations.

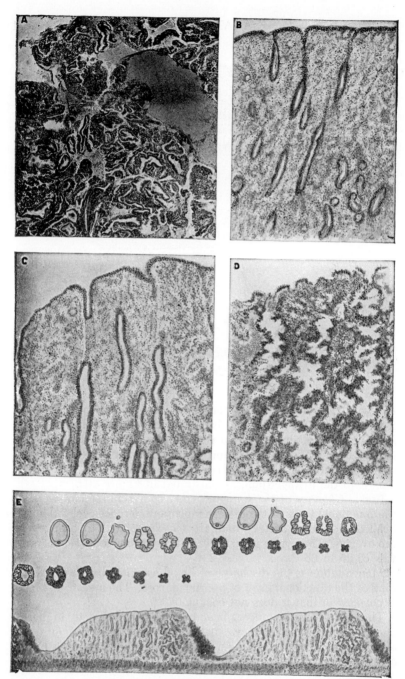

Fig. 410 (*Caption on facing page*)

Although the menstrual flow is really the terminal event of the cycle, we shall begin with it, as it is a time that is easily fixed by any woman. The menstrual flow may last from 1 to 5 days. Before it starts, the surface of the endometrium appears pale, which indicates that there is a decrease in its blood supply. This is due to a marked constriction of certain arteries (spiral arteries) in the myometrium, and, since the endometrium now lacks a proper blood supply, there is a progressive disintegration of the superficial or functional layer. Then, here and there, a superficial artery suddenly dilates and seems to burst, and there is a small hemorrhage around it.

One small area at a time is involved; there would be an uncontrollable and very severe hemorrhage if all areas of the endometrium were involved at one time. As patches of hemorrhage appear, pieces of the superficial layer of the endometrium become detached.

This process spreads gradually until the entire superficial layer of epithelium has disintegrated, in turn, and has joined the discharge. The uterine glands discharge their secretions and collapse. The edema fluid that has been present is lost. The mucosa is now very thin, since only the basilar layer of epithelium remains. This layer has a separate blood supply and is left intact throughout the menstrual cycle. It is responsible for the regeneration of a new functional or superficial layer after each menstrual flow.

Even before the menstrual flow ceases, repair begins in the areas which first underwent destruction. The repair is evident by the abundant mitotic figures (mitosis) in the cells of the basilar layer. The ensuing phase of the cycle is called the *reparative, estrogenic, follicular, proliferative, postmenstrual* or *preovulatory* phase (by various authors).

The covering epithelium is regenerated first, and then the superficial layer grows until it becomes at least 3 times as thick as the basilar layer. The glands elongate during this phase. The estrogenic phase is associated with a rapidly growing ovarian follicle

FIG. 410. Sections through the human endometrium at various stages of the menstrual cycle. (A) Menstrual phase; (B) proliferative phase; (C) at time of ovulation; (D) premenstrual phase. In (E) the changes in the thickness of the mucosa are shown; it is thinnest during the 3 menstrual flows shown; its great thickness just before the 3 periods is shown. Two complete sets of changes in the ovary are shown; the ovaries are thought to alternate in ovulation; one is regressing and the other developing simultaneously. (After Schroeder)

FIG. 411. CORRELATION OF INTERNAL SECRETIONS AND UTERINE CHANGES

Pituitary: Anterior Lobe

FSH; stimulates growth of follicle and production of estrogen; production of FSH checked as estrogen concentration reaches a peak

LH and luteotrophic; rupture of ovarian follicle and development of corpus luteum and production of progesterone. Estrogen level in blood decreasing. FSH production beginning again, and LH production decreasing due to rising progesterone concentration and falling estrogen concentration

Ovarian Hormones

Period of rapidly developing ovarian follicle

Concentration of estrogen rising

Period of corpus luteum.

Concentration of progesterone rising and estrogen falling

Events in the Ovary

Unripe follicle; developing rapidly and moving toward surface of ovary

Rupture of the follicle; ovulation. Developing corpus luteum; matures about 19th day; then degenerates, if ovum is not fertilized

Ovum

Growing, as follicle develops; maturation beginning

Ovum in tube; maturation completed. Being moved toward uterus; disintegrates. Fertilization possible for a day or two after ovulation

Uterine Mucosa

Extravasation of blood, following ischemia of superficial or functional layer of the mucosa. Desquamation of epithelial cells; mucosa very thin. Glands have extruded their secretion and are collapsed; low glycogen content. Elimination of blood, secretion and dead epithelial cells

Repair of functional layer of mucosa begins even before the flow has ceased; regenerated by basilar layer of the mucosa. Mucosa becoming thicker; blood supply increasing; glands elongating and becoming dilated in their deeper parts

Mucosa reaches its maximal thickness; glands increased in width, tortuous and distended with secretion; rich in glycogen. Blood vessels congested. Preparation for implantation, but if ovum is not fertilized, corpus luteum involutes, production of progesterone ceases, FSH is again produced, the superficial vessels of the mucosa constrict, the epithelial cells begin to degenerate and the next menstrual flow begins again

Day of Cycle: 1 2 3 4 5 6 7 8 9 10 11 12 13 14 15 16 17 18 19 20 21 22 23 24 25 26 27 28 1 2

Menstrual flow

Follicular, estrogenic, proliferative, preovulatory phase

Secretory, progravid, progestational, premenstrual phase

Menstrual flow

and lasts from 7 to 10 days, or from the fifth to the fourteenth day of the cycle. At the end of this phase, ovulation occurs.

After ovulation, a corpus luteum develops in the ovary. The next 2 weeks, or from the fifteenth to the twenty-eighth day of the cycle, is the secretory, progestational, progravid (meaning "before pregnancy") or *premenstrual* phase. It is characterized by a very active secretion by the glands in the uterine mucosa, which have become tortuous and greatly distended with secretion (Fig. 410). Their cells contain a large amount of glycogen.

The superficial or functional layer of the mucosa becomes thicker than it was during the preceding phase, due to an accumulation of fluid (edema) in the endometrium. The endometrial stroma (lamina propria) is loose and edematous. The stromal cells begin to enlarge and are now very sensitive to any mechanical stimulus, to which they respond by a decidual reaction (p. 799).

During the first part of the progestational phase, the ovum is being moved along toward the uterus. The changes in the endometrium are such as prepare it to receive and nourish the ovum, if it is fertilized. In this case, the mucous membrane becomes the decidua (p. 799).

If the ovum is not fertilized, the corpus luteum begins to degenerate, the mucosa becomes pale, and the menstrual flow begins again. The appearance of the endometrium at various times of the menstrual cycle is shown in Figure 410.

The changes in the uterine mucosa, in relation to the events in the ovaries and the anterior lobe of the pituitary gland, are shown in chart form in Figure 411. The changes are, in summary: The early development of the uterine mucosa, after the menstrual flow ceases, is due to estrogen produced by a rapidly developing ovarian follicle, which meanwhile is arriving at the surface of the ovary. The development of the follicle and the production of estrogen are under the control of FSH of the anterior lobe of the pituitary gland. Estrogen, in addition to the change in the uterine mucosa, keeps all the reproductive organs in a functional state and stimulates the production of LH by the anterior lobe of the pituitary gland.

FSH and LH together bring about a rupture of the mature ovarian follicle, and then the development of the corpus luteum and production of progesterone are controlled by LH and the luteotrophic hormone of the anterior lobe of the pituitary gland. Progesterone brings about further development of the endometrium and inhibits the production of FSH. The anterior lobe of the pituitary gland later stops secreting LH because of the falling estrogen level in the blood and the rising progesterone level. Then, if no fertilization has occurred, the corpus luteum undergoes involution, the progesterone level falls, and the anterior lobe of the pituitary gland again secretes FSH, and the cycle is repeated.

The ovaries, therefore, are responsible for the cyclic changes of the uterine mucosa and for the changes essential to the maintenance and the development of the embryo, particularly in the early period of pregnancy.

The ovaries, in turn, are controlled by the anterior lobe of the pituitary gland. Estrogen initiates the changes in the uterine mucosa that prepare it for the reception of the fertilized ovum. Progesterone is responsible for the final changes in the uterus and for nourishment and development of the embryo in early pregnancy. In other words, as one author says, "estrogen sets the stage for gestation and then calls forth progesterone for indispensable aid in getting the product of gestation embedded and maintained."

The uterine mucosa is prepared periodically for pregnancy. If fertilization does not occur, there is withdrawal of hormone support and a decrease in blood supply to the functional layer of the mucosa, with sloughing and menstrual flow.

The functions of the uterus are to implant and permit development of the new individual and to expel the fetus and the placenta at the end of pregnancy.

BLOOD SUPPLY. Blood is supplied to the uterus by way of branches of the hypogastric arteries. The veins, after forming a plexus, empty into the tributaries of the hypogastric veins. The blood supply of the superficial or functional layer is separate from that of the basilar layer of the endometrium; the former is by way of "spiral" or coiled arteries.

NERVE SUPPLY. The uterus is supplied with fibers from both divisions of the autonomic nervous system. Visceral afferent fibers transmit impulses to the central nervous system.

The vagina is a muscular tube about 3½ in. long, which lies between the bladder and the urethra, in front, and the rectum, behind. It is shown in Figures 406, 404 and 407. It extends from the uterus to the external opening in the vestibule (Fig. 412). It is attached to the cervix a short distance above the lips. The portion of the vagina above the end of the cervix is called the *fornix* (Fig. 407). It is a circular groove that surrounds the cervix. In the virgin, the external opening of the vagina is closed partially by a fold of mucous membrane called the *hymen*.

The wall of the vagina is composed of smooth muscle and fibro-elastic connective tissue, lined with mucous membrane, which is thrown into transverse folds called *rugae*. The epithelium of the mucous membrane is stratified, squamous, nonkeratinizing in type.

The mucous membrane of the vagina undergoes cyclic changes by which the stage of the menstrual cycle can be estimated. Vaginal smears are used to aid in determining the time of ovulation. (Such smears are useful also as a means of testing for the presence of cancer of the body of the uterus or of the cervix, since a characteristic type of cell is noted when cancer is present.)

The outer layer of the vaginal wall is composed of fibrous tissue.

ACCESSORY ORGANS

The external genitalia are shown in Figure 412.

THE CLITORIS is the homologue (counterpart) of the penis in the male. It contains erectile tissue.

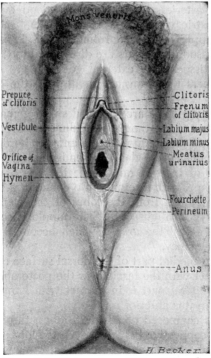

FIG. 412. External genitalia of female.

THE LABIA MINORA are 2 folds of delicate skin that arise just anterior to the clitoris. They partly cover the clitoris and then pass backward to enclose the vestibule (the cleft between the labia minora and behind the clitoris).

The urethra and the vagina open into the vestibule. The vestibular glands (Bartholin) in the lateral walls of the vestibule are called *vulvovaginal* glands also, and they correspond to the bulbourethral glands in the male.

THE LABIA MAJORA are folds of skin that pass from the mons pubis backward. They join each other over the ridge formed by the body of the clitoris. Behind, they unite to form the posterior commissure, which is called the *perineum* by obstetricians. The skin of the labia majora contains hair follicles, sweat glands and sebaceous glands.

THE MONS PUBIS is the rounded pad of fat above the labia majora. It is covered by dense skin and hair.

The blood supply of the external genitalia is from branches of the hypogastric arteries, and the venous blood eventually drains into the hypogastric veins.

The nerve supply is derived from both divisions of the autonomic system; vasodilator fibers are distributed to the blood vessels of the erectile tissue. The external genitalia are supplied richly with afferent fibers that transmit impulses to the central nervous system.

The mammary glands are modified sweat glands. They lie on the ventral surface of the thorax, extending from the second to the sixth rib, and from the sternum to the anterior border of the axilla. The size is variable; each gland is hemispherical in shape.

At the center of the ventral surface there is a nipple. This is cylindrical in shape, with a rounded tip containing 15 to 20 depressions into which ducts from the lobes of the gland empty. The structure is shown in Figure 413. The nipple is surrounded by a pigmented area called the *areola*, which becomes deep brown in color during pregnancy.

The upper and medial part of the dorsal surface of the mammary gland is in contact with the fascia over the pectoralis major muscle. The lower and lateral part is in contact with lymph nodes in the axilla and the serratus anterior muscle.

Each gland is composed of 15 to 20 lobes; there is an increase in the fat in the connective tissue between the lobes and the lobules at the age of puberty. Each lobe consists of many lobules. Each main lactiferous duct gives rise to many intralobular ducts. The nonlactating breast probably contains no secretory alveoli but consists only of a duct system. The glands are composed of epithelial glandular tissue and supporting connective tissue. The blood supply is by way of the internal mammary artery. Lymphatic vessels drain into the axillary lymph nodes. Both efferent and afferent nerve fibers are abundant.

DEVELOPMENT OF THE REPRODUCTIVE SYSTEM

There is no structural difference in early human embryos that reveals the sex of the developing individual. This means that both sexes possess the same embryonic structures and that differentiation of the sexes takes place later. The names of the embryonic structures and the *homologous* (meaning "the same") forms in male and female are shown in the following table. The structures that function in the adult are shown in bold type.

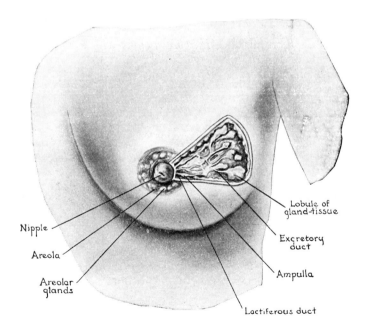

Nipple

Areola

Areolar
glands

Lobule of
gland-tissue

Excretory
duct

Ampulla

Lactiferous duct

Fig. 413. Left mammary gland; drawn from living subject. Ducts and glandular tissue drawn from dissection.

Embryonic Structure	Male	Female
Genital ridge	Testis; gubernaculum testis (fetal) cord to guide descent of testis	Ovary; ovarian and round ligaments
Wolffian body	Head of epididymis; paradidymis; vas aberrans	Epoophoron; paraoophoron
Wolffian duct	Body and tail of epididymis; ductus deferens; ejaculatory duct	Longitudinal tubule of epoophoron; canal of Gartner
Müllerian duct	Prostatic utriculus	Uterine tubes; uterus; vagina
Urogenital sinus	Cavernous portion of urethra	Vestibule
Genital tubercle	Penis	Clitoris
Genital folds	Skin and prepuce of penis	Labia minora; prepuce of clitoris
Genital swellings	Scrotum	Labia majora

SEQUENCE OF EVENTS IN REPRODUCTION

The process of reproduction really begins with the development and the maturation of germ cells of the parents, then progresses through ovulation, fertilization, implantation, development of the ovum through the embryonic and the fetal phases and, eventually, birth (parturition) or delivery of the new individual from the uterus to the external world.

The entire life span of an individual comprises both intra-uterine and extra-uterine periods.

The intra-uterine or prenatal period lasts about 280 days and may be subdivided into the following:

Pre-embryonic or Period of the Ovum. The duration is from 10 to 14 days. It extends from the time of fertilization to implantation or until the zygote (fertilized ovum) is separated into embryonic and nonembryonic portions.

Period of the Embryo. This extends from the time of implantation (10 to 14 days) to the end of the second month. During this time the rudiments of all the main organs of the adult are evolved.

Period of the Fetus. This extends from the beginning of the third month to birth, and during fetal life the organs and the systems of the body develop. The developing individual assumes a human appearance at the beginning of this period. During the periods of the embryo and the fetus the nourishment of the new individual is taken care of by the mother, since the growing organism is parasitic until birth.

The extra-uterine or postnatal life may be subdivided into the following:

PERIOD OF THE NEWBORN OR NEONATAL PERIOD. This extends from birth to the end of the second week.

PERIOD OF INFANCY. This extends from the end of the second week to the end of the first year or until the assumption of the erect posture which usually is between the twelfth and the fourteenth months.

PERIOD OF CHILDHOOD. This extends from the end of the first year to about the fourteenth year in girls and the sixteenth year in boys, when puberty occurs.

PERIOD OF ADOLESCENCE. This extends from puberty to the late 'teens in girls and to the early twenties in boys.

PERIOD OF MATURITY. This extends from the end of the adolescent period to senility or old age.

Development continues throughout mature life, until the retrogressive or degenerative changes of senility occur.

HUMAN EMBRYOLOGY; DEVELOPMENTAL ANATOMY

Human embryology is a study of the changes during intra-uterine life or the development of the individual from fertilization to birth. It is properly begun with the origin of the parents who are to reproduce or give origin to a new individual of the next generation.

Each parent began existence as a single cell (fertilized ovum), and all of the more than 25 trillion cells of the body grew from this one cell. The mother originated from the ovum of the new individual's maternal grandmother and a spermatozoon of the maternal grandfather. The father originated from the ovum of the new individual's paternal grandmother and a spermatozoon of the paternal grandfather.

The cells that developed from the fertilized ovum of either the maternal or the paternal grandmother were of 2 types: soma cells and germ cells.

The soma cells gave rise to almost all of the cells of the entire body and also produced membranes and other structures that were necessary for the nourishment and the protection of the growing organism during intra-uterine life.

The germ cells were those upon which the life of the species depended, as they linked one generation with the next, and it is these that are concerned with the child which the parents are to produce.

The germ cells of each parent became differentiated when the mother and the father were embryos of 6 weeks. At this early date they could be distinguished from the soma cells. The germinal tissue differentiated into gonads (ovaries of the mother and testes of the father) by the tenth or the eleventh week of intra-uterine life, but the germ cells did not become functional until puberty.

MATURATION OF GERM CELLS

In the course of their complete development, germ cells undergo a change, called *maturation,* that is peculiar to them and never occurs in any other cells of the body. It begins at the age of puberty. It is a modified mitosis, in which, although there is a division of the cytoplasm, there is no splitting of the chromosomes, so each of the 2 daughter cells formed contains only one half of the number of chromosomes of the original cell. Sometimes maturation is called *reduction division,* since the number of chromosomes is reduced to one half.

In the development of the ovum, the primary germ cell (oogonium) grows and becomes a primary oocyte. The primary oocyte, in turn, undergoes maturation or reduction division (while still in the growing ovarian follicle), and the chromosomes are reduced in number. The 2 daughter cells are unequal in size; the larger is called a *secondary oocyte,* and the smaller or abortive cell is called the *first polar body.* This process is shown in Figure 401.

During ovulation, the secondary oocyte undergoes an ordinary mitosis, with a splitting of the chromosomes, and, again, the two daughter cells are unequal in size. The larger is the mature ovum, and the smaller is the second polar body. This mitosis probably is completed after the ovum has entered the uterine tube. The first polar body may undergo ordinary mitosis and produce a third polar body. Thus, from each primary oocyte, 1 mature ovum and 3 polar bodies are produced, each with 24 chromosomes. The polar bodies perform no function. Figure 414 (from *a* through *e*) shows maturation of an ovum.

The mature human ovum is the largest cell in the body; it is enclosed in protective structures and contains stored food material, called the *yolk,* that serves to nourish the new individual in the earliest stages of development. The nucleus is large and spherical and is surrounded by a nuclear membrane. Mitochondria are present in the cytoplasm. The nucleus contains chromatin material (23

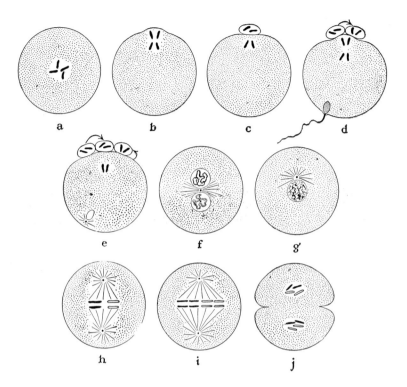

FIG. 414. Diagram of maturation (a, b, c, d, e), fertilization (d, e, f, g) and first division of segmentation (h, i, j). *Maturation.* In b and c, the first division is a modified mitosis, with no splitting of chromosomes; in c, the two resulting cells are unequal in size; reduction in chromosome number is indicated; the abortive cell is called the first polar body. In d, the second division is beginning, and the first polar body divides as indicated by arrows. In e, the second division is like an ordinary mitosis; the second abortive cell is formed.

Fertilization. In d and e, fertilization is indicated by the entrance of the head and middle piece of the spermatozoon into the ovum. In f, the nuclear material of the spermatozoon becomes the male pronucleus; and the nucleus of the ovum, the female pronucleus. In g, the pronuclei unite to form the fusion or cleavage nucleus of the zygote.

Segmentation. In h, the chromosomes are formed again and the centrosomes have moved to the poles. In i, the chromosomes on the equatorial plane have divided. In j, the fertilized ovum completes division; each daughter cell contains chromosomes from each parent cell; those from one parent are shown as solid bodies; those from the other are shown in outline.

regular and 1 "X" chromosome) and a nucleolus. The path that the ovum follows after ovulation is shown by diagram in Figure 406.

In the testes, the male germ cells (spermatogonia) become primary spermatocytes that undergo modified mitosis and maturation, in which there is no splitting of chromosomes. Two types of cells, called *secondary spermatocytes*, are formed from each primary spermatocyte. In one type, there are 23 regular chromosomes and an "X" chromosome, and in the other type there are 23 regular chromosomes and a "Y" chromosome.

Secondary spermatocytes undergo ordinary mitosis, and again 2 equal cells are produced, each with 24 chromosomes; these cells are called *spermatids*. Thus, in the testes, each germ cell produces 4 spermatids (2 with an "X" and 2 with a "Y" chromosome, in addition to 23 regular chromosomes). This is in contrast with the ovaries, in which each germ cell produces only 1 mature ovum, and all mature ova contain 23 regular and an "X" chromosome.

Spermatids are transformed into spermatozoa (p. 758); the beginning of the tail formation is shown in the spermatids in Figure 401, and the various phases of spermatogenesis are shown in Figure 400.

The head of the spermatozoon contains the nucleus and the 24 chromosomes; the middle piece contains the centrosome. The tail serves as a propeller. The course of spermatozoa after they are released from the testes is shown in Figure 397, and the course in the female genital tract is shown in Figure 406.

Thus the mature germ cells (called *gametes*) of the mother and the father are prepared for fertilization (union). The genes (units in the transmission of hereditary characteristics) of their chromosomes are concerned in inheritance of heredity; they carry all the factors that determine the constitution of the new individual. The germ plasm produces many different structures with widely different functions, including body characteristics (somatic) and the possibility of reproduction (germ cells).

The male and the female gametes are highly specialized cells; each contains 24 chromosomes, hence it cannot undergo mitosis. They have only two possible courses to follow. The first is to unite with a gamete of the opposite sex to produce a new individual. The second possibility is to disintegrate. An unfertilized ovum begins to degenerate in a day or two after ovulation and is completely disintegrated in the uterus. Spermatozoa disintegrate within 2 days.

FERTILIZATION

Fertilization consists of the entrance of the head and the middle

piece of one spermatozoon into a mature ovum; it is illustrated in
Figure 414.

If an "X" chromosome-bearing spermatozoon unites with the
ovum, the resulting individual is a female. If a "Y" chromosome-
bearing spermatozoon unites with the ovum the resulting individual is a male. Thus, sex determination is established by the type of
spermatozoon that fertilizes the ovum, but the differentiation is
due to the action of hormones and perhaps other factors at a later
time.

The nuclear material in the head becomes the male pronucleus,
and the nucleus of the ovum becomes the female pronucleus. The
two pronuclei unite to form a fusion or cleavage nucleus (shown
in g, Fig. 414). Since each pronucleus contributes 24 chromosomes,
the fertilized ovum contains 48 chromosomes, which is the number
characteristic for the body cells of man.

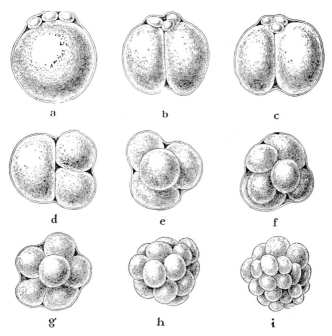

FIG. 415. Segmentation of the fertilized ovum. The ovum
divides into 2 then 4, and so on indefinitely. The resulting solid
mass of cells, i, is called a morula, since it resembles a mulberry.
(Modified from Sobotta)

The chromosomes break down into chromatin granules, which intermingle to form a typical nucleus. The father's part in reproduction is now complete, but the mother's part continues through the intra-uterine life of the new individual and ends only after she has expelled the fetus from the uterus.

The fertilized ovum is called a *zygote;* it is the beginning of the new individual of the next generation, who at this time is a 1-celled organism with 48 chromosomes. In this 1 cell are contained all the potentialities of the new person, such as body build, intellectual capacity, ambition, special talents and the power to do right or wrong. These are latent possibilities; the use one makes of them depends on the person himself. Few persons live up to the best of which they are capable, in intellectual and other attainments. So much depends on whether one forms good or bad habits early in life and whether or not he feels responsible for the privilege of living and contributing to the welfare of the human race.

SEGMENTATION

The zygote begins immediately to divide by ordinary mitosis, and the new individual passes rapidly through a 2-celled, 4-celled, 8-celled stage, and so on. The new cells are much smaller than the ovum.

As cell division continues, a solid mass of cells called a *morula* (because it resembles a mulberry) is formed. This is illustrated in Figure 415. Differentiation has begun already, since the cells are varied in size. The segmenting mass is being moved along toward the uterus, which it reaches in 3 to 6 days, probably while in the morula stage.

Next, a cavity appears in the mass of cells, and the dividing cells now differentiate into an outer layer or shell, called the *trophoblast* or *trophectoderm,* and a cluster of cells called the *inner cell mass* (Fig. 416), by the time it is 10 days of age.

The trophoblast forms the chorion or outer covering of the growing mass and also gives rise to the membranes that nourish and protect the embryo and attach it to the uterine mucosa of the mother. By the time the developing mass is 10 to 12 days of age it is sinking into the uterine mucosa and establishing connection by means of the chorionic villi. After this a period of very rapid growth ensues.

Two cavities appear in the inner cell mass, and the zygote appears as 3 spheres. The upper cavity is called the *amniotic* cavity, and its side walls form the amniotic membrane. The lower cavity is the yolk sac; both are shown in *c* of Figure 416 and in *a* of Fig-

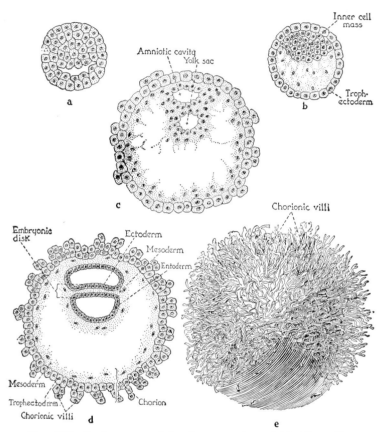

FIG. 416. Early stages of development. (a and b) The cells are separated into a peripheral layer and an inner cell mass. The peripheral layer is called the trophoblast or trophectoderm; the entire structure is called a blastodermic vesicle. (c) The formation of the amniotic cavity and yolk sac is indicated; the former is lined by ectoderm; the latter is lined by entoderm. (d) The location of the embryonic disk, and the 3 germ layers are shown, together with the beginning of the chorionic villi. (e) The external appearance of the developing mass is shown; the chorionic villi are abundant.

ure 417. The 2 cavities are separated by a plate of cells called the *embryonic plate* or *disk*. While this is going on, a new layer of cells appears on the outer surface of the inner cell mass and is called the *extra-embryonic mesoderm*. These cells grow until they form a complete lining for the original cavity of the morula, and

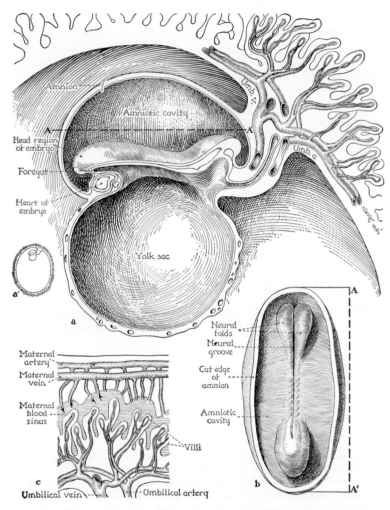

FIG. 417. (a) The developing embryonic disk is shown, between the amniotic cavity and the yolk sac; the umbilical vessels are shown in the body stalk. (a′) The entire blastodermic vesicle is shown in its actual size, at the same age. (b) The structures of the embryonic disk, as seen on looking down from above, are shown. The neural folds and neural groove are evident. The section is indicated by the line A-A′ on a and the orientation is indicated on b in the same manner. (c) The structure of the placenta is shown diagrammatically; the maternal and fetal circulations are distinct.

this cavity is now called the *extra-embryonic coelom*. The meso-dermal cells also form a short connecting stalk between the inner cell mass and the trophoblast.

The embryonic disk, which lies between the amniotic and the yolk sac cavities, gives rise to the embryo. In the third week of life 3 sheets of cells are present, which are called the *germ* layers: ectoderm, entoderm and mesoderm.

The ectoderm or upper layer forms the floor of the amniotic cavity and becomes continuous with the walls of the amnion at the margins of the embryonic disk.

The entoderm or lower layer forms the roof of the yolk sac and is continued as the inner walls of this cavity at the margins of the embryonic disk.

The embryonic mesoderm or middle layer is an incomplete plate of cells between the ectoderm and the entoderm. At the margins of the embryonic disk, it becomes continuous with the extra-embry-onic mesoderm that covers the outer surface of the inner cell mass. The 3 layers are shown in Figure 418.

By means of further changes and differentiation, the following struc-tures arise from each germ layer.

From the Ectoderm: (1) the nervous system; (2) the epithelium of the skin and its appendages; (3) the lining of the oral, the nasal and the anal passages, the paranasal sinuses, the enamel of teeth and the salivary glands; (4) parts of the eye (lens, iris, retina, epithelium or cornea, conjunctiva, lacrimal glands) and part of the ear; (5) the vesti-bule in the female and a portion of the urethra in the male, with asso-ciated glands; (6) the anterior lobe of the pituitary gland and the medulla of the adrenal gland.

From the Entoderm: (1) epithelial lining of the digestive tract with exception of the mouth, part of the pharynx and the anal canal; (2)

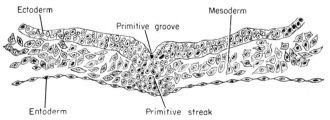

FIG. 418. Origin of mesoderm from the primitive streak, as shown in a human embryo (Mateer) cut transversally (after Streeter) ×185. (Arey, L. B.: Developmental Anatomy, ed. 6, Philadelphia, Saunders)

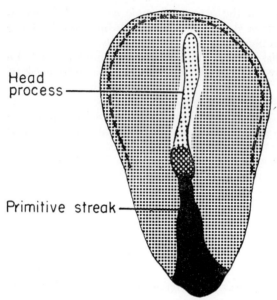

Head process

Primitive streak

FIG. 419. Embryo with primitive streak and head process. ×26. (Arey, L. B.: Developmental Anatomy, ed 6, Philadelphia, Saunders)

parenchyma of the digestive glands, including the pancreas and the liver; (3) the lining of the respiratory tract; (4) lining of part of the urinary bladder, the female urethra, part of the male urethra and associated glands; (5) parenchyma of the thyroid and the parathyroids and part of the thymus.

From the Mesoderm: (1) skeletal, muscular and connective tissues of the body; (2) vascular system, with lymphatic and blood-making organs (hemopoietic); (3) lining of pleural, pericardial and peritoneal cavities; (4) kidneys, ureters and part of urinary bladder; (5) gonads, ducts and accessory structures; (6) dentin and cementum of the teeth; (7) cortex of the adrenal gland.

CHANGES IN EMBRYONIC DISK

The ectoderm and the entoderm in the posterior part of the longitudinal axis of the embryonic disk fuse, forming a band of cells, called the *primitive streak,* that is indented by the dorsal primitive groove.

In front of the primitive streak the cells multiply, and the 3 germ layers fuse to form the primitive node or knot, which is concerned with the formation of the head process. The roof of the head process forms the notochord. The notochord is the foundation of the axial skeleton or the primitive backbone. It extends throughout the length of the future vertebral column.

A structure called the *allantois* arises from the posterior end of the roof of the yolk sac and grows upward into the connecting body stalk. Some of these structures are shown in Figure 419.

The flat embryonic disk now becomes transformed into the cylindrical form of the embryo. The portion near the head process grows more rapidly than the parts farther away and folds over, forming a cylinder with ectoderm on the outer wall and entoderm on the inner. The cavity inside the cylinder becomes the primitive gastro-intestinal cavity; it opens into the yolk sac through a large opening that later becomes much smaller.

EARLY CHANGES IN THE GERM LAYERS

The ectoderm along the mid-line of the embryonic disk thickens into the neural plate. The lateral margins of the plate grow rapidly and rise from the surface of the disk as a pair of longitudinal neural folds (Fig. 417, *b*). These folds fuse in the mid-line and form the neural tube that gives rise to the brain, the spinal cord, the retinae and the optic nerves. The ectoderm that covers the periphery of the embryonic disk is carried over the dorsal surface of the neural tube with the infolding of the neural folds and forms the external covering of the embryo.

The entoderm folds into the primitive digestive tube. The greater part of the permanent alimentary canal is derived from the yolk sac and is lined with entodermal cells.

The mesoderm has 2 origins: extra-embryonic mesoderm of the inner cell mass and the embryonic mesoderm from the primitive streak, the node and the head process. The embryonic mesoderm appears as a pair of plates on either side of the longitudinal embryonic axis and is continuous with the extra-embryonic mesoderm laterally.

Each plate of embryonic mesoderm is composed of 3 parts:

MEDIAL MESODERM, which forms somites. These later divide into dermomyotomes and sclerotomes. The dermomyotomes form the muscles, and the sclerotomes form the axial skeleton. Probably both parts of the somite contribute to the mesenchyme that forms the connective tissue of the body wall and the supporting structures and the voluntary muscles of the extremities. The anterior portion of the medial mesoderm does not form somites; it gives origin to muscles of the head region, the cranial bones and the connective tissues.

INTERMEDIATE MESODERM gives rise to the genito-urinary systems.

LATERAL MESODERM divides into somatic and splanchnic layers, with a cavity or coelom between. Later this cavity will contain the heart, the lungs and the abdominal viscera.

DEVELOPMENT OF VARIOUS SYSTEMS

This material is condensed greatly; for further information text-books on embryology should be consulted.

The face and some of the other structures in the head and the neck region arise from a series of branchial arches. The face begins to assume human form in 5 to 8 weeks. The nose is broad and flat, and the nostrils are far apart, at first. Later the bridge of the nose is elevated and prolonged into the tip, and the nostrils point downward.

The limb buds appear as elevations on ridges on either side of the embryonic disk, during the fifth week. The future limbs grow rapidly, and the distal parts soon flatten. Constrictions appear at the sites of the wrist, the elbow, the ankle and the knee. Furrows appear on the flat distal ends and later are converted into fissures that separate the fingers and the toes.

The primitive gastro-intestinal tract is a tube of entoderm rolled up on the roof of the yolk sac; digestive glands, as well as the respiratory system, are outgrowths of the digestive tract. The primitive tract differentiates into 3 chief segments: mouth, pharynx and digestive tube. The lining consists of entoderm; accessory coats come from the splanchnic mesoderm, as does the mesentery (a part of the peritoneum). At each end, the alimentary tract comes in contact with ectoderm and forms the oral and cloacal (meaning "sewer") membranes. The oral membrane ruptures in the fifth week. The cloaca, or caudal end of the gut, receives the allantois, the urinary and the genital ducts. It subdivides dorsally into the rectum and ventrally into the urogenital sinus. The subdivision is complete during the seventh week, and the cloacal membrane ruptures at this time. The liver and the pancreas arise as outpouchings from the walls of the duodenum.

The lungs and the respiratory passages arise from the ventral wall of the pharynx. At first the pleural cavity communicates with that of the abdomen, but during the eighth week it is separated from it by the diaphragm.

The urinary and the genital systems arise from the mesoderm of the intermediate cell mass (intermediate mesoderm) and are intermingled during development. There is a common fold, called the *genital* fold, that appears during the fifth week and later differentiates into nephric and genital ridges.

Three pairs of kidneys appear in sequence in the human embryo.

THE FIRST KIDNEY is called the *pronephros,* the tubules of which degenerate early. The only part of the pronephros that functions and persists is the long excretory duct (called the *wolffian* or *mesonephric* duct) that perforates the wall of the cloaca.

THE SECOND KIDNEY, called the *mesonephros,* has a larger and more complete set of tubules, which become attached to the wolffian or mesonephric duct. These tubules arise from the urogenital fold on the posterior abdominal wall. The second kidneys function for a time, that is, from the fifth to the ninth weeks of intra-uterine life. The tubules begin to degenerate during the sixth week.

THE THIRD KIDNEY. The mesonephros is replaced by the third or permanent kidney called the *metanephros*. An evagination from the lower part of the wolffian duct develops into the ureter, the renal pelvis, the calyces and the collecting tubules of the kidney. The remaining parts of the kidney develop from the caudal part of the urogenital fold.

Wolffian Duct. The main portion of the wolffian duct does not enter into the formation of the final kidney. The main part of the wolffian duct degenerates in the female; in the male it becomes the ductus deferens. The various portions, that is, the structures from the lower part of the wolffian duct and those from the urogenital fold, unite to form the permanent kidney.

Genital System. So far as the genital system is concerned, the ducts of both the male and the female develop from the genital fold before the sex is evident. After the sex is established by the gonads, the ducts of the opposite sex degenerate. In the male, some of the mesonephric tubules are transformed into the efferent ducts of the epididymis. The rest of the wolffian duct forms the duct of the epididymis, the ductus deferens and the ejaculatory duct. It dilates to form the ampulla from the wall of which the seminal vesicles evaginate.

Müllerian Ducts. A second pair of ducts arises in the embyro, called the *müllerian ducts*. They lie near the wolffian ducts. In the female the upper parts of the müllerian ducts form the uterine tubes, and the lower portions fuse to form the uterus and the vagina. The ovaries develop from the urogenital fold. The müllerian ducts degenerate in the male.

The testes develop from the mid-portion of the urogenital fold. They lie in the abdominal cavity, at first; late in intra-uterine life they descend into the scrotum through the inguinal canal.

The external genitalia arise as a bud on the anterior body wall. They are similar in the two sexes at first and can be distinguished only after the eighth week of intra-uterine life.

Circulatory System. The development of the circulatory system is complicated. Blood corpuscles arise from the mesenchyme (a diffuse mesoderm consisting of a spongy network of branching cells). Spaces or blood islands appear in the mesenchyme that fuse and form networks or channels. The development of the blood vessels in the embryo follows that of the blood vessels in the wall of the yolk sac and the body stalk. Blood islands appear in the yolk sac during the fourth week and in the body mesenchyme in the fifth week. The liver forms blood corpuscles during the sixth week, and the spleen, the thymus and the lymph nodes form them in the second and third months. From the third month on, the bone marrow and the lymph nodes are the source of the blood corpuscles.

As the blood spaces form, the surrounding cells flatten into endothelium, and networks of blood vessels appear. The mesenchyme furnishes the accessory coats around the endothelium to form the walls of blood vessels. The vascular system begins as a paired, symmetrical system. The first paired vessels serve to establish chorionic circulation in the placental area; the aortae give off umbilical arteries that pass into the body stalk and branch in the wall of the chorion (Fig. 417, *a*). Blood returns through the umbilical vein.

Eventually, 2 large arteries and many veins are formed. Between the 2 arteries and veins are 2 heart tubes, at first unfused, lying side by side. The heart is formed as a single tube by the fusion of these 2 heart tubes. After the fusion, the tube folds into a loop, and dilatations appear. These dilatations are the forerunners of the atria and the ventricles, which are separated by septa formed later.

The third dilatation becomes the beginning of the aorta and the pulmonary artery. The 2 large arteries mentioned above now form the primitive right and left aortic vessels, which fuse at the origin and later in the abdominal region. This leaves 2 large primary aortic arches, one on either side of the body. Five pairs of communicating vessels appear between the arches. Some of these disappear and others remain. Those that remain become the common carotids, the aortic arch, and the innominate, the subclavian and the pulmonary arteries. Branches are given off to form the other arteries of the body.

Three systems of paired veins arise early. These are: the umbilical veins from the chorion, the vitelline vein from the yolk sac and the cardinal veins from the body of the embryo itself. The vitelline veins pass to the liver; these and the cardinal veins undergo transformations and replacements in the development of the venous system in its final form.

The lymphatic vessels have a separate origin from spaces in the mesenchyme. Fetal circulation is described on pages 464 to 465. The embryology of the nervous system is described on pages 316 to 320.

Fetal Organs

As soon as the developing zygote is embedded in the uterine mucosa, a whole set of fetal organs develops, which have to do with the nutrition, the respiration and the protection of the embryo and elimination of its waste products. The fetal organs are the yolk sac, the amnion, the chorion, the allantois and the umbilical cord.

The Yolk Sac. The entodermal roof of the yolk sac provides epithelium that lines almost the entire alimentary tract. In the earliest human specimens observed, the yolk sac is a small vesicle, lined with a single layer of entoderm and covered with splanchnic mesoderm. In embryos of 4 weeks the entodermal roof of the yolk sac begins to form the fore and the hind gut that are connected by means of a narrow strip to the yolk sac proper. This strip becomes the yolk stalk and later is incorporated into the umbilical cord. The stalk detaches from the gut during the sixth week and soon degenerates.

The Amnion. The amniotic cavity begins as a cleft in the inner cell mass. By the end of the third week, the primitive ectodermal roof of the amniotic cavity is covered with somatic mesoderm. The primitive amnion and the outer layer of the trophoblast are joined by mesoderm; the union is called the *body stalk*. The embryonic disk forms the floor of the amniotic cavity. The amniotic cavity enlarges and by the end of the second month fills the chorionic

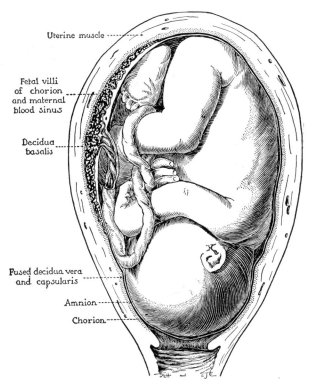

Fetal villi of chorion and maternal blood sinus

Uterine muscle

Decidua basalis

Fused decidua vera and capsularis

Amnion

Chorion

FIG. 420. Section of the uterus, showing the relation of an advanced fetus to the placenta and membranes. (Modified from Bumm)

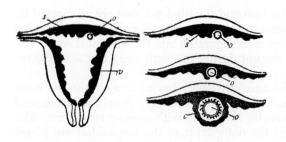

Fig. 421. Various stages in the process of implantation; the relation of the uterine mucosa to the embryonic vesicle during implantation is shown. s, Decidua basalis; v, decidua parietalis; c, decidua capsularis; and o, the ovum.

sac. The amnion (Figs. 417, 420 and 425) then fuses with the chorionic wall.

The amniotic sac is filled with clear, watery fluid that serves as a protective watery cushion. The amniotic membrane with its contained fluid forms a wedge to dilate the cervix of the uterus at the time of birth. The amnion and the amniotic fluid are called the *bag of waters.* Since the fetus is immersed in fluid during intrauterine life, the skin is protected from maceration by the fatty covering called *vernix caseosa,* which is composed of secretions of sebaceous glands together with the debris and the castoff outer cells of the epidermis. The newborn infant is covered with vernix caseosa.

The Chorion. The trophoblast attaches itself to the uterine mucosa, destroys this area and buries itself, as shown in Figure 421. The destruction of the mucosa is due to enzymes secreted by the trophoblast, and the superficial wound is closed by a portion of the trophoblast and a fibrin clot. The trophoblast with the underlying extra-embryonic mesoderm compose the chorion (Fig. 416, *d*).

Projections called *villi* develop on the outer layer of the chorion (Fig. 416, *e*); the villi branch, and mesoderm soon spreads into some of them. Blood vessels develop in the mesoderm (Fig. 417, *c*).

Due to changes in the uterine mucosa produced by the trophoblast, the embryo is surrounded by disintegrating, liquefying, mucosal components that serve as food for the embryo for a time.

The embryo is connected with the chorion by the body stalk, as shown in Figures 422 and 423. The villi in this region enlarge to form the chorion frondosum, which establishes close connections with the maternal blood spaces in the wall of the uterus. The villi on other parts of the chorion may disappear and leave a smooth surface called the *chorion laeve* (Fig. 422).

The allantois appears before the gut has assumed the tubular form. At 3 weeks it is a slender, entodermal tube, located near the dorsal surface of the yolk sac and extending into the body stalk. Only the remnants of the allantois remain by the fourth month. Its chief value lies in the fact that blood vessels accompany it, reach the chorion and vascularize it. These are the allantoic (Fig. 426) or umbilical vessels, and by means of them the embryo is put into functional connection with the maternal circulation. At 3 weeks, the umbilical vessels pass from the embryo through the body stalk to the chorion, by way of the allantois.

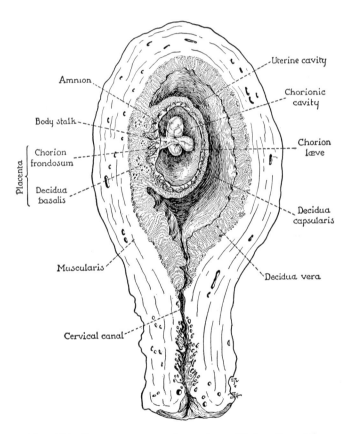

FIG. 422. Pregnant uterus, shown in sagittal section. The embryo is about 1 month of age. (Modified from Bumm)

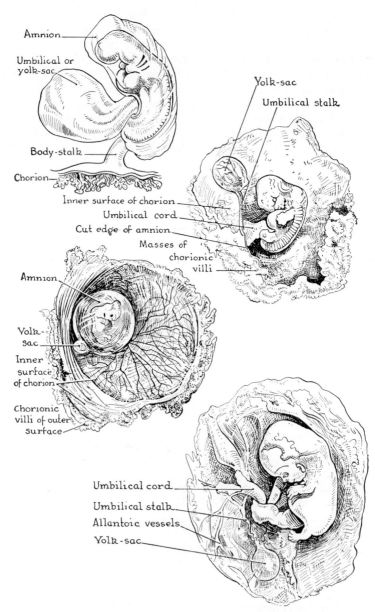

Amnion

Umbilical or
yolk-sac

Body-stalk

Chorion

Inner surface of chorion

Umbilical cord

Cut edge of amnion

Masses of
chorionic
villi

Yolk-sac

Umbilical stalk

Amnion

Yolk-
sac

Inner
surface
of chorion

Chorionic
villi of outer
surface

Umbilical cord

Umbilical stalk

Allantoic vessels

Yolk-sac

FIGURES 423 to 426 *(Captions on facing page)*

The Umbilical Cord. The primitive umbilicus is the open area at the junction of the embryonic and the extra-embryonic mesoderm, through which the yolk stalk, the body stalk and the allantois pass. During the sixth week the umbilical cord comes into existence. It is formed by wrapping the amnion around the above structures. The umbilical cord contains the yolk stalk, the vitelline vessels, the allantois and the allantoic or umbilical vessels. It connects the fetus to that part of the chorion that constitutes the fetal half of the placenta throughout intra-uterine life. The umbilical cord is shown in Figures 420, 424 and 426.

MATERNAL MEMBRANES

Structures derived from the uterus are essential to the nourishment of the embryo by the mother. The endometrium of the pregnant uterus becomes the decidua. That portion of endometrium that lies under the implanted mass is called the *decidua basalis*. It lies between the chorionic sac and the myometrium. The decidua basalis is shown in Figures 420 and 422.

The portion of the endometrium that is reflected upon and surrounds the embryo is called the *decidua capsularis* (Fig. 422), and the remainder of the endometrium is called the *decidua parietalis* or *vera* (Fig. 422).

The placenta consists of fetal and maternal portions, the chorium frondosum and the decidua basalis, respectively. Each part has its own separate circulation, and there is no communication between the fetal and the maternal circulations (Fig. 417, *c*). The umbilical vessels are shown in Figure 417, *a*. The placenta is shown in Figures 417, *c*, 420 and 422.

During the third week of pregnancy the placenta occupies one fifteenth of the internal uterine surface; by the end of the second month this has increased to one third of the uterine surface. The decidua, together with the fetal membranes, is thrown off soon after the delivery of the infant, and they constitute the after-birth.

FIG. 423. (*Top*) Human embryo of about 24 days enclosed within the amnion. ✕30. FIG. 424. (*Middle, right*) Human embryo of about 38 days. ✕4. Amnion and chorion have been cut and turned aside. FIG. 425. (*Middle, left*) Chorion sac of 45-day embryo laid open, showing embryo closed by amnion. ✕2. FIG. 426. (*Bottom*) Human fetus of about 9 weeks. ✕3½. Amnion has been cut and reflected, but still covers the umbilical vesicle and its stalk. (All figures after Piersol)

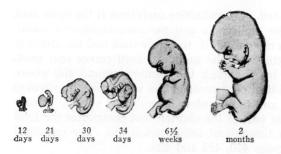

FIG. 427. Various stages in the development of the embryo and fetus, actual size. (Keibel and Mall)

| 12 days | 21 days | 30 days | 34 days | 6½ weeks | 2 months |

SUMMARY OF GROWTH OF THE EMBRYO
(From *Gray's Anatomy of the Human Body*)

First week: fertilization, segmentation to blastocyst with trophoblast and inner cell mass.

Second week: implantation. Actively invading uterine mucosa; chorionic villi. Amnion. Inner cell mass becomes embryonic disk and yolk sac begins to form. Primitive streak forms and gives off mesoderm. Notochord begins to form. Eleven days is the age of the youngest known human embryo.

Third week: neural folds appear, allantoic duct begins to develop, yolk sac enlarges, and blood vessels begin to form. Neural folds begin to unite before end of week. Primitive segments begin to form.

Fourth week: neural folds close; segments increase in number; branchial arches appear; connection of yolk sac with embryo narrower; limb buds begin to show; heart increases in size; rudiments of otic vesicles appear.

Fifth week: embryo curved; head increased greatly in size, and limb buds begin to show segments. Branchial arches change and begin to disappear. Superficial nose, eye and ear rudiments become prominent. Ear sinks into interior of head.

Sixth week: rudiments of fingers and toes recognized. Head grows rapidly. Lens of eyes formed; olfactory pits evident; lateral parts of primitive lip formed.

Seventh and eighth weeks: neck longer; upper lip completed; rudiments of fingers appear. Nose more prominent; nostrils directed forward. Eyelids present as folds. Margins of auricles of ears defined. Tips of fingers and toes free. Assumes human appearance.

Third month: head extended and neck lengthened. Eyelids fuse, and eyes remain closed until the end of the sixth month. Limbs well developed. Nails begin to appear on digits. Anal pit formed. Can tell sex by external genitalia.

Fourth month: hair begins to appear on body; increase in size of all parts of body.

Fifth month: fetal movements felt by mother; hair on head. Vernix caseosa produced by sebaceous glands of fetus.

Sixth month: body covered with fine hairs, called lanugo. More vernix caseosa. Papillae of skin; nails project from corium of dermis. Skin wrinkled; eyelashes and eyebrows appear.

Seventh month: eyes open. Testes descend into scrotum with a sac of peritoneum (tunica vaginalis). Weight of fetus about 3 pounds.

Eighth month: skin pink; well coated with vernix caseosa. Lanugo begins to disappear. Subcutaneous fat appears; fetus looks plump. Weighs 4½ to 5 pounds.

Ninth month: lanugo gone; testes in scrotum. Skin paler. 6½ to 8 pounds.

The appearance of the embryo and the fetus at various ages is shown in Figure 427.

PREGNANCY

We must consider again the mother in whose uterus the development of the embryo and growth of the fetus has been taking place. From the beginning of pregnancy the uterus enlarges to keep pace with the growth of the fetus. By the end of the fourth lunar month the fundus of the uterus is about halfway between the symphysis pubis and the umbilicus. By the end of the sixth month the fundus is at the level of the umbilicus. By the end of the ninth month the fundus has risen to the end of the sternum, but as the fetus now settles into the pelvis the fundus falls a little below the sternum during the tenth lunar month of pregnancy. The factors that enter into the increase in size of the uterus are discussed on pages 770 and 776.

Throughout the period of pregnancy, the mother carries, protects and nourishes the new life. The period of pregnancy lasts about 280 days (10 lunar months of 28 days each) or 40 weeks, after which the new individual is ready for extra-uterine existence. The mother can feel "life" from the fifth month on. The fetal heart sounds can be heard through the mother's abdominal wall as early as the fifth month.

The mother supplies oxygen and eliminates carbon dioxide for the fetus; she furnishes food, water and inorganic salts and eliminates waste. The mother must eat for two during pregnancy; the demand for extra calcium is great, as the bones and the teeth of the fetus require large amounts of it. An extra load is placed on the mother's kidneys to eliminate nitrogenous waste. Frequent urine analyses and blood pressure determinations are advised during pregnancy to detect any signs of toxicity or kidney failure.

Because of increased pressure in the pelvis, the mother may have frequency of urination; she may note nausea, vomiting and constipation during the early months of pregnancy. As a rule,

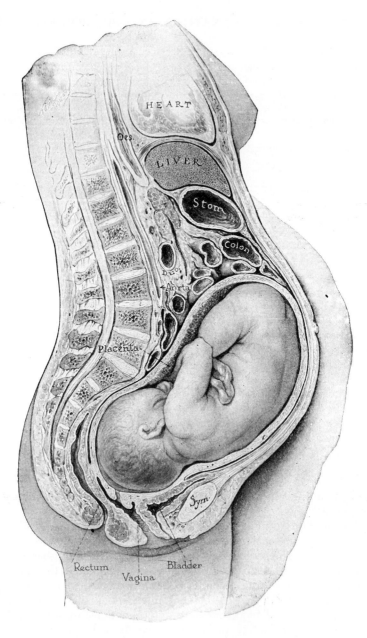

FIG. 428. Fetus in uterus at term. Sagittal section, showing head
engaged about the beginning of labor.

when the uterus rises out of the pelvis at the fourth month the nausea and the vomiting cease. Figure 428 illustrates the size of the uterus at term.

There are no nerve connections between the mother and the fetus; the possibility of maternal impressions affecting the fetus is surely very slight.

PARTURITION

The delivery of an infant at the end of pregnancy is called *parturition*. The muscles of the uterus begin to contract at term. The contractions are accompanied by severe pains that are called *labor pains*. With each uterine contraction the amniotic sac is forced into the cervical canal and acts as a wedge to dilate the canal. The first stage of labor consists of the dilatation of the cervix. In a typical delivery, the amniotic sac ruptures just at the close of this stage, and the amniotic fluid escapes. This is called the *rupture of the bag of waters*.

When the dilatation of the cervical canal is completed, the second stage of labor begins. This refers to the delivery of the infant, normally head first, through the cervical canal and vagina. It is at the time of the delivery of the head that tears may occur in the

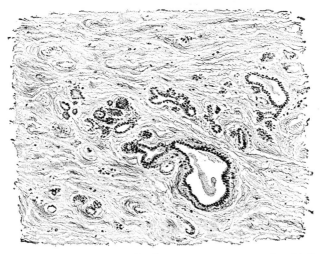

Fig. 429. Mammary gland as seen in section at the third month of pregnancy. There are no well-developed lobules, but there are scattered glandular elements. ×90.

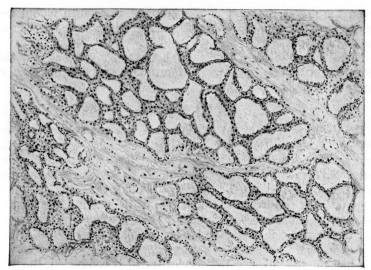

Fig. 430. Mammary gland during lactation. ×90.

pelvic floor. Many obstetricians perform an episiotomy (surgical incision of the vulvar orifice) to prevent spontaneous tears, and they repair the pelvic floor before the mother leaves the delivery room.

In the third stage of labor the delivery of the placenta or after-birth takes place. After this the uterus decreases in size rapidly. Part of this decrease is due to elastic tissue, but much of it is due to the contraction of the smooth muscle fibers of the myometrium. This tends to close the open spaces of the endometrium or denuded walls of the uterus and prevent bleeding. A fatal hemorrhage can occur if the uterine muscle relaxes at this time.

LACTATION

Estrogens produce growth of the duct system of the mammary glands, and progesterone stimulates development of the alveoli. The mammary glands reach their final development at the end of pregnancy. The lactogenic or luteotrophic hormone of the anterior lobe of the pituitary gland stimulates the production of milk in the mammary glands that have been prepared by estrogen and pro-gesterone. The mammary glands secrete milk for the nourishment of the newborn infant. The process is called *lactation*.

Changes begin to take place in the mammary glands as soon as the developing zygote is implanted in the uterus. During the first half of pregnancy the epithelium of the lobes increases rapidly, and secretory portions are formed, as shown in Figure 429. During the latter half of pregnancy the cells begin to produce a secretion so that at the end of pregnancy colostrum appears. This is the fluid that is obtained from the breasts before the secretion of true milk begins. It may be expressed from the breasts immediately after delivery and is ingested by the child during the first 2 days of postnatal life.

Colostrum, which is formed in small quantities, is a yellowish fluid, containing fat globules and multinucleated cells loaded with particles of fat. Colostrum differs from true milk in that it contains little or no caseinogen but, instead, contains about 8 per cent of lactalbumin and lactoglobulin. Lactose and fat are present in smaller, and inorganic salts in greater, amount than in true milk. Colostrum is supposed to have a laxative effect on the newborn. The lactating gland is illustrated in Figure 430.

For the maintenance of secretion, removal of milk is absolutely essential. If milk is not removed, the swelling of the breasts eventually disappears, milk ceases to be produced, and the mammary glands undergo involution. Under normal conditions, the production of milk continues for 6 to 9 months after the infant is born. The changes in the glands during pregnancy are due to the internal secretions of the ovaries. At parturition, the lactogenic hormone (luteotrophic) of the anterior lobe of the pituitary gland stimulates the secretion of milk; after delivery, the repeated emptying of the breast is the stimulus for continued secretion.

PRACTICAL CONSIDERATIONS

Castration is the removal of the gonads.

Hermaphrodism is the condition in which there is actually, or apparently, a combination of both sexes in one individual, in that both ovaries and testes are present. The external genitalia show mixed male and female components; the secondary sexual characteristics are intermediate.

Undescended Testes. The testes normally migrate from their original position on either side of the upper 2 lumbar vertebrae, opposite the lower extremity of the kidney, into the scrotum. The descent may be stopped at any point between the original and the final positions. If the arrest occurs in the abdominal cavity the result is called *cryptorchidism*. Spermatogenesis does not occur in the undescended testes, because of the higher temperature in the abdomen.

Anorchidism. In this condition there is a congenital absence of the testes.

Orchitis is inflammation of the testes; usually it is due to mumps, gonorrhea, syphilis or tuberculosis.

Sterility means an inability to reproduce; it may occur in either men or women. In men, the germ cells of the seminiferous tubules are very sensitive to infectious diseases, alcoholism, dietary deficiencies, local injury and inflammation. In such conditions the seminiferous tubules undergo degenerative changes. Exposure to x-rays likewise produces degeneration, if the exposure is sufficiently great. In women sterility may be due to changes in the ovaries or a failure of ova to pass along the uterine tubes.

Varicocele. The most frequent pathologic condition associated with the spermatic cord is varicocele. This is an enlargement of the veins of the cord.

Vesiculitis is inflammation of the seminal vesicles. It is due most commonly to gonorrhea or tuberculosis.

Enlargement of the Prostate Gland. This occurs frequently in men as they grow older and is usually due to adenoma of the mucous glands. The enlargement leads to compression of the prostatic portion of the urethra and makes micturition difficult. The bladder is not emptied completely, and the residual urine leads to dilatation of the bladder and the possibility of cystitis. The patient may become incontinent, that is, unable to control the emptying of the bladder. Cancer of the prostate gland occurs fairly frequently in elderly men, with the same difficulties in urination listed above. The cancer metastasizes to bones and alters the level of phosphatase in the blood. Sometimes malignant tumors of the prostate are treated by castration, since the growth of tumor cells, like the prostatic cells, is influenced by testosterone.

Enlargement of the prostate usually is treated by surgical removal.

Circumcision refers to removal of a part or all of the prepuce.

Hypospadias is the condition in which there is an abnormal opening of the urethra on the under side of the penis. In the female it is an abnormal opening of the urethra into the vagina.

Epispadias is the condition in which there is an abnormal opening of the urethra on the dorsum of the penis. In the female, it is a fissure of the upper wall of the urethra.

Salpingitis is inflammation of the uterine tubes and is due most often to gonorrhea. Usually it is accompanied by vaginitis, cervicitis, endometritis and oophoritis. Infections of the ovaries and the tubes readily spread to the peritonium and set up a local peritonitis. In this condition a large part of the pelvic contents becomes adherent to surrounding structures, and pus may be formed.

Tumors. Frequently, the uterus is the site of cancer. It also is involved frequently by a hard, fibrous tumor growth called a *fibroid.* Ovarian cysts are common and are due to a variety of causes. Cancer of the breast is common; it spreads to the axillary lymph nodes, and these are removed, together with the breast, in a radical breast operation.

Position of the Uterus. *Retroversion* of the uterus refers to a backward displacement of the body of the uterus; it is the chief function of the round ligaments to prevent retroversion. When the uterine ligaments are stretched and the pelvic floor weakened, the uterus may descend to a lower level than usual, and then it is said to be *prolapsed.*

Hygiene of Menstruation. Women should suffer no undue difficulties during the menstrual period. Dysmenorrhea (difficult menstruation) may accompany poor posture or constipation. General exercise is permitted during the period. A daily warm bath is conducive to comfort and is not harmful. Mental depression, backache and headache frequently precede the period. Amenorrhea is the absence of the menses; it may occur temporarily with changes in routine of living. It characterizes some glandular disorders and commonly is characteristic of pregnancy.

Hygiene of the Menopause. There are subjective symptoms during the early years of the menopause. Due to instability of the vasomotor system, hot flashes and outbursts of sweating occur. There may be vague muscular and joint pains, headache and temporary edema of the ankles. Many women experience emotional instability at this time. It seems as if women who are busy with interesting work take the menopause and its slight discomforts in their stride; they have no time to think of their hot flashes and headaches. Women who have time on their hands, with nothing that demands their attention, are more inclined to think of themselves and, in becoming self-centered, they capitalize on every discomfort. It is entirely up to each woman how she reacts to this natural phase of her life.

Ectopic Pregnancy. Fertilization normally takes place in the uterine tube. In some cases the ovum does not enter the tube but remains in the abdominal cavity and is fertilized there. This condition is called an *abdominal ectopic pregnancy.* The ovum may remain attached to the ovary and be fertilized there; the result is an *ovarian ectopic pregnancy*. Even if the ovum enters the tube and is fertilized there, its subsequent passage to the uterus may be prevented by adhesions. The result is a *tubal ectopic pregnancy*. In ectopic pregnancy there is great danger of fatal hemorrhage; the uterine mucosa is the only place that is properly prepared to withstand the strain of the growing embryo. Pregnancies that begin to develop elsewhere are a threat to both the new individual and the mother whose function it is to provide a "proper home" for the newcomer in her uterus. Whenever the course of nature is impeded, as in ectopic pregnancy, there is difficulty.

Early Termination of Pregnancy. If the fetus is expelled during the first 3 months of pregnancy, the process is called an *abortion*. This does not refer to abortion in the lay sense, in which there is a criminally induced termination of pregnancy. When spontaneous, it indicates some abnormality in either the embryo or the mother, as a rule. If the fetus is expelled during the fourth, the fifth or the sixth month of pregnancy, it is called a *miscarriage* and may be due to abnormality of the fetus or toxicity in the mother. If the fetus is born after the sixth month but before the full term has expired, it is called *premature labor*. Numerous factors may lead to an early termination of pregnancy.

Eclampsia refers to toxemia of pregnancy. It is characterized by the appearance of albumin in the urine and hypertension. Convulsions are common. In eclampsia, usually it is necessary to induce labor prematurely in order to save the life of either fetus or mother.

Breech Presentation. The head of the child is born first in the majority of deliveries. Occasionally, the breech (buttocks) presents; in these cases labor is attended with additional difficulties.

Cesarean Section. If the diameters of the mother's pelvis are so small that spontaneous delivery seems to be impossible, or if the mother is unable to bear the strain of normal labor, the fetus is delivered by cesarean section. This consists in removing the fetus by the abdominal route. An incision is made through the abdominal wall and through the uterine wall to deliver the fetus by hand.

Abnormalities of the Fetus. Some of the abnormalities that may occur due to disturbances in development of the embryo or the fetus are: harelip, cleft palate, web-hand, web-foot, incomplete formation of the diaphragm so that the pleural and the abdominal cavities are connected, patent foramen ovale, patent ductus arteri osis, acrania, spina bifida and amputation of a part of a limb. Text-books of embryology or anatomy should be consulted for information about such anomalies.

Hygiene of the Reproductive System. From puberty on, the instinct for reproduction makes itself felt. This instinct is fundamental to the preservation of the race. Love and bearing and rearing children are manifestations of the instinct for reproduction. This instinct, as well as many other instincts (such as the instinct for self-preservation) has great driving power, and is accompanied by profound emotional states. One cannot handle this situation on an instinctive basis, as animals do.

Since this is the case, conflicts arise between the instinct and the standards of society and one's personal ideals. Each individual has such conflicts to solve, and 3 ways are open.

THE FIRST is to give instinct full play. This is an easy solution in the beginning, as one goes gaily from one marriage venture or love affair to another with no more sense of responsibility than a cat or a dog in heat. However, the individual reverts to a lower standard of living and eventually is overcome by degradation and disease, with a sense of deep unhappiness and worthlessness, as well as frustration.

THE SECOND solution is to give intellect full play. The individual represses the instincts that are natural and valuable if correctly used. Faulty adjustments may occur; the individual may take refuge in deceit, since he is unwilling to face reality and admit the driving power of the instinct.

THE THIRD solution is a compromise. The present social standards are accepted. The issue is faced squarely, and the instinct for reproduction is recognized, admitted and controlled. If an individual has learned to control other instincts, he will have little difficulty in controlling this one. The impulse is redirected into channels that are acceptable; work is undertaken that will involve the use of one's best efforts. This will represent almost as truly as physical reproduction the expression of one's self. Any work that can be done with the force of one's whole personality is creative work. If one redirects the instinct for reproduction until it may be expressed in the natural way without incurring the criticism of society and one's self, there will be no regrets.

The instinct for reproduction, if dealt with properly, is not a disadvantage, as some seem to think. Situations that lead to undue stimulation may be avoided. "Petting" approaches closely the narrow margin that separates it from intercourse. Usually it is not realized that the margin is so narrow. Petting or "necking" leads to a definite physical response in men; there is a strain on the nervous system in approaching intercourse and then having to inhibit it.

Young people who cannot solve their difficulties with the opposite sex in an acceptable manner before marriage will find themselves even more incapable of solving them after marriage. In order to succeed, marriage must be based upon mutual respect and admiration, as well as upon physical attraction.

Nothing in the world can contribute so much to unhappiness as a failure to control the instinct for reproduction. Nothing in the world can contribute more to happiness than a fine, wholesome love and the establishment of a home and a family in which there is real teamwork between a man and the woman of his choice. This is not easy but it is worth working for.

SUMMARY

1. Male reproductive system
   A. Testes: location, description, germinal epithelium, function, blood supply and nerve supply
   B. Duct system: epididymis, ductus deferens, ejaculatory duct and urethra
   C. Acessory structures: seminal vesicles, prostate gland, bulbo-urethral glands and penis
   D. Semen
2. Female reproductive system
   A. Ovaries: location, description, germinal epithelium-ovarian follicles; ovulation, corpus luteum, fate of unshed ova, menopause, blood supply of ovaries and nerve supply of ovaries
   B. Duct system: uterine tubes; uterus; location, ligaments, gross structure, microscopic structure (serosa, myometrium, endometrium); cyclic changes in the endometrium (menstrual cycles); hormones involved; blood supply of uterus; nerve supply of uterus. Vagina; location: description; parts; structure
   C. Accessory organs: external genitalia (clitoris, labia minora, vestibule, labia majora and mons pubis); blood supply; nerve supply. The mammary glands: description; structure
3. Development of the reproductive system; comparison of male and female structures
4. Sequence of events in reproduction
   A. Periods of life span
      a. Intra-uterine or prenatal period: 3 periods
      b. Extra-uterine or postnatal period: 5 periods

5. Human embryology; developmental anatomy
   A. Definition
   B. Development of parents to maturity
   C. Maturation of germ cells; ovum; spermatozoon
   D. Fertilization
   E. Segmentation
   F. Formation of embryo
      a. Germ layers
      b. Changes in embryonic disk
      c. Early changes in the germ layers
   G. Development of various systems: face, limb buds, gastro-
intestinal, lungs and respiratory passages; urinary and genital sys-
tems; circulatory system
6. Fetal organs
   A. The yolk sac
   B. The amnion
   C. The chorion
   D. The allantois
   E. The umbilical cord
7. Maternal membranes
   A. Decidua
   B. Placenta; both fetal and maternal portions
8. Summary of growth of embryo
9. Pregnancy
10. Parturition
11. Lactation

SITUATION AND QUESTIONS

Mrs. Rohr, suspecting she was pregnant, visited her obstetrician
to confirm the diagnosis.

1. One of the first questions that the physician asked was one to
determine the ovulation period. Which of the following statements
regarding ovulation is true? _____(a) In a 28-day cycle, ovulation usually occurs 14 days after the onset of menstruation;
_____(b) Ovulation is the rupture of a corpus luteum with
the release of the ovum; _____(c) Ovulation is the shedding
of the uterine mucosa in preparation for a fertilized ovum;
_____(d) Ovulation occurs immediately before the onset of
menstruation.

2. After the history was taken and the physical examination completed, the doctor told Mrs. Rohr that she was 3 months pregnant.
Mrs. Rohr asked many questions concerning her pregnancy. The
doctor explained that some of the symptoms that she was experi-

encing were due to the rapid enlargement of the uterus. Concerning the uterus she learned: _____(a) that it is located anterior to the urinary bladder at the level of the symphysis pubis; _____ (b) that the expanded upper portion is called the *body;* _____ (c) that the increase in the size of the uterus is due, in part, to an increase in the size and the number of cells; _____(d) that it is the structure concerned with the production of female germ cells.

3. Mrs. Rohr was thrilled to think that much of herself and her husband would be transferred to the new individual. The structures of the germ cells concerned with heredity are: _____(a) spindles; _____(b) genes; _____(c) gametes; _____ (d) centrosomes.

4. Mrs. Rohr received specific instructions about her diet during pregnancy. She learned that she was responsible for the nutrition of the new individual. The medium for the exchange of nutrients is the: _____(a) amniotic fluid; _____(b) endometrium; _____(c) decidua basalis; _____(d) placenta.

5. Mrs. Rohr was told that the new individual at 3 months gestation now had the rudiments of all the main organs. This period from 3 months on is known as the: _____(a) period of the ovum; _____(b) period of the embryo; _____(c) period of the fetus; _____(d) neonatal period.

6. Mr. Rohr was equally happy about the coming event. In the process of fertilization the male germ cell unites with the ovum of the female. The mature male germ cell is called: _____(a) a gonad; _____(b) the testes; _____(c) spermatozoon; _____(d) spermatocyte.

7. During the process of maturation, the chromosomes are reduced to one half the original number. By union of the male and the female germ cells, the characteristic number of chromosomes is obtained. This number is: _____(a) 24; _____(b) 48; _____(c) 96; _____(d) 12.

8. The male germ cell is motile. The motility of the germ cell is enhanced by secretions from the: _____(a) scrotum; _____ (b) seminal vesicles; _____(c) testes; _____(d) epididymis.

Reference Books and Journals

PHYSIOLOGY

Adolph, E. F.: Physiology of Man in the Desert, New York, Interscience, 1947.

Albright, F., and Reifenstein, E. C., Jr.: The Parathyroid Glands and Metabolic Bone Disease, Baltimore, Williams & Wilkins, 1948.

Alpers, B. J.: Clinical Neurology, ed. 3, Philadelphia, Davis, 1954.

Alvarez, W. C.: Introduction to Gastro-enterology, ed. 4, New York, Hoeber, 1948.

Anderson, W. A. D.: Pathology, ed. 2, St. Louis, Mosby, 1953.

Baldwin, E.: Dynamic Aspects of Biochemistry, New York, Cambridge, 1949.

Beaumont, G. E., and Dodds, E. C.: Recent Advances in Medicine, ed. 13, New York, Blakiston, 1952.

Bell, G. H., Davidson, J. N., and Scarborough, H.: Textbook of Physiology and Biochemistry, ed. 2, Baltimore, Williams & Wilkins, 1953.

Best, C. H., and Taylor, N. B.: Physiological Basis of Medical Practice, ed. 5, Baltimore, Williams & Wilkins, 1950.

Brazier, M. A. B.: The Electrical Activity of the Nervous System, New York, Macmillan, 1951.

Cecil, R. L., and Loeb, R. F.: Medicine, ed. 8, Philadelphia, Saunders, 1951.

Cournand, A., Baldwin, J. S., and Himmelstein A.: Cardiac Catheterization in Congenital Heart Disease, New York, Commonwealth Fund, 1949.

Davson, H.: The Physiology of the Eye, Philadelphia, Blakiston, 1949.

Drinker, C. K.: The Lymphatic System, Stanford, Stanford Univ. Press, 1942.

————: Pulmonary Edema and Inflammation, Cambridge, Harvard, 1945.

DuBois, E. F.: Fever and the Regulation of Body Temperature, Springfield, Ill., Thomas, 1948.

Evans, C. L.: Starling's Principles of Human Physiology, ed. 11, Philadelphia, Lea & Febiger, 1952.

Fulton, J. F.: Physiology of the Nervous System, ed. 3, New York, Oxford, 1949.

————: A Textbook of Physiology, ed. 16, Philadelphia, Saunders, 1949.

Gamble, J. L.: Chemical Anatomy, Physiology and Pathology of Extracellular fluid, ed. 5, Cambridge, Harvard, 1949.

Gaunt, R., and Birnie, J. H.: Hormones and Body Water, Springfield, Ill., Thomas, 1951.

Glasser, O. (ed.): Medical Physics, Chicago, Yr. Bk. Pub. 1944 (ed. 1) and 1950 (ed. 2).

Goldring, W., and Chasis, H.: Hypertension, New York, Commonwealth Fund, 1944.

Harrison, T. R.: Principles of internal medicine, New York, Blakiston, 1950.

Hartridge, H.: Recent advances in the Physiology of Vision, New York, Blakiston, 1950.

Heilbrunn, L. V.: An Outline of General Physiology, ed. 3, Philadelphia, Saunders, 1952.

Karpovich, P. V.: Physiology of Muscular Activity, ed. 4, Philadelphia, Saunders, 1953.

Kolmer, J. A., Spaulding, E. H., and Robinson, H. W.: Approved Laboratory Technic, New York, Appleton, 1951.

Krantz, J. C., and Carr, C. J.: Pharmacological Principles of Medical Practice, ed. 3, Baltimore, Williams & Wilkins, 1954.

Langworthy, O. R., Kolb, L. C., and Lewis, L. G.: Physiology of Micturition, Baltimore, Williams & Wilkins, 1940.

Lewis, T.: Pain, New York, Macmillan, 1946.

Livingston, W. K.: Pain Mechanisms, New York, Macmillan, 1944.

Macleod, J. J. R.: Physiology in Modern Medicine, ed. 9, edited by Philip Bard et al., St. Louis, Mosby, 1941.

Morehouse, L. E., and Miller, A. T.: Physiology of Exercise, St. Louis, Mosby, 1948.

Nelson, W. E. (ed.): Mitchell's Textbook of Pediatrics, ed. 5, Philadelphia, Saunders, 1950.

Neurath, H., and Bailey, K.: The Proteins, New York, Acad. Press, 1953.

Pepper, O. H. P.: Medical Etymology, Philadelphia, Saunders, 1949.

Peters, J. P., and Van Slyke, D. D.: Quantitative Clinical Chemistry, Vol. 1, Interpretations, ed. 3, Baltimore, Williams & Wilkins, 1946.

Pincus, G. (ed.): Recent Progress in Hormone Research, Vol. 9, New York, Acad. Press, 1954.

Pinner, M.: Pulmonary Tuberculosis in the Adult, Springfield, Ill., Thomas, 1945.

Potter, E. L.: Rh: Its Relation to Congenital Hemolytic Disease and to Intragroup Transfusion Reactions, Chicago, Yr. Bk. Pub., 1947.

Reynolds, S. R. M.: Physiology of the Uterus, ed. 2, New York, Hoeber, 1949.

Sebrell, W. H., Jr., and Harris, R. S. (editors): The Vitamins, New York, Acad. Press, 1954.

Smith, H. W.: The Kidney, New York, Oxford, 1951.

Soskin, S., and Levine, R.: Carbohydrate Metabolism, ed. 2, Chicago, Univ. Chicago Press, 1952.

Todd, J. C., and Sanford, A. H.: Laboratory Diagnosis, ed. 12, Philadelphia, Saunders, 1953.

Town, A. E.: Ophthalmology, Philadelphia, Lea & Febiger, 1951.
West, E. S., and Todd, W. R.: Textbook of Biochemistry, ed. 2, New York, Macmillan, 1954.
Wiggers, C. H.: Physiology in Health and Disease, ed. 5, Philadelphia, Lea & Febiger, 1949.
Williams, R. H. (ed.): Textbook of Endocrinology, Philadelphia, Saunders, 1950.
Wintrobe, M. M.: Clinical Hematology, ed. 3, Philadelphia, Lea & Febiger, 1951.
Wright, S.: Applied Physiology, ed. 9, New York, Oxford, 1952.

For original sources, consult the following Journals:
Acta physiologica scandinavica (many articles in English)
American Journal of Medicine
American Journal of Physiology
Annals of the New York Academy of Sciences
Annual Review of Physiology
Bulletin of the New York Academy of Medicine
Circulation
Geriatrics
Harvey Lectures
Journal of the American Medical Association
Journal of Applied Physiology
Journal of Gerontology
Medicine
Physiological Reviews
Proceedings of the Society for Experimental Biology and Medicine
Quarterly Cumulative Index Medicus

ANATOMY

GENERAL

Brash, J. C.: Cunningham's Text-Book of Anatomy, ed. 9, New York, Oxford, 1951.
Goss, C. M.: Gray's Anatomy of the Human Body, ed. 26, Philadelphia, Lea & Febiger, 1954.
Schaeffer, J. P.: Morris' Human Anatomy, ed. 11, New York, Blakiston, 1953.
Spalteholz, Werner: Hand-Atlas of Human Anatomy, ed. 7 (translated and edited by L. F. Barker), Philadelphia, Lippincott, 1949.

MICROSCOPIC ANATOMY

Cowdry, E. V.: Textbook of Histology, ed. 4, Philadelphia, Lea & Febiger, 1950.
Ham, A. W.: Histology, ed. 2, Philadelphia, Lippincott, 1953.
Maximow, A. A., and Bloom, W.: A Textbook of Histology, ed. 6, Philadelphia, Saunders, 1952.

Smith, P. E., and Copenhaver, W. M.: Bailey's Textbook of Histology, ed. 13, Baltimore, Williams & Wilkins, 1953.

DEVELOPMENTAL ANATOMY

Arey, L. B.: Developmental Anatomy, ed. 6, Philadelphia, Saunders, 1954.

Patten, B. M.: Embryology of the Pig, ed. 3, New York, Blakiston, 1948.

NEURO-ANATOMY

Buchanan, A. R.: Functional Neuro-anatomy, ed. 2, Philadelphia, Lea & Febiger, 1951.

Krieg, W. J. S.: Functional Neuroanatomy, ed. 2, New York, Blakiston, 1953.

Kuntz, A.: The Autonomic Nervous System, ed. 4, Philadelphia, Lea & Febiger, 1953.

————: A Textbook of Neuro-anatomy, ed. 5, Philadelphia, Lea & Febiger, 1950.

Ranson, S. W., and Clark, S. L.: Anatomy of the Nervous System, ed. 9, Philadelphia, Saunders, 1953.

Rasmussen, A. T.: Principal Nervous Pathways, ed. 4, New York, Macmillan, 1952.

Strong, O. S., and Elwyn, A.: Human Neuroanatomy, ed. 3, Baltimore, Williams & Wilkins, 1953.

APPLIED ANATOMY

Callander, C. L.: Surgical Anatomy, ed. 3, Philadelphia, Saunders, 1952.
For original sources, consult:
Anatomical Record
American Journal of Anatomy
Journal of Anatomy
Journal of Neurophysiology

DICTIONARIES

American Pocket Medical Dictionary, ed. 19, Philadelphia, Saunders, 1953.

Blakiston's Illustrated Pocket Medical Dictionary, New York, Blakiston, 1952.

Blakiston's New Gould Medical Dictionary, New York, Blakiston, 1949.

Dorland, W. A. N.: The American Illustrated Medical Dictionary, ed. 22, Philadelphia, Saunders, 1951.

Price, A. L.: American Nurses Dictionary, Philadelphia, Saunders, 1949.

Taber, C. W.: Cyclopedic Medical Dictionary, ed. 6, Philadelphia, Davis, 1953.

Glossary

Abdomen (ab-do'men). The part of the body extending from the diaphragm above to the pelvis below.

Abduction (ab-duk'shun). Movement away from an arbitrary mid-line.

Abortion (ab-or'shun). The emptying of the uterus prior to the fourth month of pregnancy.

Acapnia (ah-kap'ne-ah). A marked diminution in the amount of carbon dioxide in the blood.

Acceleration (ak-sel-er-a'shun). A sudden change in speed.

Acetone (as'et-ōn). An organic compound having the formula $(CH_3)_2CO$; it is found in the urine in any condition in which insufficient carbohydrate burns in the body.

Acetone bodies. Aceto-acetic acid, beta-hydroxybutyric acid and acetone; found in blood and urine in increased amounts whenever too much fat in proportion to carbohydrate is being oxidized. Also called *ketone bodies*.

Achlorhydria (ah-klor-hid're-ah). The absence of hydrochloric acid in the gastric juice.

Acidophil or **eosinophil** (as-id'o-fil, or e-o-sin'o-fil). A leukocyte whose granules stain readily with eosin.

Acidosis (as-id-o'sis). Diminution in the reserve supply of fixed bases (especially sodium) in the blood.

Acromion (ak-ro'me-on). The outward extension of the spine of the scapula, forming the point of the shoulder.

Acuity (ak-u'it-e). Sharpness or clearness, especially of vision.

Adaptation (a-dap-ta'shun). Adjustment to a stimulus; also used to denote changes in the retina on exposure to different intensities of light; retina may be light-adapted or dark-adapted.

Adduction (ad-uk'shun). Movement of a part toward an arbitrary midline.

Adhesion (ad-he'zyun). Abnormal union of two surfaces as a result of inflammation; adhesions may form after an abdominal operation.

Adolescence (ad-o-les'ens). Period between puberty and adult life.

Adventitia (ad-ven-tish'e-ah). The outermost covering of a structure that does not form an integral part of it.

Albuminuria, orthostatic (al"bu-min-u're-ah, or-tho-stat'ik). Postural albuminuria; albuminuria that disappears when the individual lies down for a time.

Alkali reserve. The total amount of alkaline salts (especially sodium bicarbonate) in the plasma and the corpuscles that is utilizable in maintaining the normal alkalinity of the blood. Also called *alkaline reserve*.

Allantois (al-an'to-is). An early tubular structure that pushes into and lies within the body stalk. Important allantoic (umbilical) blood vessels accompany the allantois and extend to the chorion, which becomes vascularized through their branches. The allantois itself disappears by the fourth fetal month.

Alloxan (al"ock-san'). An oxidized form of uric acid; when injected, it produces selective necrosis of the beta cells of the islets of the pancreas. It is used in the production of experimental diabetes.

Alveolar air (al-ve'o-lar ār). The air in the alveoli of the lungs; the residual air.

Alveolus (al-ve'ol-us). A small cell or cavity; an air cell, one of the terminal dilatations of the bronchioles in the lungs; an acinus or terminal lobule of a compound gland (numerous branching ducts); a tooth socket.

Ameboid movement (ah-me'boid moov'ment). Movement of a cell by extending from its surface processes of protoplasm, which are called pseudopodia.

Amenorrhea (am-en-or-e'ah). The absence of the menses.

Amorphous (a-mor'fus). Without definite shape or visible differentiation in structure; not crystalline.

Ampulla (am-pul'ah). A saccular dilatation of a canal.

Amyl nitrite (am'il ni'trīt). A volatile organic compound, which, when inhaled, produces dilatation of the blood vessels; it is used in attacks of angina pectoris.

Analgesia (an-al-je'ze-ah). Loss of sensitivity to pain.

Anaphylactic (an-af-il-ak'tik). Increasing the susceptibility to an infection or to the action of any foreign protein introduced into the body following a primary infection or previous introduction of the same protein; decreasing immunity.

Anastomose (an-as'to-mōz). To open one into the other; used in connection with blood vessels, lymphatics and nerves.

Anesthesia (an-es-the'ze-ah). Loss of sensation.

Aneurysm (an'ur-rizm). A sac formed by the dilatation of the walls of an artery and filled with blood.

Anisocytosis (an-i-so-si-to'sis). A lack of uniformity in the size of red blood corpuscles.

Ankylosis (ang-kil-o'sis). Abnormal immobility and consolidation of a joint due to bony union.

Anoxemia (an-oks-e'me-ah). Deficient aeration of the blood; deficiency in the oxygen content of the blood.

Anoxia (an-ox'e-ah). A diminished supply of oxygen to the body tissues.

Antibody (an'te-bod-e). A specific substance produced by and in an animal or person as a reaction to the presence of an antigen. Antibodies react as agglutinins, lysins, precipitins, etc., with specific or related antigens; they are associated with certain globulin fractions of the plasma proteins.

Antigen (an'te-jen). Any substance which, when introduced into the blood or the tissues, incites the formation of antibodies or reacts with them.

Antiketogenic (an"te-ke-to-jen'ik). Inhibiting the formation of ketone (acetone) bodies.

Antrum (an'trum). A cavity or chamber, especially one within a bone, such as a sinus; the pyloric end of the stomach.

Aortic body (a-or'tik). *See* carotid body.

Aperture (ap'er-chur). An opening or orifice.

Aphasia (ah-fa'ze-ah). A loss of the faculty of language in any of its forms.

Aponeurosis (ap"on-u-ro'sis). One of the types of muscle attachment that takes the form of a fibrous sheet; it may invest a muscle.

Apoplexy (ap'o-plek-se). A sudden loss of consciousness, followed by paralysis due to cerebral hemorrhage, or blocking of an artery of the brain by an embolus or a thrombus.

Aqueduct (ak'wē-dukt). A canal for the conduction of a liquid; the cerebral aqueduct of Sylvius connects the third and the fourth ventricles of the brain.

Arachnoid (ar-ak'noid). The delicate fibrous membrane forming the middle of the three meninges (coverings of the brain and spinal cord).

Areola (ar-e'o-lah). Any minute space in a tissue; the pigmented ring around the nipple.

Articulate (ar-tic'u-late). To join together so as to permit motion between parts; enunciation in words and sentences. Divided into joints.

Ascites (as-i'tez). An accumulation of serous fluid within the peritoneal cavity.

Asphyxia (as-fiks'e-ah). Unconsciousness due to interference with the oxygenation of the blood.

Astereognosis (ah-ste"re-og-no'sis). Loss of power to recognize the form of an object by touch.

Asthenia (as-the'ne-ah). Weakness.

Asthma (az'mah). A disease characterized by recurrent attacks of dyspnea, wheezing and cough, due to spasmodic contraction of the bronchioles.

Ataxia (ah-taks'e-ah). A loss of the power of muscular co-ordination.

Atresia (ah-tre'ze-ah). Congenital absence or pathologic closure of a normal opening or passage; involution of ovarian follicles.

Atrophy (at'ro-fe). A wasting or diminution in the size of a part of the entire body.

Atropine (at'ro-pin). An alkaloid obtained from atropa belladonna; it inhibits the action of the craniosacral division of the autonomic system.

Auricle (aw'rik-l). The pinna or flap of the ear; a small pouch forming the upper portion of each atrium.

Auscultation (aws-kul-ta'shun). The act of listening for sounds within the body; employed as a diagnostic method.

Azygos (az'ig-os). An unpaired anatomic structure; the azygos vein arises from the right ascending lumbar vein and empties into the superior vena cava; it receives the right intercostal veins.

Basophil (ba'so-fil). A cell that stains readily with basic dyes.
Bolus (bo'lus). A rounded mass of soft consistency.
Broca's area (bro'kahz). The supposed speech center, situated in the third left frontal convolution in right-handed persons; it is on the right side in left-handed persons.
Bronchiectasis (brong-ke-ek'tas-is). Dilatation of the bronchi or of a bronchus. It is characterized by offensive breath, spasms of coughing and expectoration of muco-purulent material.
Bronchitis (brong-ki'tis). Inflammation of the mucous membrane of the bronchial tubes.
Buffer (buff'er). Any substance that tends to lessen the change in hydrogen ion concentration (reaction) which otherwise would be produced by adding acids or bases.
Bursa (bur'sah). A closed sac lined by synovial membrane containing fluid, found over an exposed and prominent part or where a tendon plays over a bone.

Caffeine (kaf'e-in). An alkaloid obtained from the dried leaves of tea or the dried seeds of coffee; employed in cardiac disorders.
Calculus (kal'ku-lus). A concretion formed in any portion of the body, such as a gallstone.
Calorie (kal'or-e). A unit of heat. A *small calorie* (cal.) is the standard unit and is the amount of heat required to raise 1 Gm. of water from 15° to 16° C. The *large calorie* (Cal.) is used in metabolism and is the amount of heat required to raise 1 Kg. of water from 15° to 16° C.
Canaliculus (kan-al-ik'u-lus). A small canal or channel; in bone, minute channels connect with each lacuna.
Cancer (kan'ser). Any malignant neoplasm (tumor or new growth).
Carbon monoxide (kar'bon mon-oks'id). A colorless, odorless, poisonous gas formed by the combustion of carbon with a limited supply of air; it has a strong affinity for hemoglobin.
Carcinoma (kar-sin-o'mah). A malignant tumor or cancer; a new growth made up of epithelial cells, tending to infiltrate and give rise to metastases.
Caries (ka're-ez). Molecular decay or death of a bone in which it becomes softened, discolored and porous. Dental caries, decay of teeth.
Carotid body (kar-ot'id). A collection of chemoreceptors located in the wall of the carotid artery (or aorta, *see* above).
Cast (kast). A mold of a tubular structure, such as a bronchial tube or a renal tubule, formed by a plastic exudate.
Castration (kas-tra'shun). Removal of testes or ovaries.

Cataract (kat'ah-rakt). A loss of transparency of the crystalline lens of the eye or of its capsule.

Celiac (se'le-ak). Relating to the abdominal cavity.

Cellulose (sel'u-lōs). A carbohydrate that forms the basis of vegetable fiber; it passes unchanged through the intestinal tract of man.

Celom (se'lom). The body cavity of the embryo, situated between the somatopleure and the splanchnopleure.

Centimeter (sen'tim-e-ter). The hundredth part of a meter; practically, ⅖ in.

Cephalin (sef'al-in). A lipid; released by platelets and injured cells; important in the coagulation of blood.

Cerumen (se-ru'men). Ear wax.

Cervix (ser'viks). The neck; any necklike structure; especially the lower cylindrical portion of the uterus.

Cesarean section (se-za're-an sek'shun). Extraction of the fetus by means of an incision through the abdominal wall and the uterus.

Chalazion (ka-la'ze-on). A small tumor of the eyelid; formed by the distention of a meibomian gland with secretion.

Cheilosis (ki-lo'sis). A condition characterized by lesions on the lips and at the angles of the mouth.

Chemoreceptor (kem-o-re-sep'tor). A receptor adapted for stimulation by chemical substances.

Chemotherapy (kem″o-ther'a-py). The treatment of disease by administering chemicals that affect the causative organism unfavorably, but do not produce serious toxic effects in the patient.

Chiasm (ki'azm). A crossing; specifically, the crossing of the optic nerves.

Choana (ko-a'nah). Posterior naris; the opening into the nasopharynx of the nasal fossa on either side.

Chokes. Violent coughing spells that may be due to nitrogen emboli in the pulmonary capillaries.

Cholesterol (ko-les'ter-ol). An organic alcohol, found chiefly in the bile, forming the greater part of gallstones.

Chromosome (kro'mo-sōm). A body of chromatin in the cell nucleus that splits longitudinally as the cell divides, one half going to the nucleus of each of the daughter cells; the chromosomes transmit the hereditary characters.

Chyle (kīl). The milky fluid taken up by the lacteals from the food in the intestine after digestion. It consists of lymph and emulsified fat; it passes into the veins by the thoracic duct.

Chyme (kīm). The semifluid mass of partly digested food passed from the stomach into the duodenum.

Ciliary (sil'e-ar-re). Relating to (1) any hairlike process, (2) the eyelashes, (3) certain of the structures of the eyeball.

Cloaca (klo-a'kah). An opening at the posterior end of the body into which the intestinal, urinary and reproductive ducts open in the embryo. It divides early into the rectum and urogenital sinus.

Clonic movements (klon'ik). A spasm characterized by alternate contractions and relaxations.

Coagulation (ko-ag-u-la'shun). Clotting, the process of change from a liquid state to that of a soft, jellylike solid.

Cocaine (ko-kān). An alkaloid from coca leaves; it is a local anesthetic, narcotic and mydriatic.

Co-enzyme (ko-en'zime). A substance (nonprotein component) associated with and activating an enzyme.

Collateral (kol-at'er-al). Accompanying; running by the side of; not direct; secondary or accessory; a small side branch of an axon.

Colloid (kol'oid). A state of matter; the matter is subdivided into particles which range from 1 to 100 millimicrons in size; the material present in the follicles of the thyroid gland and in the pituitary gland.

Colostomy (ko-los'to-me). Establishment of an artificial anus by an opening into the colon.

Colostrum (ko-los'trum). The first milk secreted at the termination of pregnancy; it contains more lactalbumin and lactoprotein than the later milk.

Coma (ko'mah). A state of profound unconsciousness from which one cannot be roused.

Commissure (kom'is-ūr). A bundle of nerve fibers passing from one side to the other in the brain or the spinal cord.

Compatible (kom-pat'i-bl). Capable of being mixed without undergoing destructive chemical change or acting in therapeutic antagonism.

Compensation (kom-pen-sa'shun). That change in the heart by which an adequate circulation is maintained in spite of valvular lesions.

Concept (kon'sept). An abstract idea or notion.

Concha (kong'kah). A structure comparable to a shell in shape, as a turbinated bone in the nose or the pinna of the ear.

Congenital (kon-jen'it-al). Born with a person; existing at or before birth.

Corpus (kor'pus). A small body or the main part of any organ.

Corpuscle (kor'pus-l). Any small mass or body.

Costal (cos'tal). Pertaining to a rib.

Crystalloid (kris'tal-oid). A body that, in solution, can pass through an animal membrane, as distinguished from a colloid that has not this property.

Curare (koo-rah're). A highly toxic extract that paralyzes muscle; it acts on the motor end-plates.

Cyanosis (si-an-o'sis). A dark, purplish coloration of the skin and the mucous membrane, due to deficient oxygenation of the blood.

Cystoscopy (sis-tos'ko-pe). The inspection of the interior of the bladder.

Decompensation (de-kom-pen-sa'shun). The condition in which a failing heart no longer maintains an adequate circulation.

Defecation (def-ik-a'shun). The discharge of excrement from the rectum.

Dentition (den-tish'un). Clinically, eruption of the teeth; morphologically, the number, shape and arrangement of the teeth.

Detrusor (de-tru'sor). The muscle fibers of the urinary bladder; three layers of smooth muscle that act as a unit in emptying the bladder.

Diabetes insipidus (di-ab-e'tēz in-sip'id-us). The habitual excretion of large amounts of pale urine of low specific gravity not containing sugar.

Diabetes mellitus (di-ab-e'tēz mell-i'tus). A disease of metabolism in which the tissues are unable to oxidize sugar; it is characterized by hyperglycemia, glycosuria, polyuria, polydipsia.

Diapedesis (di"ah-pe-de'sis). The passage of blood or of leukocytes through the unruptured walls of the blood vessels.

Dicumarol (di-koo'mar-ol). Proprietary name for a compound occurring in spoiled sweet clover and made synthetically; it is a useful anticoagulant in venous thrombosis.

Digitalis (dij-it-a'lis). The dried leaves of purple foxglove; it is used in the treatment of certain cardiac disorders.

Diopter (di-op'ter). The unit of refracting power of a lens; noting a lens whose principal focus is at a distance of 1 M.

Diurnal (di-er'nal). Daily.

Divers' palsy (dīv'erz pawl'zē). A condition in divers, who ascend too rapidly, similar to decompression sickness in aviators.

Eclampsia of pregnancy (ek-lamp'se-ah of preg'nan-se). Convulsions occurring in the latter part of pregnancy or during labor.

Ectopic (ek-top'ik). Out of the normal place.

Edema (e-de'mah). An abnormal accumulation of clear, watery fluid in the lymph spaces of the tissues.

Effusion (ef-u'zhun). The escape of fluid from the blood vessels or the lymphatics into the tissues or a cavity.

Electrolyte (e-lek'tro-lite). Any substance that, in solution, conducts an electric current.

Embolism (em'bol-izm). Obstruction or occlusion of a vessel by a transported clot, a mass of bacteria or other foreign material.

Emissary (em'is-a-re). One of the channels of communication between the venous sinuses of the dura mater and the veins of the diplöe and the scalp.

Emphysema (em-fis-e'mah). Dilatation of the pulmonary air vesicles, usually through atrophy of the septa between the alveoli.

Empyema (em-pi-e'mah). The presence of pus in any cavity; when used without qualification, an accumulation of pus in the pleural cavity.

Emulsify (e-mul'se-fi). To divide a fat into very fine particles.

Enema (en'em-ah). A fluid injected into the rectum for the purpose of clearing out the bowel or of administering drugs or food.

Enuresis (en-u-re'sis). Involuntary passage of urine after the age of 3 years.

Epicritic (ep-ik-rit'ik). Noting a set of sensory nerve fibers supplying the skin; by means of these a person is enabled to appreciate the finer degrees of touch, pain and temperature and to localize the same.

Epistaxis (ep-e-staks'is). Nosebleed; hemorrhage from the nose.

Erectile (e-rek'til). Noting a vascular tissue, found in the nasal cavities, the penis and elsewhere, which, when filled with blood, becomes swollen and more or less rigid.

Ergosterol (er-gos'te-rol). Vitamin D or the mother substance thereof; intensely powerful in its antirachitic effects.

Estrogen (es'tro-jen). A generic term for estrus-producing compounds.

Estrus (es'trus). The period of sexual excitement in the female of the lower animals.

Evagination (e-vaj-in-a'shun). A protrusion of some part or organ.

Exophthalmos (ex-of-thal'mus). A protrusion or prominence of the eyeball.

Extension (ex-ten'shun). The movement at a joint in which the angle between the parts is increased.

Extravasation (ex-trav-as-a'shun). The act of escaping from a vessel into the tissues, said of blood, lymph or serum.

Extrinsic (ex-trin'sik). Originating outside of the part where found or upon which it acts.

Fascia (fash'e-ah). A sheet of fibrous tissue enveloping the body beneath the skin and also enclosing the muscles and groups of muscles and separating their several layers.

Fasciculation (fa-sick"yoo-lay'shun). Localized contraction of muscle fibers or an in-co-ordinated contraction of skeletal muscle in which the fibers of one motor unit contract.

Feces (fe'sez). The matter discharged from the bowel.

Fimbria (fim'bre-ah). Any fringelike structure; especially the fringelike end of the uterine tube.

Fissure (fish'ur). A furrow, cleft or slit.

Fistula (fis'tu-lah). A pathologic or abnormal passage leading from an abscess cavity or a hollow organ to the surface or from one organ to another.

Flaccid (flak'sid). Relaxed, flabby, soft.

Flatus (fla'tus). Gas or air in the stomach or the intestine; commonly used to denote passage of gas by rectum.

Flexion (flek'shun). Bending of a joint so as to approximate the parts it connects and decreasing the angle between them.

Fovea (fo've-ah). A cup-shaped depression or pit.

Fulminating anoxia. (ful'min-a-ting). Sudden, intense and severe anoxia.

Fundus (fun'dus). The bottom of a sac or hollow organ; that farthest removed from the opening; the cardiac end of the stomach.

Ganglion (gang'le-on). An aggregation of nerve cells within the brain, along the course of a sensory nerve, in one of the organs of special sense or in the autonomic system.

Gangrene (gan'grēne). A form of necrosis combined with putrefaction; death of the tissue.

Gavage (gah-vahzh'). Feeding by stomach tube.

Gel (jel). A colloidal system comprising a solid and a liquid phase that exists as a solid or semisolid mass; a jelly or solid or semisolid phase.

Glossitis (glos-si'tis). Inflammation of the tongue.

Glycerol (glis'er-ol). A tri-atomic alcohol; a constituent of all fats.

Hematuria (hem-at-u're-ah). The presence of blood in the urine.

Hemiplegia (hem-e-ple'je-ah). Paralysis of one side of the body.

Hemorrhoids (hem'or-oidz). Piles, a varicose condition of the external hemorrhoidal veins causing painful swellings at the anus.

Hemostasis (hem-os'tas-is). The arrest of bleeding; the checking of the flow of blood through any part of a vessel.

Heparin (he'par-in). A liver extract that prevents the coagulation of the blood.

Heredity (he-red'it-e). The transmission of qualities from parent to offspring.

Homeostasis (ho-me-os'ta-sis). A tendency to uniformity or stability in the normal body states of the organism (Cannon).

Homologous (ho-mol'o-gus). Corresponding; having similar relations.

Hordeolum (hor-de'o-lum). A sty, an inflammation of a sebaceous gland of the eyelid.

Hormones (hor'mōns). Chemical substances formed in one organ or part of the body and carried in the blood to another organ or part, where they stimulate functional activity or secretion.

Humidity (hu-mid'it-e). Moisture, dampness; relative—the percentage of moisture in the air.

Hyaluronidase (hy"a-lu-ron'i-dase). An enzyme causing breakdown of hyaluronic acid in protective polysaccharide barriers, promoting invasion of cells and tissues by the invading agent; it is a spreading factor.

Hyperpnea (hi-perp-ne'ah). Exaggerated breathing movements.

Hypertrophy (hi-per'trof-e). Overgrowth; this is not hyperplasia, which is an increase in the bulk of an organ by an increase in the number of individual tissue units.

Hypodermic (hi-po-der'mik). Subcutaneous; beneath the skin.

Hypodermoclysis (hi"po-der-mok'lis-is). The subcutaneous injection of a large quantity of saline solution.

Illusion (il-u'zhun). A false perception, the mistaking of something for what it is not.

Image (im'aj). The representation of an object made by rays of light emanating or reflected from it; a memory picture.

Inflammation (in-flam-a'shun). A morbid series of reactions produced in the tissues by an irritant; it is marked by an afflux of blood with exudation of plasma and leukocytes.

Infundibulum (in-fun-dib'u-lum). A funnel-shaped structure or passage.

Inguinal (in'guin-al). Relating to the region between the abdomen and the thigh (groin).

Intravascular (in-trah-vas'ku-lar). Within the blood vessels or the lymphatics.

Intravenous (in-trah-ve'nus). Within a vein.

Intussusception (in"tus-sus-sep'shun). The infolding of one segment of the intestine within another segment.

Invagination (in-vaj-in-a'shun). The pushing of the wall of a cavity into the cavity.

Involuntary (in-vol'un-ta-re). Performed independently of the will; when used in connection with muscle, it refers to the nonstriated muscle tissue.

Involution (in-vo-lu'shun). The return of an enlarged organ to normal size; retrograde changes.

Ions (i'onz). A group of atoms or parts of molecules that carry a charge of electricity; elements of electrolytes. Cations, such as Na^+ and K^+, bear positive charges and migrate toward the cathode or negative pole in an electric field. Anions, such as Cl^- and HCO_3^-, bear negative charges and migrate toward the anode or positive pole.

Kenny method. A method of treating infantile paralysis devised by Sister Kenny.

Ketogenic (ke-to-jen'ik). Producing ketones (acetone).

Ketosis (ke-to'sis). The condition marked by excessive production of ketone bodies in the body.

Kilogram (kil'o-gram). 1,000 grams; about 2.2 pounds avoirdupois.

Kinesthetic (kin-es-thet'ik). Pertaining to muscle sense or to the sense by which muscular movement, weight, position, etc., are perceived.

Lamella (lam-el'ah). A thin sheet or scale; one of the plates.

Lamina (lam'in-ah). A thin plate or flat layer; the flattened portion of either side of a vertebral arch.

Lecithin (les'ith-in). A lipid composed of choline, glycerol, phosphoric acid and fatty acids.

Leukemia (lu-ke'me-ah). A disease of the blood marked by persistent leukocytosis, associated with changes in the spleen and the bone marrow or in the lymphatic nodes.

Ligament (lig'a-ment). A band or sheet of fibrous (usually nonelastic) tissue connecting two or more bones, cartilages or other structures, or serving as support for fasciae or muscles; a fold of thickened peritoneum supporting any of the abdominal viscera.

Ligature (lig′at-ūr). A thread or wire tied tightly around a blood vessel, the pedicle of a tumor or other structure in order to constrict it.

Linin (li′nin). The faintly staining substance composing the fine netlike threads found in the nucleus of the cell, where it bears the chromatin in the form of granules.

Lumen (lu′men). The space in the interior of a tubular structure such as an artery or the intestine.

Macula (mak′u-lah). A spot.

Malaise (ma-lāz′). A feeling of general discomfort or uneasiness, an out-of-sorts feeling, often the first indication of an infection.

Maternal (mat-er′nal). Pertaining to the mother.

Meatus (me-a′tus). A passage or channel, especially the external opening of a canal.

Meninges (men-in′jēz). Membranes; specifically, the membranous envelope of the brain and the spinal cord.

Meningitis (men-in-ji′tis). Inflammation of the membranes of the brain or the spinal cord.

Menopause (men′o-pawz). Termination of the menstrual cycle.

Metabolism (me-tab′o-lism). The sum of the chemical changes whereby the function of nutrition is effected; it consists of anabolism or the constructive and assimulative changes and catabolism or the destructive and retrograde changes.

Meter (me′ter). A measure of length; 100 cm.; the equivalent of 39.371 in.

Microgram (mi′kro-gram). One one-millionth of a gram, or $\frac{1}{1,000}$ of a milligram.

Micron (mi′kron). One one-millionth of a meter or $\frac{1}{1,000}$ of a millimeter; $\frac{1}{25,400}$ of an inch.

Millimeter (mil′im-e-ter). $\frac{1}{1,000}$ of a meter; about $\frac{1}{25}$ of an inch.

Miscarriage (mis-kar′ij). Expulsion of the product of conception during the fourth, fifth or sixth month of pregnancy.

Morphine (mor′fin). The chief narcotic principle of opium; used as an hypnotic and analgesic.

Mucus (mu′kus). The viscid watery secretion of the mucous glands; it consists of water, mucin, epithelial cells, leukocytes and inorganic salts.

Myelin (mi′el-in). The lipid substance that ensheaths the axis cylinder of a myelinated nerve fiber; a myelinated nerve fiber, therefore, is one with a myelin sheath.

Myoneural (mi-o-nu′ral). Relating to both muscle and nerve, denoting the nerve terminations in muscular tissue.

Narcosis (nar-co′sis). Stupor or unconsciousness produced by some narcotic drug.

Nares (na′rēz). The nostrils.

Necrosis (ne-kro'sis). Local death of tissue.

Neuromuscular junction. Same as myoneural.

Neutrophil (nu'tro-fil). Having no marked affinity for either acid or basic dyes; a leukocyte that does not stain readily with either acid or basic dyes.

Nissl granule (nis'el). Chromophil granule constituting one of the stainable substances of the cytoplasm of a nerve cell.

Notochord (no'to-kord). A cord of cells that serves as a primitive backbone in the embryo; it is later replaced by vertebrae.

Nystagmus (nis-tag'mus). Rhythmic oscillation of the eyeballs, either horizontal, rotary or vertical.

Opaque (o-pāk'). Impervious to light.

Optic (op'tik). Relating to the eye.

Optimal (op'tim-al). The best or most favorable.

Orifice (or'if-is). Any aperture or opening.

Ostium (os'te-um). A small opening, especially one of entrance into a hollow organ or canal.

Oxidation (oks-id-a'shun). The combining of food and oxygen in the tissues; chemically, the increase in valence of an element.

Oximeter (ox-im'e-ter). An instrument for measuring the oxygen saturation of hemoglobin in the circulating blood; it consists of an ear piece, a control box and a galvanometer.

Pacchionian bodies (pak-ke-o'ne-an). Small projections of the arachnoid tissue, chiefly into the venous sinuses of the dura mater.

Palpitation (pal-pit-a'shun). Forcible pulsation of the heart perceptible to the individual.

Papilla (pap-il'ah). A small, nipple-shaped elevation.

Paralysis (par-al'is-is). A loss of power of voluntary movement in a muscle through injury or disease of its nerve supply.

Parturition (par″tu-rish'un). The act of giving birth to young.

Pectoral (pek'to-ral). Pertaining to the breast or the chest.

Perimeter (per-im'et-er). An instrument delimiting the field of vision.

Perineum (per-e-ne'um). The portion of the body included in the outlet of the pelvis, extending from the pubic arch to the coccyx and between the ischial tuberosities.

pH. The symbol commonly used in expressing hydrogen ion concentration. It signifies the logarithm of the reciprocal of the hydrogen ion concentration expressed as a power of 10.

Phenolsulfonphthalein (fe″nol-sul-fōn-thal'e-in). A red powder that is nontoxic and is excreted in the urine with great rapidity; it is used as a test for kidney function.

Phlebothrombosis (fleb″o-throm-bo'sis). Thrombosis of a vein without inflammation of its walls.

Phrenicectomy (fren-is-ek'to-me). Resection of the phrenic nerve for the same purpose as phrenicotomy.

Phrenico-exairesis (fren″ik-o-ex-i-re'sis). Extraction of a piece of the phrenic nerve through an incision at the base of the neck to paralyze the corresponding side of the diaphragm.

Phrenicotomy (fren-ik-ot'o-me). Surgical division of the phrenic nerve; the result is paralysis of one side of the diaphragm.

Physiotherapy (fiz″e-o-ther'ap-e). The use of natural forces, such as heat, light, air, water and exercise, in the treatment of disease.

Pilocarpine (pi-lo-kar'pin). An alkaloid that stimulates the craniosacral division of the autonomic nervous system.

Plexus (plex'us). A network or tangle of interweaving nerves, veins or lymphatic vessels.

Polarity (po-lar'it-e). That quality of a synapse that permits the passage of an impulse in only one direction.

Potential (po-ten'shal). Possible, but not actual; capable of doing or being, though not yet doing or being.

Pressor (pres'or). Exciting vasoconstrictor activity, producing increased blood pressure; denoting afferent nerves that when stimulated, excite the vasoconstrictor center.

Prolapse (pro'laps). The falling down of an organ or other part, such as the uterus.

Proliferation (pro-lif″er-a'shun). The reproduction or multiplication of similar forms, especially of cells.

Psychosurgery (sigh″cho-sur'ger-y). Frontal lobotomy or operative section of the frontothalamic fibers of the brain; used in the treatment of certain mental disorders.

Puberty (pu'ber-te). The age at which the reproductive organs become functionally operative.

Pulmotor (pul'mo-tor). An apparatus for supplying oxygen to the lungs and inducing artificial respiration in cases of asphyxiation.

Punctiform (punk'tif-orm). In points.

Pus (pus). A fluid product of inflammation consisting of a liquid containing leukocytes and the débris of dead cells.

Rachitic (ra-kit'ik). Relating to or affected by rickets.

Ramus (ra'mus). A branch; one of the primary divisions of a nerve or a blood vessel; a part of an irregularly shaped bone that forms an angle with the main body.

Receptor (re-sep'tor). Nerve ending that receives a stimulus.

Reflection (re-flek'shun). The throwing back of a ray of light from a surface that it does not penetrate.

Refraction (re-frak'shun). The bending of a ray of light as it passes from one medium into another of different density.

Regurgitation (re-gur-gi-ta'shun). The flowing backward of blood through incompletely closed heart valves; the return of small amounts of food from the stomach.

Rh antigen or factor. An agglutinogen or antigen first found in the erythrocytes of the rhesus monkey, hence the Rh. Normally it is present in 85 per cent of white people; Rh positive and Rh negative are terms denoting the presence or absence, respectively, of this antigen. It can cause antibody formation only in Rh-negative persons or animals.

Rehfuss tube (ra'fus tūb). A fine tube devised for studying gastric secretion or for nasal feeding.

Reticular (re-tik'u-lar). Netlike.

Retroversion (re-tro-ver'shun). The tipping of an entire organ backward; turning backward without flexion or bending of the organ, as of the uterus.

Seborrheic dermatitis (seb"or-rhe'ik der-mat-i'tis). A disorder of the sebaceous glands of the skin, leading to the appearance of greasy scales.

Secretion (se-kre'shun). The production by a cell or an aggregation of cells of some substance differing in chemical and physical properties from the material from which or by which it is produced.

Sella turcica (sel'ah tur'sik-ah). A saddlelike prominence on the upper surface of the sphenoid bone, in which the hypophysis lies.

Sensation (sen-sa'shun). The translation into consciousness of the effects of a stimulus exciting any of the organs of sense.

Sinus (si'nus). A channel for the passage of blood; a hollow in a bone or other tissue; antrum; one of the cavities connecting with the nose; a suppurating cavity.

Sinusoid (si'nus-oid). A blood space in certain organs, as the spleen and the liver.

Somatic (so-mat'ik). Relating to the trunk, the wall of the body cavity.

Spasm (spazm). An involuntary, convulsive, muscular contraction.

Spectrum (spek'trum). The band of colors formed by passing white light through a prism.

Spermatogenesis (sper"mat-o-jen'es-is). The process of formation and development of the spermatozoa.

Sphincter (sfingk'ter). A circular muscle that serves, when in a state of normal contraction, to close one of the orifices of the body.

Sphygmomanometer (sfig"mo-man-om'et-er). An instrument for measuring blood pressure.

Splanchnic (splank'nik). Pertaining to the viscera.

Squamous (skwa'mus). Scalelike.

Sterility (ster-il'it-e). Infertility, lack of progeny, unproductiveness.

Stethoscope (steth'o-skōp). An instrument for conveying sounds to the ear.

Stricture (strik'tur). A circumscribed narrowing of a tubular structure.

Subarachnoid (sub-ar-ak'noid). Situated or occurring beneath the arachnoid.

Subcutaneous (sub-ku-ta′ne-us). Situated or occurring beneath the skin.
Supination (su-pin-a′shun). Position of the hand in which the radius and ulna are parallel, as in the anatomic position.
Susceptibility (sus-sep-tib-il′it-e). The characteristic that makes one liable to infection by disease.
Synovial (sin-o′ve-al). Of, or pertaining to, or secreting synovia; synovia is the viscid fluid of a joint or similar cavity.
Synthesis (sin′the-sis). Building up of a compound by union of its elements.
Syphilis (sif′il-is). A contagious venereal disease.
Syringomyelia (sir-in″go-mi-e′le-ah). The existence of abnormal cavities filled with fluid in the substance of the spinal cord.
Systole (sis′to-le). The contraction of the heart muscle.

Tactile (tak′til). Pertaining to the sense of touch.
Tetanus (tet′an-us). Lockjaw; an acute infectious disease in which there is more or less persistent tonic spasm of some of the voluntary muscles; the first sign is stiffness of the jaw.
Tetany (tet′an-e). Intermittent tonic muscular contractions of the extremities.
Thrombin (throm′bin). Fibrin ferment; it converts fibrinogen into fibrin.
Thrombosis (throm-bo′sis). The formation or development of a clot.
Tinnitus (tin-i′tus). A ringing or singing sound in the ears.
Trabecula (tra-bek′u-lah). A septum that extends from an envelope into the enclosed substance, forming an essential part of the stroma of the organ.
Transmethylation (tranz-meth″il-a′shun). The type of metabolic chemical reaction in which a methyl group is transferred from a donor to a receptor compound; methionine and choline are important sources of methyl groups.
Trigone (tri′gōn). Noting a triangular area, especially of the interior of the bladder between the opening of the ureters and the orifice of the urethra.

Ulcer (ul′ser). An open sore other than a wound; a loss of substance on a cutaneous or mucous surface causing necrosis of the tissue.
Umbilicus (um-bil-i′kus). The navel; the cicatrix (scar) that marks the site of attachment of the umbilical cord.
Urticaria (er-tik-a′re-ah). Nettle-rash; hives; elevated, itching, white patches.

Variocele (var′ik-o-sēl). Enlargement of the veins of the spermatic cord.
Varicose veins (var′ik-ōs). Unnaturally swollen and tortuous veins.
Vasa vasorum (va′sah vas-o′rum). The small nutrient arteries in the walls of the larger blood vessels.

Vasodilator (vas″o-di-la′tor). An agent or nerve that causes a dilatation or increase in lumen of an arteriole, capillary or venule.

Vasomotor (va-so-mo′tor). Causing dilatation or constriction of blood vessels; noting the nerves that have this action.

Vena comitans (ve′nah com′it-ans). A deep vein following the same course as its corresponding artery.

Vertigo (ver′tig-o). Dizziness, giddiness.

Vesicle (ves′ik-l). A small bladder or sac containing liquid.

Vestibular (ves-tib′u-lar). Pertaining to a vestibule; such as of the inner ear, larynx, mouth, nose, vagina.

Villus (vil′us). A minute, fingerlike projection from the mucous membrane of the intestine; a vascular chorionic tuft.

Visceral (vis′er-al). Pertaining to a viscus.

Viscosity (vis-kos′it-e). A condition of more or less adhesion of the molecules of a fluid to each other so that it flows with difficulty.

Viscus (vis′kus). An internal organ, especially one of the large abdominal organs.

Volatile (vol′at-il). Tending to evaporate; passing into vapor at ordinary temperature.

Voluntary (vol′un-ta-re). Relating to or acting in obedience to the will.

Volvulus (vol′vu-lus). A twisting of the intestine, causing obstruction.

Wassermann test (vahs′er-mahn). Test for syphilis.

Combining Forms and Prefixes

These forms, with a prefix or a suffix, or both, are those most commonly used in making medical words. G indicates those from the Greek; L, those from the Latin. Properly, Greek forms should be used only with Greek prefixes and suffixes; Latin, with Latin. Often a vowel, usually a, i or o, is needed for euphony.

A- or **Ab-** (L) *away, lack of:* abnormal, departing from normal.
A- or **An-** (G) *from, without:* asepsis, without infection.
Acr- (G) *an extremity:* acrodermatitis, a dermatitis of the limbs.
Ad- (L) *to, toward, near:* adrenal, near the kidney.
Aden- (G) *gland:* adenitis, inflammation of a gland.
Alg- (G) *pain:* neuralgia, pain extending along nerves.
Ambi- (L) *both:* ambidextrous, referring to both hands.
Ante- (L) *before:* antenatal, occurring or having been formed before birth.
Anti- (G) *against:* antiseptic, against or preventing sepsis.
Arth- (G) *joint:* arthritis, inflammation of a joint.
Auto- (G) *self:* auto-intoxication, poisoning by toxin generated in the body.

Bi- or **Bin-** (L) *two:* binocular, pertaining to both eyes.
Bio- (G) *life:* biopsy, inspection of living organism (or tissue).
Blast- (G) *bud, a growing thing in early stages:* blastocyte, beginning cell not yet differentiated.
Bleph- (G) *eyelids:* blepharitis, inflammation of an eyelid.
Brachi- (G) *arm:* brachialis, muscle for flexing forearm.
Brachy- (G) *short:* brachydactylia, abnormal shortness of fingers and toes.
Brady- (G) *slow:* bradycardia, abnormal slowness of heartbeat.
Bronch- (G) *windpipe:* bronchiectasis, dilation of bronchial tubes.
Bucc- (L) *cheek:* buccally, toward the cheek.

Carcin- (G) *cancer:* carcinogenic, producing cancer.
Cardi- (G) *heart:* cardialgia, pain in the heart.
Cephal- (G) *head:* encephalitis, inflammation of brain.
Cheil- (G) *lip:* cheilitis, inflammation of the lip.
Chole- (G) *bile:* cholecyst, the gallbladder.
Chondr- (G) *cartilage:* chondrectomy, removal of a cartilage.
Circum- (L) *around:* circumocular, around the eyes.
Cleid- (G) *clavicle:* cleidocostal, pertaining to clavicle and ribs.
Colp- (G) *vagina:* colporrhagia, vaginal hemorrhage.
Contra- (L) *against, opposed:* contraindication, indication opposing usually indicated treatment.
Cost- (L) rib: intercostal, between the ribs.
Counter- (L) *against:* counterirritation, an irritation to relieve some other irritation (e.g., a liniment).
Crani- (L) *skull:* craniotomy, surgical opening in skull.
Crypt- (G) *hidden:* cryptogenic, of hidden or unknown origin.
Cut- (L) *skin:* subcutaneous, under the skin.
Cyst- (G) *sac or bladder:* cystitis, inflammation of the bladder.
Cyto- (G) *cell:* cytology, scientific study of cells, a device for counting and measuring cells.

Dacry- (G) *lachrymal glands:* dacryocyst, tear-sac.
Derm- or **dermat-** (G) *skin:* dermatoid, skinlike.
Di- (L) *two:* diphasic, occurring in two stages or phases.
Dis- (L) *apart:* disarticulation, taking joint apart.
Dys- (G) *pain or difficulty:* dyspepsia, impairment of digestion.

Ecto- (G) *outside:* ectoretina, outermost layer of retina.
Em- or **En-** (G) *in:* encapsulated, enclosed in a capsule.

Encephal- (G) *brain:* encephalitis, inflammation of brain.
End- (G) *within:* endothelium, layer of cells lining heart, blood and lymph vessels.
Entero- (G) *intestine:* enterosis, falling of intestine.
Epi- (G) *above or upon:* epidermis, outermost layer of skin.
Erythro- (G) *red:* erythrocyte, red blood cell.
Eu- (G) *well:* euphoria, well feeling, feeling of good health.
Ex- or **E-** (L) *out:* excretion, material thrown out of the body or the organ.
Exo- (G) *outside:* exocrine, excreting outwardly (opposite of endocrine).
Extra- (G) *outside:* extramural, situated or occurring outside a wall.

Febri- (L) *fever:* febrile, feverish.

Galacto- (G) *milk:* galactose, a milk-sugar.
Gastr- (G) *stomach:* gastrectomy, excision of the stomach.
Gloss- (G) *tongue:* glossectomy, surgical removal of tongue.
Glyco- (G) *sugar:* glycosuria, sugar in the urine.
Gynec- (G) *woman:* gynecology, science of diseases pertaining to women.

Hem- or **hemat-** (G) *blood:* hemopoiesis, forming blood.
Hemi- (G) *half:* heminephrectomy, excision of half the kidney.
Hepat- (G) *liver:* hepatitis, inflammation of the liver.
Hetero- (G) *other* (opposite of homo): heterotransplant, using skin from a member of another species.
Hist- (G) *tissue:* histology, science of minute structure and function of tissues.
Homo- (G) *same:* homotransplant, skin grafting by using skin from a member of the same species.
Hydr- (G) *water:* hydrocephalus, abnormal accumulation of fluid in cranium.
Hyper- (G) *above, excess of:* hyperglycemia, excess of sugar in blood.
Hypo- (G) *under, deficiency of:* hypoglycemia, deficiency of sugar in blood.
Hyster- (G) *uterus:* hysterectomy, excision of uterus.

Idio- (G) *self, or separate:* idiopathic, a disease self-originated (of unknown cause).
Im- or **In-** (L) *in:* infiltration, accumulation in tissue of abnormal substances.
Im- or **In-** (L) *not:* immature, not mature.
Infra- (L) *below:* infra-orbital, below the orbit.
Inter- (L) *between:* intermuscular, between the muscles.
Intra- (L) *within:* intramuscular, within the muscle.

Kerat- (G) *horn, cornea:* keratitis, inflammation of cornea.

Lact- (L) *milk:* lactation, secretion of milk.
Leuk- (G) *white:* leukocyte, while cell.

Macro- (G) *large:* macroblast, abnormally large red cell.
Mast- (G) *breast:* mastectomy, excision of the breast.
Meg- or **Megal-** (G) *great:* megacolon, abnormally large colon.
Ment- (L) *mind:* dementia, deterioration of the mind.
Mer- (G) *part:* merotomy, division into segments.
Mesa- (G) *middle:* mesaortitis, inflammation of middle coat of the aorta.
Meta- (G) *beyond, over, change:* metastasis, change in seat of a disease.
Micro- (G) *small:* microplasia, dwarfism.
My- (G) *muscle:* myoma, tumor made of muscular elements.
Myc- (G) *fungi:* mycology, science and study of fungi.

Necro- (G) *corpse, dead:* necrosis, death of cells adjoining living tissue.
Neo- (G) *new:* neoplasm, any new growth or formation.
Neph- (G) *kidney:* nephrectomy, surgical excision of kidney.
Neuro- (G) *nerve:* neuron, nerve cell.

Odont- (G) *tooth:* odontology, dentistry.
Olig- (G) *little:* oligemia, deficiency in volume of blood.
Oo- (G) *egg:* oocyte, original cell of egg.
Oophor- (G) *ovary:* oophorectomy, removal of an ovary.
Ophthalm- (G) *eye:* ophthalmometer, an instrument for measuring the eye.
Ortho- (G) *straight, normal:* orthograde, walk straight (upright).
Oss- (L) *bone:* osseous, bony.
Oste- (G) *bone:* osteitis, inflammation of a bone.
Ot- (G) *ear:* otorrhea, discharge from ear.
Ovar- (G) *ovary:* ovariorrhexis, rupture of an ovary.

Para- (G) *irregular, around, wrong:* paradenitis, inflammation of tissue in the neighborhood of a gland.
Path- (G) *disease:* pathology, science of disease.
Ped-[1] (G) *children:* pediatrician, child specialist.
Ped-[2] (L) *feet:* pedograph, imprint of the foot.
Per- (L) *through, excessively:* percutaneous, through the skin.
Peri- (G) *around, immediately around* (in contradistinction to para): periapical, surrounding apex of root of tooth.
Phil- (G) *love:* hemophilic, fond of blood (as bacteria that grows well in presence of hemoglobin).
Phleb- (G) *vein:* phlebotomy, opening of vein for bloodletting.
Phob- (G) *fear:* hydrophobic, reluctant to associate with water.
Pneum- or **Pneumon-** (G) *lung* (pneum—air): pneumococcus, organism causing lobar pneumonia.
Polio- (G) *gray:* poliomyelitis, inflammation of gray substance of spinal cord.
Poly- (G) *many:* polyarthritis, inflammation of several joints.
Post- (L) *after:* postpartum, after delivery.
Pre- (L) *before:* prenatal, occurring before birth.
Pro- (L and G) *before:* prognosis, forecast as to result of disease.
Proct- (G) *rectum:* proctectomy, surgical removal of rectum.
Pseudo- (G) *false:* pseudoangina, false angina.
Psych- (G) *soul or mind:* psychiatry, treatment of mental disorders.
Py- (G) *pus:* pyorrhea, discharge of pus.
Pyel- (G) *pelvis:* pyelitis, inflammation of pelvis of kidney.

Rach- (G) *spine:* rachicentesis, puncture into vertebral canal.
Ren- (L) *kidney:* adrenal, near the kidney.
Retro- (L) *backward:* retroversion, turned backward (usually, of uterus).
Rhin- (G) *nose:* rhinology, knowledge concerning noses.

Salping- (G) *a tube:* salpingitis, inflammation of tube.
Semi- (L) *half:* semicoma, mild coma.
Septic- (L and G) *poison:* septicemia, poisoned condition of blood.
Somat- (G) *body:* psychosomatic, having bodily symptoms of mental origin.
Sta- (G) *make stand:* stasis, stoppage of flow of fluid.
Sten- (G) *narrow:* stenosis, narrowing of duct or canal.
Sub- (L) *under:* subdiaphragmatic, under the diaphragm.
Super- (L) *above, excessively:* superacute, excessively acute.
Supra- (L) *above, upon:* suprarenal, above or upon the kidney.
Sym- or **Syn-** (G) *with, together:* symphysis, a growing together.

Tachy- (G) *fast:* tachycardia, fast-beating heart.
Tens- (L) *stretch:* extensor, a muscle extending or stretching a limb.

Ped—from Greek *pais,* child.
Ped—from Latin *pes,* foot.

Therm- (G) *heat:* diathermy, therapeutic production of heat in tissues.
Tox- or **toxic-** (G) *poison:* toxemia, poisoned condition of blood.
Trache- (G) *trachea:* tracheitis, inflammation of the trachea.
Trans- (L) *across:* transplant, transfer tissue from one place to another.
Tri- (L and G) *three:* trigastric, having three bellies (muscle).
Trich- (G) *hair:* trichosis, any disease of the hair.

Uni- (L) *one:* unilateral, affecting one side.

Vas- (L) *vessel:* vasoconstrictor, nerve or drug that narrows blood vessel.

Zoo- (G) *animal:* zooblast, an animal cell.

Suffixes

-algia (G) *pain:* cardialgia, pain in the heart.
-asis or **-osis** (G) *affected with:* leukocytosis, excess number of leukocytes.
-asthenia (G) *weakness:* neurasthenia, nervous weakness.
-blast (G) *germ:* myeloblast, bone-marrow cell.
-cele (G) *tumor, hernia:* enterocele, any hernia of intestine.
-cid (L) *cut, kill:* germicidal, destructive to germs.
-clysis (G) *injection:* hypodermoclysis, injection under the skin.
-coccus (G) *round bacterium:* pneumococcus, bacteria of pneumonia.
-cyte (G) *cell:* leukocyte, white cell.
-ectasis (G) *dilation, stretching:* angiectasis, dilatation of a blood vessel.
-ectomy (G) *excision:* adenectomy, excision of adenoids.
-emia (G) *blood:* glycemia, sugar in blood.
-esthesia (G) *(noun) relating to sensation:* anesthesia, absence of feeling.
·ferent (L) *bear, carry:* efferent, carry out to periphery.
-genic (G) *producing:* pyogenic, producing pus.
-iatrics (G) *pertaining to a physician or the practice of healing* (medicine): pediatrics, science of medicine for children.
-itis (G) *inflammation:* tonsillitis, inflammation of tonsils.
-logy (G) *science of:* pathology, science of disease.
-lysis (G) *losing, flowing, dissolution:* autolysis, dissolution of tissue cells.
-malacia (G) *softening:* osteomalacia, softening of bone.
-oma (G) *tumor:* myoma, tumor made up of muscle elements.
-osis (-asis) (G) *being affected with:* atherosis, arteriosclerosis.
·(o)stomy (G) *creation of an opening:* gastrostomy, creation of an artificial gastric fistula.
-(o)tomy (G) *cutting into:* laparotomy, surgical incision into abdomen.
-pathy (G) *disease:* myopathy, disease of a muscle.
-penia (G) *lack of:* leukopenia, lack of white blood cells.
-pexy (G) *to fix:* proctopexy, fixation of rectum by suture.
-phagia (G) *eating:* polyphagia, excessive eating.
-phasia (G) *speech:* aphasia, loss of power of speech.
-phobia (G) *fear:* hydrophobia, fear of water.
-plasty (G) *molding:* gastroplasty, molding or re-forming stomach.
-poiesis (G) *making, forming:* hematopoiesis, forming blood.
-pnea (G) *air or breathing:* dyspnea, difficult breathing.
-ptosis (G) *falling:* enteroptosis, falling of intestine.
-rhythmia (G) *rhythm:* arrhythmia, variation from normal rhythm of heart.
·rrhagia (G) *flowing or bursting forth:* otorrhagia, hemorrhage from ear.
·rrhaphy (G) *suture of:* enterorrhaphy, act of sewing up gap in intestine.
·rrhea (G) *discharge:* otorrhea, discharge from ear.
-sthen (ia) (ic) (G) *pertaining to strength:* asthenia, loss of strength.
-taxia or **-taxis** (G) *order, arrangement of:* ataxia, failure of muscular co-ordinatio
-trophia or **-trophy** (G) *nourishment:* atrophy, wasting, or diminution.
-uria (G) *to do with urine:* polyuria, excessive secretion of urine.

Index

Artery (*Continued*)
  gastric, 441
  hardened, 476, 504, 742
  hepatic, 441, 606
  hypogastric, 444
  iliac, common, 443
    external, 444
  innominate, 435
  intercostal, 440
  lumbar, 443
  mammary, internal, 438
  maxillary, internal, 435
  meningeal, middle, 436
  mesenteric, inferior, 441
    superior, 441
  nerve supply of, 425, 510, 706, 708
  nutrient of bone, 84
  ovarian, 442
  palpation points of, 435, 437, 440,
      449
  peroneal, 447
  phrenic, inferior, 443
    superior, 440
  plantar arch, 447
  popliteal, 447
  pulmonary, 430, 541
  radial, 440
  renal, 442
  sacral, middle, 443
  spermatic, 442
  splenic, 441
  structure of, 424
  subclavian, 437
  suprarenal, middle, 442
  systemic, 434-449
  temporal, superficial, 435
  thoracic aorta, 440
  thyrocervical trunk, 438
  tibial, anterior, 447
    posterior, 447
  ulnar, 440
  umbilical, 464, 797
  velocity of blood flow in, 506
  vertebral, 438
  volar arch, 440
Arthritis, 135
  rheumatoid, 135, 743
Articular cartilage, 126
Articulations. *See* Joints
Artificial, kidneys, 693
  respiration, 235, 572-574
Aschheim-Zondek test, 743

Ascites, 411
Ascorbic acid, 626
Asphyxiation, 574
Aspirate, 542
Assimilation, 54
Astereognosis, 321, 348
Asthma, 543, 570
Astigmatism, 374
Asynchronism, 224, 235
Ataxia, 321, 348
Atelectasis, 543
Athetosis, 237, 323
Atom bomb victims, 407
Atresia, 768
Atretic follicles, 768
Atria of lungs, 540
Atrioventricular, bundle (His), 422,
      489
  node, 422, 490
Atrium, of heart, 420, 540
  fibrillation of, 516, 520
Atrophy, of muscles, 237, 279
  progressive, muscular, 237
Atropine, 280, 379, 543
Attachments of muscles, 152
Audiometer, 380
Auditory, center, 333
  meatus, external, 366
  tube, 367, 532
Auerbach's plexus, 585
Auscultation, 494
Autonomic (visceral efferent) system,
      269-276
  disorders of, 281
  divisions of, 270-272
  effect of drugs on, 280-281
  functions of, 274-276
  ganglia of, 270-272
  structure of, 270-272
Axis cylinder, 249
Axon, 249
Axon reflex, 510

Babinski reflex, 325
Bacterial action in large intestine, 637
Bag of waters, 796
Bainbridge reflex, 515
Balance, in temperature regulation,
      706
Barium, enema, 653
  meal, 653
Baroceptors, 496, 508, 513-515, 558

Tuberosity, 86
  ischial, 98
  ulnar, 93
Tumor(s), of adrenal cortex, 737, 745
  of adrenal medulla, 746
  of pituitary, 742
Tunica, adventitia, 424, 427
  albuginea, 758
  intima, 424, 427
  media, 424, 427
  vaginalis, 758
Tympanic membrane, 367

Ulcer, of cornea, 373
  in diabetes mellitus, 742
  of gastro-intestinal tract, 281, 613, 614, 653, 655
  syphilitic, 49
Umbilical, cord, 464, 799
  vessels, 464, 797
Umbilicus, 799
Unconscious muscle sense, 291
Undifferentiated mesenchymal cells, 31
Universal donor, 410
Urea, 639, 648, 692
Uremia, 693
Ureters, 666-668
Urethra, 671-672
  female, 671
  male, 672, 762
Urethritis, 677
Urethrovaginal fistula, 671
Urinary bladder, 320, 668-670
Urine, 681
  albumin in, 690
  casts, 692
  composition of, 681
  production of, 681
  specific gravity of, 690
  sugar in, 691
  suppression of, 693
  voiding of (micturition), 671
Urticaria, 49, 409
Uterine, muscle, 723
  tubes, 768
Uterus, 769-776
Utricle, 371
Uvula, 594, 629

Vagina, 776
Vaginal smears, 777

Valves, action of, 491-493
  of heart, 420, 491-493
  lesions of, 475, 518
  of lymphatics, 465
  of veins, 427
Vaporization, 704-706
Varices of esophagus, 613
Varicocele, 806
Varicose veins, 477
Vasa vasorum, 425, 427
Vasoconstrictor nerves, 510, 706, 708
Vasodilator nerves, 510, 706, 708
Vasomotor, center, 510-511
  nerves, 501
Vater, ampulla of, 610
Vater-Pacini corpuscles, 339
VDM (vasodepressor material), 522
Vein(s), accessory hemiazygos, 454
  anterior tibial, 460
  axillary, 453
  azygos, 454
  basilic, 452
  brachial, 453
  cardiac, 450
  central, of liver, 607
  cephalic, 452
  common iliac, 462
  coronary, of stomach, 458
  coronary sinus, 450
  cystic, 458
  deep, 449
  emissary, 451
  external, iliac, 462
    jugular, 452
  femoral, 461
  great saphenous, 460
  hemiazygos, 454
  hemorrhoidal, superior, 458
  hepatic, 459, 607
  hypogastric, 462
  iliac, common, 462
    external, 462
  inferior, mesenteric, 458
    phrenic, 455
    vena, cava, 462
  innominate, 453
  internal, jugular, 452
    mammary, 454
  jugular, external, 452
    internal, 452
  lumbar, 455